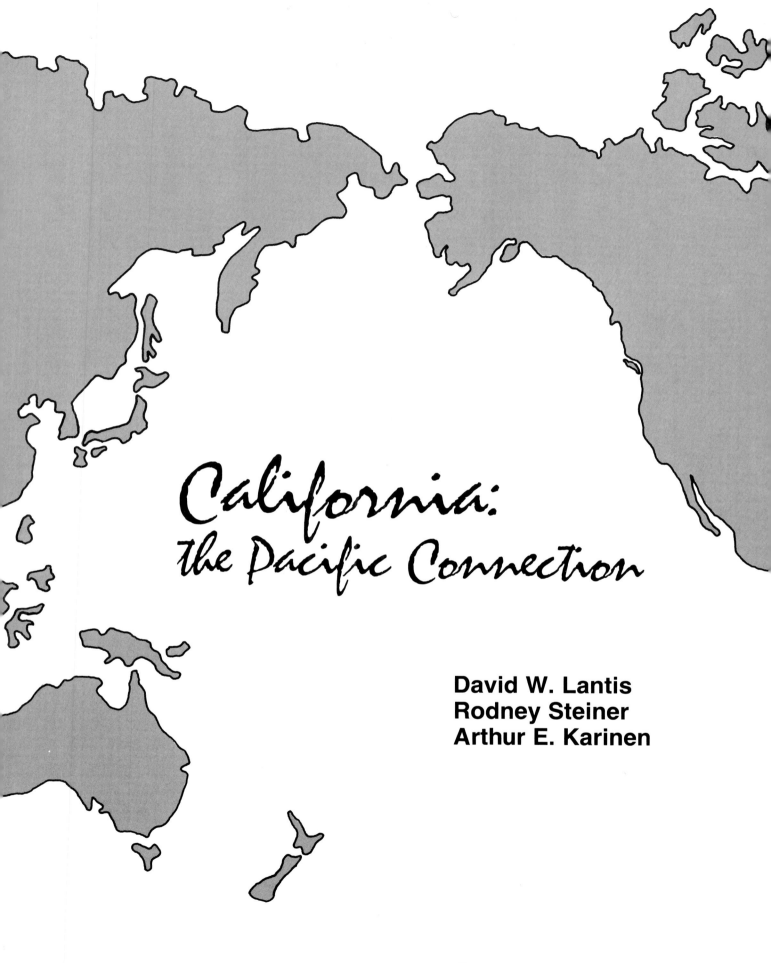

# California:
## the Pacific Connection

**David W. Lantis**
**Rodney Steiner**
**Arthur E. Karinen**

**Creekside Press**

Sketches by Phyllis Steiner

Original index by Helen Lantis

Cover by Tom Best and Nina Birks

**CREEKSIDE PRESS**
1616 Oak Park Avenue
Chico, California 95928
(916) 343-1443

**Library of Congress Cataloging–in–Publication Data**

Lantis, David W.
    California, the Pacific connection / David W. Lantis, Rodney
Steiner, Arthur E. Karinen.
        p.   cm.
    Bibliography: p.
    Includes index
    ISBN 0–9620015–1–1.        ISBN 0-9620015–2–X (pbk.)
    1. California—Description and travel.    I. Steiner, Rodney,  1928–
    II. Karinen, Arthur E., 1919–        III. Title.
F861.L36  1988                                              88-14988
917.94—dc19                                                      CIP

Dedicated to Helen, Phyllis and Florence

and

Written for the people of California



With appreciation
to those thousands of students
in our California classes who have contributed
so much to our knowledge of our Golden State



Our thanks to

Larry Jackson and Gail Taylor–Collins of Heidelberg Graphics
and Andy Wilson of TextStyle Publishing

# CONTENTS

# Forethoughts

Eons before people first came to the Golden State physical relationships with the Pacific Basin had been established. They began with the creation of the ocean itself and the beginnings of the landmass that is now California. The tie between Pacific and the Golden State is atmospheric as well as earthly: California's equable climes and water supplies have close relations with the great water body to the west.

From a human standpoint California's links with the Pacific Rim were established when the earliest people crossed the Bering land bridge and located in California.

Coming north out of Mexico, on the eastern rim of the Pacific, the colonial Spanish "discovered" California before the middle of the sixteenth century. But for some generations the single contact remained the view of the California shore which sailors on the Manila galleons enjoyed as they sailed southward with the winds on their trans-Pacific crossings.

For three-quarters of a century California's Pacific connection was primarily that between New Spain (and then Mexico) and Alta California—travel tended to be by sea rather than overland.

People from the Pacific Basin participated in the Gold Rush and later commerce between China and San Francisco expanded. Soon many Chinese, then Japanese and Filipinos came to California to work in the fields and elsewhere, succeeded by even more migrants from Mexico.

Wars in the Pacific and eastern Asia since 1941 have brought many new trans-Pacific connections, social as well as economic and political.

In the second half of the twentieth century California has truly become a Pacific "nation." Large numbers of immigrants, coming from Americas, from Pacific islands and from the Asian rim seem to be converting California into America's first Hispanic-Asian majority state.

In increasing numbers Californians vacation in Canada, Latin America, Hawaii, Australia and New Zealand and eastern Asia...and people from these realms come to California. Import-export trade between California and Asia especially has expanded.

Many believe that the twenty-first century will be the century of the Pacific Basin. Los Angeles may become America's leading "world city." Already financial relations with the entire Pacific Basin are extremely important.

The Pacific connection seems strongest in Southern California and the San Francisco Bay Area, yet it exists everywhere in the Golden State: the resident of Crescent City who visits China, the person in Bishop who buys a Korean car, the farmer in the Imperial Valley who sells his cotton abroad, the waiter in Death Valley who serves food to Chilean visitors. These and a myriad of other examples demonstrate the importance of the trans-Pacific relations of the Golden State.

## THIS BOOK

Vivid description, factual detail, scholarly documentation, provocative generalities and imaginative theory apply to studies of humankind on the earth. The authors wish that each of these could been woven into this book. In our quest for the ideal we have had another desire too: to provide a work that can be read pleasurably by those who wish to amplify their knowledge of the Golden State. Excluding basic research the impelling need seems to be a reader-oriented work. There are thousands of books about the state including many that have made unique contributions to literature of California. Sources documented in the bibliography reflect this. The reader is encouraged to refer to these materials for additional information.

The approach in this book is both regional and topical. Chapters 2 to 12 consider California's eleven subregions and relate them also to the rest of the American West. For California is not a nation apart. Part IV, Overviews, considers specific topics.

Hopefully, a two-style approach has been used effectively. We are grateful to Professor Richard Logan of University of California, Los Angeles for suggesting it. Paragraphs begin with "major ideas". Detail is inset several spaces.

**ACKNOWLEDGEMENTS**

The authors express their appreciation to the many professional geographers, the thousands of students who have sat in our courses on California, and the countless others who have helped to expand the voluminous knowledge of California.

Portions of the manuscript were reviewed by many of our friends in California colleges and universities. Their assistance has been identified in individual chapters. There are others whose aid we should have enlisted. Such oversights were not deliberate.

The original text was prepared by David W. Lantis and modified with the assistance of Rodney Steiner and Arthur Karinen. Steiner has prepared the overviews and has contributed to extensive re-writing of the manuscript, especially as it concerns Southern California. Map preparation has been the responsibility of Karinen.

This book will be dated before it reaches the library shelves and the bookstores. Such is the fate of a work on a dynamic state like California. Over a two-year period Lantis made 16 field reconnaissance trips, driving over 20,000 miles and visiting all 58 California counties. More time and more trips would have been desirable. Appreciation is extended especially to professional geographers, city and county planners, agricultural commissioners and superintendents of schools. Thousands of people through casual conversation provided ideas and clues.

We acknowledge particular appreciation to Richard F. Logan, University of California at Los Angeles, William Bowen of California State University, Northridge and Patricia Chapla of California State University, Chico. Logan has supported the project almost from its inception in 1953. Bowen and Chapla have reviewed the entire manuscript for this work for us. We have given particular attention to printed reviews written by Logan, John Crowley (University of Montana), Herbert Eder (California State University, Hayward) and Howard Gregor (University of California, Davis).We felt much honored when Lawrence C. Powell (University of California at Los Angeles) wrote in Westways, "This is my book on California." We are pleased too that A.R. Ottley of the California State Library listed it as one of a "basic dozen" books on California. We acknowledge also the kind words in print of William H. Hutchinson (California State University, Chico) and Neil Morgan of San Diego.

We anticipate that this book will be revised and welcome suggestions for improvement from readers.

**Figure 1-1.** The Golden State affords many recreational (upper left) activities—fishing at O'Neill Forebay, San Luis Reservoir near Los Banos is seen here. (California Department of Water Resources)

**Figure 1-2.** California, a Pacific Rim state—a land of (upper right) many complexions. Broadway, downtown Los Angeles. (dwl)

**Figure 1-4.** Expanding national defense budgets during the Reagan presidency much affected California—new housing at U.S. Marine Corps mountain training center north west of Bridgeport. (dwl)

**Figure 1-3.** Electronics and computers loom large in (lower left) California, a post-industrial Pacific Rim land. (Apple Computer, Inc.)

Chapter One

BACKGROUND

# BACKGROUND*

California has intrigued people in many parts of the world for almost half a millenium, since the early Spanish conquerors applied the name of a mythical island peopled by Amazons to a largely unexplored area northwest of New Spain. Almost everything about the Golden State seems to be newsworthy—be it a midwinter flood up north, a severe brushfire near Los Angeles, a new television series emanating from a Hollywood studio, the decision of the governor to run for the Senate or the presidency, and on and on and on.

During the years 1940 to 1969 California experienced a boom, fostered to a considerable extent by defense monies. Then there was there was a brief slowdown until the 1980's brought an impressive portion of the nation's defense monies and an increase in immigrants, coming from scattered parts of the Pacific Rim. As the population of the Golden State rises toward 30 million (a number six times larger than in 1940) many American out-of-staters feel that there are too many people to warrant migration. Yet they still regard California favorably and come by the millions to visit.

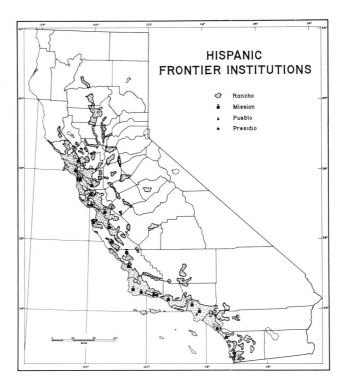

**Map 1-1.** The colonial Spanish and Mexicans concentrated their efforts in coastal (especially southern) California.

## AN ECCENTRIC LAND

Location of California within the nation and the world has much affected its development. It remains apart from eastern United States, separated by extensive near-empty lands—mountains and plateaus which tend to be arid. Such spatial detachment led to shipping costs that made it difficult for some California products (although not aircraft and motion pictures) to be marketed east of the Rocky Mountains. Contrariwise this helped local and eastern-branch enterprise to prosper with expanding Golden State markets.

California might have experienced greater intellectual provincialism with such remoteness had it not been for an ongoing migration into the state. With present-day rapid communication and transportation, of course, conditions have changed—the whole world is now beset with ideas, both good and poor, originating with California media, especially television.

Doubtless California's "wrong shore" location, apart from Europe and the Atlantic, contributed to a "regional consciousness" and perchance to the innovative tendencies sometimes attributed to Califor-

nians. Now, as the Pacific Basin becomes more meaningful in world affairs, California increasingly seems to be on the "right ocean".

Third largest (158,683 square miles) among the 50 states, California is the second longest, with a Pacific shoreline of 1264 miles—almost ten degrees of latitude. While a few excellent harbors favor maritime trade, the oft-clifted shores coupled with interior highland walls, contain seaward and landward passages alike. These barriers, along with extensive area and diversified environments foster the Golden State's subregional distinctions noted at this chapter's end.

## A VARIETY OF RESOURCES

Despite nature's generosity to the Golden State, off-center location is not the single handicap. Summer aridity especially and rough terrain are widespread; threat of major earthquakes is ongoing, recurrence of floods likely. Increasing urbanization eliminates

---

* This chapter has been reviewed by Clarence McIntosh, history professor, California State University, Chico.

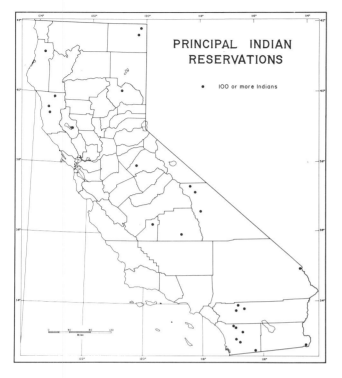

**Map 1-2.** The present distribution of Indian reservations in the Golden State bears slight relationship to the distributuion of First Californians in pre-Columbian times.

farm land while intensifying atmospheric pollution. Now, with insufficient fossil fuels, Californians, like other Americans, must seek substitutes or face energy problems.

The attenuated Pacific frontage has provided abundant water for potable conversion, coolant for electric plants, sites for space research and recreation opportunities, minerals (such as magnesium and salt) and seafoods. Lamentably it has been regarded too for waste disposal. The attractiveness of the sea strand is often preferred to interior location. With its advantages it has been rather easy to forget occasional oil spills, storm damage and infrequent "tidal waves." But whose shoreline is it. Of late Californians have realized that too much of it is privately held, to be developed at the owner's whims.

Along Pacific North America, only California has been blessed by lowlands. Valleys often contain alluvium, washed from adjacent mountains, that provides some of the world's most productive soils. Many basins have had abundant groundwater despite absence of surface flow. Yet sometimes overdraft has produced salt intrusion or subsidence or both. Despite initial cost, irrigation (and drainage) facilities have produced long-time advantages; reliable irrigation

water in a predictably rainless land can prove more productive than a humid habitat with erratic precipitation. But increased facilities lead to more people and thus urban encroachment upon farmlands.

Highlands, in places among the world's roughest, include some of the earth's snowiest and wettest mountains in winter. Legacies include water and soils for lowlands, sought-after scenery, forests, and river gradients suitable for hydroelectric development. Naturalists and river rafters oppose additional reservoir developments, thus reducing opportunities for still-water recreation, water and power output. There is contention too over timber exploitation and management of mountain resort sites—resources are obviously too limited for all contemporary demands.

The California earth has yielded minerals impressive in variety and product value—recovery began with the Gold Rush. Natural gas and petroleum have been found in diverse spots (Chs. 6,7 and 9); billion-dollar industries have resulted. Despite national or even international demand, other minerals, such as asbestos, diotomite, iron ore, mercury, "rare earths", salines and tungsten, have been more localized. Awareness of their finity has increased. Yet in the near future California demands for cement, gas, solar and geothermal energy may increase.

Appreciable portions of California have dry-summer subtropical (Mediterranean) environments (see Overview A) that, suitably watered, can be receptive to scores of agricultural commodities. This realm has enticed migrants in general, the military, tourists, retirees and sundry industries. By encouraging native and "foreign" investments, net outflow of wealth has been minimized. The vaunted California lifestyle (casual, outdoor, mobile) coupled with architecture, arts and literature, seems much attuned to this climatic environment.

As population has increased in the more productive and amenable parts of the Golden State, erstwhile "wastes" (i.e., mountains and deserts) have gained value as "escape areas" for affluent urbanites. More and more, California resources and space have become inadequate for esthetic, health and utilitarian demands as well as contrasting recreational preferences. Hence allocation for contrary uses has become increasingly difficult.

## THROUGH THE CENTURIES

Four basic periods in the successive occupance of California have occurred: (1) First Californian (In-

**Figure 1-5.** Statue honoring the First Americans, Plaza Hill Park, Old Town, San Diego (Helen Lantis).

dian) (2) California under Spain (3) California under Mexico and (4) Anglo American.* In latter years the Anglo period has experienced considerable immigration from Latin America and east Asia. Thus a fifth period, *Pacific Basin Post Industrial,* may be evolving. Despite the dominance of the Anglo period for over a century, influences of the earlier times persist.

### The First Californians

A comparable diversity of pre-Columbian Indians did not exist in other states; partially this reflected the diverse habitats of the several Californias. Anthropologists have identified five language stocks and 26 tribal groups within California. Penutian, the largest group, has few affiliations with Indian tongues outside present-day California. The multiple environments were seemingly attractive—pre-Spanish density was among the highest in the United States. Descendants of the 24 still-extant groups exceed 40,000 plus augmentation from recent influx of non-California Indians. Over much of California these first residents have disappeared; place names and land routes still reflect their heydey. In pre-European times the Indian was more widely dispersed, reflecting needed closeness to water and food, as contrasted with the extinction threat presented by the white man. The number of reservations and Indian groups on reserves in northwestern California

and in the Sierran and Southern California foothills still occupy habitats that have been relatively unattractive to non-Indian Californians.

The usual lifestyle of the First Californians was hunter-gatherer. Thus they made little change on the landscape. Those in dry locations and mountains had less material wealth. As today, most environments permitted simple shelters and little clothing. Southern California Indians possessed a mild environment. Those in the Central Valley held lands that required somewhat more effort. The Northwest, with its perennial salmon streams and its conifer forests, provided a wealthier portion of early-day California.

### Vaqueros and Friars (Colonial Hispanics)

Spanish knowledge of California existed for over two centuries before the first colonial occupance—this was the northwestern edge of Spanish settlement in the Americas. Between 1769 and 1822 a chain of 21 missions was constructed on near-coastal lowlands which had suitability for agricultural self-sufficiency, sizable Indian populations and accessibility to sea navigation. Introduction and irrigation of European crops constituted a prelude to present-day farming. But attempts to "civilize" the First Californians met

---

* The term *Anglo* is broadly used in this book to identify people of north European descent whose native tongue is English from birth.

**Figure 1-7.** Although these nineteenth century houses on Bunker Hill, Los Angeles, have been torn down one still finds many older homes, especially in the northern half of California (dwl).

with only partial success. Many Indians were converted to Christianity, learned Spanish and acquired a knowledge of agriculture.

Beside the Franciscan priests *(padres)* at the missions there were presidios manned by soldiers at well-chosen embayments in Southern and Central California. Additionally, small numbers of colonists came north from Mexico. Among California's presently largest cities, Los Angeles and San Jose originated as planned farm villages *(pueblos)*; other communities (as San Diego, Monterey and San Francisco) "just grew" near presidios or missions. Place names, farming practices, customs, architecture, highway routes (particularly *El Camino Real*), basically U.S. 101 today), foods and even contemporary California speech reflect the Spanish years—some of these traits have been reinforced through ongoing Hispanic influx.

Fewer than 800 *ranchos* (large individual holdings) were awarded, mostly during the brief period of Mexican control (1822-1846). Cowboys *(vaqueros)* followed their herds. But Mexico, weak and newly independent, could hardly colonize its most distant province. Ranchos were principally in Southern California and the Central Coast, with a lesser number in the Central Valley. Some properties, especially in the 1840's, were given to Europeans and Anglo Americans who were willing to accept Mexican citizenship. Thus California afforded a tempting opportunity for an expansionist United States. Lasting results of this period included wider dispersal of Hispanic place names, road and property patterns, ranchsteads and the tradition of the gentleman farmer.

## Next Came the Anglos

After cession of the Hispanic Southwest at the end of the Mexican War, the Anglo-American period began. Within a year (in 1849) the nation's most spectacular Gold Rush was underway. A constitutional convention, held in Monterey at the time, decided the outline and contemporary dimensions of the Golden State. These locational considerations prevailed: California should reach the 42nd parallel, undefined northern limits of Hispanic claims in North America; the value of shoreline warrant maximization; because of the importance of San Diego Bay, California would extend to the Mexican border established in 1848 (a straight line from the Colorado-Gila confluence to a point on the Pacific five miles south of San Diego Bay. In establishing an eastern boundary the convention excluded most of the *Great American Desert* which already contained the socially-distinct Mormons and which seemed unpromising economically. Too, California engulfment of the entire *Mexican Southwest* would have been unacceptable to a Congress embroiled in the free state-slave state issue. After much debate the eastern border was drawn, north to south, along the 120th parallel to its intersection with the 39th parallel, thence southeastward to the contact of the 35th parallel and the Colorado River. It was felt that the Colorado offered a potential navigable waterway. The resultant bisection of Lake Tahoe apparently resulted from observation of an inaccurate map in Monterey.

## STAGES OF AGRICULTURE

Since 1850 farming in California has experienced three economic successions: a pastoral era of sheep and cattle (prevalent until the 1880's); grain farming, dominant from the 1870's until about 1900: and irrigation agriculture, principally since 1900. These stages have overlapped—not all portions of the Golden State have experienced all three.

### Land of Sheep and Cattle

The countryside was largely pastoral before the Gold Rush—a logical scheme for small numbers of Hispanics in a summer-desert environment. Rural population density was low; cattle grazed across vast open ranges. The principal products were hides and tallow; much of the meat was discarded. Ascendancy of Anglo farmers combined with unprecedented drought in the 1860's ended the dominance of cattle ranching. Grazing persists, however, as the most

**Figure 1-8.** In the late nineteenth century California was a leading wheat producing state. (Historical Collection, Title Insurance and Trust Company, Los Angeles)

widespread form of productive land use. Huge ranches still exist and livestock also are run on many public lands, although less densely than in the past.

### Wheat and Barley

Where soils and climate assured reasonable yields, Anglo farmers began to substitute wheat and barley for livestock. Like pasturage, the grains were wholly dependent upon winter and spring rains but higher monetary returns allowed more settlers on small holdings.

Ease of storage and handling facilitated export by ship in a time of inadequate overland transport. Briefly California led the nation in production of wheat; later it became the leading producer of barley. Grains, despite their widespread eviction by irrigated crops, still occupy larger acreages than any other crop category. Among other uses they have much demand within California as livestock feed.

### Watering the Land

The value of irrigation was appreciated in Mission days but artificial watering remained modest until railroads connected California with eastern markets and technical improvements such as refrigerator cars and water pumps appeared. Other retardants included initial irrigation costs, uncertain consumer response and litigation over water rights.

Nearly half of California's irrigated acreage was developed in the years 1890-1930, principally for vineyards and orchards whose output was marketed nationwide in raw as well as processed forms. Once

again, high crop values permitted smaller (and more numerous) farms. Quests for cheap labor resulted in the migration of people from many lands into California.

Additional water became available in the 1940's with the Central Valley Project and the All-American Canal system and after 1960 with the California Aqueduct. Now California's irrigated crop land, occupying less than a tenth of the state's area, contains the bulk of the farms, cultivated acreage and crop output.

### THE MANY MILLIONS

Essentially the Anglo period has reflected the westward movement, or "westerling", as suggested by journalist Horace Greeley in 1846: If you have no family or friends to aid you, and no prospect opened to you there (like a father's workshop or his farm), turn your face to the great West, and there build up a home and a fortune.

Earlier years witnessed immigration from the Atlantic seaboard—particularly New England and the Middle Atlantic states. From the 1880's until World War I this movement was subordinate to that of Middlewesterners to California as California almost became New Illinois. Victims of depression combined with Great Plains drought and dust came in the 1930's. There almost seemed a Confederate invasion during the second World War, including blacks, with a lesser number coming from the Rocky Mountain states. After the war ex-servicemen and their brides populated the housing tracts and filled the schools with their offspring.

**Figure 1-9.** Mexican nationals transplanting celery near Arroyo Grande. Despite extensive use of machinery, hand labor remains vital to present-day agriculture in California. (dwl)

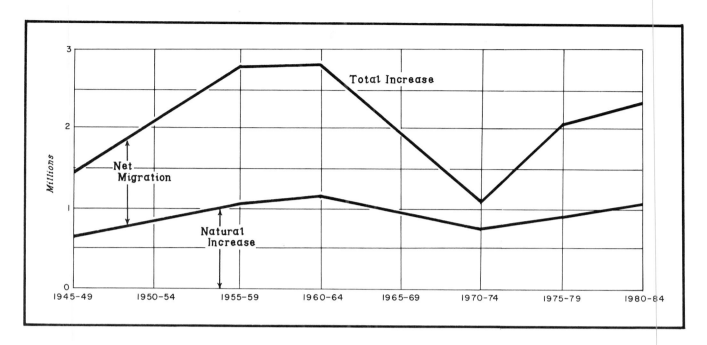

**Chart 1-1.** Sources of population growth in five-year increments, 1945-1985.

Migration slowed in the late 1960's but continued to have diverse origins, with Texas the leading source, followed by Illinois and New York. Since the late 1970's there has been an international migration, especially from the Pacific basin (Latin America and eastern Asia).

### An International Potpourri

The "Anglo period" warrants qualification. First Californians and Hispanic peoples remained after statehood, albeit with some difficulties. Soon other non-Anglos migrants arrived. In the 1980's more than one of every four Californians is either nonwhite or speaks some other first language than English. The Chinese particularly had identification early with the Gold Rush and railroad and levee projects. Considerable numbers of Irish too came during the second half of the nineteenth century. Demands for farm labor encouraged Filipinos, Hindus, Japanese, Mexicans, Sikhs and others to migrate. Likewise such "Mediterranean" peoples as Armenians, Italians and Portuguese found their way into rural California.

In the 19th and early 20th centuries the state experienced less direct European influx than eastern United States. Still the migration was significant. California lacked the factories and mines and found its farm labor elsewhere. As the depressed 1930's saw wholesale deportation of alien Mexicans they were soon replaced, among others, by fellow ethnic migrants from other states. The European exodus of Jews and other refugees from Hitler's Nazism brought additional new Californians.

A period of economic boom (1940-1969) witnessed immigrating war brides and various refugee groups, augmenting California's traditional ethnic mix with such sundry newcomers as Cubans, Dutch, Guamanians and Samoans, Indonesian Dutch, Hungarians and Navajos. But the prime destinations were the evolving megalopolitan centers where factories and service trades offered sources of lower wage employment. Besides half a million (locally born plus interstate migrants) new California blacks, a million people joined the state's "foreign stock" during the 1960's.

Since 1970, with the post-industrial trans-Pacific era, an increasing number have been Latin Americans and east Asians. Economic recession in the 1970's. as in earlier difficult periods, prompted concern for the pace of immigration, most notably of unauthorized Mexican entrants who became so numerous that some concernedly half-joked about California's "peaceful reconquest" by Mexico. For a while refugee Vietnamese, fewer yet more conspicuous, were also debated.

### Natality, Mobility and Such

The inflow of California migrants, 1940-1969 and subsequently, has been renowned for the immensity of its numbers as well as its bias toward young adults who reinforced a swollen birth rate. Such services as education, health and transportation has lagged at times behind statewide population increments that occasionally exceeded a thousand persons daily. California has led all states in growth volume, absorbing so many Americans and foreign-born that since the early 1960's it has been the nation's most populous state.

Migration slowed for a time after the early 1960's, dropping to near-zero by 1970; subsequently it increased. The high post-World War II birthrate declined too. In the late 20th century the "natural increase" (excess of births over deaths) has been markedly lower than the natural increment a few decades earlier (map 1-3). Yet it has exceeded immigration as a source of native Californians so much that the proportion of locally-born versus out-of-state births has nearly equalized.

Presently California's growth per cent (added population proportional to base population) no longer ranks in the top tier of states even though the total increment (nearly a quarter million annually) remains second only to Florida.

An upward trend, coupled with a diminished birth rate, seems to exist. State population may reach 30 million or so by 2000. Zero population growth, while closer than in some earlier decades, seemingly remains distant. The fertility must shrink more and migration entirely cease for the population to stabilize.

Beginning in the late 1960's outmigration from California received publicity. While seldom approaching immigration numbers, emigration volume impacted conspicuously less-populous recipient states. Whether these were "new" or "old" Californians is unclear (many were California-born) but the geographical direction of their movement since the late 1950's has been consistent. Vicinal states (Arizona and Oregon) have been the recipients. California has continued to "import" from the Northeast (Massachusetts to Illinois).

Migration into and out of California has been impressive. Some years ago a sample of "movers" revealed that 12 persons changed states for every single net migrant added to the California populace. Foreign influx has become a more important component, providing a larger share of California growth than the national norm of 20 per cent annually. The Golden State's portion of the nation's registered alien populace is twice the state's share of the national population. Illegal immigrants into California have been of greater magnitude, estimated in the late 20th century to total some millions.

**Figure 1-6.** Railroads have had an important role in California for over a century— this is the *C.P. Huntington* locomotive of the Central Pacific (now the Santa Fe Southern), on display at California State Railroad Museum in Sacramento. (dwl)

The percentage of California oldsters has lessened with slowed migration and doubtless a normalization of migrants' traits. Hence California is approaching national norms in age and sex structure, frequency of interstate migration and marriage, birth and death rates. In recent years its growth rate has exceeded that of the nation again—possibly California's per cent of the total national population could increase from 10 to 14 per cent of the total United States numbers before rates balance. Of late California's birth rate has been below the national average while its illegitimate rate has been higher.

The Golden State seems to rank distressingly high in such realms of social pathology as broken families, alcohol and drug addition, suicide and some crimes. Although defects are apparent it is moot whether the causes relate to such California aberrations as selectivity of migrants, social "climate" or possibly the state's end of trail location in the 48 conterminous states.

## SPACECRAFT AND STRAWBERRIES

If residents of the Golden State flourish, it is necessary to offer services and goods beyond it borders. *Basic* activities, earning *exogenous* income, balance Californians' expenditures elsewhere to sustain such *non-basic* (although equally essential) pursuits such as retail trade, transportation and construction. Hence basic economic activities have particular concern in interpreting California's viability. In essence there are three broad categories—amenities, natural resources and defense expenditures. Each has been in sufficient demand to offset the eccentric location internationally and nationally. All three bear close affinity to the uniqueness of California's resource base and natural setting although each is the immediate product of human initiative and circumstances.

## The Resource Base: Tomatoes and Oil

Golden State activities directly concerned with the earth and its resources developed earliest and predominated until the 1940's. Despite augmentation by newer basic activities this group is the most widespread and evenly distributed across the state. This resource group is dominated by agriculture (see Overview F for additional information). Productive soils combined with climatic mildness and reliable supplies of "artificial" rain have been marshalled to produce farm goods that lead the nation in variety (more than 250) and value. Produce for out-of-state markets (such as cotton, fruits, nuts, rice and vegetables) have provided major economic cornerstones. About two dozen California counties remain chiefly agricultural, in part because of a growing in-state consumption of perishable commodities that cannot be grown in some states.

California has exported also quantities of fish, lumber and minerals, so that it has ranked first, second and third among the 50 states in their output. Again, in-state consumption has expanded. A one-time leader in petroleum export, California has long been a deficit producer. Forest output too is needed increasingly within the state, as are livestock products. Yet California retains a near-national monopoly in such commodities as borates and redwood and almonds (and other fruits, nuts and vegetables). As natural resource output has inherent limits, other activities share responsibility in supporting the current Golden State population and in attracting or repelling the newcomers.

## Hillside Viewspots and Ocean Vistas

Amenities are basic activities stimulated by the "livable" qualities of California, principally scenery (as a hilltop view or a seascape) and climate. Many regard California to be the nation's most beauteous state and its summer-desert subtropical climate the world's choicest. The valuable tourist and retirement "business", commencing in the 1870's, is amenity-related. It has accelerated with American affluence, mobility, leisure time, advertisement and creation of man-made attractions to supplement (or even substi-

tute for) environmental appeal. In bygone decades when winter visitation was paramount, Southern California tended to dominate tourist trade. Presently there is more dispersal around the state and more balanced seasonal continuity.

Retirement by out-of-staters (who thereby bring their incomes to California) has suffered from high living costs, environmental and social problems and alternate-locale promotion.

The cinema industry initially was identified with climate and scenic attractions. It fostered such "style goods" industries as cosmetics, fashions, ceramics and furniture—all have been consequential "export" enterprises. Style goods and motion pictures (and subsequently television) have contributed to expanded tourism and probably to migration in general. They have glamorized and popularized California more than agriculture despite the "retreat" of movie making in the latter half of the twentieth century.

## Missiles and Navy Bases

Military-related activities in the Golden State have included shipyards, military bases, ordnance and much electronic manufacture and much of the wide array of research installations and factories identified as "aerospace." All these are actuated principally by federal contracts related to "security needs." Since 1940 California has received more from the national treasury than it has contributed chiefly because of military spending in these diverse forms. California has led all other states in aerospace employment, federal research and development contracts and location of military personnel (in part because of its "Pacific connection")—these have much stimulated population growth during these decades.

National and international situations are basic to defense activities although conditions within the state are influential. The Golden State has excelled in design quality and productive efficiency in electronics and aerospace. It possesses research facilities, requisite talent and assembly lines. Advantageous natural conditions are important: Pacific shores, harbors, flattish open terrain and climatic mildness. Such conditions favor military operations and some have favored shipbuilding as well as aerospace. Geographic allocation of defense expenditures, based on technical and economic considerations, have commended California. Other factors could attain greater importance in the future with unpredictable consequences for the Golden State. Prominent among these are political decisions, safety through areal dispersal and alleviation of national poverty pockets.

While dispersed, defense activities tend to be concentrated California's warmer subtropical realms (see map 4-2). They focus upon metropolitan areas to draw upon urban labor and facilities; in turn defense plants and military bases have fostered city growth. The few communities resulting principally from military activities are mostly in the "dry east" where there is available space.

## COMMERCE AND TRADE

A world political map demonstrates that California's location makes it the portal between the interior American West and lands overseas. This is a comparable position to that of the Middle Atlantic seaboard for eastern United States. In the past the Golden State formed a "side door", *not t*he main entrance. California has become the *other* front door with expansion of the Pacific Basin commerce. The Western interior is relatively unproductive and empty, unlike the Middle West. California alone has twice the population of the remainder of the trans-Rocky Mountain West while Los Angeles and San Francisco metropolitan areas have far more people than their primary service areas. Thus their ports mainly serve California's own hinterlands, despite publicized "land bridge" traffic between Europe and eastern Asia. San Diego and Humboldt bays, seemingly more developable, have been "offcenter" with poor hinterlands and inferior land access to the interior. Thus the ports of San Francisco Bay and Los Angeles-Long Beach have experienced limited competition from them. Likewise major airports are concerned more with locally-generated traffic than with through service, though stopovers on international flights surely aid the Golden State's tourist industry.

Major east-west overland corridors cross the state immediately inland from Los Angeles and from San Francisco Bay. Inland heavy truck (carrying eastbound agricultural products especially) and rail traffic is notable. Considerable maintenance population resides along these arteries, particularly at junctions, pass towns (such as San Bernardino, Bakersfield, Sacramento and Redding, and strategically-placed waypoints and water sources. Transport facilities have attracted military bases to some sites but have not generally stimulated large-scale manufacturing and sundry activities.

Traffic north-south represents shorter hauls than trans-continental movement; it is mostly aerial or overland rather than maritime. The Central Valley, with agricultural productivity, is the easiest pathway and presents the chief corridor between the Pacific Northwest, the Bay Area and Southern California. Such cities as Sacramento and Stockton, both of which lie at overland crossroads with seaport facilities, have become transport centers. These and other cities have local importance as wholesale nodes.

## A DIVERSE LAND

Southern California and the San Francisco Bay Area suggest northeastern United States: crowded landscapes with depleted resources, where problems of close living increasingly so precede those of simply wrestling a livelihood from the land. In excess of 90 per cent of Californians are urban dwellers; migrants tend to select cities because of economic opportunities.

Most of the Golden State is neither urban nor genuinely agricultural. Extensive tracts of mountains, foothills, deserts, forests and brushland remain dominant—optimum use remains an important challenge and opportunity for California. Ownership problems and natural resource management are as vital over much of California as in much of the sparsely-populated American West. It may be increasingly easy to convince the urbanite of the importance of these assets—concern for environment has increased, especially among younger citizenry.

### Multiple Use

California approaches the natural diversity of the other 49 states (see Overviews A through D)—it furnishes examples of nearly all geologic processes. And summer temperatures reach the national maximum while winter minimums in the Northeast (see Ch.2) suggest stations in Maine and Minnesota. Some sections of our golden land approach Washington or British Columbia in winter wetness while altitudes in the High Sierra (Ch.10) impart summer temperatures equivalent to those along Alaska's Arctic Coast. These exemplify the variety and uneven distribution of California's biotic, soil, mineral (including water) resources. Physiographic distinctiveness provides an economic advantage over topographic uniformity in view of California's near-juxtaposition of *dry subtropical* and *cool humid* habitats—one offers warmth and productive soils, the other water and timber. Multiplicity of environments likewise permits varied farming and recreational opportunities over extended periods of the year.

The Golden State's diverse landscapes pose certain physical barriers; they have been conducive to uneven distribution of resources, occupations and attitudes; thus they predispose California to elements of disunity. Although these problems have been mitigated by unification of statehood, economic linkages and transport improvement, they have not been eliminated. They contribute moreover to other elements of diversity. considered next.

### Shopping Malls and Farmsteads

California's early dominance by rural livelihoods and outlooks has been progressively eroded through urbanization—strong disparities now prevail. Farmland occupies far more of the state yet metropolitan populace is numerically dominant; there are still two hundred thousand "rural" farm inhabitants. An even larger portion of California remains uncultivated—scarcely a third of the state has as many as ten inhabitants to the square mile (Fig. E-5). Even in the past when location was more of a basis for political representation, little influence could be exerted by this sizable portion of the Golden State; sometimes as much energy was devoted to separatism as to leadership.

California's rural-urban distinction has been blurred by several conditions. There has been too late a start and too much mobility and urban interdependence for rural loyalties to intensify in California as they have done in some states. A disproportionate share of the state's rural dwellers actually live in hamlets or even cities and depend upon industrial or other nonfarm activities; admittedly many are ultimately attached to farming.

Urban agglomerations reveal the same socioeconomic areal difference found in metropolitan America, with central districts (and some downtown deterioration), suburbs, ethnic groups and distinct "class" neighborhoods. Such mini-regions have become more relevant to the state's geography as additional towns became cities and cities attained metropolitan status.

### The Tehachapi "Wall"

One of the most enduring geographic schisms within California has been the one that has existed between north and south; the traditional divide has been the Tehachapi Mountains (the southwestern fringe of the Sierra Nevada).

A more-meaningful distinction today would be three-fold: southern California (south of a Santa Ynez Valley-Tehachapi Mountains-Owens Valley "line,"

central California (north approximately to Ca. 20 or even Ca. 32) and northern California. The cultural distinctiveness of the latter tends to be ignored. And Sacramento and the Bay Area are not really northern.

The dichotomy on opposite sides of of the Tehachapi has continued since the Hispanic colonial times, engendered by distance, mountain barriers, climatic modifications and historic circumstances. Most certainly to the early Hispanics the Bay Area was northern. The schism continues today and remains formidable, attested by renewed proposals to sever the state into two. "Realms" of water and waterpower have been magnified; the South does need part of what nature gave the North. Again it is seen in the sphere of old versus north: Southern California as an Anglo area is the latecomer with the population majority to challenge the supremacy and pride of the North, especially San Francisco. The Los Angeles versus San Francisco "thing" exists between adjacent communities across the nation, especially in athletics. Polarized in these two leading urban centers is the enduring concept between conservative (Los Angeles) and liberal (San Francisco). This generalization overlooks the real north (i.e., "beyond" Chico and Santa Rosa), with its small towns and rural areas). Some have ascribed the difference between north and south as based upon historic immigration to the "two" Californias.

## THE MANY CALIFORNIAS

Variations in landscape, urban and rural habitats and the just-noted North versus South, can be visualized better if examined in terms of those numerous smaller units that in total form the California mosaic. For the Golden State is complex. The state is initially identified with several larger units ("regions") of western United States which geographers currently recognize.*

---

* In an overview of United States and Canada California is commonly regarded as part of The Pacific Coast (or Pacific Borderlands). But eastern California, beyond the barrier of the Peninsular Ranges, Sierra Nevada and Cascade Range, is commonly considered part of the Intermontane Region. The reader is referred to such standard texts on United States and Canada as C.L. White, E.J. Foscue and T.L. McKnight, Regional Geography of AngloAmerica, 6th edit., (Englewood Cliffs, N.J.: PrenticeHall, 1985; J.H. Patterson, North America, 7th edit., (New York: Oxford University Press, 1984); and S.S. Birdsall and J.H. Florin, Regional Landscapes of the United States and Canada, 2nd edit., (New York: John Wiley and Sons, 1981).

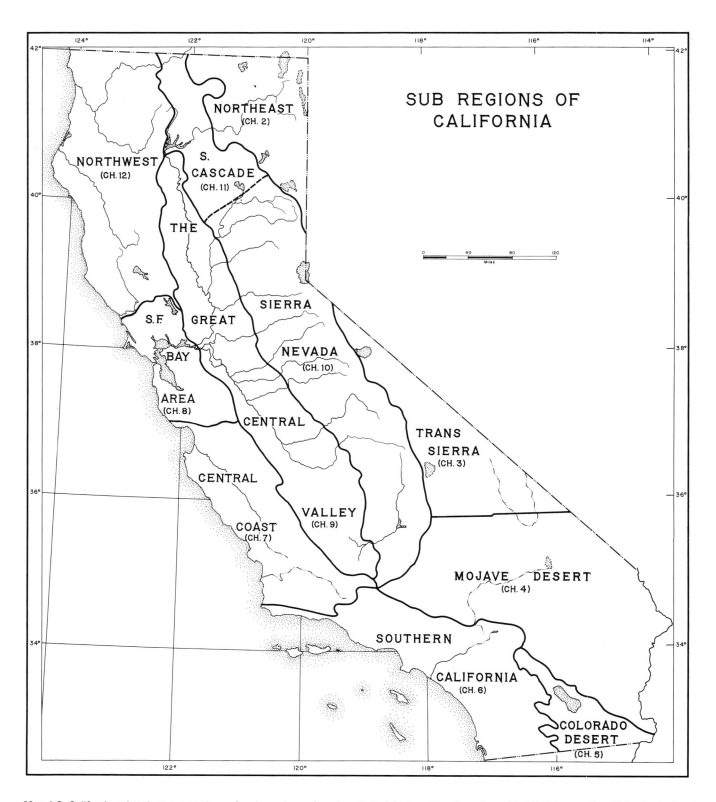

**Map 1-3.** California subregions are portions of major regions of western United States. They have been identified bases of multiple physical and cultural attributes. An attempt has been made to use names which have local acceptance. The dashed line reflects the impossibility of delineating the Sierra Nevada-southern Cascade transition.

To delineate a more detailed survey of the Golden State, this book identifies 11 subregions within the regions (i.e., *Intermontane Region, Heartland, and Northern Highlands).* *

The eastern marches of California penetrate into the *Intermontane Region* which covers a sizable area between the Pacific Highlands and the Rocky Mountain system. Four California segments of this region are identified: *Northeast, Trans-Sierra, Mojave Desert and Colorado Desert.*

Long considered the "Great American Desert" by explorers and even pioneer settlers, most of it is uninhabited although locally it is productive or scenic. Since it forms the traditional overland entry into the Golden State from the east, this realm makes an appropriate place to start the regional investigation of California.

The Heartland is definitely preeminent in renown, productivity, population and influence.

This is what the world generally accepts to be California. Logically it is assigned more space than other portions of the Golden State. Generally it coincides with parts of California which have the vaunted Mediterranean (dry-summer subtropical) climate. It encompasses nearly all of the Hispanic colonial province (Southern California, the Central Coast, the San Francisco Bay Area and the Great Central Valley)

Four mountainous areas, Sierra Nevada, Southern Cascade, Klamath and northern Coast Ranges (the

---

*The senior author is uncertain about the word region. This term seems to mean "everything" and almost "nothing". Lantis prefers to use *region* for large multicharacteristic areas and s*ubregion* for subdivisions thereof. Steiner and many others feel differently.

latter two are considered a single subregion, The Northwest) have been included within the final section as the Northern Highlands.

This sparsely-populated realm provides a delectable "dessert" after the complexity of the "main course" (i.e., The Heartland). Within United States and Canada, these highlands logically extend north into Alaska—they tend to be seasonally damp, relatively chilly and forested.

Within California, north and east of the Heartland, the Northern Highlands and the Intermontane Region suffer from climatic limits and rough terrain. They do not connote California to people of other states and nations. In fact their own residents sometimes have felt that they are California's forgotten people.

While relatively empty, these peripheral areas enrich the Heartland with water, power, lumber, mineral and ranch products. And they provide escape areas for urbanites. Where they adjoin large-populous areas they are experiencing inflow of urban-based residents. Elsewhere these marginal locales help service overland travel between the Heartland and other parts of United States, provide space for military operations not accommodated in the Heartland and afford priceless recreation sites for the increasingly-crowded millions in California's core areas.

So how many Californias are there? The first edition of California, Land of Contrast identified ten, including the Bay Area within the Central Coast. In the late twentieth century the State Office of Tourism finds twelve. Regardless of how many subdivisions of California one may choose to find, the regional approach seems to be the logical way to examine this fascinating and complex land.  So we now proceed.

PART ONE

THE
INTERMONTANE
REGION

# THE INTERMONTANE REGION

A vast land between the Sierra-Cascade on the west and the Rocky Mountains on the east, the Intermontane Region* reaches from the Canadian border on the north to the Gulf of California. Although an Occidental heritage dates from Spanish conquistadors, the Lewis and Clark expedition and the mountain men of the early nineteenth century, this broad expanse remains nearly devoid of human occupancy over wide areas. J. Russell Smith, in describing portions of it, wrote:

This is a vast region. everywhere the rain is so slight, the summer so hot, that the farmer with his plow is not the symbol of settlement. Instead it is the cowboy with his lariat and leather leggings that keep the cactus from pricking him. Someone has said that this is a region where there are more streams and less water, more cows and less milk, and where one can look farther and see less, than any other place in the world. **

Little of the Intermontane Region is actually within California. The general description presented here is provided as a background for subsequent consideration of its California subregions. The four segments of the Golden State that are encompassed within this region are not what the world's citizenry identifies with the word California. Considered in the first part of the book, these four subdivisions, which describe the driest fourth of the state, are: the Northeast, the Trans-Sierra, the Mojave Desert and the Colorado Desert. Had the borders of our eleven western states been determined simultaneously, quite probably no part of the Intermontane Region would have been included within California.

While human activities may differ on the wooded slopes of the Blue Mountains of Oregon and in the scorching deserts of southern Arizona in summer, nearly everywhere they are hampered by insufficient water. In essence the Region is bordered by mountains sufficiently high that moisture from either the Pacific or Atlantic is removed before it reaches this parched land.

Since the Coronado expedition of the sixteenth century, many renowned explorers have traversed portions of the Intermontane Region. But their efforts seldom attracted settlers into this dry country. The population density remained low even after the At-

lantic and Pacific slopes were linked by railroads in the second half of the nineteenth century. Cycles of heavier rainfall encouraged occupance of the Great Plains but the ongoing dryness of the Intermontane Region only locally allowed hope for dry-land farming.

An important inducement to attract humankind into these barren lands has been provided by mineral deposits. Famed mine camps boomed, then usually declined into ghost towns. Among the more renowned of such places, some still active, have been Bingham Canyon, Bisbee, Bodie, Cerro Gordo, Death Valley and Douglas.

The Mormons moved into the Salt Lake Basin a century and a half ago and demonstrated that, with irrigation, agriculture could succeed in this sunny land. In time, irrigation farming developed elsewhere—in the Yakima and Wenatchee valleys of Washington, along the Snake River in southern Idaho, in the Imperial Valley of California and in the Salt-Gila Basin of Arizona. Construction of such dams as Roosevelt, Hoover and Grand Coulee was permitted by technological advances, and the drilling of pump wells in the Coachella and Antelope valleys, enabled expansion of cropped land. Still, much of the water used to irrigate the land must come from peripheral mountains. The stinginess of the rain gods negates agricultural utilization of most of the Intermontane Region.

Especially since the late 1920s, in the automotive age, highway travel and recreation have helped to diversify the regional economy. Today interstate highways 8, 10, 40, 80 and 90 follow major transcontinental routes that contribute considerably to the economic well-being of the Intermontane Region. In the twentieth century Bryce Canyon, Death Valley and the Grand Canyon have gained recognition as natural wonderlands. Human works like Hoover and Grand Coulee dams are on the agenda of expanding numbers of visitors to western America.

Man has erected such places of sport, relaxation, and retirement in the desert as Las Vegas, Palm Springs, Reno and Tucson.

Portions of the Intermontane Region have been called the "modern American frontier." One accustomed to thinking of exceedingly small populations for Nevada and Arizona reads the latest census statis-

---

* Most authors of recent textbooks on the geography of Anglo-America, although the specific names they employ may vary somewhat, identify such a region.
** J. Russell Smith and M. Odgen Phillips, North America (New York: Harcourt, Brace and World, Inc., 1942), p. 545.

tics and the anticipated growth predictions in astonishment.

The four subregions within the Golden State have differing relationships to the remainder of California. The Northeast, particularly, has loose ties with the rest of California. The Northeast, unlike the two southern subregions, the Colorado Desert and the Mojave Desert, is not crossed by a major east-west rail line or highway. The Trans-Sierra has more affiliation with Southern California; many urbanites traverse U.S. 395 enroute to recreation areas. In fact the Trans- Sierra, with Death Valley, is a recreational objective. While water, via the Los Angeles Aqueduct, and hydro-electricity from the Trans-Sierra are dispatched to Southern California, the high Sierran wall hampers contact between the Trans-Sierra and central portions of California.

By contrast the Mojave has close contacts with central California as well as Southern California. Products of its ranches and mines are shipped to Southern California and an expanding number of Mojave residents commute to employment in the Los Angeles conurbation. Ties between the Colorado Desert and Southern California are likewise strong. The Los Angeles metropolis created Palm Springs; Southern Californians also frequent the Colorado River and the Salton Sea. Also, Southern California provides a primary market for the agricultural products of the Coachella and Imperial valley portions of this Desert.

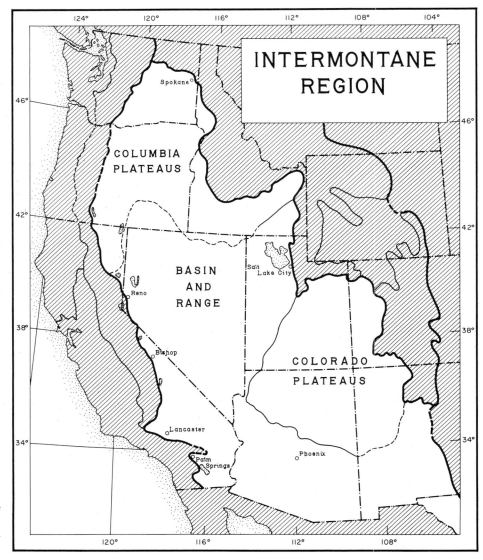

**Map 1-1.** Only four smaller segments of the Intermontane region (the Northeast, Trans-Sierra, Mojave Desert, and Colorado Desert) are located within California.

**Figure 2-1.** The Northeast is a lonesome land where the physical earth is conspicuous. This is the Modoc Plateau, viewed northeast from Schonchin Butte east toward Tule Lake. (Mary Hill)

# Chapter Two

# THE NORTHEAST

This chapter has been reviewed, as previously, by Robert Middleton, Lassen College. The predecessorial work was also reviewed by Robert Pease, University of California, Riverside and Rolland Berger, C.S.U., Chico.

# THE NORTHEAST

Surely this lonesome land, with its broad empty spaces, cannot be California. Assuredly it is not the California that the world and most Californians know. Sometimes flattish, but with mountains often in view, this crudely triangular jumble of lava, essentially in Modoc and Lassen counties, is separated from the remainder of the Golden State by the Sierra Nevada (see map 2-1). Some find suggestions here of Colorado or Wyoming (Fig.2-1). There appears to be a climatic analogue between Alturas and Cheyenne in average January and July temperatures, in snowfall totals and in annual precipitation. Vegetation over wide stretches is sparse—like Wyoming, sagebrush is often the dominant plant.

With a surfeit of porous rocky surfaces and a dry-summer climate, water and cultivable land tend to be cherished. Hence streams from highlands are tapped carefully in those few areas where alluvial soils and terrain permit irrigation—one map shows 36 irrigation reservoirs in the Northeast. Yet paradoxically, poor drainage forms a major obstacle to vernal grazing on numerous wet meadows otherwise valuable.

Although its total population of around 30,000 would hardly make a respectable suburb in the Bay Area, the area of the Northeast is larger than any of the nation's nine smallest states. While many residents are either ranch or hamlet dwellers, wide stretches are empty. Well over half of the total inhabitance is found in two areas, the **Upper Pit Basin** and the **Honey Lake Plain,** with more than 15,000. There are few cities; Susanville, the largest community gains much support from highlands to the west.

The dominant source of Northeastern livelihood is ranching. Livestock, primarily beef cattle but also sheep, determine ranch economy and provide the leading source of rural income.

Summer feed comes from the open range, extensively regulated by the federal government within national forests or Taylor grazing districts.* Government policy prescribes the adjustment of animal population to the natural carrying capacity of these lands; there are additional restrictions where timber growth of watershed protection is involved. Growing season variability (range grass is available one year in February, perhaps in May the next year) plus the multiple use program for the national forests makes ideal grazing intensity difficult, both scientifically and politically, and can still precipitate controversy between rancher and federal administrator. Winter feed is provided by

hay and grain, the most extensively cultivated crops in the Northeast. Irrigated lands commonly produce livestock feeds although some grain is dry-farmed and some natural forage comes from wet meadows. The most significant variation from this theme occurs in the Tule Lake Basin.

Forestry, the other major source of income, is likewise sharply restricted by federal policy (as well as the availability of timber) thus assuring some degree of permanency. Here, as elsewhere in the West, much timberland is outside the national forest, whereas much non-timbered land is with such preserves. The Northeast produces about five per cent of California's log output, chiefly western yellow (Ponderosa and Jeffrey) pine.

Processing has declined significantly; Susanville is now the single center and there are only two operating mills in Modoc County. In the Northeast, like the eastern slopes of the nearby Sierra Nevada and Cascade, sawtimber cut long exceeded regrowth. Much of the annual growth in the area is classed as cull and breakage, indicating less than ideal soil and climate for tree growth. Appreciable areas of the Northeast have greater *immediate* value for grazing.

The abundance of open space is another major asset of the Northeast. But, despite spiraling metro-

---

* Suitable portions of the federal public domain, not reserved for other uses, are leased under the Taylor Grazing Act to private ranchers, particularly to long-established operators. The number of livestock are regulated in accord with range capacities as ascertained by the Bureau of Land Management (B.L.M.). In California Taylor districts are largely confined to the Northeast and the Trans-Sierra subregions. Exchange of land between the Forest Service and B.L.M. is under consideration.

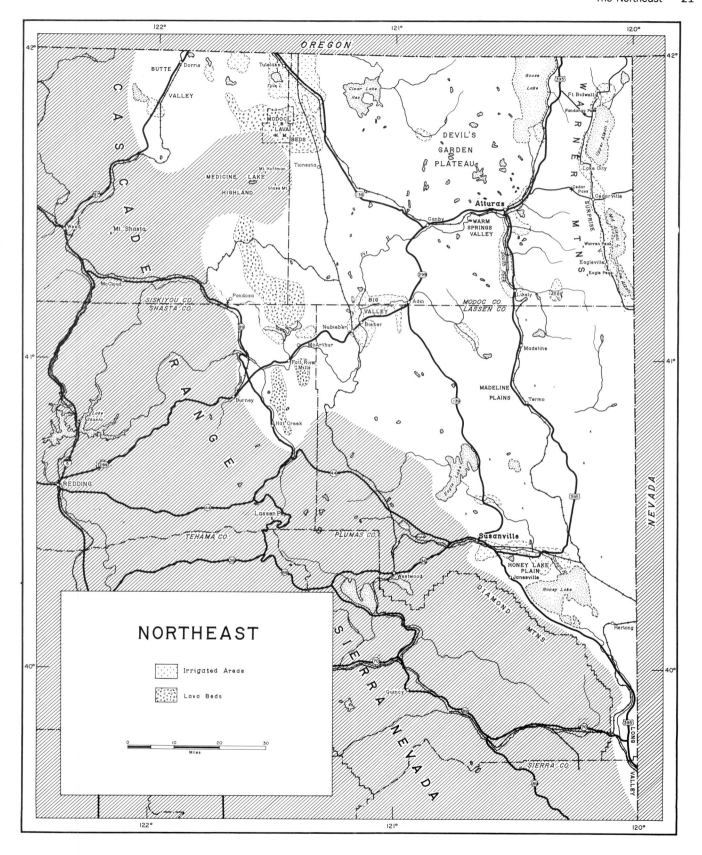

**Map 2-1.** The Northeast includes all of Modoc County, most of Lassen County and the eastern portions of Siskiyou and Shasta counties.

**Figure 2-2.** The harvest of barley, Tule Lake Basin. Considerable barley is sold to brewers; the remainder is used for livestock feed locally. (Tulelake Chamber of Commerce and Tulelake Growers Association)

politan growth, the Golden State retains an adequacy of this resource in areas more accessible than the Northeast and more climatically benign.

Few fishermen and hunters visit this area because of the out-of-the-way location and somber-hued lava fields do not excite many tourists. Position alone sets the Northeast apart from major interstate travel routes (save for Butte Valley in the extreme northwest, athwart the main California-Oregon rail route). Thus scenic attractions like Eagle Lake, Glass Mountain, Lava Beds and the Warner Mountains remain comparatively unvisited; even the military has limited its activities to the **Sierra Ordnance Depot** at Herlong.

Nowhere else in California is there such an extensive area of nearly flat lava surfaces—the Northeast is a distinct, albeit relatively isolated portion of California. No other section has an economy so singularly dependent upon extensive livestock ranching.

Even as it is more akin physically to eastern Oregon and Nevada than the "other Californias" to be considered, the Northeast culturally too tends to maintain an out-of-state orientation.

Residents of northern Modoc County read the Portland *Oregonian*, watch southern Oregon television stations and shop in Klamath Falls. Since improvement of Ca. 36 however residents of the Honey Lake Plain have strengthened their connections with lands to the west of the Sierra Nevada. They watch television programs from the Sacramento Valley and read the Sacramento *Bee* but often risk the known hazards of U.S. 395 to shop in Reno. Federal land policies formulated in Washington, D.C. prompt letters to the local congressman. Following reapportionment of the California

Senate (in 1965) some residents of Modoc County threatened to repeat their secession attempts of the 19th century. And they are forced to "share" a state senator who represents much of the Sierra Nevada as well as the distant city of Modesto. Still the Northeast is linked to the California Heartland by such all-compelling political ties as markets for much of its forest products and livestock, sources of tourists and inclusion within the San Francisco wholesale trade area.

The people of the Northeast can be classified in two general groups: "old timers" (as Indians, ranchers and retail merchants, often the descendants of pioneers) and newcomers, including exurban Social Security recipients.

The latter group shifts more rapidly—some individuals do not adjust to this "different California." Recently outside money has purchased land. Many ambitious youth depart after high school; there are limited economic opportunities in the Northeast. Conservatism is strong and welfare loads light. The feeling of "white backlash" seems incongruous in hamlets without blacks or Asians.

## AN OBTRUSIVE EARTH

### Fault Blocks and Tablelands

While the Northeast is plateau country it does not represent the textbook example of billiard-ball flatness. Surfaces vary from 3000 to 10,000 feet—"typical" elevations approximate 4500 feet.

Successive basaltic lava outpourings from multitudinous vents created much of the present topography before or during the Pleistocene ice age (i.e., the last two million years). The flows buried older north-south trending fault-blocks. Oldest flows postdate the formation of Mount Shasta while the youngest, only a few centuries old, are weathered so little that the rocky surface is barren of plant cover.

There are three principal physiographic units: (1) the Warner Mountains and contiguous Surprise Valley (2) the Honey Lake Plain (3) the Modoc Plateau (a segment of the extensive Columbia Plateaus to the north). The prior two areas form small segments of the Great Basin. But the largest portion is the Modoc Plateau.

**Honey Lake Plain**, between the Diamond Mountains segment of the Sierra Nevada (west) and the Amadee-Skedaddle Range (east), has a pluvial basin history.

This is the California portion of the bed of Pleistocene Lake Lahontan, an extensive Ice Age surface that was largely in Nevada. Honey Lake itself a relict of Lake Lahontan, whose greater depth and

**Figure 2-3.** The Warner Mountains and Surprise Valley, viewed southward with Cedarville in the foreground. Alluvial aprons at the base of the fault scarp are used for cattle ranching. The meadows in the foreground are flood irrigated or by sprinklers and pumps. (dwl)

size are revealed by prominent wave-cut terraces. The discharge of Susan River and lesser streams enters the lake but much flow has been diverted for irrigation while summer evaporation from the surface of this shallow body is high.

Appreciable portions of the Northeast, including the Honey Lake Plain, are covered with lake silts of Pleistocene origin. Much of the cropped land, is either of such origin or is alluvial. Included are Surprise Valley, Tule Lake Basin and the Pit River Valley.

Most of the lakes are Ice Age relicts, remnants of once-larger bodies much diminished as result of desiccation, drainage and irrigation.

**The Warner Range**, westernmost Basin Range in this subregion, is suggestive of a miniature Sierra Nevada.

It is a complex fault block about 90 miles long, varying in width from eight to 20 miles. Higher peaks, with small glacial lakes, attain elevations of 8000 to 10,000 feet. The Surprise Valley Fault, along the steep eastern face, has vertical displacement of about 6000 feet (Fig.2-3).

The **Modoc Plateau** is covered with widespread basaltic lava flows and scattered cinder cones. *

Its principal subdivision is the *Devil's Garden Plateau* north of the Pit River Valley, bounded by an impressive scarp to the east and south. South of the Pit Valley, Modoc lavas have almost buried older fault blocks although bold cliffs, such as the Hat Creek Escarpment are pominent locally. On the Modoc's northwestern edge *Lava Beds National Monument* has appeal for earth scientists as well as vacationers, with its cinder cones, Mammoth Crater and several hundred caverns (lava tubes).

The Plateau is less arid than is suggested by the paucity of surface flow. The lavas are highly permeable—this is one of the principal areas of large springs within the United States. The principal river, the Pit, rises in the Warner Mountains but crosses the width of the Modoc and the Southern Cascade to become an important tributary of the Sacramento.

## Pines and Sagebrush

The natural vegetation forms a transition between the Great Basin types and those of the mountains to the west.

---

* Despite the widespread acceptance of the term Modoc, Pease in his published dissertation suggested substitution of the name Volcanic Tableland because of the poor definition of the extent of the Modoc Plateau. His tableland would include the Warner Mountains.

The Northeast is the largest area of Great Basin sagebrush in California—it is found in association with saltbush, bitterbrush and bunch grass (the chief forage plant). The eastside Sierran forest, primarily firs and pines, covers sizable tracts in the western half of the area and also in the Warner Mountains.

Timber constitutes a ranking natural resource of the Northeast.

Travelers along U.S. 395 do not appreciate this, since there is a belt of western juniper along the highway, extending north-south through the central portion of the Northeast.

Terrain, altitude, water availability and soils all influence the distribution of vegetation.

If young lava flows are not weathered sufficiently the ground has limited cover. However, aspen glades are found locally within the Warner Mountains forests while tule rushes extend along some stream courses on the Tule Lake Basin and the Honey Lake Plain.

### Thunderstorms and Snow Flurries

The Northeast generally has a dry-summer humid middle-latitude climate (identified as *Ds* by Russells, considered semi-arid by Thornthwaite—see Bibliography) which contrasts with the aridity of Intermontane California farther south.

Most of the precipitation, frequently as snow, is brought by cyclonic storms out of the north Pacific in winter. Annual totals are modest in comparison with mountain areas farther west but the snowfall compares favorably with that received by portions of central United States with a continental climate. Limited summer moisture comes from either tropical disturbances or polar-front passage.

Seasonal changes are suggestive of those associated with interior middle latitude environments.

The January to July mean monthly range is 35 to 50 degrees Fahrenheit; altitude tends to produce rather cool summers ( Alturas averages 67 degrees in July). The growing season ( approximately four months) tends to be short, and frosts have occurred in all months. Winter temperatures average only slightly below freezing but polar outbursts can bring sharp cold spells; -36 degrees F. recorded in Madeline represents the all-time minimum winter extreme. At such times, a person may suspect that the only barrier holding back the cold blasts is a barbed wire fence. Weather stations commonly record a seasonal snowfall of 3 to 4 feet. In midwin-

ter, dense radiation fogs sometimes occur around Tule Lake and Honey Lake.

### Soils: Less than the Best

Good soils are restricted; thus only a tenth of the Northeast is suitable for cultivation.

Loams and silts of lacustrine or alluvial origin are characteristic in tilled areas. But over wide stretches the young volcanic rocks have weathered insufficiently to produce good soils.

## INHABITANCE

The Northeast has experienced a less-elaborate occupance than some parts of California. It was beyond the confines of Spanish and Mexican habitation. More recently, the settlement has been relatively simple. For instance, the subregion has not attracted large numbers of Asians and Hispanics.

### Four Peoples

Prior to Anglo-American settlement, representatives of four American Indian groups shared the Northeast. None was agrarian yet all except the Northern Paiute were semisedentary.

The periphery of *Northern Paiute* lands extended into Surprise Valley and the eastern Honey Lake Plain.

These Uto-Aztecans, late arrivals among Native Americans, were materially inferior to the other three peoples. Crude conical huts, bark or brush covered, provided winter shelter. Insects, nuts and seeds were common foodstuffs; grasshoppers were regarded as delicacies and small game (especially rabbits) was prized in the winter diet.

A Penutian people, the *Maidu*, occupied the northern Sierra Nevada and the Cascadian basins west of Honey Lake Plain—the western edge of the Plain formed peripheral territory.

Hokan family members, the *Achomawi*, dominated the largest portion of the Northeast, the Pit River drainage basin. The resource economy of these riparian people included deer, fish and waterfowl.

A small, closely-knit tribe, the *Modoc*, resided around northern lake basins.

The Modoc have been considered valorously warlike because of their success in delaying Anglo settlement through the Modoc War (1872-1873). These lake dwellers used tules (bulrushes) for basketry, clothing, dwellings and rafts.

Possibly a thousand semi-Indians (there has been

intermingling, especially with Mexicans in recent generations) still live in the Northeast.

Indians who have acquired more formal education often leave the area—their former white neighbors speak of them with respect. A subtle prejudice remains towards the others— perhaps it is best described as bewilderment over their reluctance to accept more fully an alien culture. The Indians have become strangers in their homeland.

### Next: Anglo-Americans

Soon after California achieved statehood Anglo settlement began; homesteads were established on favorable surfaces near Alturas, Susanville and Cedarville.*

The easily-flooded alluvial meadows provided forage and cattle ranching was the principal way of life. Livestock were naturally expected to forage for themselves, then were slaughtered for their tallow and hides if not trailed to markets west of the Sierra Nevada.

Market conditions were unfavorable and transportation was arduous hence settlement came slowly. The Northeast was not a too-appealing part of the West as long as less isolated areas were available.

Isolated geographically from more populous portions of California, with physiographic ties to the desert country of Nevada, early Northeastern residents tended to have a spirit of independence.

Isaac Roop and Peter Lassen proclaimed the *Territory of Natagua* in 1855 but Congress never accepted the short-lived entity. The Sagebrush War of the following decade resulted from disagreement between California and Nevada over the interstate boundary. Much later, in 1959, a prominent Nevada legislator questioned the validity of the state line.

### LAND OF BEEF AND TIMBER

The uncomplicated economy of the Northeast is dependent upon cattle ranching, lumbering and tourism. Thus its population understandably remains sparse.

An individual can walk for many hours or even days, apart from the few larger towns and main roads, and possibly not see another person. With possible exception of the Trans-Sierra, considered in the next chapter, nowhere else in California has man altered the landscape so modestly.

The Northeast is no longer a surplus timber pro-

ducer—private stands have been depleted.

Decline followed a generation of accelerated lumbering that ended in 1959. Although the output of pine decreased in the late 1950's, the harvest of white pine was increased. But by the 1960's the last private stands of timber were being cut and some once-large lumber camps vanished. Regrowth will take many years.

In the 1980's the forest industries have been relatively stable; several hundred are employed.

The last sizable private stand of first-growth timber (the Weyerhauser Tract on the Devil's Garden) was cut between 1965 and 1975—it is now on a 70-year regrowth cycle. Thus much of the current logs come from national forests. Trucks, transporting logs 70 to 100 miles, have replaced the logging railroads of the past. With trucks, logging of smaller acreage is economic when combined with rail operations. Location east of the Sierra front creates slightly lower rail rates; considerable lumber moves east by rail.

Minerals have never been of much economic consequence in the Northeast but geothermal energy may gain importance. Surprise Valley and the Honey Lake Plain seem to afford prospects.

Some power is now being generated with geothermal energy. The high school in Susanville is warmed with earth heat, as are some commercial greenhouses.

Early in the 20th century a small amount of gold and silver was taken from the Warner Mountains. Various deposits have produced highway construction materials. A drained lake bed in Jess Valley has been one of California's commercial sources of peat moss since 1937. The mining may continue for another decade.

Southern California syndicates have sold considerable "vacation retirement" acreage.

The largest venture has been *California Pines* southwest of Alturas. Streets have been laid out and some homes have been built. Many buyers have chose to camp their recreational vehicles on their lots instead of constructing houses.

### THE SEVERAL REALMS

Varied physical, economic and historic factors warrant discussion of portions of the Northeast separately.

---

* It should be stressed that much land in California was too dry to farm without irrigation. Moreover, many choice lands had been claimed during the colonial period.

## Surprise Valley

Locally, the densest rural population within the Northwest is found in Surprise Valley. * Its area (250 square miles) is small and its easterly portion has intermittent lakes, salt flats and migrating sand dunes. Cultivation is limited to a narrow belt where a score of small creeks issue from the eastern flank of the Warner Range. In the past two decades pump wells have permitted expanded acreage of alfalfa but increased costs for electricity have been ruinous for some ranchers in the 1980's.

The Valley's four long-withering ranch villages seem to have stabilized with some retiree residence.

Currently few dwellings are vacant and numbers of mobile homes have been brought in. The largest hamlet, **Cedarville,** even has limited medical facilities and several eateries. A crossroads junction (Fig. 2-3) with white frame cottages like of a rural New England place, it suggests the nineteenth century.

Surprise Valley, despite its ongoing seclusion, became the first center of livestock ranching in Modoc County.

Through the years ranches have been consolidated, hence the population has not increased. Recently, as elsewhere in America, higher operating costs have been ruinous for some ranchers. There never has been a local railhead and beef is trucked to market.

Transhumance (seasonal migration) is practiced; livestock are still hauled eastward into the uplands of northeastern Nevada in spring. The abrupt fault face of the Warner Range has discouraged its use from the east. Haymaking for local winter feed is the principal summer activity, with alfalfa seed as a commercial product. As elsewhere in the Northeast, cattle are marketed in autumn as "long yearlings" (about 700 pounds).

Livestock are meadow pastured much of the winter (because of rainshadow location snow cover is limited), reducing hay consumption. With pump wells and sprinklers, slopes at the base of the Warner now produce alfalfa, much of which is shipped westward.

## The Warner Range

Due to isolation the Warner Range has never gained deserved recognition.

A prime value is to provide a "reservoir" for winter moisture falling from east-moving storms. Thousands of cattle graze on its meadows in summer and a little logging has been conducted. If this alpine fastness was adjacent to Los Angeles, with its attributes, it would be a nationally-known playground. For the limited number who know the range and enjoy these mountains, trout fishing, autumnal deer hunting and hiking are attractions.

The *South Warner Wilderness Area*, with 70,000 acres, occupies the higher southern portion of the range.**

As yet there is no immediate threat of overuse of the Warner wilderness despite the thousands who now visit this locale each summer. Here are found *Eagle Peak* (9934 ft.) and other summits, snowfed glacial lakes stocked with trout, a scenic summit trail and campsites.

The Range is not a serious barrier to east-west movement due to Cedar Pass (6350 ft.).

Long-desired *Winnemucca-to-the-Sea Highway*, which would utilize Ca. 299 through Cedar Pass, lacks the support of Reno. Yet appreciable truck traffic from the east uses the unpaved (and dusty) road westward from Nev. route 140 to the California line. Another deep notch farther north, Fandango Pass, was used by pioneers but has never been paved.

## The Pit River Valley

The Pit River and its two headwater forks occupy a crudely "Y-shaped" depression across the Modoc Plateau. There are two foci of ranching—the upper basin just west of the Warner Mountains and Big Valley downriver.

### The Upper Pit Basin

Three segments (Goose Lake Valley, South Fork Valley and Warm Springs Valley) comprise the basin of the upper Pit River (map 2-1).

Ranching in Goose Lake Valley is limited due to insufficiency of water from the less-lofty northern portion of the Warner Mountains, unfavorable soils and small pastoral allotments within the Warner.

---

* In *California Place Names* (Berkeley, University of Cal. Press), Gudde suggested that early wayfarers on an offshoot of the *Oregon Trail* named the Valley after they had crossed Nevada's Black Rock Desert and found grass and potable water. Pease (personal communication) believes that Valley was named by its settlers in 1863.
**Wildernesses, portions of national parks and forested to remain largely in the primitive state for enjoyment by nature lovers, were finally afforded statutory protection by Congress in 1964. Thirteen of California's areas were given "charter status" under the legislation. Additional areas have been approved with major increments in 1984 (as described in Chapter 10).

Contemporary land use in the South Fork Valley was established nearly a century ago with consolidation of properties into a single sizable unit.

Formerly owned by a Southern California oil company and more recently by an insurance firm, the property (formerly called the Corporation Ranch and now the Lyneta Ranch) has been enlarged to include 18,000 acres in the Madeline Plains. Cultivation has been improved and in the mid-1980's there was experimentation with wild rice.* Company cattle have long been pastured in the Warner Mountains.

Westward from Alturas, the *Warm Springs Valley*, has more productive acreage than the two segments of the upper Pit just mentioned.

Its ranches tend to generate incomes above the countywide average, especially as larger properties have replaced smaller ranches through consolidation of homesteads of past times. This is reflected sometimes in abandoned houses and barns. Traditionally flooded meadows along the Pit produced native hay but expansion of alfalfa has occurred. Adjacent uplands provide summer pasturage; some ranchers use the Devils Garden Plateau to the north.

**Alturas** (3000),** the second city of the Northeast, is the seat of Modoc County. As the service center for an extensive area (including Surprise Valley) its commercial importance is enhanced by limited availability elsewhere in its county.

About half way between Seattle and Los Angeles, Alturas lies at the junction of U.S. 395 and Ca. 299. Hence restaurants, motels and service stations have appeared adjacent to older two-story structures on Main Street. This is the single Modoc town with a radio station, specialty shops and automobile agencies. A westside lumber mill, established later than many in the Northeast, has benefited from the Southern Pacific railhead. Long the junction for the railroad's Lakeview branch line, Alturas has lost its cattle shipments by rail; animals are now trucked to market. Around 50 Indians reside in improved housing on the southwest outskirts (*physically* the most attractive site in town because a hillock affords protection against north winds). Mansions are absent in Alturas; most residences are unpretentious.

*Big Valley*

An erstwhile lake bed along the middle Pit River, Big Valley has been drained partially. Homesteaders occupied land after areas around Alturas and Susan-

ville were settled.

The original 160-acre homesteads proved too small; holdings have been consolidated so that contemporary ranches average between 1000 and 2000 acres, partially irrigated. Such hamlets as Bieber, Aden and Fall River Mills have local importance.

A producer of "long yearlings" for California markets, Big Valley is hampered by poor marginal land for summer pasturage.

Shallow-rooted alfalfa and native hay are grown and lately bedding strawberries have been added. Once dairying was important here but as in other quasi-isolated area to be noted later, this district no longer competes (since highway improvement) with larger operators west of the Sierra-Cascade.

**Madeline Plains**

Another ancient lake bed, the Madeline Plains, south of the upper Pit Basin, has productive soils but long lacked sufficient water (despite winter swamps which produced excellent duck and geese hunting). Now there are pump wells on the portion which is part of the Lyneta Ranch noted previously.

With wheel-line irrigation, this area now produces alfalfa. Elsewhere dry-farmed grains remain typical. There are also a few large cattle ranches scattered across the treeless expanse. Several diminutive communities have rail sidings, service stations, shanties and taverns. Still, many travelers on U.S. 395 scarcely slacken their speed as they cross the Plains.

**Northern Basins**

Much of the western portion of the Northeast is by nature forested. Two settlement nuclei are beds of pluvial lakes in northeast Siskiyou County: Tule Lake Basin and Butte Valley, partially separated by volcanic uplands containing *Lava Beds National Monument*.

Geologically, Lava Beds suggests a larger *Craters of the Moon* (Idaho). But it has the legacy of the *Modoc War* and nearness to Tule Lake. Its improved campgrounds are increasingly frequented.

The Northern basins had limited use until the area was crossed by rail lines and improved highways.

---

**Wild rice, grown commercially in California since 1981, is a grass indigenous to Minnesota and adjacent Canada. By 1987 18,000 acres were under cultivation, chiefly in the Sacramento Valley flood basins but also in the Northeast and Lake County.
*** Throughout the book population has been postulated to anticipated size in 1990.

In recent decades lumbering was significant; there were once considerable reserves of sugar pine, white pine, cedar and red fir. Now mills are closed and some of the camps have vanished completely.

*Butte Valley*

Butte Valley, in the far northwest corner of the subregion (map 2-1) has about 50 large ranches which produce alfalfa, fall-harvested potatoes and beef cattle.

*Dorris* (1000), the single noteworthy town, is a highway stop frequented by sportsmen and truckers. Following construction of the Southern Pacific's Shasta Line into Klamath Falls, a group of Brethren (or Dunkards, a Pennsylvania Dutch sect from the Middle West), established a colony in the early 1900's and tried to apply humid-land farming techniques. Their irrigation district remained water-short until pump wells were drilled through the volcanic cap rock. The Dunkards and their small farms are gone. In the early 1980's the area's prosperity lessened due to "farm problems," especially the rising costs of pumping.

*Tule Lake Basin*

The Basin, the ranking agricultural area of the Northeast, is a segment of Oregon's *Klamath Basin* that happens to be in California (map 2–1 and Fig. 2–2).

Farm evolution came late; after the Bureau of Reclamation constructed Clear Lake Reservoir on Lost River the level of Tule Lake dropped, permitting agricultural utilization of the Basin. World War I veterans began homesteading in 1922. During World War II Nisei (second generation Japanese immigrants), placed in a resettlement center, reclaimed additional land. Thus, after the war, more land was available for homesteading. So many ex-servicemen applied that it was necessary to hold a lottery to determine successful applicants.

The cultural landscape differs in detail from the remainder of the Northeast despite some similarity in product. Besides anticipated grains, alfalfa and livestock, there are other commodities.

Homesteads have been consolidated into larger properties. Many of the veterans are now gone. Drain ditches are conspicuous; there are also more shade trees than in most parts of the agricultural Northeast.

Of late there have been some changes in agriculture. And because of a lengthy Bureau of Reclamation contract for electricity, energy costs are less burdensome here than in other parts of the subregion.

Tule Lake, like the contiguous Klamath Basin, produces autumnal potatoes. Use of row-line irrigation has eliminated the fear of early frost and more economic use is made of fertilizer. While total output is insufficient to justify local processing (as frozen french fries), an improved type of storage cellar, employing nitrogen to delay spoilage, permits year-round marketing. Barley acreage has declined but raising of Sonoran wheats (suitable for both feed and food) has increased. Onion acreage fluctuates with U.S. exports; for a time in the 1980's the high value of the dollar was a problem. The Basin was once the single West Coast producer of durum wheat. With its production in the San Joaquin Valley, acreage in the Tule Lake has declined. An unique specialty, horseradish, is processed locally.

**Tulelake** (350), fifth largest community in the Northeast, provides a modicum of services (there is much shopping in Klamath Falls) despite limited facilities (Fig. 2-5).

Relative to change in the village, one local resident observed, "Mister, nothing is gonna change here. The action is in Klamath Falls. This is just a little farm town." Earlier, there was a little growth during agricultural expansion. Tulelake provides residence, shipping facilities and local needs (there is no local doctor).

**Honey Lake Basin**

Most populous portion of the Northeast, Honey Lake Basin suggests irrigated landscapes elsewhere in the Intermontane West— it has pastures, cropped fields, groves of trees and farm buildings.

Productive land continues southward on well-drained terraces southwest of ancient Lake Lahontan nearly 40 miles along Long Valley towards Reno, paralleling U.S. 395.

The Plain is a locale with a proud legacy of early California history.

For more than a century it has afforded a major gateway into the Sacramento and northern California. *Noble's Road, Humboldt Road* and other routes extended across the mountains northwest from Susanville, averting higher Sierran summits and deeper snowpacks to the south. Discovery of gold in the northern Sierra produced a brief period of lawlessness and boom. Disagreement over the northern Nevada-California border centered here—hence the would-be "Sagebrush War" in the early 1860's.

The Plain was long the only occupied portion of Lassen County; much of the county's population is still concentrated here. The area northeast of Honey Lake, drier and hotter, is little-utilized. Lands northwest of the lake along the Susan River are cultivated. Irrigation works came only with the arrival of the Southern Pacific in the 1880's; increased settlement resulted.

Land leveling, then pump wells and lately, wheel-line irrigation, has led to expanded tilled acreage.

Output of alfalfa, the principal irrigated crop, has increased; much is used locally for winter feed. Such grains as barley, wheat and rye are either grown under irrigation or dry-farmed. More recent changes include vegetables, grown in greenhouses with geothermal water and bedding strawberries, formerly raised around Redding in the northern Sacramento Valley.

In late summer ripe grain fields provide an attractive pattern against blue skies and the forested

**Figure 2-4.** Wildfowl, Tule Lake Wildlife Refuge. This preserve hosts the largest concentration of waterfowl in North America—millions of ducks visit this area on the Oregon border. Hunters come by the thousands in autumn. (Klamath Basin National Wildlife Refuges).

**Figure 2-5.** Tulelake and the Tule Lake Basin. This town provides local needs and is an agricultural shipping point for the Basin, a structural depression whose western wall rises a thousand feet. (Tulelake Chamber of Commerce)

**Figure 2-6.** Rural scene, Honey Lake Basin. Grain stubble and livestock are familiar sights on western edge of this relict of pluvial Lake Lahontan. The Diamond Mountains (rear) form northeastern fringe of the Sierra Nevada. (Lassen County Chamber of Commerce)

Diamond Mountains background. Potatoes yield well but market limitations long restricted vegetable production. Some milk is marketed locally but beef cattle are more important.

**Susanville** (6500), ranking community of the Northeast and seat of Lassen County, is the only town in the subregion showing appreciable population gain.

The city has traditionally been divided into a southside "mill town" and a more prestigious northside by the Susan River. Wide Main Street is flanked by older business blocks with newer establishments (especially travel-oriented) toward the east. As in Alturas deciduous shade trees create a changing seasonal aspect. Newer homes overlook the community and Honey Lake Plain from volcanic Cascadian slopes (Fig. 2-7).

Although it not experiencing spectacular growth, Susanville is supported by a diversity of incomes.

County business, state and local government district offices, rail traffic, ranch trade and lumber mills contribute to its viability. It is the site of a California Correction Center (men). As an eastern entryway to Lassen Volcanic National Park (and the Sierra-Cascade border country) and the Sacramento Valley, it is visited by increasing numbers of travelers. Lassen College, the Northeast's single center of higher education, doubled in enrollment after 18 year-olds were declared adults and many "academic refugees" from urban California began attending Lassen (and other outlying California colleges).

**Herlong** (2700) is a military installation whose population has fluctuated with changing military circumstances (Fig. 2-10).

The site of Sierra Army Depot, it was established east of Honey Lake in 1942; it affords advantages of dry climate and isolation. Its permanence became enhanced after it was deemed a wiser atomic-age storage site than Benicia (Ch.8). Much temporary housing for military retirees and civilian employees has been removed but maturing Chinese elms and permanent structures have reduced

**Figure 2-7.** Susanville is the largest city of the Northeast. This view is west into the wooded Cascadian tableland where the Susan River issues from its canyon onto the Honey Lake Plain. (Lassen County Chamber of Commerce, photo by Eastman's Studio)

### Eagle Lake

Sixteen miles north of Susanville, Eagle Lake is one of California's larger fresh water bodies. Despite moderate alkalinity it has gained as a recreational center with vacation dwellings, camping, aquatic recreation and a California State University, Chico environmental laboratory (the fauna is distinctive). Under-surface outflow makes it unique from the typical Great Basin terminal lake.

Like Tahoe and other lakes, Eagle has a fragile environment. The Forest Service has installed a "model" sewage system and hundreds of campsites (now managed by C.S.U., Chico). Some planners feel that this is a serious mistake as the density of use might upset the ecologic balance.

### AN UNIQUE LAND

Presently the Northeast tends to be an uncertain land. It has been a realm of "sagebrush aristocracy"— the large-holding rancher has been a prince whose voice has been respected locally. Descendant of successful pioneers, he has tended to be college educated

its bleakness. Many workers commute from Susanville or even Reno.

Figure 2-9. Camping at Eagle Lake. The vacationist savors the absence of congestion which is common at more frequented spots in the Golden State. Yet even here campgrounds are likely to be filled during popular summer weekends. (Shasta-Cascade Wonderland Association, photo by Ken Molino)

**Figure 2-8.** Eagle Lake and the southern Cascade Range. Attempts in the past to drain water from the lake failed. Recreation is having an expanded role but the environment is fragile! (Lassen County Chamber of Commerce, photo by Eastman's Studio)

and somewhat worldly although conservative by tradition and livelihood. Social stratification, while less rigid than in metropolitan California, does exist. Dedication to the arts is limited but a strong affection for nature prevails— Northeasterners fish and hunt! But as the end of the twentieth century approaches many ranchers are confronted with economic problems that tend to make the future uncertain. People here may be less directly affected by the Pacific Rim and national and world affairs, but they are still concerned.

This is a portion of California where a stranger can return after an absence of some years and not feel lost. Percentage-wise (but numerically involving only hundreds of people) the subregion has outgained the state in population.

Although roads are paved bus service is infrequent, airline and Amtrak service absent, distances considerable. Moreover two-lane highways, especially U.S. 395 between Susanville and Reno, can be somewhat unsafe. Perhaps there is less isolation than in earlier times but the Northeast remains a land apart from the California Heartland, with ties to Klamath Falls and Reno.

Land prices are somewhat higher than in the past, reflecting urban encroachment on farms elsewhere. Significant increase in sprinkler irrigation has occurred and the wheel-line is much seen. But higher pumping costs are hurting many ranchers. Short growing season and soil limitations remain impediments. Although employment in lumbering has stabilized, there are few mills now.

It is difficult to envision hordes of visitors despite beauty spots like Eagle Lake and the Warner Mountains. One recent migrant, a retiree from Southern California, commented, "This is a mighty good place to live if one likes isolation. And I reckon that after 30 years in the city, with that darned traffic and smog, I do. His wife was not available for comment (p.s.: Three years later this couple had moved to Red Bluff).

Figure 2-10. "Historic" street scene, Herlong. This photograph reflects the life style of employees at the base, except that they now live "off base", probably in Susanville. (dwl)

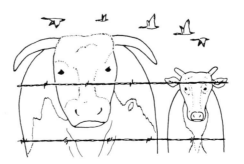

**Figure 3-1.** Death Valley, more than a mile deep, looking north with the Panamint Mountains in rear. View taken from Dante's View (5704 feet elevation). The playa surface near the middle of the picture contains the lowest spot in the hemisphere (-282 feet). (Mary Hill)

Chapter Three

# THE TRANS-SIERRA

* As previously, this chapter has been reviewed by John Carthew, Pierce College. Initially it was reviewed by the late Ruth E. Baugh, University of California at Los Angeles.

# THE TRANS-SIERRA

The silver gray of the mesa. The alkali blotch below
The water pool's sheen where the grass grows green

And the far peaks tipped with snow *

One poet thus envisages the landscape of California on the "far" (east) side of the Sierra Nevada. Triangular in shape, this Trans-Sierra subregion encompasses 13,000 square miles. It is delimited on the east by the Nevada border, on the south by the northern limits of San Bernardino County (map 3-1), and on the west by the abrupt front wall of the mighty Sierra. Representative features of this environment overlook human delimitation and reach eastward into Nevada. Like the ruler-edge political boundary on the east, which most certainly distressed the first surveyors, the southerly definition is pure literary convenience and is not indicative of conspicuous physical change.

The generosity of Vulcan's fires, coupled with Jupiter's niggardly rains, have fashioned Trans-Sierran terrain into a striking succession of naked north-south trending mountain blocks and intervening elongated basins with glaring playas.

In the vast and near-empty Trans-Sierra, man is a persistent intruder. About three quarters of the 26,000 permanent residents live in Owens Valley. Sizable tracts of federal lands give a practical indicator of sparse population and meager resources over most of the subregion.

Specifically these include (1) the unassigned lands still under the Bureau of Land Management in the public domain (2) Death Valley National Monument (3) national forests in the White-Inyo Mountains and the Volcanic Tableland (between Owens Valley and Mono Basin), dedicated primarily to range and watershed protection rather than forest preservation (4) military testing grounds—over 700 square miles (to the southeast of Owens Lake). Forty four per cent of all California land, a share exceeded in six other states, but third in acreage only to Alaska and Nevada, is controlled from Washington. Federal holdings in California consist mainly of national forests (20 million acres); Taylor Act grazing districts (7 million acres) and undedicated public domain (9 million acres), both administered by the Bureau of Land Management and particularly extensive in the Intermontane Region of the state; military reservations (4 million acres); national monuments (2.3 million acres); national parks (1.7 million acres); and Indian reservations (3.5 million acres).

The dominant source of income is derived from services to travelers to or through the subregion; overall, economic supports are limited.

Mining and ranching form the other two significant activities in the area. Mining output generally exceeds ranching in annual value of product but operations fluctuate considerably. The latter is localized and modest in scope. The important role mining has had in settlement justifies its primary consideration.

## IN QUEST OF GOLD—AND BORAX

The first economic activity that prompted Anglos to tarry in the Great Basin was mining—this has been as true in the Trans-Sierra as of the larger portion within Nevada (but not of Utah's Wasatch Front).

While the California segment of the Basin has lacked the dramatic story of renowned Virginia City, many of its hillsides have resounded with the ring of the prospector's pick against stone. The several centers of major significance in California have included *Bodie, Cerro Gordo* and *Death Valley*. Major strikes have involved a small portion of this province.

### Twenty-Mule Teams

The Trans-Sierra, with the adjacent Mojave Desert, has provided almost the entire world output of borate minerals.

Initially the borates were associated with waters and gases that accompanied volcanism; later these

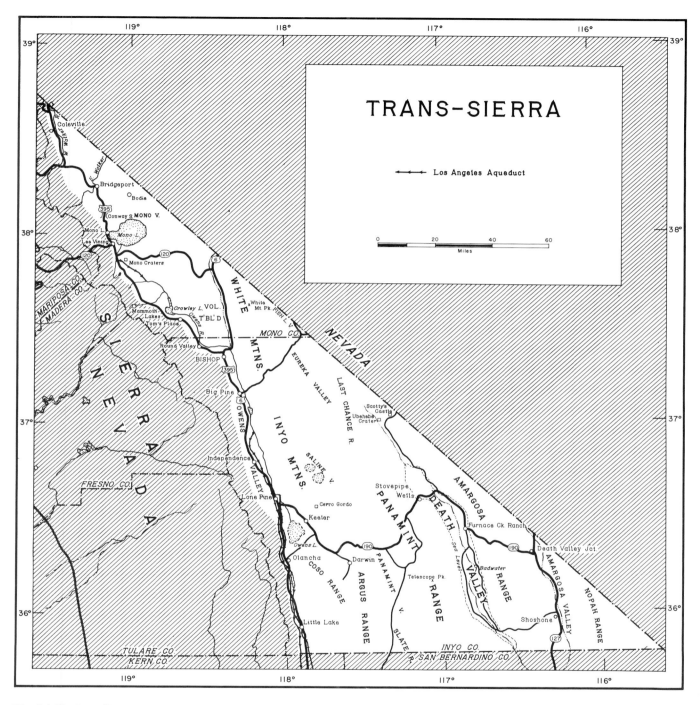

**Map 3-1.** The Trans-Sierra, covering most of Mono and Inyo counties, is part of the Great Basin within California. The Basin forms part of Intermontane Region of western United States.

salines were deposited in lakes that in time became playas (dry lakes or alkali flats). Borax deposits were found near the center of Death Valley in the final quarter of the nineteenth century. In 1882, operations began at the Harmony Borax Works. The refined products were hauled to Mojave, the closest railhead, for shipment to Los Angeles.* Production continuedfor five years; a

sharp decline in prices halted operations. Soon thereafter a richer borax-bearing mineral, *colemanite,* was discovered and production resumed

* Allegedly the 20-mule teams were 18 mules and two lead horses. The trip (165 miles) required 10 days each way. Each wagon-trailer outfit carried 36 1/2 tons and animal feed and water. Major output in Death Valley followed construction of the Tonopah and Tidewater Railroad northward from Ludlow (on the Santa Fe Southern) in 1907.

in 1890. The Pacific Coast Borax Company finally halted operations at Ryan, its largest mine, in 1927 when lower production costs were achieved at Kramer (and still more recently at Boron) in the Mojave Desert (Ch.4).

**Silver and Gold**

Three silver camps (Panamint City, Darwin and Cerro Gordo) developed in this area shortly after the Comstock Lode. Less spectacular than the major Nevada silver center or the gold mines of the Sierra's Mother Lode Country, they have been almost forgotten.

**Cerro Gordo**, two miles above sea level in the White-Inyo Range nine miles northeast of Keeler, was a major factor in the economic growth of Los Angeles in the 1870's, according to Remi Nadeau in *The City Makers*. Some millions of dollars were taken from Cerro Gordo between 1868 and 1877. Early in the 1900's the mine was again the state's leading silver producer. It has not been operative since 1940.

Gold was recovered in the 19th century. Among the more important centers was **Bodie**, home of the mythical "bad man." Gold was discovered at Bodie in 1859, but production did not crest until the 1870's, when the town had 12,000. A little mining was conducted in the 1930's. Bodie is a ghost camp visited by increasing numbers of tourists; it is now a state historic park.

**Talc and Tungsten**

What a lively land the Trans-Sierra would be if all the mines ever operated were still active! Yet as this brief review has shown, mining has been as ephemeral as desert lakes. Presently products are commonly extracted mechanically and shipped after minimal processing; hence much of the ultimate income is "exported" too.

Most of the mining is marginal economically hence it is extremely responsive to slight price changes and especially to federal policies involving protective tariffs, defense purchases and direct exploration incentives.

A good example of intermittent operation has been Black Rock mine in the Benton Mountains 25 miles north of Bishop, which yielded more than $10 million in tungsten from 1954 to 1956, but closed in 1963 due to cessation of the government purchase program. Another prime example is intermittent operation is the *Darwin district* east

of Owens Lake, where there has been irregular activity since 1874.

Two other minerals, soda ash and talc, have been extracted more consistently.

Soda ash, for window glass and detergents, has been obtained from the dry bed of Owens Lake. Talc from Deep Springs and Keeler districts is used in such ceramics as wall tile.

**Owens Lake** has yielded such salines as soda ash continuously since the early 1880's and qualifies as the most enduring "mine" in the subregion.

Climatic change after the pluvial period in the late Great Ice Age eliminated overflow southward; and, as the lake shrunk, saline concentration occurred. Despite the mining, the limited population around Owens Lake emphasizes the inability of mining to sustain a permanent Trans-Sierran population. Although Bishop has served as the concentration and supply center for Black Rock and Sierran tungsten and Lone Pine continues to be a supply point for Darwin and Owens Lake, no major Trans-Sierran town depends principally upon mining. Both these communities derive much more support from tourism.

Currently the Trans-Sierra produces more than a dozen minerals of economic value. Some, like clay and stone, are commonplace construction materials.

Others are more exotic, like zeolite and talc. Still others are "traditional", like sodium carbonate from Owens Lake and boron from Death Valley.

In the 1980's the Trans-Sierra has participated in the "statewide revival" of gold exploration and mining, albeit less activity has occurred than in the deserts to the south and in the Sierra Nevada. The largest operation has been in the Inyo Mountains northeast of Lone Pine, where helicopters have been used to transport mining and earthmoving machinery preparatory to reworking old mine dumps.

**A DESOLATE LAND**

Many city dwellers find the Trans-Sierra a barren land, a wilderness of sparsely vegetated mountains and seemingly flat basins. But to the student of earth sciences, the prospector and the "rock hound," it seems a paradise.

For the workings of nature lie exposed without the dense blanket of soil and vegetation characteristic of humid lands. To many a stranger from wetter climes it seems monotonous and barren. To one familiar with dry regions, the land has a maze of intricacies resulting from slight variations in slope, relief, rocks, soils and water availability.

## This is the Great Basin

Physiographically the Trans-Sierra belongs to the portion of the Basin and Range known as the Great Basin, nine-tenths of which is outside of California. Its trademarks are attenuated youthful north-south trending "splinter" ranges separated by alluvial-filled basins.

No Trans-Sierran streams drain to the sea; this Great Basin characteristic also applies to much California desert country farther to the southeast. In fact, most basins have no external drainage—thus they are bolsons. The flattish central portion of a bolson is a playa, which was a lake bottom during the pluvial period of the Great Ice Age. With internal drainage playas become intermittent, though shallow, lakes.

Trans-Sierran mountains form three general files and include some of the most majestic ranges in the Great Basin (map 3-1 and Chart 3-1).

Their structures, lithologies and geologic histories are too complex to allow simple description. It is sufficient here to note that these three rows generally decrease in elevation eastward and consequently in moisture supply.

The western file includes a magnificent horst, the *White-Inyo Range* (called the Inyo Mountains in Inyo County), with its ancient bristlecone pines and a group of high summits culminating in 14,242 *White Mountain Peak,* site of the University of California's High Altitude Research Area and the *Coso-Argus-Slate* ranges in the south. The middle grouping includes the *Last Chance Range* in the north and in the south the anticlinal *Panamint Range,* sufficiently cool to serve as headquarters for Death Valley National Monument. Its single crestline reaches an apex in *Telescope Peak* (11,049 ft.). The eastern tier, collec-

tively the *Amargosa Range,* is generally remembered by visitors who have explored its colorful formations along Titus Canyon.

The four series of elongated basins that occur between the Sierra Nevada and the Nevada line are as remarkable as the ranges.

The westernmost row, the *Sierra Forelands,* includes West Walker Valley and Bridgeport Valley in the extreme north and **Owens Valley**, 120 miles long, towards the south (Fig. 3-2). Between these depressions is *Mono Basin* with its *Volcanic Tableland* through whose southern edge the Owens River has cut the gorge containing the sites for city of Los Angeles hydroelectric production. The second group, least frequented, consists from north to south of Fish Lake, Eureka, Saline and Panamint valleys. The four are separated by outliers of adjacent ranges so that each has a separate drainage system and playa floor. The third trough is occupied by **Death Valley**, a great depression with graben-like structure and including a salt-encrusted playa and bordering alluvial fans that often merge into the pediments of surrounding mountains (Fig. 3-1). The easternmost basin is the *Amargosa Valley,* not a true bolson since it contains the intermittent Amargosa River, which follows a U-shaped course around the south end of the Amargosa Range to terminate in Death Valley.

## A Summer Furnace (but not everywhere!)

The Trans-Sierra is known for its sizzling summers—with noticeable smog for over a decade. Heat is more common in lower-lying Death Valley (lowest elevation -282 ft.), where Furnace Creek averages 102 degrees F. in July and in Panamint Valley than it is in Owens Valley (Long Pine has a July average of 75 degrees F.) and Mono Basin.

There is sufficient difference in temperature that the latter areas are recognized as middle-latitude

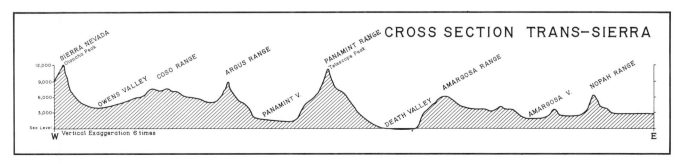

**Chart 3-1.** Cross section of the Trans Sierra across southern Inyo County. One can readily visualize the succession of north-south fault-block ranges and intervening bolsons that are so typical of the Great Basin.

desert-steppe transition while the former as sub-tropical deserts (see Overview A). A dome of high pressure over the area yields high temperatures and clear skies in summer; by contrast, midwinter days are generally pleasant (Furnace Creek has an average December temperature of 52 degrees F.). Dominance of the Trans-Sierra by polar air, however, may bring subfreezing temperatures. Vertical zonation prevails in such mountain ranges as the Panamint and higher summits in the White Mountains display alpine conditions.

Precipitation everywhere is slight; only on higher summits does it exceed 10 inches annually (Bishop averages 6 inches).

Within proximity of the snow-laden Sierra Nevada, surface water is somewhat more plentiful; scorched eastern portions of the subregion lack sufficient grass for grazing.

The chief source of moisture is winter storms from the north Pacific, although much of the moisture has been wrung out of the air masses in crossing the Coast Ranges and the Sierra Nevada. Although specific figures are generally lacking, the upper slopes of the ranges receive more precipitation. Such summits as White Mountain Peak and Telescope Peak are likely to wear snowy caps above 10,000 feet during much of the winter.

Uncommon but sometimes locally spectacular rainfall in summer may occur from cloudbursts. Such precipitation results from disturbances in moist upper air that originates over the Gulf of Mexico or other subtropical waters. Turbulence over the ranges more frequently produces cumulus cotton balls that delight the photographer of Trans-Sierran landscapes. Usually, however, the precipitation from the cumulo-nimbus clouds (thunderheads) is modest—it may even evaporate before striking the ground.

## Shadscale and Sagebrush

There are four principal vegetation associations in the Trans-Sierra.

Sagebrush prevails in the north and throughout much of Owens Valley. In the south its struggle against heat and drought is reflected by stunted size. It is gradually replaced by creosote bush, which is dominant over much of southwestern Inyo County, including the lower mountain slopes. The low, dry eastern basins carry a shadscale formation. Higher slopes of the ranges possess a pinyon pine and juniper woodland, which usually includes mountain mahogany. Lesser cover includes bunch grass over parts of Owens Valley and the east Sierran pine forest, which prevails upon the Volcanic Tableland at elevations above 6000 feet. This is the single stand of marketable timber, although the pinyon-juniper at one time provided charcoal to smelt the lead-silver ores in local mining operations.

To the stranger, the vegetation of the Trans-Sierra may seem monotonous, and yet

...Along springs and sunken watercourses, one is surprised to find such water-loving plants as grow widely in moist ground, but the true desert breeds its own kind, each in its particular habitat. The angle of the slope, the frontage of a hill, the structure of the soil determines the plant. South-looking hills are nearly bare, and the lower tree line higher here by a thousand feet. Canons running east and west will have one wall naked and one clothed. Around dry lakes and marshes the herbage preserves a set and orderly arrangement. Most species have well-defined areas of growth, the best index the voiceless land can give the stranger of his whereabouts.*

## THE SIERRA FORELANDS

Consisting of the better-watered slopes along the eastern face of the Sierra Nevada from West Walker Valley southward through Owens Valley (map 3-1), the Sierra Forelands is the favored portion of the Trans-Sierra (Fig. 3-3).

This dry land, whose stream flow comes from an adjacent mountain oasis might well have become comparable agriculturally on a smaller scale to Utah's Salt Lake Basin or the Colorado Piedmont if much of its water supply had not been tapped by the city of Los Angeles through its aqueduct (Fig. 3–4).

### Land of the Mono

The Forelands was occupied by the Mono, a little-known primitive Uto-Aztecan people, before its Anglo settlement.

Food gatherers and hunters, not farmers, these folk doubtless had an arduous existence. Still the streams provided fish and there was game on the grass-covered plains. Hence life was less difficult for the Mono than it was for their cousins the *Koso* who occupied less fertile country farther east.

---

* Mary Austin, The Land of Little Rain (Boston: Houghton Mifflin Company, 1904), pp. 9-10.

**Figure 3-2.** Owens Valley landscape. Farming declined after Los Angeles built its Aqueduct but some grazing continues. White-Inyo Range is in the distance (Mary Hill).

Presently about 8 per cent of the Trans-Sierran populace is Indian; a third reside on five small reservations in Owens Valley; water is allocated by the city of Los Angeles.

## Farmers and Ranchers

Cattlemen first settled in the Forelands in 1861 although Mono hostility discouraged settlement until Ft. Independence was established the next year; intermittent Indian troubles continued until 1865. The mine camp at Cerro Gordo afforded an early outlet for beef. Gradually as the homesteaders increased, there was a shift toward irrigation agriculture.

Ditches were constructed in the 1870's and the 1880's but lack of a local market hampered farming for many years. Sheep and cattle, sold irregularly to mining camps but more often in Los Angeles, were the dominant products. In the north some dairying was attempted. Unseasonable frosts discouraged attempts to raise deciduous fruits.

By the early years of the twentieth century much of the readily-available water was being used in Owens Valley; about 40,000 acres were under cultivation (in contrast to less than 10,000 acres now).

Much of the ranching was concentrated in the northern part of the Valley (known locally as Round Valley and Bishop Valley), although Lone Pine and Independence farther south were growing market towns. Agricultural prosperity of the

Valley had been enhanced by the gold boom at Tonopah, Nevada. At this time, a Bureau of Reclamation survey party visited the area and located an excellent reservoir site at the north end of Owens Gorge; this prompted Forelands ranchers to anticipate much agricultural expansion. Before their hopes could be realized the city of Los Angeles had acted to construct the *Los Angeles Aqueduct.*

## Quest for Water

Through the nineteenth century the city of Los Angeles relied upon the waters of the Los Angeles River. But as the metropolis grew it became obvious that in times of recurrent drought this supply was inadequate. Los Angeles embarked upon construction of its Aqueduct in 1908.

This monumental municipal program, a five-year project, cost $23 million. It created a 223-mile conduit comprising open and concrete-lined ditches and steel and concrete pipes, which in places were tunneled through mountain ranges. The Aqueduct (Fig. 3-4), now with a capacity of 600 second-feet, takes water from the Owens River north of Independence (map 3-1) and delivers it to the Los Angeles Lakes (Fig. 6-32) for distribution to Los Angeles mains.

**Figure 3-3.** Representative Trans-Sierra landscape— southeastern fringe of Owens Lake and the Coso Range. The gravelly surface and the sparse vegetation cover (foreground) are typical of its structural depressions. Owens Lake was perennial until Los diverted its natural sources (Mary Hill).

**Figure 3-4.** The Los Angeles Aqueduct in Owens Valley with south end of the High Sierra (rear). The Aqueduct provides the chief source of water consumed within the political city of Los Angeles. Olancha Peak (rear) attains 12.135 feet above sea level. ( Los Angeles Department of Water and Power)

Continued growth of the city, coupled with cycles of drier years, prompted Los Angeles in the 1920's to purchase ranch lands and water rights (to augment municipal water supply) in the northern part of Owens Valley. Construction of the Long Valley Dam, storing 183,000 acre-feet in Crowley Lake, was undertaken in 1935 to supplement the supply. A few years later the *Mono Extension* was made, including an 11-mile tunnel through the dormant Mono Craters, so as to divert waters of Sierran streams contributing to Mono Lake into the Aqueduct.

Ranching population in Owens Valley and the Mono Basin has been severely restricted since Los Angeles requisitioned a water supply.

Presently the city obtains two thirds of its water and a tenth of its electricity from these areas. Having acquired much land as well as water rights, Los Angeles leases some 200,000 acres for grazing as well as providing water for irrigation, as is, from time to time, excessive of city needs. Inyo County leads the state in proportion of lease-operated ranch land.

**The Farmer Departs**

The economy of Owens Valley was markedly altered by removal of much of its water supply. In the southern part of the area it ended plans for irrigation expansion with water that would have been available from a dam projected in Long Valley.

The well-being of the basin was much changed too by purchase of properties and water rights in northern Owens Valley in the 1920's. And decline of their rural trade was especially difficult for the merchants of Owens Valley towns.

Pump well installation on city-owned ranch land lowers the water table during drier years. An appreciable population decline in Owens Valley took place in the 1930's. This decline occurred during years of economic depression elsewhere. Valley farmers were fortunate in being able to sell to the city at a fair price, but the methods used in acquiring water rights (secrecy and an uncompromising attitude) created much hostility. Ill-will towards Los Angeles still exists; currently Inyo County is contesting groundwater withdrawals that threaten to denude the vegetation and further restrict ranching.

**Cattle Truckers, Skiers, and Others**

The Forelands, traversed by the Sierra Highway (U.S. 395), forms a north-south corridor of increasing significance (Fig. 3-6).

This might be called "the back" door into Southern California. Repeated road improvement, coupled with a lack of large cities, permits rapid movement despite growing queues of vehicles.

U.S. 395, easternmost of California's three major north-south routes, is popular with commercial travelers between Southern California and the Pacific Northwest and constitutes the principal thoroughfare between Reno and Los Angeles.

Increasingly, the highway is used by truckers engaged in hauling livestock from diverse parts of the Intermontane West into Los Angeles. In summer the route is the all-important avenue of approach for eastern Sierran vacation spots. During peak winter weekends hordes of snow enthusiasts create the impression of a Los Angeles freeway. Between Reno and Bishop, where four summits exceed an elevation of 7000 feet (causing brief closure during winter storms) the landscape is especially inviting with sage, grass and cattle, conifer forests and aspen glades and vistas of the Sierra and the White-Inyo.

All Forelands towns experience appreciable tourism; motels display "no vacancy" signs on summer weekends.

Autumn brings many hunters and in winter,

streets are sometimes filled with sports cars bearing ski racks, bound chiefly to or from Mammoth (Ch. 10). Owens Valley towns have benefited much from the eastern Sierra ski boom. Bishop alone anticipates a million or more visits annually.

Most Forelands towns are of the single street village *(strassendorf)* form, thus seasonally green ribbons along U.S. 395.

With groves of willow or cottonwood, they remind one more of typical irrigated oases than of desert hamlets. Importance of tourism is reflected in the ubiquitous cafes, curio shops, motels, service stations and sporting goods stores. The breadth of the single thoroughfare (the highway) is similar to that of Mormon communities in Utah.

For many years, Owens Valley lacked a rail connection with the rest of California.

In conjunction with construction of the Los Angeles Aqueduct the Southern Pacific built a broadgauge line northward from Mojave to link with the now abandoned narrowgauge that once served mine camps. The line has functioned in more recent years as a freight route, facilitating the export of mineral products. It no longer carries passengers except on trains used for motion picture or television films.

### Owens Valley

The dominant pre-irrigation activity in Owens Valley, sheep and cattle ranching, again became the chief mode of rural land use after the construction and expansion of the Los Angeles Aqueduct.

The previous position of farm houses is hinted by occasional groves of trees. Aqueduct seepage has significance in providing grass forage around such communities as Independence and Lone Pine.

The city of Los Angeles is now a major employer in Owens Valley.

Besides the maintenance crews required by the Aqueduct it self, there has been construction of additional facilities, including dams and power plants.

Coupled with the construction of paved highways leading to the eastern Sierra, the tourist trade, a reflection of the growth of Los Angeles, has been a major force in the economy of the Forelands for nearly half a century.

Due primarily to this trade, the population of Inyo County is more than double what it was before the Aqueduct was built. Most Owens Valley towns form recreational gateways into the canyons of the Sierra's eastern face.

**Lone Pine** (1200), the TransSierra's second city, is the hub of southern Inyo County, with a hospital and specialty shops as well as service stations and motels (Fig. 3-5).

At the junction of a Death Valley highway (Ca. 190) and U.S. 395, it is an eastern approach into the Mt. Whitney area. It serves as a center for scattered mining operations.

**Independence** (1000) is dominated by the yellow Inyo County courthouse and the Los Angeles Water and Power maintenance structure.

It has a cluster of singlestory false fronts and residences along the Sierra Highway, including a museum and historic homes.

**Bishop** (circa 12,000; many outside city limits), sufficiently-distant from Los Angeles and Reno, acts as a service center for an extensive area and contains a third of the entire TransSierra population.

It is fragmented by Indian properties, somewhat like Palm Springs (Ch.5). Land control by the Paiute Indians and by the city of Los Angeles has created a confinement that results in absurd prices for new residential sites. Along Main Street newer business blocks have replaced false fronts. There is a radio station, as well as varied specialty shops. The town's several functions include highway commerce, operations center for tungsten mining, headquarters for Inyo National Forest, third most-frequented in California, and various other governmental facilities, modest lumbering, and supply point for scattered ranches.

### Mono County

Rural land use in the northern basins of the Forelands (i.e., Mono County) is restricted to Bridgeport Valley and West Walker Valley (which reflects the absurdity of the rulerstraight California-Nevada border; much of the cultivated land is in Nevada). The Mono Basin is largely a barren volcanic wilderness, with little opportunity even for grazing.

Highly mineralized **Mono Lake**, once designated as "undrinkable" on a city of Los Angeles map, is the landmark of the area. It shrank notably as result of water exportation to Los Angeles; recent efforts have reduced the outflow. The shoreline has been incorporated into a *Tufa State Reserve.*

Near the junction of U.S. 395 and Ca. 120 (leading over Tioga Pass into Yosemite Park) is **Lee Vining** (500), a near-treeless highway stop.

Mountain-girt Bridgeport Valley, well-watered by the East Walker River, provides summer pasturage for hundreds of cattle.

**Figure 3-5.** Lone Pine, the Alabama Hills and the High Sierra. The town provides a gateway to Mt. Whitney (14,495 feet), seen on the skyline in the middle of the picture. (Southern Inyo Chamber of Commerce, photo by Bob White's Flying Service).

Early-day homesteaders sold hay and cattle at such mine camps as Aurora and Bodie. When the mine camps declined, the homesteaders sold out to two would-be cattle barons. When their firm went bankrupt, their holdings were divided into five sizable parcels, averaging 4000 acres each. Because of the altitude (7000 feet) and cold winters, no attempt is made at year-round feeding. Cattle are taken in late autumn to lower lying basins in Nevada.

**Bridgeport** (unincorp.,circa 200), Mono County seat, has an ornate Victorian courthouse but no high school (students are bussed to Lee Vining!).

Mono County is a historical accident. Bridgeport became the seat when early settlers learned their courthouse in Aurora was in Nevada. The town has a strassendorf pattern; false-front blocks are prettied with white paint—but some of the street has no sidewalks.

## THE WESTERN GREAT BASIN

The eastern Trans-Sierra, almost vacant and lonesome, better typifies the Great Basin overall than does the Forelands.

Neither Panamint Valley nor Saline Valley nor Eureka Valley even possesses a village today.

**Figure 3-6.** Mono Basin and the High Sierra with the Sierra Highway (U.S. 395). View taken southward from Conway Summit (8138 ft.)—note snow markers (Caltrans).

Mining operations are scattered (and spasmodic). Remote *Deep Springs Valley* has a few cattle ranches and has had a "dude ranch" private "preparatory " college that has stressed social ideals.

**Figure 3-7.** Furnace Creek is the center of human activity in Death Valley. View westward to Panamint Mountains with Texas Springs campground in foreground (National Park Service, photo by Dwight Warren).

**Figure 3-8.** The "lure" of Death Valley. An "almost" pristine geologic museum. (Union Pacific Railroad, National Park Service).

## The Koso Lived Here

The Koso, aboriginal people of the eastern Trans-Sierra, materially were among the poorest Uto-Aztecans.

These people, whose numbers apparently never exceeded 500, had a difficult life. They resided in mountain canyons but roamed widely in quest of food. They made good use of an impoverished environment; their diet included rabbits and lizards, pinyon nuts, sundry seeds, mesquite beans and even prickly pear cactus.

## Death Valley: A National Park?

Death Valley remained a wasteland for decades after its discovery, feared for tales of summer heat (the American record, 134 degrees F., was recorded there) and encumbered since immigrant days by its appropriate appellation.

Borax mining over half a century contributed to a tourist industry through transportation and resort facilities developed by the mining company.

The Valley became a national monument (3000 square miles) in 1933; it is operated by the National Park Service to preserve its landscape for recreational use.*

Mining facilities and commercial resorts that pre-date establishment of the Monument remain privately owned. There has been much argument over re-opening of borax properties.

Construction of paved roads plus accessibility to densely populated portions of California have been major factors in Death Valley's increased popularity as a winter playground.

The season, lasting from October until May, usually has pleasant weather except during periods of winter storms.The Valley is now crossed by some thousands each summer— publicity given several hikers testifies to the climate. Rangers regularly patrol the roads in air-conditioned pickups. Visitors are given specific instructions regarding behavior in case of vehicular breakdown.

The Valley has diversified physical appeal. Geologically it is veritably a geomorphic museum.

Climate, in season, is another attraction, as is historic background.

*Dante's View* (in the Black Mountains), provides the best panorama of the area that is auto-accessible. Visitors commonly examine relics of the borax-mining era. The limited accommodations become congested during holiday periods; campgrounds near the park headquarters are especially popular.

Already more frequented than some of the national parks,the Valley was being proposed for national park status, with extended boundaries, in the late 1980's.

---

* Unlike national parks, approved by Congressional action, national monuments are established by and may be abolished by Presidential decree with approval of Congress.

## AN ALMOST CHANGELESS LAND

Utilization of the TransSierra seems less likely to change than any California subregion. "Anything" could happen in mining, always unpredictable, *even* the equivalent of another Comstock Lode. But mineral developments are by nature localized. Albeit unlikely now would be the establishment of a major military installation. The importance of the Sierran Forelands as a commercial corridor and as a Sierran gateway seems likely to increase; Death Valley tourism likewise continues to expand. As elsewhere in California's dry east, Los Angeles and urban Southern California provides both economic impetus and visitors. Ties with central and northern California are more limited.

The **California Desert Plan** (q.v. Chapter 4) will definitely affect the Trans-Sierra too, by designating (and publicizing) special attractions and land uses, especially in the emptier segments.

Prospects for agriculture seem remote. "Futuristically", sea water conversion (and even the California Water Project) could precipitate significant change in Owens Valley. Even more remotely possible, the city of Los Angeles might become a local entrepreneur of water and land, particularly if desalinization of sea water in Southern California becomes sufficiently inexpensive. In that instance Owens Valley could reclaim its own water supply and take its place as an important area of irrigation agriculture in the Intermontane West, raising produce for metropolitan Southern California.

Meanwhile, those individuals who are able to garner a living in this sparsely populated land continue to appreciate the clear skies, absence of urban pressures and easy access (of the Forelands) to the Sierra Nevada. A less-happy thought is the proposal to make Panamint Valley a site for nuclear waste. But the Valley has no one to "push" the idea.

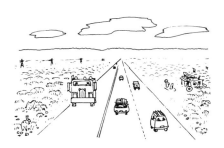

**Figure 4-1.** The Mojave—a land to be crossed. This is the introduction to the Golden State gained by travelers on I-15. Note piedmont apron with its many washes and hamlet (right, rear) which provides highway services. (Caltrans).

Chapter Four

THE MOJAVE DESERT

This chapter was originally reviewed by Jeanne Garrison, El Camino College.

45

# THE MOJAVE DESERT

Anaheim, August 6

Dear Mom and Dad,

Los Angeles is really spread out! And so much traffic— it will be a relief to get home. Bill says he's glad
our car has air conditioning. We recall Gramps tell-
ing about crossing the Mojave in a Model T Ford. It
must have been h-o-t. Now Bev says they take "your"
other grand kids to the Colorado River to water ski
any time of the year. We did Disneyland yesterday—
p-e-o-p-l-e!

love,

Sherry

Annually numerous postcards with such messages
are mailed east. Such a note reveals these facts about
the Mojave: (1) its once-dreaded summer heat—and
the value of air conditioning (2) its position athwart
major transportation routes between coastal California and the North American interior and (3) its
importance as a playground for Southern California.

Perhaps nowhere else in California does one feel
the openness and spaciousness of the Golden State so
completely as in the Mojave. The contrast with the
millions of people in the San Francisco Bay Area and
the Los Angeles Lowlands is dramatic.

Possibly the Mojave is as naturally appealing to
humans as any desert of its size can be.

Water is locally available; seasonal temperatures
are less extreme than those of dry lands to both
south and north; the terrain provides scenic variety; mineral-rich rocks are widely exposed; and it
is accessible from Southern California.

While its population approximates 300,000, settlement is limited to small areas.

Most of its inhabitants reside in a belt within 50
miles of its southwestern edge, especially in the
Mojave-Boron, Antelope Valley, Victorville-
Barstow and Twentynine Palms-Yucca Valley
areas. Blythe and Needles house the balance except for less than five per cent widely scattered in
such places as highway hamlets and mine camps.

The Mojave Desert encompasses a sixth of California. Its general position is readily identified but its
extent is less precise.

There seems to be common accord that the Desert
is basically a natural (rather than cultural) phenomenon. It is restricted entirely to California by
common acceptance. The Desert, as identified in
this chapter, has these boundaries: on the west
and south by an almost continuous mountain wall
(from northwest to southeast, the Sierra Nevada,
the Tehachapi, San Gabriel, San Bernardino,
Little San Bernardino, Orocopia, and Chocolate
mountains); on the east by Arizona and Nevada;
and on the north by the southern limits of Inyo
County.

Leading supports of Mojavian livelihood include
(1) transportation , (2) military installations, (3) tourism and recreation, (4) mining, (5) farming.

## A LAND TO CROSS

The Desert has been challenged by transcontinental traffic for over a century.

**The Old Spanish Trail** from Santa Fe to Los
Angeles across Cajon Pass was opened in 1830.
Neither "old" nor "Spanish", this route represented a continuation of the **Santa Fe Trail**,
which linked Mexican outposts in New Mexico and
California; it had been projected by the Spanish
even in the eighteenth century. The Mojave is still
athwart the major gateways (Needles or Las
Vegas through Barstow and over Cajon Pass) or
Blythe-Coachella Valley into Southern California from the continental interior.

### Rail Corridors

Two major rail routes into California from the
east cross the Mojave; and the main line between
southern and central California traverses its western
edge.

The routes initially followed the shortest courses

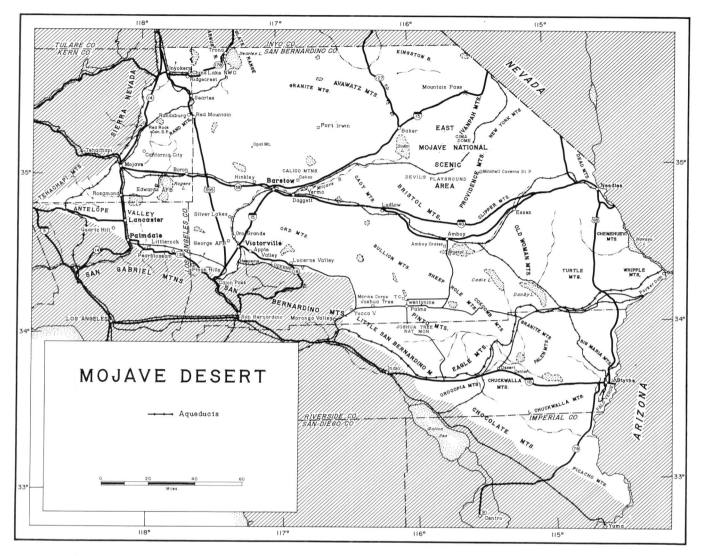

**Map 4-1.** The Mojave, California's big desert, encompasses a fifth of the Golden State and parts of five counties. It is not devoid of people, especially along its southwestern edge adjacent to Southern California.

permitted by water and terrain. Topography remains a major consideration but the waterhole, once so essential for locomotives is no longer important (since the advent of diesel engines). Transcontinental traffic commenced on the Santa Fe route from Needles to Barstow in 1885; it crosses Cajon Pass into the Los Angeles Lowlands. Construction (in 1905) between Salt Lake City and Daggett gave the Desert a second route, which became part of the Union Pacific system in 1921. In 1967 another line was completed between Cajon Pass and Palmdale. Branch lines have been extended to such mineral centers as Lucerne Valley (cement) and Trona (chemicals). A branch lines also serves the Palo Verde Valley.

Until the 1920's railroads dominated traffic. Local lines favored mining developments and permitted more successful settlement of Antelope Valley, the Mojave River Valley and the Palo Verde Valley.

Some communities, especially Mojave and Barstow, still gain much economic benefit from the railroads.Elsewhere,as at Needles, the importance of railroad payrolls has declined or vanished.

**Pipes and Wires**

The average highway traveler gives little attention to another vital aspect of Mojave "transit"—the wires and pipes that deliver fresh water, natural gas, and electricity to coastal California.

The Los Angeles Aqueduct is only one of such facilities, reaching across the western Mojave from the Trans-Sierra into Los Angeles (Fig. 4-5). **The**

**Colorado River Aqueduct** was completed across the southeastern Mojave from Parker Dam into the Los Angeles Lowlands in 1941 (Fig.4-8). Hoover Dam affords a major source of electrical energy for metropolitan Southern California; transmission lines cross the Desert. Natural gas has been piped across the Mojave since 1947. The first line, from the Permian Basin (eastern New Mexico), enters California at Blythe and crosses the Mojave into Southern California. A decade later, another gas line, from New Mexico's San Juan Basin, was completed into California; it enters the state at Topock to provide fuel for central and northern California.

### Back Roads and Freeways

Highways gained increasing importance in the economy of the Mojave from the 1920's.

Early, routes tended to parallel the rail lines. Now the subregion is traversed by important east-west and north-south routes (map 4-1).* Highways have tended to become more direct, showing less regard for terrain, older trails, and water holes; principal thoroughfares are being converted into freeways.

The Desert is crisscrossed by numerous unpaved roads.

These frequently extend for miles over empty areas; strangers are advised to traverse them with caution, especially in summer.

### Highway Places

Perhaps a thousand families rely directly for their livelihood by providing services to highway travelers.

Services for wayfarers have fostered establishment of many retail businesses. Larger towns are major nocturnal stopovers with motels and restaurants prominent. The life of many Mojave towns depends upon the motorist.

*Baker* is a classic example of a town whose entire existence is related to tourist services—it is largely an assemblage of motels, cafes, service stations, garages and bars.

Highway "travel towns", inevitably tiny, were once as closely spaced as mine camps or railroad settlements. But the advent of faster automobiles and highways with restricted access has caused abandonment of the "one gas station" hamlet in favor of the larger towns with more complete services. Present-day motorists thus find much greater

**Figure 4-2.** Joshua trees, the "trade marks" of less-arid parts of the Mojave. Although creosote bush grows much more widely, these giant lilies are among are among the most distinctive plants of the Desert, especially on well-drained slopes above 2500 feet. (dwl)

distances between service stops than did the wayfarers of yesteryear.

### THE DESERT

A stranger to dry lands may assume all deserts are alike—an oft-conjured image is sand dunes and oasis groves of palms. True, all deserts suffer water deficiency and generally have sparse populations. But each of the several California deserts has its distinctive characteristics.

There are differences in climate, topography and vegetation; there is likewise difference in human utilization. For example some Mojave surfaces (steep slopes, sandy areas, playas) hamper land-use; but over wide areas terrain is not a handicaps. As noted in earlier chapters, much of the Northeast is a volcanic tableland with quite cold winters. Essentially, the Trans-Sierra has three files of "over-lapping" fault blocks and extreme summer heat in Death Valley.

---

* Two east-west roads, Interstate 10 and 40, are segments of major transcontinental ways. The Sierra Highway (Ca. 14 and U.S. 395 which becomes a single road across Owens Valley to the north) is the major California artery east of the Sierra Nevada, as was indicated in the two previous chapters. Interstate 15, from Barstow northeastward carries much of Los Angeles-Las Vegas traffic (Fig. 4-1); a western connection (Ca. 58) of I-40 has been used increasingly in recent years.

**Figure 4-3.** A "typical" playa—Rosamond Dry Lake. Such barren surfaces are scattered around the Mojave. Evaporation of ephemeral lakes leaves a maze of cracks on the sun-baked clay and saline minerals. This particular surface serves as an emergency landing field. (U.S. Air Force)

## Worn Mountains and Playas

The Mojave is a land of broad flattish basins and usually-low mountains, much eroded. The same processes operated here as those that produced the geologically-younger Great Basin—but the geologic time frame is much different. The Mojave has four principal topographic types: (1) untilted blocks (2) young fault blocks (3) old fault blocks, and (4) bolsons (basins).

*Antelope Valley* epitomizes the untilted block—it is a triangular area whose apex points westward.

Its southwestern and northwestern sides are flanked respectively by the *San Andreas* and *Garlock fault* zones. The brunt of upward thrust was exerted apparently against the San Gabriel and Tehachapi masses, whereas the Antelope itself has has retained limited elevation. Consequently it has received alluvial burden from adjacent highlands, with a series of coalescing alluvial fans. Several small tectonic protuberances, locally called "buttes", disrupt its surface regularity.

Especially typical of the central Mojave is the older fault block, long worn by erosion and perhaps almost buried by its surrounding alluvial waste heap.

Names of some ranges suggest their dissected physiognomy: *Old Woman, Old Dad, Dome.* Yet contemporary highland surfaces may be quite

**Figure 4-4.** "Cloudburst" sky near Providence Mountains. Sufficient rain fell from this thunderhead to produce "several years" average precipitation. (Richard F. Logan)

craggy, even angular. Terrain at the base of of fault cliffs may be rocky still, and rugged with steep stream gradients. The deposits of intermittent streams flare outward—they are gravelly upslope but become sandy as they they descend towards the adjacent basin, which is often extensive. The

**Figure 4-5.** "All sorts of things" move across the Desert. Here at Jawbone Gap is an arm of the California Aqueduct. Scarcely visible on the ridge is one of ten inverted siphons of the Los Angeles Aqueduct. (dwl)

detective work of the geologist is frustrated as one endeavors to trace the history of the Desert.

Loftier and younger fault blocks are more conspicuous in the eastern Mojave—they include the *Ivanpah, New York, Turtle, Avawatz* and *Providence* ranges.

The abrupt west face of the Providence Mountains, almost a mile high, prompts difficult climbing and is suggestive of the eastern wall of the Sierra Nevada (Fig. 3-5). By contrast the nearby Cima Dome is so gently rounded as to suggest a giant blister on the earth—it is easily traversible with four-wheel drive. (This difference suggests the intricacy of Mojave Desert geology, as do the impressive sand hills of this locality known as the **Devil's Playground.**

Many small ranges separate the lower-lying terrain into about 50 individual basins of varying size and altitude. Alluvial basins, including Antelope Valley, encompass about half of the entire Mojave (see map B-1).

From a mountain top the typical basin seems flat but from its low point it slopes gently upward in all directions like a shallow bowl. Many of these depressions are separated by low watershed divides, so that "mountains" can be bypassed easily by

**Figure 4-7.** Chemical works on the edge of Searles Lake, an important source of saline minerals. This playa has a solid crust ten feet thick, wth overlayering of bromine, calcium, lithium, potassium and sodium salts. (dwl)

travel routes. Natural vegetation differences reflect varying soils, salinity and depth of water table.

The centers of many basins contain relicts of extensive Ice Age lakes, such as *Rosamond, Muroc and Soda.* These intermittent lakes, or playas, are usually dry and their hard-packed clay surfaces sometimes glisten with mineral salts (Fig. 4-3)

After winter cyclonic precipitation or summer flash storms they may briefly be covered with shallow water. The most conspicuous of these playas are found southeast of Amboy. It is inferred that in wetter times (the pluvial period), these playas were not only interconnected but had a common outlet into Colorado River and may even have carried discharge from the Mojave River, if not from Death Valley and the Owens River.

### Wind Swept—Even Oven Hot

Unfamiliar with the Desert, the stranger may dread its summer heat and with some justification, as this news account indicates:

**DESERT HEAT KILLS TWO
ON SEARCH FOR GOLD**
L.A. Men's Truck Fails Near Amboy
The bodies of two Los Angeles men who died from heat and exposure when their truck broke down during a desert prospecting trip were brought out of Bristol Dry

**Figure 4-6.** Lake Havasu, formed behind Parker Dam, backs up for 55 miles along the Colorado River. It is much used for recreational purposes and provides an intake spot for the *Colorado River Aqueduct,* which delivers water to Southern Califorinia cities. (dwl)

Lake in San Bernardino-County yesterday by a four-wheel Sheriff's caravan. (Los Angeles Times, August 17, 1957).

The above lead tells of an incident decades ago that occurred only 25 miles south of Interstate 40. The Mojave Desert is a land that can experience blistering summers yet frequent winter mildness, little rain, and abundant sunshine. Despite its latitude (33 to 36 degrees) it is best considered middle-latitude rather than subtropical.

While statistics are limited, obviously topographic differences between basins and adjacent ranges create climatic variations. Average annual precipitation tends to be slight everywhere.

The limited precipitation follows the usual California seasonal pattern.

There is a winter maximum, with annual totals ranging from less than five inches over much of the eastern and central desert to about 15 inches in western Antelope Valley.

East-moving Pacific storms, with tracks usually well to the north, lose much moisture over the Coast Ranges and the Sierra Nevada; thus even when overcast skies prevail across the Mojave, slight rainfall is likely. The storms are relatively infrequent—even in winter the Desert receives 60 to 80 per cent of potential sunshine. At Bagdad, over a period of seventeen years, the average rainfall was 2.28 inches— this included three years during which no precipitation was recorded! Winter precipitation, which increases on slopes of such higher ranges as the Providence Mountains, may even fall as snow.

The eastern Mojave is particularly subject to summer cloudbursts.

They occur when low pressure prevails over the interior of southwestern United States and the position of the Azores (North Atlantic) High fosters westerly movement of unstable superior (i.e., upper altitude) tropical Gulf air masses.

Even if no rain falls, impressive cumulus thunderheads may form (Fig.4-4), Blythe and Needles are "rarities" among California weather stations— they receive more precipitation in August than in any of the winter months!

Temperature ranges in the Desert, seasonal as well as diurnal, tend to be considerable.

Because of clear air and nocturnal cooling, the daily summer range may be 30 to 45 degrees F. and maximums above 100 degrees are frequent.* The lower-lying eastern Mojave tends to be 10 to 15 degrees F. warmer than the western Desert. Winter daytime temperatures are usually pleasant (with a maximum of 50 to 70 degrees F., except for periods when a polar air mass pushes southward or during passage of a cyclonic storm). Winter mildness contributes to the recreational use discussed later.** Nocturnal temperatures, often well below freezing, preclude growth of mid-winter or early spring crops.

Winds are a characteristic feature of Mojave climate.

In spring and winter, they tend to be stronger and more frequent, owing to sectional differences in temperature and pressure. Winter northers may cover the entire desert.

Upon occasion it is possible for a car to receive a sandblast, with the windshield becoming so pitted as to require replacement. Additional winds include little dust devils— rising currents suggestive of a miniature tornado, common on summer afternoons. Relatively strong valley and mountain breezes also prevail.

California's sunniest area (over 90 per cent of the possible amount) prevails in a broad stretch from Death Valley to the Mexican border. Mean daily solar radiation (important for solar electric production) is highest in the northwest Mojave (around the junction of Los Angeles, Kern and San Bernardino counties).

## Water by the Barrel

Water supply is a critical factor in Mojave occupance.

Much of the water used in the subregion comes from nearby highlands through surface or subterranean flow; Antelope Valley and the Mojave River Valley are more fortunate than most of the Desert because of the adjacent Transverse Ranges.

Historically, over wide stretches of the Mojave, water was shipped in by tank or barrel for the highway points, railroads, mines and towns, except where wells tapped a subterranean supply of potable water. Locally there are a few springs at the base of mountains but the flow is limited. It is understandable that Desert residents have had a keen interest in the California Water Project and

---

* Lantis recalls reading a temperature of 114 degrees on the outside wall of an Amboy cafe at 10:30 p.m one August night.
** Barstow diurnal temperature varies from 30 to 60 degrees F. in January; 12 degrees F. is the record low there. Contrast this with the record minimum of -36 degrees F. at Madeline in the Northeast, cited in Chapter Two.

importation of water from northern California (see Ch. 9).

### Burroweed and Creosote

Once significant to American Indians as a food source, the natural vegetation of the Mojave Desert, now has value for scenic appeal. The dominant vegetation type is the brownish-green creosote bush, sometimes called "false greasewood," which grows in association with burroweed.

Widespread distribution of the resinous, evergreen creosote bush, growing 2 to 7 feet high, lends landscape monotony for the highway traveler. Seemingly everywhere, it obscures the variety of vegetation types. In actuality there is considerable variation as result of soil conditions, slope, depth of water table, and precipitation, although meager rainfall assures a limited density.

Four vegetation associations merit mention. (1) Such **salt-tolerant** species as pickleweed or sea blite may grow upon playas, even though these highly alkaline surfaces are sometimes devoid of plants. (2) On better drained hills and plains where desert shrubs are characteristic, burroweed and encelia lend variety to the widespread **creosote bush.** (3) Along the floodplains of the Mojave and Colorado rivers are **riparian groves** of cottonwood and mesquite thickets. (4) On upper mountain slopes there may be thin stands of **pinyon and juniper.**

Well-known California desert plants add variety to these associations.

The yucca, known also as "Spanish bayonet," is found on many hillsides below 2500 feet elevation, whereas another lily, the Joshua tree, grows 10 to 20 feet high in groves on well-drained alluvial fans and lower mountain slopes above 2500 feet elevation (Fig. 4-2)—it is especially prevalent in Antelope Valley and Joshua Tree National Monument. The palo verde, honey mesquite, and ironwood are particularly common along sandy washes in the southeastern basins.

The somber-hued desert becomes splashed with color when the perennials burst into bloom at the end of the winter "rainy" season.

The red-flowered ocotillo, the yellow-blossomed palo verde and the white waxy spikes of the yucca have particular attraction. When rainfall is sufficient, the long-dormant seeds of annuals grow rapidly. California poppies and lupines are especially abundant in Antelope Valley. After a cloud-burst, annuals with a brief life cycle may appear on basin floors despite summer heat.

### Scorpions and Kangaroo Rats

Animal life is surprisingly varied—the numbers of lower forms are especially impressive.

Burrowing animals include the kangaroo rat, the white-footed mouse, and the jack rabbit. One occasionally hears the mournful yip of the coyote. There are spotted skunks, badgers and diminutive kit foxes. Many of these creatures are nocturnal and seek shade during the heat of summer days. Reptiles include numerous lizards, the desert tortoise, the desert rattlesnake (and also the sidewinder, a rattler that has adopted a curious sideward method of keeping as much of its body off as possible off the hot ground. There are multitudes of insects, including ants, flies, grasshoppers and beetles; some, like the scorpion, are poisonous. The density of larger herbivores (and carnivores also) tends to be low, despite the bighorn sheep found in higher ranges like the Providence Mountains.

### ENTER HUMANKIND

Though broad expanses are now considered wasteland, the Desert has been frequented by mankind for thousands of years.

Pinto Basin (in Joshua Tree National Monument) is a significant site in investigation of early man in western America. During the pluvial period, the Mojave was quite possibly a more attractive home for primitive peoples than it has been during the Christian era. At the time of the Spanish conquest, the Desert was sparsely populated by three American Indian groups, Serrano and Chemehuevi (representing the Uto-Aztecan family) and the Mojave (warlike Hokan people). Yet the Desert was sufficiently empty that the Europeans could occupy it without serious aboriginal opposition.

### Hunters and also Tillers

The *Chemehuevi* was a group which occupied the central Mojave after moving northward during historic times.

A small tribe of less than a thousand members, the Chemehuevi were hunter-gatherers who eked out a scanty living. Their favored habit appears to have been the higher, slightly damper area around the Providence Mountains. They avoided the hot basin floors as they migrated from range to range.

More recently, the creation of Lake Havasu in the eastern Mojave flooded irrigable portions of their reservation and several hundred remaining tribe members moved downstream to the Colorado River reservation at Parker.

The *Serrano* representatives, not the "true" Serrano of the San Bernardino Mountains, were also hunters whose livelihood was difficult.

The *Mohave* by contrast were sedentary riparian folk who dwelled along the Colorado River in the Needles area and practiced flood basin agriculture.

Their farming, a type practiced elsewhere in the Southwest, depended upon utilization of the high water table immediately following recession of vernal Colorado River flood waters. Actual application of water to the land was not undertaken. In addition to corn, beans, pumpkins and melons,the Mohave planted wild grasses and collected seeds from untilled floodplain plants. They relied too upon fish from the river, which were caught by seines or by driving the fish into scoops along sloughs.

### Gold Seekers, then Farmers

Before the American period the Mojave remained largely unknown. The Franciscan explorer Francisco Garces visited the Desert but the Spanish established no settlements. The Old Spanish Trail was opened in the Mexican period.

This route, pursued by the first American immigrant party overland in 1841, was also employed by Fremont on the eastward lap of his second expedition. He is usually credited with naming the Mojave River Valley—extension of the name to the entire Desert came later.

The Gold Rush, railroad construction, population growth in Southern California, and the rise of desert mine camps were important factors in the founding of nineteenth century towns in the Mojave. Earliest agricultural settlement (along the Mojave River) occurred in the 1860's.

This predated the first Desert bonanza strike. But the dramatic increase in population has not taken place until the mid-twentieth century.

### SHAFTS AND OPEN PITS

While mining in the Mojave has been less dramatic than in some parts of California, it has had intermittent economic moment since the 1880's.

Until 1900 only a few of the camps, among all the settlements of the subregion, were more than mere hamlets. Sometimes water has been the vital economic factor; if returns from operations could "pay the bill", water would be hauled long distances by rail tanks or by trucks.

Gold is often associated with popular images of desert mining. But contemporary production of gold in the Mojave is negligible.

It is true that over 200 gold claims have been located in the subregion (and outstanding producers have included the Yellow Aster in Randsburg and the *Bagdad-Chase* south of Ludlow). But it has been silver that brought early development in the Mojave, even though the area has never been a leading source. Brief activity at *Calico* (1880's) soon subsided when market prices declined. After a long period of decadence the town was restored as a tourist attraction in the 1950's (Fig.4-15).

Intermittently the Rand District has been a producer of both silver and gold.

Following discovery of gold in the 1890's a cluster of camps flourished. The open-pit Yellow Aster, worked for many years, yielded some millions of dollars. The *Rand Silver Mine* at Red Mountain, operated until after World War II, has been California's major silver producer. The new California "gold rush" of 1980's led to modest renewal of gold mining.

### Boron and Potash

The value of mineral products from the Desert remains substantial. Unspectacular industrial mineral products have been especially important.

These have included cement, iron ore, potash, borax and tungsten (scheelite). If petroleum is excepted, the Desert has ranked high in mineral output in California—several score of different varieties have had importance.

Salines, particularly potash and borax, are the most important.

**Trona** (2000) is wholly supported by chemical plants that pump brine from beneath the crusted surface of Searles Lake and by complex processes, provide various products for export from the Desert (Fig. 4-7). The largest (and oldest) of the saline plants was phased out in the late 1980's.

Southeastern California contains 90 per cent of the world's known borate reserves.

At **Boron** (3200) in eastern Kern County (Antelope Valley), longtime borax mining expanded drastically in the 1950's as a result of demand for

**Figure 4-8.** This vast open-pit mine, west of Barstow off Ca. 58, is the world's leading source of borates. (John W. Reith)

boron fuels and other compounds. In the late twentieth century its principal use has been in the glass industry.

Now an open-pit mine and nearby processing plant dominant the landscape and settlement has followed (Fig. 4-8). Saline output has declined in the 1980's.

The nearby towns of Desert Lake (founded as a planned community) and Kramer have been stimulated by mining as well as by nearby Edwards Air Force Base.

Cement processing from local minerals is consequential in the Mojave Desert and production has expanded.

This is largely a reflection of proximity to Southern California markets. Production commenced around 1910; additional plants have been opened and older ones enlarged. Specific location has been influenced by sizable limestone deposits and rail facilities. The major concentration is in the Mojave River Valley, where Southwestern Portland (at Victorville) and Riverside Cement (at Oro Grande) constitute two of the larger plants in western United States. Additional plants have been constructed by Permanente Cement (in Lucerne Valley) and by California Portland Cement (near Mojave).

The Desert provided *iron ore* for Kaiser Steel at Fontana (see Fig. 6-57) from 1942 until 1983.

Initial operations were conducted in the Providence Mountains. Following completion of a 50-mile rail link with the Southern Pacific, Vulcan was abandoned in favor of Eagle Mountain in 1948. The magnetite replacement deposit here contained more than 40 million tons of ore, varying in content from 30 to 50 per cent. Prior to mine closure **Eagle Mountain** was cited as a model company camp.

The Mojave is characterized by many smaller dispersed enterprises. Some are oriented towards the Los Angeles market hence tend to conduct steady operations.

Common *table salt* and *calcium chloride* come from the brines of Bristol Lake. The Bristol salt is used in industrial chemicals and in the water-softening operations of the Metropolitan Water District. Some lesser operations are related to the erratic federal defense program, such as manganese from the Little Maria Mountains and tungsten from Atolia; hence production tends to be spasmodic. Production of europium oxide occurs in the Ivanpah Mountains east of Baker. This mineral became valuable for use in color television tubes; at $600 a pound (after processing) it qualifies as both rare and precious. The world's only source of Hectorite (a lithium-bearing clay with varied uses) has been mined at Newberry Springs. Zeolite, used in England to clean up nuclear waste at power plants, has been quarried near Barstow and and a mine in the Little Maria Mountains is an important source of agricultural gypsum.

## ALFALFA AND SPARSE PASTURES

The Mojave cannot be considered a major California agricultural area.

Still, where water is available, agriculture has had importance and, though they may depend slightly upon surrounding ranches, many of the larger towns of the Desert are located in basins where farming has been conducted.

Agriculture in the Mojave has benefitted from the growth of Los Angeles.

The Desert supplies, as much as it can, livestock, poultry and feeds for the metropolitan area. These agricultural pursuits are able to tolerate summer heat and winter cold.

Most of the Mojave is not well suited for livestock ranching.

Its natural vegetation does not provide much forage; it permits more than five head of cattle per square mile in the northeast. Too, the low dry mountains lack suitable alpine grasslands for transhumance. Thus vast stretches are devoid of sheep and cattle ranches. Still, it was stockmen rather than miners who formed the first Anglo group to settle in the Desert. More recent dry-land grazing has been limited largely to the higher ranges in the northeast Mojave.

### The Essex District

An anomoly in the Mojave, usually too barren for livestock without irrigated pastures, the Essex District (in the northeastern Mojave) has greater vegetative density (especially grass) than is usual in the subregion.

Somewhat higher (between 3000 and 4000 feet) the surfaces of the District carry a cover of bunch grass and shrubs that afford sparse cattle pasture. The loftier New York and Providence Mountains trap more moisture than most of the Mojave ranges. Even so there are fewer than a dozen ranches. Headquarters are situated in canyons at the base of the mountains where water from limestone formations provide a steady spring flow.

### CLUSTERS OF PEOPLE

One senses the overall emptiness of the Mojave while driving one of the interstate highways. But flying over this dry land one really appreciates how much of it lacks people. Most residents of the Desert are found in a few clusters.

These "concentrations" of human activity will be considered: **Palo Verde Valley, the Needles District, Barstow, the Mojave River Valley, Apple and Lucerne valleys, the Morongo Valley** and **Antelope Valley.**

### THE PALO VERDE VALLEY

The Palo Verde Valley,* remindful of a miniature Nile or Indus, is a crescentic segment of the lower Colorado River floodplain in the southeastern Mojave. Now the Desert's ranking agricultural area, it suggests Colorado Desert agricultural landscapes (Ch.5). The cultivated fields contrast vividly with the barren untilled Chuckwalla Desert to its west.

Irrigation development in the Palo Verde was delayed until the early twentieth century.

Thomas Blythe, a San Francisco financier, ac-

**Figure 4-9.** Segment of the Palo Verde Valley, the ranking agricultural producer of the Mojave Deser. (dwl)

quired title to 39,000 acres through his "controlled" entrymen under the Desert Act in 1877. He died before development was scarcely started; during a lengthy estate litigation, most of the original irrigation works were destroyed by floods. After court decisions finally allowed development, the Palo Verde Mutual Water Company sold land and built a new irrigation system. Inadequate market outlets posed a problem until ranchers floated bonds and constructed their own rail line, the California Southern, to connect with the Santa Fe main line. After completion of the rail outlet, cotton became the leading crop and remained so until the depressed years of the 1930's.

Agricultural expansion was delayed until construction of Hoover Dam.

Repeated Colorado River rampages crippled irrigation works and destroyed crops. The Valley has been plagued too by drainage problems; since the land slopes downward (from the slightly higher natural levee, fields towards the west have had a higher water table.

Despite its small size (170 square miles), the Valley has subsequently (i.e., post-Hoover Dam) become

---

* The Palo Verde, although "barely" within the Mojave, is physically and economically more akin to the Colorado Desert although its winters are colder. Its growing season is two weeks shorter than Imperial Valley and its record low of 5 degrees F. is far colder than the minimum temperatures experienced in the Colorado Desert.

a prosperous agricultural oasis.

It ranks third in desert California (after the Imperial and Coachella valleys) in value of agricultural product. Yet the countryside retains a suggestion of newness and rawness; the visitor also notes the conspicuous absence of fences and outbuildings.

There have been a series of agricultural shifts; now, with alfalfa, grains, lettuce, melons and livestock, it suggests a miniature Imperial Valley (Ch.5).

There was almost monoculture of cotton in the past. But for half a century alfalfa (for shipment to the Los Angeles Lowlands) acreage has been higher. More recently cotton allotments have been restricted by federal controls.

Melons (cantaloupes, honeydews and watermelons) harvested "early" (i.e., May to July) have tended to yield premium prices traditionally. After elimination of the bracero program in the 1960's) cantaloupes declined—much of the early crop now comes from Mexico.

The Valley is California's earliest source of processing tomatos (shipped to Fullerton) and onions (shipped north). For both vegetables, processing plants "open" their season with Palo Verde offerings.

Livestock are imported from Western rangelands in autumn, fattened and shipped to metropolitan Los Angeles in late winter. Improved Mexican wheats, suitable for both food and feed, have replaced barley. The wheat is consumed locally and in Imperial Valley feedlots; "topped off" cattle are shipped to Los Angeles.

Corporate-owned lemon groves, using shallow well irrigation, have appeared on The Mesa (west of the Valley floor). Since winter frost may occur, helicopters, wind machines and water spray are used to protect the fruit. Local packing sheds are anticipated. But an approach to record low temperatures might eliminate production.

**Blythe** (7900), marketing and shipping center for the Valley, is suggestive of Imperial Valley cities.

Like El Centro, it has a high volume of retail trade, a sizable black population and a considerable number of residents who work on surrounding farms. It is more like Brawley, however, with its relatively low incomes, lesser educational attainments and limited number of retirees. Understandably there is much shabby housing. Hobson Way (I-10 Bus.), with stately palms and sidewalk canopies, has most of the retail activity (including two mini-malls). Its east-west reach suggests a

larger town. Blythe is a major way point between Phoenix and Los Angeles, hence a gateway into California. Thus travelers services (G.E.M.) are conspicuous.* Expanding interstate movement has benefitted it establishments. The city is supported also by retail trade derived from an extensive surrounding area.

## THE NEEDLES DISTRICT

The Needles Oasis, long utilized by the Mohave Indians, lacks the agricultural output of the Palo Verde Valley.

While it is larger than floodplains "downvalley" along the Colorado, it was long handicapped by Colorado River inundations. There is little arable land on the California side of the river.

The *Mohave* practiced flood irrigation until Hoover Dam was constructed. Subsequently they were employed as railroad workers.

The Mohave never effected a treaty with the federal government but their land was divided checkerboard fashion with alternate sections granted to the Santa Fe Railroad, similar to division of Cahuilla lands (Ch.5). Currently the Mohave are looking to the future more optimistically than in past decades.

They feel they have been plagued by governmental "bureaucracy." They have finally leased 2500 acres

---

* G.E.M., for gas-eats-motels, is a term coined by Frank Seawall, C.S.U., Chico, to identify travel facilities.

**Figure 4-10.** Hayfield Pumping Station on the Colorado River Aqueduct. This facility , which requires lifting to reach its markets, differs from the gravity-flow Los Angeles Aqueduct. (dwl)

to an Imperial Valley farmer with the understanding that they will be taught contemporary agricultural techniques.

Despite frustrations (which cause many youth to drop out of high school) the tribe is considering such possibilities for their lands as a shopping center, recreation, agriculture and a gambling casino (within Nevada). Many Mohave have been voluntary converts to Christianity. One Mohave joked, "Who needs Heaven—we have Lake Havasu City."

Presently the Mohave hold much of the Needles Area. Despite the extent of their *Fort Mohave Indian Reservation* which encompasses land in both California and Arizona, most of the tribe (around 300) reside in Needles (on an enclave just outside of the city limits), locale of the Tribal Council. Indians and whites alike consider relations to be good.

The functions of **Needles** (5600) include services for an extensive area, entry point into California, highway stop (g.e.m.), recreation spot and retirement place.

Projected as a Santa Fe division point, Needles was established in 1883. Earlier the largest community in the Desert it has not achieved the growth of such communities as Victorville and Lancaster.

"Everyone" who drove westward into California on U.S.66 (now I-40) recalled Needles as "that hellhole" in a subtropical desert whose modest amenities could not compensate for the heat. Surely in winter, and even in summer with air-conditioning it is not that bad. Before cooled air, Needles was a "transit" town—railroad families escaped to the Coast in summer. Now railroaders retire to Needles!

After Hoover Dam "Mexican town" (flood bottoms) became a golf course. Aquatic activity adds to the recreational appeal. Visitors are often Canadians and other middle income "northerners."

Compact in area, Needles is surrounded by federal lands. There is a strong civic spirit, reflected in the City-County Center on the mesa (Needles is a sub-county seat).

The contrast between the "old" Needles along the railroad with modest frame cottages, light-asphalt roofs and the newer stucco ranch-type dwellings on the mesa, with their white crushed-rock roofs (where a third of the residents now live) is pronounced.

### The Mojave River Valley

Extending for more than 60 miles crescent-like, the Mojave River Valley creates an attenuated ribbon of greenery amid the gray desert hues.

The Mojave River, rising on the northeastern slopes of the San Bernardino Mountains, constitutes one of the major streams of the Desert. While its surface flow generally disappears into its sandy bed upstream from Victorville, subsurface flow continues 50 miles east of Barstow; it can be tapped by shallow wells. During the late Pleistocene the river flowed into Death Valley.

For a century and a half the Valley has provided a commercial corridor.

Initially it formed a segment of the Old Spanish Trail, then was used by emigrant trains and by Mormons traveling between Salt Lake and San Bernardino. Then came the main line of the Santa Fe and eventually U.S. 66. Now I-15 avoids the Valley, and there is a string of decaying travel facilities along "old" Route 66.

The agricultural value is higher than highway travelers probably realize.

The Desert's earliest cattle ranching (which continues today) began here. Currently the Valley is a source of riding horses. for the Los Angeles Basin; alfalfa fields are commonplace. Small poultry ranches are no longer consequential while fields of onions and potatoes have modified older land-use patterns.

Victor Valley (the upper Valley) lacks adequate water despite a county agency; while the California Water Project supplements pumping in Middle Basin (between Victorville and Barstow) and eastward, there is overdraft and the "whole" Valley is

**Figure 4-11.** A dispersed residential area, Apple Valley is merging into the Victorville urban complex. (dwl).

Figure 4-12. "Flight line", Edwards Air Force Base, with Rogers Dry Lake in the rear. The U. S. Air Force tests new spacecraft designs here. (U.S. Air Force)

contesting water allocation.

Population of the Valley continues to rise. It forms one of the major clusters of the entire Desert.

### Barstow and Environs

**Barstow** (22,000), leading community of the central Mojave (and a major city in the entire Mojave) is bolstered by highway trade, local services, military and railroads.

It began in 1886 as a rail junction town where transcontinental lines from central and southern California join. Barstow has extensive freight classification yards and since 1945 has been the site of the Santa Fe's "running" diesel repair shops.

Barstow's location has been called "a tank of gas from Los Angeles, Las Vegas and Needles" by Garrison (see bibliography). The G.E.M. function is important; service stations, restaurants and motels are much evident. Desert habitues ("desert rats"),who tend to gather here, frequent older motels downtown; the city is the shopping place for a hinterland of approximately 10,000 square miles. Threading through the city the freeway (I-l5-40) exits allow ready city entry and egress. A recent westward "extension" of I-40, Ca. 58 continues through Bakersfield to the Pacific Coast. Yet central Barstow has been affected less by new downtown facilities than Victorville.

Figure 4-13. The Colorado River at Needles. There are not too many places in interior California where aquatic frolic is comfortable in late March. (dwl)

Several thousand military and civilian personnel are employed at the Marine Corps Depot. The ethnic population (8 per cent black, 27 per cent Hispanic) is conspicuous. A number of Marine veterans have retired in the city.

The temporary closure of Fort Irwin (Army) hurt Barstow.but subsequently the city has changed due to a community college, automation of the Santa Fe yards (installation of a "hump"), expansion of diesel yards, growth as a truck terminal, and an enclosed shopping complex. Population, with the fringes, approaches 40,000 people yet the

Figure 4-14. Cholla Gardens in Pinto Basin, Joshua Tree National Monument. (dwl)

conspicuous "scatteration" of Victorville is lacking. There are two museums plus nearby Calico, a "restored" mine camp (now a county park).

### Victor Valley (the Upper Basin)

**Victorville** (30,000), Upper Basin focal point, is a highway stop, local node and residence place. It is the site too of Victor Valley College.

It developed as an outfitting point for nineteenth century miners. Later its false fronts provided a popular setting for "western" motion pictures. Now it has income from travelers, George Air Force Base personnel, retirees and commuters (to the eastern Los Angeles Basin) and employees at two large cement plants. A state prison is projected for nearby **Adelanto** (5,000).

Besides retail trade (a strip along old U.S. 66 and around freeway exits) Victorville is a low-density residential community. Two entire Los Angeles suburban-type retail complexes have developed apart from the central district. Growth has continued with much new housing "upvalley" to the south. Here 5000-acre Jess Ranch, long known for its beef, turkeys and pond grown trout), is the focus of housing, especially for senior citizens.

Conversion of "old" U.S. 395, northeastward from San Diego across Cajon Pass, into I-15 has made Victorville a favorite stopover point for San Diegans to and from Las Vegas. The Roy Rogers-Dale Evans Museum provides an added excuse to tarry.

Although they are discussed later, Apple and Lucerne valleys have been fused into the Victorville "metropolitan" complex.

**Hesperia** (unincorp.,circa 15,000 in "environs") houses retirees and commuters.

It began as a "cheap land" scheme and now sprawls across the upland west of Victor Valley. Some residences were constructed in low-cost (federal funds) tracts. usually occupied by retirees from Fontana or Rialto.

### Apple and Lucerne valleys

Southeast of Victorville along the eastern base of the San Bernardino Mountains, Apple and Lucerne valleys are being absorbed into the "greater" Victorville complex.

Residential development in Apple Valley can be attributed to the alchemy of a Long Beach oil fortune, a barrage of advertizing and proximity to metropolitan Los Angeles (Fig. 4-11).

Half a century ago **Apple Valley** (unincorp., circa 12,000) would have seemed highly unlikely to become the "Palm Springs of the Mojave."

Then it gained a country club, an airport, a crisscross of paved roads and a number of horse "ranchettes."

In the closing years of the twentieth century its looks increasingly like suburban Victorville, complete with apartments, "normal" commuter-oriented tracts and shopping malls.

Until the final decades of the century Lucerne Valley seemed a "way out" rural environment with alfalfa fields and pasturage of feeder cattle.

Since the late 1970's the Valley has acquired the appearance of the urban fringe. There is still a rurban feel to the Valley.

### Morongo Valley

Population is expanding along Ca. 62 northeast of San Gorgonio Pass.

Earlier growth here tended to be retirees with fondness for the desert and who could not or would not afford Palm Springs. In the closing decades of the century, a considerable population increase represents commuters. The area is accessible to the Los Angeles Basin via. I-10.

**Morongo Valley** (unincorp., circa 5000), although closer to the millions in the Los Angeles Basin, remains a dispersed rurban type of community.

A few miles farther east, **Yucca Valley** (circa 20,000) has become one of the larger towns in the Desert.

It stretches for several miles along the highway and has definitely become the service center for the "far" southern edge of the Mojave.

**Twentynine Palms** (6000) has been affected by the nearby Joshua Tree park and the Marine Corps facility.

But much growth during the past half century has been due to the affection of retirees for the area.

### Antelope Valley

Occupying 1500 square miles in the westernmost Mojave, Antelope Valley retains agricultural value although much of its population growth and urban economy has been unrelated to farming.

Yet farming has been favored more than in most parts of the Mojave.

Circumstances have included availability of ground water (now augmented from the California

Aqueduct), water from peripheral mountains and favorable highway (Ca.14) and rail (Valley Line of Southern Pacific) access to the Los Angeles Lowlands. Precipitation is usually sufficient on its western edge for dry-farmed grains. About 90,000 acres have been utilized although about half of the cultivated land has been fallowed (strip farming is practiced).

Agriculture commenced in the Valley over a century ago.

Bunch grass permitted localized winter and spring grazing in the early 1880's. The "Boom of the Eighties" in Southern California encouraged agriculture in the west and around Palmdale. Promoters sold many parcels of land for grain farming usually to newcomers unfamiliar with rainfall cycles in this near-arid land.

Six irrigation districts were established in eastern Antelope Valley, paralleling the grain farming farther west. Thousands of acres of prunes and almonds were planted. After an 11-year period of extreme dryness (from1893-1894), one district survived. Many trees perished while other orchards were severely curtailed.

By the middle 1920's the contemporary agricultural mosaic had been established.

Presently there are grains in the west, relict orchards in the south, and alfalfa, truck crops and poultry elsewhere. Elevation, latitude and northerly exposure of the High Desert (circa 2000 feet) means harsher winters and lesser cropping possibilities than in the Colorado Desert and the Palo Verde Valley (i.e., the "Low Desert").

The rural economy of Antelope Valley has persisted for some decades.

Holdings in the west have been consolidated. Use of strip farming conserves moisture and reduces erosion. Dry farmed grains yield well in years of adequate rainfall—approximately 40,000 acres are thus used. Farms, owner-operated and highly mechanized, average about 1000 acres each. The pump-well belt to the east has been hampered by steady decline in water table (60 to 200 feet deep). Five and a half cuttings of alfalfa are customary; much hay has been trucked to the metropolitan dairy belt. Urban markets also have afforded outlets for such truck crops as melons and carrots. Urbanization of the San Fernando Valley prompted relocation of poultry farms in Antelope Valley.

Some of the most spectacular urban growth in the Desert has occurred around the "twin" communities

**Figure 4-15.** Calico, northeast of Barstow. Now a county park, this old mine camp was the inspiration for Ghost Town at Knott's Berry Farm in Orange County. (dwl)

of Palmdale and Lancaster.

There has been a definite correlation with activities at Palmdale Airport and Edwards Air Force Base. There has also been an expansion of services for travelers on Ca. 14. And impressive commutation to the Los Angeles Basin takes place.

Aircraft companies in metropolitan Los Angeles established testing facilities at Palmdale Airport (circa 1950). In the late 1960's, with the shift of aerospace firms from "conventional" aircraft, prospects seemed to diminish. For a time there were plans of making Palmdale Southern California's supersonic air terminal. Subsequently Lockheed's space shuttle contract became all-important (flights began in 1981). With their housing tracts both communities suggest newer Los Angeles suburbs.

**Lancaster** (75,000) is the largest city in the Mojave and the ranking service center of the western Mojave.

There are sprawling housing tracts, apartments and retail facilities. The city is not unusually attractive despite more expensive custom homes around Antelope Valley College on the west side.

**Palmdale** (30,000) is less diversified in function than Lancaster.

Its economy has directly affected by fluctuations in employment at its airport. Its central district, which long suggested a country hamlet, has been redeveloped.

**Mojave** (2600), a pass town at the eastern base of the Tehachapi crossing, has experienced limited growth.

It has a considerable ethnic population and lower

**Figure 4-16.** Downtown Lancaster early on Sunday morning. The largest city in the Mojave suggests a suburb of Los Angeles. (dwl)

"socioeconomic" rating. Highway services are conspicuous (Mojave is at the junction of Ca. routes 58 and 14). It suffered economically after closure of a military base and cutback in railroad employment. There is commutation to Edwards Force Base and Lancaster-Palmdale.

## DESERT TRAINING AND MISSILE RESEARCH

Military activities, beginning with the Pacific Theatre in World War II, and the continued importance of the Pacific Basin, have accounted for the persistence of installations in the Mojave.

At least one large establishment is maintained by each of the major services (and the Coast Guard operates on the Colorado River!). Duplicate utilization irritates those who decry unnecessary preemption of the Desert despite the seeming worthlessness of much of these reserved tracts. Assuredly thousands of military and civilian personnel have have added considerably to Mojave payrolls.

Installations tend to be space oriented.

Acreages necessary for testing aircraft and missiles, for target practice, maneuvers and storage have been available. Approximately a sixth of the entire Mojave is contained within military bases (Map 4-2); elsewhere, wanderers have been warned against picking up "duds" (explosives

remaining from past activities).

Military operations tend to be climate-related.

This has been a reason, along with better accessibility, for concentration here rather than in the Trans-Sierra or Northeast. Dryness permits outdoor preservation of many stores at the **Marine Corps Logistics Base** east of Barstow, for example. The depot provides the Marines' chief storage and repair center in western United States. It has excellent rail and highway access.

Another locational factor is communications and allied services.

While space oriented, operations have tended to be located where supplies and civilian labor forces are available. Thus Barstow, Lancaster, Palmdale, Victorville and Twentynine Palms have gained population because of nearby installations. The tendency of military activities to gravitate into the western Mojave demonstrates that many of the functions represent "spillovers" from Southern California, where congestion precluded their establishment where they were deemed strategically vulnerable. Noteworthy examples are Palmdale Airport and Edwards Air Force Base; here large civilian staffs have been employed to test material produced around Los Angeles.

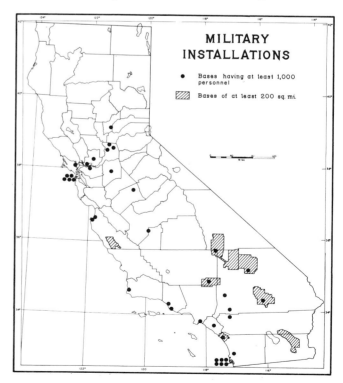

**Map 4-2.** Military bases occur widely in the Golden State. The largest installations are inland but many personnel are stationed near the Pacific Rim.

The **Naval Weapons Center** at China Lake has created one of the largest Mojave communities, China Lake-Ridgecrest.

In the entire Desert it represents the single new (post-1940) concentration based wholly upon the military. **China Lake** (12,000), within the military reserve, contains offices, laboratories and housing for military and select civilian personnel. The Center has been used to test ship-fired rockets, many of which have been manufactured in Southern California. Recent emphasis has been upon advanced research rather than testing.

**Ridgecrest** (23,000) has changed considerably to become a "modern" Desert city.

In its early years there was uncertainty about its permanency and it resembled a shanty town. Now it has air-conditioned stucco dwellings, Cerro Coso College and shopping facilities that serve much of the northwestern Desert and the Trans-Sierra to the north.

**Edwards Air Force Base** is the oldest military installation in Mojave—it is used to test Air Force and Navy aircraft and for missile research.

Established in the 1930's as a bombing range Edwards covers 300,000 acres (Fig. 4-12). Its site has about 350 "flying days" annually. At the time of its development its runway was the longest in the world.

**George Air Force Base**, which has been used recently for advanced jet training, provides a staging point for dispatch of fighter aircraft to "trouble spots" around the world.

Established north of Victorville in 1941, it served as headquarters for interceptor defense of metropolitan Los Angeles in "pre-missile" days.

**Fort Irwin**, sometimes inactive, has been the main Army establishment in the Mojave. It is now the home of the **U.S. Army National Training Center** and also contains N.A.S.A.'s Goldstone Tracking Station.

During World War II it was used as a center for training of personnel destined for the North African theatre. It was inactive between 1944 and 1951. Later it was expanded (to 600,000 acres) to become the largest contiguous installation in the Mojave, although China Lake and Test Range B together are nearly twice as spacious. Later, "inactive" again, the Fort was under the California State Military Headquarters. It provided space for Reserve and National Guard training. Its present use commenced in 1981 with the Reagan administration's expanded program of "na-

tional defense." It is used for combat training with frequent rotation of personnel nationwide and has had a "workday" populace of 10,000 military plus civilians. Complete facilities (multi-story residences, recreation facilities, hospital and others) have been constructed. The impact upon Barstow has been "overwhelming."

The **Marine Corps Base** north of Twentynine Palms affords a desert-setting place for artillery and missile range.

Established in 1952 in a Sahara-like setting, it represented the single site the Corps could find in the Desert with the amount of land (560,000 acres) it wanted. With a capacity of 10,000 trainees, the base is well located relative to the Corps' Southern California centers in San Diego and at Camp Pendleton. It is used most heavily in summer.

## FISHERFOLK AND ROCK HOUNDS

The Mojave, as a recreation area, benefits from its position relative to metropolitan Southern California—and the "High Desert" allows bird watchers, campers, flower lovers, hunters and rock hounds (as well as "off the road" 'wheelers) the opportunity to escape briefly from the gargantuan metropolis.*

Many a grizzled prospector who endured much hardship in the Mojave in pre-automobile days would be dismayed at the idea of the Desert as a recreation land.

Admittedly Red Rock Canyon is not another Bryce, nor is Mitchell Caverns (northwest of Essex) comparable to Carlsbad, but these places are accessible to Angelinos.

Leading visitation areas include (1) the northern base of the San Bernardino Mountains, from Cajon Pass to Lucerne Valley, (2) the northern piedmont of the Little San Bernardino Mountains and (3) along the Colorado River.

The appeals of **Joshua Tree National Monument** suggest those of Death Valley (Ch.3) and Anza-Borrego Desert (Ch.5). All three are arid wastes, albeit distinctive.

Joshua Tree, established as a preserve in 1936, was little frequented for many years. More recent popularity seems to result from the desire of

---

* Residents of Southern California distinguish between "High Desert" (i.e., most of the Mojave) and "Low Desert" (Colorado Desert and lower Colorado River Valley). Lamentably San Francisco Bay Area news media sometimes apply the term High Desert to Northeast California.

**Figure 4-17.** "Walking" a nature trail near Cottonwood Springs, Joshua Tree National Monument. This preserve may become a national park in the near future. (dwl).

Southern Californians for open space. Thus its altered status to **national park** seems probable. Its campgrounds are "dry" (one brings one's own water, firewood or fuel).

There is a diversity of attractions. Salton View (5148 ft.) affords an overlook of the Coachella Valley and the Salton Sea—on those days when the air is not smoggy. Near park headquarters is the Oasis of Mara. Other appeals include Cottonwood Springs, numerous Joshua trees, Pinto Basin with its Cholla Gardens, and some good examples of spheroidal weathering of granite in the Little San Bernardino Mountains.

There are a number of spots for camping, fishing, and boating along the **lower Colorado River.**

Southern California offers its millions few spots for fresh-water fishing. Thus many Middlewestern refugees (and their offspring) will drive several hundred miles, often towing a boat-laden trailer, to fish in the Colorado.

Activity is noticeable wherever there is access by road. The clear waters here provide bass, bluegill, channel catfish, catfish, and crappie. Principal locales include Lake Havasu behind Parker Dam, Needles, the 15-mile section from Parker Dam to Earp and Blythe. An increasing number of enthusiasts take boat trips along the lower river.

## "OUTLIERS" OF "GREATER" LOS ANGELES

Increasingly, the Mojave Desert has been sharing in the population spiral of Southern California.

Despite separation from the Los Angeles Low-lands by the walls of the San Gabriel and San Bernardino mountains, the southwestern fringe of the Mojave, from Palmdale to Yucca Valley has become a detached outlier of the evolving megalopolis that focuses on metropolitan Los Angeles.

Contributing to the growth are such factors as the beauty and solitude of the Desert, availability of cheaper land, publicity and promotion, the desire to "do one's own thing" allowed by more permissiveness in county territory, technological advances (such as air conditioning, swimming pools and access by paved highways) that tend to make this land more habitable. Considerations too include polluted air and other repelling aspects of life in metropolitan Los Angeles.

Quite often the "encounter" of the Southern California urbanite with the Mojave begins casually.

Oft-times it is doubtless a search for affordable housing. In time many of the occasional visitors become full-time residents. Some have outside incomes (investments or pensions); others have creative ability (artists and writers) but many seek local employment.

The thousands of desert homesteads provided by the federal government have posed such problems to San Bernardino County as road maintenance and fire and police protection. A problem is given too to the census taker, who must decide who is and who is not a "resident" of the Desert. Meanwhile realtors try to attract more people while local chambers of commerce strive to widen the economic base by attracting industry.

The High Desert, lying above 2000 feet elevation, especially along the northern base of the Little San Bernardino, San Bernardino, and San Gabriel ranges, has been the focus of much of the development.

Devotees contend that the area lacks the intolerable summers of the Low Desert (i.e., Colorado Desert) whereas enthusiasts for the latter argue that the summers are miserable in both areas but that the Mojave winters lack the pleasantness found farther south.

## THE REST OF THE DESERT

Most of the Mojave, almost wholly in possession of the federal government, remains in a semi-pristine state. As the end of the century approaches there is considerable debate about its future.

## THE DESERT PLAN

A **California Desert Conservation Area** of 25 million acres has been established on public lands in eastern California (Trans-Sierra, Mojave Desert and Colorado Desert).

This was achieved under a special section of the Federal Land and Management Act of 1976. Logically, Congress has delegated the Bureau of Land Management (B.L.M.) to develop the Plan since the public domain is already under that agency. However the Bureau is not too enthusiastic and has not had sufficient expertise to do so. Most of the Plan entails recreation, which is not a prime goal of B.L.M.. Unfortunately the federal budget is not adequate and it is debatable whether B.L.M. can enforce the Plan.

The Plan is supported by such conservation groups as the Sierra Club and the Wilderness Society, with many supporters in Congress. Opposition comes from the California Desert Coalition (i.e., ranchers, miners, private recreation developers, off-the-road vehiclers).

The Plan entails a variety of land uses.

It will include wilderness areas (to be designated by Congress), recreational facilities, wildlife habitats, range management, survey of mineral resources (and monitoring of mining operations), land tenure and management of critical environments. B.L.M. is seeking cooperation of private individuals and local agencies. It anticipates vehicular access will continue and that probable development of wind and solar energy facilities will take place within the Area.

Progress has taken place. B.L.M. has identified a multitude of natural features to be preserved and others to be studied Primitive campgrounds have been created and more are anticipated. Four "Multiple Land-Use Classes" have been established, ranging from mining to wilderness.

A key unit is the **East Mojave National Scenic Area.** Portions of this new entity have been proposed to become a national park.

## LOOKING FORWARD

Anticipating the future of the Mojave, or any other part of California, borders on the absurd. Many transplanted residents of the Desert are escapees from metropolitan Southern California, especially commuters or retirees who prefer the Desert to the frantic, less-affordable life in the city. Many older retirees originally came from "back east" but prefer the dryness of the climate in the Mojave.

One interesting gamble with future growth is **California City** (3000), an incorporated community containing 160 square miles. Its original planners, members of a Beverly Hills firm, optimistically ignored the problems and talked of a city of one million people!

Technological advances have not resolved the Desert's problems of inadequate water. Yet delivery of northern California water to the southern Antelope and Mojave River valleys is taking place. Technology is allowing solar-electric production at Daggett, with anticipation and others in this "sunniest" part of the Golden State.

But the economic base remains precariously narrow in much of the Mojave. A few industrial firms have located in the northern Antelope Valley along transportation routes but the Mojave has obvious impediments to expanded population. The future for mining camps and communities dependent upon military bases tends to be problematic.

The Mojave has been altered noticeably in this century as result of its juxtaposition with Southern California athwart principal surface corridors to coastal areas. Because of transportation, the importance of the Mojave to California's circum-Pacific connections is magnified.

Increasingly, the southern edge of the Desert is becoming a continuation of the Southern California sprawl, stimulated by metropolitan industry, recreation, tourism, travel and mining. Housing costs in the Mojave tend to be lower than in some parts of the Los Angeles Basin. County planners are prepared for a possible "invasion." As was undertaken with the San Fernando Valley in the early 1940's, a comprehensive plan for development of southern Antelope Valley has been prepared.

There are several hints that a burgeoning growth of the southern Mojave is underway, such as the Santa Fe Southern's Colton-Palmdale rail link, water deliveries from the California Aqueduct, and expansion of population along the northern flanks of the San Bernardino and San Gabriel mountains. Some residents fret over visual pollution, created by street signs, the increased number of transmission lines, and hilltop communications facilities. Still, one ponders: Are industry and suburbia compatible for the Mojave? Is there, even in this sizable Desert, space for more cement mills and expansion of amenable residential sites? And what about use of the Desert as a dumping ground? Some job-short towns like the idea, even though the numbers of permanent jobs would be low.

As population of the Desert increases, frustrations with a county seat in San Bernardino increase. It has been proposed that the nation's largest county should be subdivided. High Desert residents feel a sense of estrangement from the metropolis "Down Below," as they term the Los Angeles Lowlands.

**Figure 5-1.** An increasing portion of the Desert, like southwestern Sun Belt areas to the east (especially Arizona) is becoming a land of retirees. (Palm Springs Convention and Visitors Bureau).

**Figure 5-2.** Date grove near Indio. A voracious consumer of water, the date palm is said to have its fronds in heaven and its roots in hell. (Bureau of Reclamation)

Chapter Five

# THE COLORADO DESERT

* The introductory portion and the section on Imperial Valley has been reviewed by Reynaldo Ayala, Imperial Valley campus, San Diego State University.

# THE COLORADO DESERT

Assigned a name that implies a wasteland, the Desert has become a productive land, unlike so many arid realms. This became possible because of access to the exotic waters of the Colorado River.

The Colorado Desert, one of the two smallest subregions in the Golden State (approximately 4000 square miles), is tucked away in the far southeastern corner of the state. To the east is Arizona, to the south Mexico and to the west is Southern California (map 5–1).

The Colorado Desert is a bonafide part of the *Great American Desert*.

For decades after early nineteenth-century surveys by Zebulon Pike and Stephen Long, much of North America between the Missouri River and the Sierra Nevada was regarded as the *Great American Desert* and was labeled thus on textbook maps. Although its extent has been much reduced since establishment of wheat farms and livestock ranches, the extreme Southwest, including the Colorado Desert, still warrants the term.

Here edible vegetation is so limited that even grazing is nigh impossible without irrigation—this is a land where a year's rainfall may not total an inch, and where it is literally possible to fry an egg in the sun of a summer afternoon. By whatever standards a scholar devises, and in the terminology of local residents, this area is truly a desert—that is, in its empty, undeveloped three quarters.

The occupied quarter of the Desert encompasses as its larger southern portion the delta of the Colorado River, whose water is supplemented by subsurface runoff from less arid mountains to the west.

Coupled with the advantages of rich soil, long growing season and access to the prosperous American market, the Colorado Desert has become one of the world's most productive oases.

It has also become one of the nation's most famous recreation places, with advantages of near-ideal winter climate and proximity to wealthy populous Southern California (Ch.6).

## THE SALTON TROUGH

The Colorado Desert approximates the landform division called the Salton Trough.

The Trough consists of a series of low-lying basins between the Little San Bernardino, Orocopia and Chocolate mountains (east) and the Peninsular Ranges of Southern California (west) (map 5-1). Its northwest corner focuses on San Gorgonio Pass, a natural and heavily-used gateway into to the Los Angeles Lowlands; its southern side is delimited by the Mexican boundary—physiographically the Trough continues southward to the Gulf of California.

The entire Trough, and perhaps the entire Gulf of California, is a structural basin with a vast thickness of downwarped sediments (see Overview B for further explanation). Medial and marginal faults are present.

The most famous of these is the **San Andreas** near the base of the Little San Bernardino Mountains; the spectacular mountain walls along the west side are considered of fault-scarp origin; and many hot springs along both east and west sides are attributed to seepage in fault zones.

From an apex at Yuma the Colorado has spread its delta.

The delta, extending westward toward the Peninsular Ranges has shut out the waters of the Gulf of California from the Salton Trough, much of which lies below sea level.

The Trough, north of the delta, has been occupied intermittently by freshwater lakes.

**Lake Cahuilla**, the most recent of these, has produced conspicuous shorelines, especially along the western side of the Trough. Colorado delta sediments were partially deposited in the lake, creating fine-textured soils that must be irrigated and drained with care, as well as frequently replowed to depths of four feet, lest salts accumulate. Traditionally the Trough is divided into three

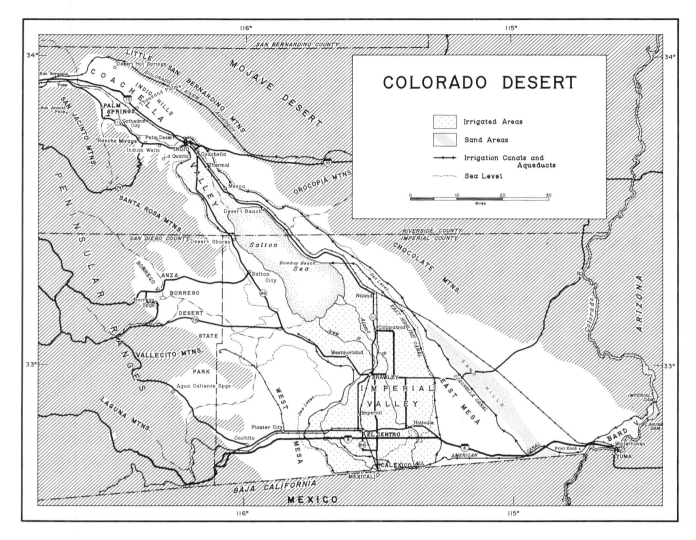

**Map 5-1.** Encompassing the non-aquatic north end of the Salton Trough, the small Colorado Desert includes most of Imperial County and small portions of San Diego and Riverside counties.

principal units (within California).

The north (California) half of the delta drains northwesterly into the Salton Sea—this portion of the Trough is called the **Imperial Valley**. The northern Trough, which slopes southward toward the Sea, is called **Coachella Valley**. It is filled with alluvium from the mountains to the northwest which is coarser than the Colorado delta sediments— hence it is too porous for agriculture in many places. The center of the depression is occupied by the **Salton Sea,** which originated as a freshwater lake in 1905 when the Colorado River surged into the irrigation works of the Imperial Canal during flood stage. Subsequently surface evaporation has concentrated the lake's salt content so that it is higher than the ocean.

Sand dunes, conspicuous locally, apparently rep-resent beach sand blown eastward from the shores of Lake Cahuilla.

The largest body, **Sand Hills**, trends northwestward between the Imperial Valley and the Chocolate Mountains for a distance of 40 miles. Some crests rise 300 feet although most of the dunes are quite low. Southwest of the Salton Sea is is also a lesser area of barchans (crescent-shaped dunes). Also there are low dunes northeast of Palm Springs.

## A HOT, HOT SUMMER LAND

During summer months the Desert is one of the hottest places on earth, closely approaching Death Valley and the subtropical deserts of the Old World in high temperatures.

Record temperatures here have reached 126 degrees F.—from June through September average midday temperatures exceed 100 degrees F. in the shade. Relative humidity, a normally low feature, does not compensate sufficiently to prevent many desert families from spending their summers in nearby mountains or along the seashore. Nocturnal cooling in this clear-sky land makes summers somewhat more tolerable but even at night the temperature regularly does not fall below 70 degrees F. in midsummer.

Fortunately winters are different—for six to seven months the Desert, with mild sunny days, is one of the more climatically-appealing places in the United States.

As in summer this is one of the sunniest portions of the nation. Agriculturally the Desert can practically considered to have a year-round growing season. However, a low of 13 degrees has been recorded so there is an element of risk in growing sensitive winter produce.

The Colorado is likewise one of the more arid portions of the earth.

Precipitation annually, at various stations, approximates 3 inches.In both summer and winter the controlling air is typically of local "tropical continental" origin. Occasional winter storms from the Pacific briefly bring overcast skies, but usually most of the potential rain has been wrung out when the storms cross the Transverse and Peninsular ranges. Accompanying winds, especially in springtime near the base of San Gorgonio Pass, are often more significant than precipitation since blowing sand is highly destructive to some crops. Windbreaks of native arrow weed, laboriously hand-set, are a common sight in truck gardens; elsewhere tamarisk trees are sometimes grown for windbreaks.

Like winter "lows", summer storms, while infrequent, are often memorable.

As moist unstable air moves northwestward, from the Gulf of California or even the Gulf of Mexico, displays of lightning, winds, unaccustomed humidity, and even torrential rains occur.

## CREOSOTE AND BURROWEED

Flora in the Colorado Desert consists predominantly of scattered species of low shrubs, able to survive for months without rainfall.

The creosote bush with its olive-colored leaves and the burroweed are most widespread. Yet overall

**Figure 5-3.** West of the Imperial Valley, semi-pristine West Mesa is part of the Sonoran Desert. (dwl)

the total vegetation has more complexity than the casual traveler along main roads realizes; botanists have collected hundreds of individual species of native plants. Besides its great variety, much of the plant life is quite distinct from that of other California deserts—so much so that the term "Sonoran" is sometimes applied in differentiating the flora of the Colorado and the other "southern" deserts from the Mojave.

A relatively large supply of succulents is included in the distinctive Sonoran vegetation.

The cholla cactus is a commonplace example. Other representative plants include the ocotillo, dramatic at Easter with monkey-tail trunks tipped with red flowers, and the low but distinctive washbank "forests" of ironwood, palo verde, mesquite and smoke tree, so celebrated in desert landscape pictures. At opposite extremes are the *Washingtonia* palms the mountain canyons and the coarse perennial galleta grass which is an important factor in stabilization of the Sand Hills east of Imperial Valley. For many plants, individual rainstorms tend to be more important than seasonal totals. Like other dry portions of California, the Desert is sometimes vivid with blooms of quick-growing annuals, particularly after spring rains.

## CAHUILLA AND YUMA

For aboriginal peoples the Colorado Desert was not too inviting.

Yet a number of sites with artifacts have been found on its western edges. Those who resided here, the Cahuilla and various Yuman groups, restricted their habitats to favored peripheral locations.

The *Cahuilla*, limited in number, concentrated about Palm Canyon, as they do today.

Formerly they were food-gatherers who took advantage of Colorado River seepage into the Salton Trough to provide sources of food. The Cahuilla, as a non-farming people residing in a land with limited game, necessarily used all available plants; Kroeber reported that they found some 60 varieties useful. The successful survival of the Cahuilla to the present is fortuitous. They hold two sizable Coachella Valley reservations, *Torres-Martinez* and *Agua Caliente*, with over 200 Indians on 22,000 acres. The former reservation consists of conspicuously barren tracts amidst irrigated fields. The latter, focusing upon Palm Canyon, is much more attractive.

The *Yuma* were a sedentary people who practiced flood irrigation in a manner akin to their near relatives, the Mohave, upstream (Ch.4).

While the name Yuman has been assigned to the family, the Yuma did not exceed the Mohave in numbers; the Yuma were apparently less given to warfare and traveling. The fertility of the Yuma oasis would have discouraged desert forages.Like the Cahuilla, the Yuma have survived to the present and Fort Yuma reservation has been set aside in Bard Valley (opposite the city of Yuma).

## A WAY WEST

The Colorado Desert, like the Mojave and the Sierra Nevada, is an area that has to be crossed to reach coastal California from the North American interior.

Between Spanish holdings in Alta California and Mexico, the overland route traversed the Colorado Desert between Anza-Borrego and Yuma. Yet the distance between watering places, plus difficulties with Indians, made this land route even more forbidding than the difficult ocean voyage up from Mexico. During the Gold Rush period, when the Desert served as an important corridor in transcontinental travel, the *Colorado Crossing* tended to parallel the earlier Spanish route directly south (to avoid the dunes) then west from Yuma to the Peninsular Ranges to minimize the waterless intervals.

The contemporary transcontinental line of the Santa Fe Southern reached the length of the Desert between Yuma and San Gorgonio Pass in 1877.

The local construction headquarters, Indio, remains a railroad service point. A branch line was extended to Calexico in 1903 after beginnings of farm settlement there. A tortuous line, opened in 1919, long provided a second rail outlet to the Pacific Coast at San Diego (before its abandonment west of Plaster City (map 5-1).

Interstate highways east from San Diego (I-8) and Los Angeles (I-10) reinforce the role of the Colorado Desert as a transport corridor.

Interstate traffic within the subregion is serviced primarily at El Centro and Indio—both towns had developed retail facilities prior to the development of the automobile age, and both are located conveniently near major highway junctions. Trucking of farm produce to coastal cities is a major commercial activity; eastbound agricultural exports still move predominantly by rail. A heavy highway traffic movement between the Palm Springs area and the Los Angeles Basin is substantial even in summer.

## THE SEARCH FOR WATER

A key factor in agricultural development of the Colorado Desert has been availability of irrigation water.

Only after dependable supplies became available could substantial settlement take place—a condition still true. The Colorado Desert remained nearly untilled before the twentieth century.

Eventually irrigation resulted from the efforts of two experienced water engineers, George Chaffey and Charles Rockwood.

Their California Development Company (the C.D.C.), aided considerably by Chaffey's renown as a developer of successful irrigation systems in Australia and in Southern California and by his willingness to reinvest his personal fortune thereby amassed, succeeded in conveying Colorado River water into the Desert by 1901.

Obstacles interposed by the Mexican and United States governments and problems of silting induced the C.D.C. to cut a unwise canal entry from the river below Yuma. Aided by untimely floods, the river ran uncontrolled into the canal and from March 1905 to February 1907, flowed through Imperial Valley to re-establish the Salton Sea (where Lake Cahuilla had recurrently been). The floodwaters turned the shallow beds of the New and Alamo rivers into impressive gullies— actually fortunate in view of their present utility as drainageways for surplus irrigation water, which lessens waterlog-

**Figure 5-4.** Imperial Dam on the Colorado River, with the headgates of the All-American Canal. The low dam, about 15 miles north of Yuma, is sufficiently high to divert water into the Canal. Water then flows downslope into the Imperial and Coachella valleys. "Desilting basins" are conspicuous in the middle of the photo. (Imperial Irrigation District)

ging and salt accumulation in fields.

Efforts to provide an assured water supply for the Desert without admitting the entire river was not readily achieved. Also, increasing demands for irrigation water on the Mexican side of the border posed a long-term threat to adequacy of the supply.

It was deemed necessary to construct a large flood-control dam and a canal entirely within the United States so as to effectively use the Colorado River.

Not until the Colorado River Compact of 1922 was approval of the states of the Colorado River obtained. Financial wherewithal was not available until Congressional passage of the Boulder Canyon Act of 1928 and availability of Public Works funds in 1933.

Construction of the world's then-highest dam (Hoover) upriver and the All-American Canal (Fig.5-4) took years to complete. The contemporary delivery system dates from 1940 when the first flow was diverted from Imperial Dam, then desilted in nearby settling basins and conveyed 80 miles into Imperial Valley via the *All-American Canal.*

World War II preempted labor from a longer extension, the Coachella Canal.

Hence Colorado River water did not reach the northern part of the Colorado Desert until 1948. Previously the Coachella Valley depended upon groundwater originating in the Transverse and Peninsular ranges—an expensive and limited source.

The additional canal systems have been a significant stimulus to Desert agriculture despite distances involved the high evaporation rates en route.

Their operation is facilitated by continuous downslope flow, which obviates the need for expensive pumping. In fact there is sufficient gradient to permit generation of hydroelectricity at four plants along the All-American Canal.

Imperial Valley settlement commenced at the turn of this century; for three decades the population grew rather rapidly as irrigation agriculture expanded. Populated portions of the Desert, dependent upon water supplies, consist of five distinct "oases" widely separated by raw desert.

These subdivisions are : (1) **Imperial Valley** (2) **Bard Valley** (3) **Anza-Borrego Desert** (4) **Salton Sea** (5) **Coachella Valley**. Each will be considered separately.

## IMPERIAL VALLEY

With an irrigated area of some 470, 000 acres and a population of 90, 000, the Imperial Valley is a focus of settlement and productivity in the Desert.

Agriculture is the predominant source of livelihood and nearly the only basic activity.

**Figure 5-5.** Hydroelectric plant on the All-American Canal. The westward downslope of the Colorado River delta allows generation of electricity. With a capacity of 15,000 second feet this man-made river is one of the world's larger irrigation canals. In the background is East Mesa; note the creosote bush. (Imperial Irrigation District).

There is also limited service to wayfarers, military activity (at El Centro Naval Air Station), and wallboard manufacture at Plaster City.

Most towns were founded before 1910; they have been influenced by the branch line of the Southern Pacific, which permitted commercial export agriculture. The earliest settlers were homesteaders who generally came from the Middle West, often enticed by promotion efforts. The developers coined the name *Imperial Valley* to allay concern that prospective settlers might have had about desert residence.

The decades since the mid-1920's have been a time of agricultural maturation in the Valley.

Production and acreage have increased slowly in comparison with the earlier decades and the general land-use patterns have become persistent.

### Cropping Shifts

An expected period of trial and error was experienced by settlers in their choice of products.

Summer heat discouraged production of deciduous fruit, eggs and potatoes. Several crops later important were not part of the earliest agriculture: cotton (since 1916), lettuce (since 1916), carrots (somewhat later), flax (since 1934) and sugar beets (since 1937). Feeding of sheep and cattle on locally-grown alfalfa and grain has been a dependable mainstay from the beginning.

Agriculture has become more diversified but livestock and feed production have tended to increase nevertheless. Raising perishable truck crops, the other major activity, has proved quite successful since the earliest settlement.

The technique of double-cropping within a single season, unknown in most parts of the United States, has been in vogue almost from the beginning.

### Out on the Farm

Characteristically there are three types of property. These are (1) the ranch of the locally-raised owner-operator (2) the corporate entity (perhaps directed from a distance but locally managed and (3) the lease operation.

The "typical" owner-operators have food factories containing many hundred acres. Many are descendants of homesteaders. As lifelong residents of the Valley, they know local methods and problems thoroughly. *Corporate* properties, some representing reinvestment of farm money "driven out" of Southern California by urbanization, have become increasingly characteristic. Considerable land is *leased*, perhaps to a Japanese-American or Filipino truck farmer or to a Salinas lettuce grower.

Farm buildings are few in number and of modest quality. Houses are generally single-story frame structures; many are shanties. Many owners are town residents, with a foreman or other employee living on the ranch. There are few outbuildings; many ranches contain no livestock, and a tin roof on poles suffices as a machinery shed. Construction of quality ranch-style bungalows in the past generation reflects a tendency for some landowners to move back to the country. Fields are large and commonly fenceless. The irrigation lateral, often concrete lined, is ubiquitous. Rural roads, while closely spaced, remain unpaved to a degree uncommon is more productive California agricultural districts. Cottonwoods, eucalyptus and tamarisk trees are widely planted for shade and as windbreaks.

## Machines—And Once-Bent Backs

The Imperial Valley needed a number of seasonal farm laborers from the earliest years.

Farmers of European descent detested work in extreme summer heat and dependable low-wage Hispanic labor was nearby. Mexican families, often encamped beside irrigation ditches, were an early sight in the Valley.

Many growers have held hostility toward "more demanding" America-born field hands; laborers represented diverse backgrounds.

Hindus migrated from Canada as early as 1907; known as "rag-heads" because of their turbans, they picked the Valley's first cotton crop in 1910. Relatively few became permanent residents— those who did have tended to become socially acceptable landowners; one of the Indian-born group served in Congress (1956-62).

Filipino importation began in 1920, prompted by fear that Congress would restrict Mexican labor; like the Hindus, they have tended to ascend the economic ladder. Many Filipinos remain in the Valley as lease farmers. Additional non-Mexican laborers, including many blacks from the South, arrived during the depression and dust years of the 1930's. Blacks, now the second most-numerous ethnic group in the Valley, are concentrated in El Centro, where their numbers total around 2000.

But the Mexican national and the Mexican-American have provided the principal supply of temporary labor since the beginnings of Valley settlement.

From 1920 to 1940 thousands came by truck from Sonora and Baja California, ostensibly for the work season; many remained during the slack period on public welfare rolls. There were numerous "wetbacks" who crossed the border easily and repeatedly in response to seasonal needs. Many

became United States citizens and permanent residents; by 1950, 30 per cent of the county population had Spanish surnames, a higher per cent of the total population than in any other county. With 19 per cent, Imperial ranks second only to San Francisco among all 58 counties in percentage of foreign born.

The illegal entrant was largely replaced by the Mexican *bracero* (contract worker) for over a decade (1950-1963).

An agreement was effected between the United States and Mexican governments. At times there were over 60,000 braceros at work in the Valley. In 1964 American organized labor persuaded Congress to eliminate this cheap competitive labor. Sociologically, the bracero program was not ideal. Women and children were left without the company and support of husbands (and fathers) for months at a time. However, elimination of the program did not make jobs for citizens. Rather, there was a "flight" of such crops as market tomatoes and melons to Mexico or work was done by hiring of Green Card holders (i.e., Mexican nationals).

Recent decades have seen significant shifts in Valley labor.

These have included changes in total numbers of workers, rancher attitudes and worker dexterity. Automation of farm production has taken place, even including "hard to mechanize" vegetables. Many a "native-born" worker who knew more humble tasks now operates impressive farm machinery. There has been a dramatic decline in the number of workers.

## Vegetables and Cattle

Climatically favored (for agriculture), the Valley could raise most crops grown elsewhere in the nation (though possibly not in in summer!). In recent years the return from Imperial agriculture has approached a billion dollars annually.

Farming is characterized by its diversity as well as productivity. A score of commodities are "million dollar" items. The Valley has an inherently wide range of possibilities ties when compared to higher latitude areas. Diversity has been affected by such considerations as ultimate limits to consumption, competitive advantages of other farm areas, local soil variations, and federal policies (price and acreage controls). Knowledgeable operators shift with trend variations— this is a "guessing game" which yields varying fortunes year to year.

**Figure 5-5a.** The American Nile— lettuce harvest east of Holtville. (dwl)

*Truck Crops*

Despite large acreage declines (with "relocation" in Mexico), truck crops remain important in the Imperial. Melons as well as vegetables have long been important.

They are raised chiefly for fresh table use thus are shipped wherever price momentarily promises the best return, be it Boston or Los Angeles. The longer the distance, the greater the potential competition; thus timing is of utmost importance here. Most truck crops in the Imperial are planted to mature in midwinter or spring—at times when there are few competing areas in operation. Planting season traditionally begins after Labor Day, at a time when many American farmers are involved with harvests.

The long-dominant vegetable crop, *lettuce,* provides a good example of the timing factor.

Many growers operate in both the Imperial and Salinas valleys by means of a carefully-planned seasonal migration of operations between the two areas (see Ch.7). By shifting key personnel onto leased land in the Imperial, and carefully fully staggering the planting periods, a steady output of lettuce is maintained during the Salinas off-season.

Most truck crops require relatively intense effort—beyond regular irrigation, weeding, regular fertilization and pest control.

For instance *melons* are given special temperature advantages by planting them on south-facing furrow ridges; each young plant is then covered with a paper "hot cap." In a different way heat is conserved for young tomato plants by constructing paper and wood shelters the length of each row, so oriented as to create a southern exposure.

Most truck crops have common need for a near-perfect water balance (hence land leveling and irrigation timing must be extremely precise). Lighter textured soils are preferred for a majority of the truck crops, partly because water control is easier and crop quality in some cases is superior. Lettuce however, absorbs wind-blown sand and hence is grown on heavier soils. Vast tracts of lettuce (it occupies more acreage than all other truck crops combined) are thus particularly appropriate for the Imperial where most soils are heavy-textured.

In some years more than two dozen types of truck crops have been harvested in the Imperial Valley.

Within the limitations posed by local growing conditions, the choice and extent of truck crops depends upon such factors as planting in other truck-growing areas.

Enterprising growers elsewhere can change marketing aspects quickly; this has been the case with Mexican tomato production, which currently dominates the western winter market. For some crops, competition is also severe from southern Texas and Florida in years when good weather conditions prevail there. Consumer preferences have a long-time impact, as in the case of carrots. Decreased carrot output reflects loss of eastern markets due to the advent of packaged topped carrots; earlier, the Imperial carrot had an advantage because of more attractive leaves.

### Alfalfa and Wheat

Much of the cultivated area in the Imperial Valley, from the earliest days, has been devoted to raising livestock feeds, including alfalfa, barley and sorghums. New Mexican wheats have largely replaced barley.

These crops are "filler" crops for lands not used for more valuable crops; for the Valley their returns tend to be minimal. They tend to be tolerant of the alkali soils that plague much of the Valley; alfalfa especially is a soil-builder. Since they can be grown later into the summer than most truck crops, the feeds permit a more complete land-use and encourage rotation with such short-lived crops as lettuce.

The most valuable feed crop, alfalfa, has traditionally been shipped in quantity to the Los Angeles Basin dairy belt. Increasingly it has been consumed locally.

Regretfully it is also the heaviest water consumer of all major Valley crops although this habit makes alfalfa especially useful on areas of heavier, water-logged soil.

### Feed Lots and Pastures

Like other irrigated areas in the dry West, the Imperial is a major feeding place where cattle and sheep from rangelands are brought for "finishing" (i.e., final fattening before marketing).

Increase of population in Southern California has been reflected directly by expanded livestock in the Valley, which is within easy trucking distance of metropolitan packing plants.

Feeding is not done on open rangeland; rather, on alfalfa pastures previously cut, or increasingly, at feed lots with automatic feed mixers and pens able to handle thousands of livestock at a time. By careful shading of feed lots, it is possible to continue volumes comparable to those of cooler seasons in summer. The summer drought of California pastures is a major incentive to summer feeding in the Imperial. By-products from other commodities, as well as bulk feed crops, are utilized, especially sugar-beet pulp and cottonseed meal. Nevertheless, the Valley has exceeded its feed supply and must import the deficit.

### Cotton

Cotton has remained a leading Valley product for some decades despite considerable fluctuation.

Cotton, when stimulated by federal price-support programs, tends to occupy as much land as acreage quotas permit. At times, as in the 1940's and again in the late 1960's, insect damage has slowed production for a time. Imperial cotton is usually *Delta Pine*, which customarily gives the southeastern deserts the state's highest yields at a good price. Following ginning and baling locally, the cotton is generally trucked to Long Beach for export to Asia or elsewhere.

### Sugar Beets

For half a century beets have been grown in the Imperial Valley.

Like cotton it is well suited to the alkaline, water-short desert environment. Government policy has stimulated (and to a degree regulated) output; its pulp furnishes supplemental cattle feed. Unlike cotton, it is a refugee from urbanized Southern California, not the South. Construction of a refinery ( north of El Centro) stimulated production. In keeping with the Valley pattern of unique timing of its crops, beets are planted in the fall; elsewhere in the state beets tend to be spring planted. Acreage has reached plant capacity but construction of another plant is unlikely as long as there is a world sugar glut.

## Townfolks

For a basically agricultural area the Imperial Valley is quite urban.

Since settlement the portion of town dwellers has risen steadily; it now exceeds two thirds the total population. Farm consolidation and automation have caused numbers of rural residents to decline. Communities are shipping points and of necessity residences for businessmen, ranchers and workers. Remoteness from large cities assures considerable retail trade. Still, ranchers have not typically retired here nor do these towns have much tourist appeal—existence is justified chiefly by

**Figure 5-6.** El Centro, principal city of the Imperial Valley. It remains an eastside-westside town. View is northeast—note contrasting density of shade trees. (El Centro Chamber of Commerce)

agriculture.

A common urban design typifies Valley towns. Arcaded store fronts are characteristic and skylines low.

Air conditioning is conspicuous; it has replaced the water-coolers of days bygone. While affluent residents have long lived in air-conditioned homes, driven air conditioned cars and worked in air-conditioned offices, now even a rude shanty will have a window air conditioner—it is considered a necessity, no longer a luxury.

Except Holtville, all larger towns are located on the north-south rail line. Near the tracks one generally finds shipping sheds and processing plants, with a central district to the west. East of the tracks is a "Little Mexico," with its modest cottages, bare ground and paucity of landscaping; it is occupied by blacks as well as Hispanics. In the southwest quadrant there is evidence of affluence in well-landscaped homes. "West side" occupancy by a few Hindu ranchers and Japanese businessmen reflects changed social conditions.

Historically there was no dominant town, as found in many California counties. But El Centro has been favored for some decades. Towns are somewhat unevenly spaced, which reflects earlier irrigation development in the southern third of the Valley as well as orientation to rail transport.

**El Centro** (30, 000) provides the Valley its governmental, shopping and travel center (Fig.5-6). It is the most-typically middle income town, reflecting governmental personnel and other white-collar employment.

Yet here, too, one finds many low incomes. Despite less concern than Brawley about sprawl, it is the most liberal Valley town and ranks first in the county in age of its residents (including older landowners) and educational attainment.

The self-acclaimed "largest town below sea level in the Western Hemisphere, " El Centro does house about a fourth of the Valley population. As the major (only!) stop on I-8 between Yuma and San Diego, its waystop function is conspicuous. Motels often display "no vacancy" signs, especially in winter.

One often heard Spanish spoken in its central district in past decades. *Se habla español* signs were common in windows. Now the C.B.D. looks "half dead." A regional shopping center is located on the westside (off I-8). Too, many Mexican nationals now shop at home in much-larger Mexicali. Boosters keep hoping the Navy will relocate some of its facilities from San Diego to the Naval Air Station—Navy "Brass" in San Diego deny this.

**Brawley** (18, 000), the ranking agricultural city of the Valley, is near the center of truck cropping.

Hence it is the principal dwelling place for farm workers, temporary and permanent alike and also affords residence for many prosperous landowners. Until mid-century Brawley rivaled (and many

**Figure 5-7.** Capitol complex, State of Baja California del Norte, Mexicali. Half a century ago Mexicali was a small adobe place. Now it is a metropolis of over 500,000. There are close ties with its "twin city" of Calexico. (dwl)

years exceeded) El Centro in population. Its central district, without shopping center competition, continues to flourish.

**Calexico** (20, 000), a border crossing and residence place for many Mexicans, is distinctive. Like other Valley towns it has a strong alliance with agribusiness. It also has a college.

Calexico began as a text-city headquarters of the Imperial Land Company at the terminus of the original C.D.C. canal. It boomed again during the Prohibition era as a weekend center for Mexicali-bound field hands—in 1920 it was the Valley's largest town.

Calexico's per capita trade exceeds that of El Centro (reflecting much cross-border retail activity).* It has the lowest average incomes, the least educational attainments, the youngest population, the most sizable households—these all are clues to a large foreign-born population. It is the single Valley town where females (wives of migratory workers) greatly outnumber males. San Diego State University has its Imperial Valley campus here.

Calexico aspires to grow. And it hopes to use the "twin plant" concept as the basis for becoming the largest city in southeast California (under the concept, a U.S.-managed plant in Mexicali could make parts, with final assembly in Calexico, employing Mexican labor.

Other Imperial Valley towns are relatively small. They serve as places for shipping, residence and weekday shopping for their environs.

The largest are **Holtville** (5000), a lettuce center, **Imperial**, site of the Irrigation District headquar-

ters and Imperial Valley College, and **Calipatria** (2900).

## BARD VALLEY

This is California's portion of the Yuma Valley on the "delta head" of the Colorado River.

The *Sand Hills* and *Pilot Knob* separate Bard Valley from the bulk of the Colorado Desert. Unlike the rest of the of the Desert, the upper delta has always had water. Hence it provided a more attractive habitat for the Yuma Indians, practicers of flood irrigation.

This locale became historically important to Anglos as the **Yuma Crossing**. Below its junction with the Gila, the Colorado River is confined to a narrow gorge.

An ill-fated mission was located there by the Spanish in 1780. Many forty-niners entered California at this point on the *Gila Trail* and *Fort Yuma* was established as an Army post. The Santa Fe Southern utilizes this crossing for its southern transcontinental rail line, and Interstate 8 enters California here. Another crossing is made by the siphon that carries Colorado River water, taken from the California , *under* the river for convenient delivery to Arizona's Yuma Valley. At the north end of Bard Valley is *Imperial Dam*, where water is diverted into the All-American Canal.

---

*In 1950 Mexicali was a small adobe village. Now, as the capital of Baja California del Norte, it approximates 500, 000. Variety of merchandise is large (including Kentucky Fried Chicken). Obviously some items are still purchased in Calexico. But a person can drive around the parking lot of the El Centro shopping center at noon and see very few cars with Baja licenses.

**Figure 5-8.** Downtown Brawley. Canopies over sidewalks are characteristic in Imperial Valley towns. (dwl)

*Fort Yuma Indian Reservation* (established in 1884) once encompassed virtually all of Bard Valley.

Political pressures subsequently forced opening of the northeasterly half of the preserve (48, 000 acres) to non-Indian homesteaders on 40-acre tracts.

The remaining floodplain was divided among the Yumans, with each Indian receiving five acres of the bottomland. The Indians long eeked out small incomes on their tiny patches and resided in substandard houses. In total there are about 800 Native Americans but they use only about a square mile of land for crops.

In recent decades conditions have improved considerably for the Yuma. The Bureau of Indian Affairs has erected new houses The Indians and the Bureau have been removing Anglo squatters. The Indians have opened a rental trailer park for visitors and they conduct bingo games. They have become more assertive of their land rights and in self-government. They are getting higher rents for the several thousand acres they "lease" to outsiders.

The agricultural environment here, as elsewhere in the Colorado Desert, permits wide choice of crops. Contemporary production tends to parallel that in Imperial Valley.

Representative output includes winter truck crops (carrots and lettuce), spring melons, cotton and livestock feeding. With numerous shanties and the willow thickets along the river, Bard Valley presents a less well-kept landscape than the Imperial Valley. A distinctive addition is made by the fishing resorts and trailer parks along the Colorado.

A tragedy of political geography is represented in partition of the Yuma Valley between Mexico, California and Arizona. It has resulted in duplication of such services as education, fire and police.

There are three separate irrigation districts. The River has in historic time shifted its course over the wide floodplain just above the Yuma Crossing, and there long has been some doubt as to which state has jurisdiction of a 10 square-mile tract that has "crossed over" to California's side of the Colorado. Further effects of the boundary are felt in time-zone change and duplicate incorporation of businesses in both Arizona and California. Many Californians have gotten married in Yuma to avoid a three-day wait.

*Winterhaven* partly owes its existence to the state line. A disorderly assemblage of service stations, cafes and farm workers' dwellings, it forms a sub-

**Figure 5-9.** Bare rock formations and Sonoran Desert vegetation are representative of Anza-Borrego State Park. (California Division of Beaches and Parks).

urb of Yuma and provides a misleading entry into "wealthy" California. When California gasoline prices are lower than those in Yuma, a disproportionate share of Yuma Valley gasoline is sold here.

## ANZA-BORREGO DESERT

The southwestern periphery of the Colorado Desert is contained within California's largest state preserve, **Anza-Borrego Desert State Park**. This is perhaps the best remaining illustration of the "natural" Desert (Fig. 5-9).

Established in 1933, the 470, 000-acre playground is suggestive of Joshua Tree and Death Valley parks in use. Included are alternating basins and offshoot ridges of the Peninsular Ranges. From November to May the park provides a refuge especially for Southern Californians—campers, hikers and sightseers. Representative Sonora Desert flora and fauna, striking rock formations and warm winter sunshine are major attractions. There is a rich history stemming from early-day travel (noted in the section on Transportation).

Privately held **Borrego Valley** is surrounded by, but is not part of, the state park.

**Figure 5-10.** Borrego Springs and its Valley, in eastern San Diego County, are surrounded by Anza-Borrego State Park. (Borrego Sun).

Di Giorgio established a ranch, watered by deep wells, in the late 1940's and raised California's earliest fresh-market grapes. Expanded acreage in the Coachella Valley (after construction of the extension of the All-American Canal) became too competitive and operations have ceased. More recently consideration has been given to the production of citrus crops. Borrego agriculture is hampered by high pumping costs, porous (sandy) soils, inferior-quality water and isolation from markets.

A highly dispersed residential community, **Borrego Springs** (Fig. 5-10), has appeared along the southwest side of the Valley.

During the cooler months it is occupied by retirees and visitors from Southern California and as far away as western Canada. Remoteness and absence of a publicity-conscious clientele result in an appreciably quieter atmosphere than at Palm Springs, despite similarities in scenery and nearly identical climates.

## SALTON SEA

The Salton Sea was created and reached its greatest extent in 1905-1907.

It rose to within 198 feet of sea level and forced the Southern Pacific Railroad to relocate on higher ground. Exclusion of the River and the high desert evaporation rates conspired to reduce the Sea by

1925 to one half of its maximum extent.

Subsequent increases in return flow from nearby irrigation have expanded the sea now to about two thirds its maximum. Irrigation water is applied by Imperial and Coachella valley farmers in quantities sufficient to flush out salts that would otherwise accumulate in their soils. The saline water is then drained into the only downhill site available—the Salton Sea. Anticipating no end to this practice, irrigators have sought flooding rights to permit a continued rise in the level of the Sea.

The Salton Sea is now a recreation place for residents of metropolitan Southern California as their home areas become ever more crowded for such activities.

*Corvina*, a near relative of sea bass, has been successfully fully planted and sports fishing is popular—perhaps ill-fated however, due to increasing salinity of the Sea. The increased enthusiasm for water sports has led many devotees to tow their boats from metropolitan areas. The long-time dumping of sewage into the Sea by Imperial Valley cities (in both Mexico and California) has posed an urgent problem, especially with the expansion of recreational facilities.

Urbanization near the Salton Sea shoreline is occurring along the north and west sides.

Building sites here near main highways are more available than around the southern shores. Earlier construction stressed commercial lodgings and services for the recreational visitor rather

**Figure 5-11.** Salton City. Improbable as it may seem to many Californians, Imperial Valley gives hints of gaining additional retirees from America's Snowbelt. (Salton City Resorter).

than individual private dwellings.

Of interest is Salton City, where a Los Angeles developer invested $10 million to create an 11 000-lot project with paved streets and water obtained from a deep well several miles away. Within the first year (1958-1959) $30 million worth of lots were sold; construction of residences has been slow but a number of mobile homes stand near the shore (Fig. 5-11).

## THE COACHELLA VALLEY*

Northernmost portion of the Salton Trough, the Coachella Valley shares with the Imperial an alluvial surface and temperatures and aridity common to the rest of the Colorado Desert. Yet there are appreciable differences.

The Coachella is considerably smaller in area and has a generally higher (much is above sea level) and coarser surface; historically it found water a scarcer commodity. On the other hand, the Coachella is bordered by higher, more scenic mountains and is closer to metropolitan Los Angeles—both in terms of distance and with regard to position along main traffic corridors.

There are distinct man-made differences between the Coachella and Imperial valleys too.

They result partially from the significant dissimilarities, physical and locational. Coachella agri-

**Figure 5-12.** Hand work by non-Anglos typifies the growing of truck crops in the Coachella Valley. (Bureau of Reclamation, photo by K.C. Middletown)

culture stresses fruit crops, such as its famous date palms, and minimizes livestock and feed production. An ever greater distinction is that, in the Coachella, recreation is virtually on a par with farming as a basis for human occupance, and the name of Palm Springs is more famous with Californians generally than the name Coachella stamped on grapefruit rinds or date wrappers.

Therefore discussion concerns (1) the *Agricultural Valley* and (2) the *Palm Springs District*.

## THE AGRICULTURAL VALLEY

Save for its hunter-gatherer Indians the Coachella Valley remained an unoccupied waste until the late nineteenth century.

The Southern Pacific laid trackage across it in 1877. Even the name seems to be of late origin, being credited to the mapping crews of the U.S. Geological Survey (refuting popular belief that it derives from the Spanish *conchilla*)—for the small shells so common in Valley soils.

Agricultural settlement of the Coachella, in typical desert fashion, proceeded hand-in-hand with development of a water supply.

The sequence was different from the Imperial Valley. Originally Colorado River water was not accessible. Seeking water for locomotives, the railroad discovered artesian flows, and in 1900, introduction of well-drilling methods, feasible for agriculture, permitted the beginnings of irrigation. For almost half a century thereafter, population and agriculture of the Valley grew relatively steadily but at a very modest rate in comparison with the Imperial Valley boom.

The first decade, and perhaps the entire first half century, might be considered as one of agricultural "infancy."

Melons and dates, among crops important early, remain significant. Although less consistently successful, other contemporary crops (especially grapefruit, table grapes and cotton) were established by 1910. The relatively high water costs, among other conditions, discouraged production of livestock feeds and even of cantaloupes, a fairly high-value item that nonetheless suffered from Imperial Valley "cheap water" competition. Irrigation water was widely shared in the beginning,

*This section was reviewed earlier by Steve McWilliams, College of the Desert.

with farm sizes often of 10 to 80 acres (much smaller than in Imperial Valley).

With heavy and often wasteful water usage, available ground-water supplies diminished rapidly.

It was obvious by 1920 that supplemental water supply was needed if more than a fraction of the Valley was to be irrigated permanently. Coachella farmers joined Imperial and Southern California water seekers in obtaining Hoover Dam and related Colorado River projects, and, in 1948 water deliveries began from the Coachella branch of the All-American Canal.

Population and cropland tripled between 1948 and 1960.

An era of expansion reminiscent of the pre-1930's in the Imperial Valley was experienced. Subsequently, acreage stabilized but some shifts have occurred in the general pattern of products that evolved prior to 1948.

There is an impressive contrast between the landscape of the lower Coachella Valley and that of the Imperial Valley.

The Bureau of Reclamation's long-time limit (see South End, Ch.9) of 160 acres has meant noticeably smaller farm properties , yet residences generally are more attractive (i.e., owner-occupied!). Trees are markedly more conspicuous— besides groves of date palms and citrus assorted varieties like tamarisk (used as windbreaks). They provide a pleasing green contrast to the colorful though barren mountain border. The Coachella has a much smaller total production than the Imperial yet its output per acre and diversity are greater. Scattered Indian reservations, with about 200 occupants in total, cover one-sixth of the Valley. While much reservation acreage is cultivable, only small portions are actually tilled, often by non-Indians.

Significant shifts have occurred in the agricultural scene during recent decades.

Although farm sizes (with additional machinery) have been expanded, acreage has essentially stabilized. Also, use of owner-operated shipping sheds, the entry of California corporate money, rising land prices and shifting labor practices have taken place. The demise of the bracero proved difficult for small farmers.

### Dates and Grapes

Vineyards and orchards dominate in the Coachella to about the same extent that livestock feeding does in the Imperial.

**Figure 5-13.** Vineyard in the Coachella Valley with Mt. San Jacinto (rear). (Bureau of Reclamation, photo by J.R. Cotterill).

Significant similarities among the three leading Coachella crops (dates, citrus and grapes) tend to be obscured by differing appearance of the plants.

First, they are relatively permanent; second, they are sufficiently high-value products to compensate for their heavy water consumption. Dates, the extreme example, are by far the "thirstiest" desert crop, but at the same time return the most value per acre. Fruits are typically grown on higher , coarser soils where waterlogging and alkalinity are at a minimum. Of all crops, the fruits are best able to repay the higher irrigation costs incurred on these droughty soils. Fruits thus provide a means of using lands that may not usable for other items. All three fruit crops are shipped predominantly in perishable form, which requires careful handling and transport.

Grapes, the most valuable Coachella crop, are predominantly of the Perlette and Thompson seedless varieties (Fig. 5-13).

They are shipped for fresh table use earlier than their counterparts elsewhere in the state. Since the 1960's, when for a while consumer antagonism created market saturation (buyers refused to pay premium prices for "sour" (under-ripe grapes), the Perlette has gained popularity at the expense of the Thompson seedless.

A variety of citrus (including grapefruit, lemons, tangerines, and oranges) is grown and acreage has increased.

Grapefruit, whose blossoms perfume the air the year round, depend heavily upon table consump-

expansion between Indio and Palm Springs.

**Figure 5-19.** Grapefruit is an important Coachella Valley crop. (Water and Power Resources Service, photo by E.E. Hertzog).

tion in California—a receptive growing market. Coachella fruit ripens too late to compete successfully "back East" against Florida and Texas output. High quality and an early ripening trait are important advantages for Coachella grapefruit, as opposed to the non-desert varieties. Citrus land in the Valley is 90 per cent absentee-owned; groves are handled by three large management firms.

Dates, once dependent upon domestic markets, are now sold also in Europe. About 90 per cent of the domestic output comes from the Valley.

United States dates have sold more successfully in Common Market countries since since Algerian independence. However a conglomerate (Tenneco), much involved in agribusiness, has dominated date shipments.

The date groves of the Coachella, like the coastal avocado and citrus districts (and the almond farms in Butte County— Ch.9) are virtually a "way of life." Their aesthetic and prestige value helps compensate for the involved, expensive efforts required for their production.

So successful is Coachella date production that Middle East growers have sent students to study local techniques. These include mechanized pollination and harvesting (since the early 1970's), which has reduced growing costs. Long stabilized, date acreage has increased somewhat. Yet the future is somewhat problematic. The groves appeal to subdividers for their shade and exotic effect—and they tend to be in the path of urban

### Sweet Corn and Other Vegetables

Vegetables (and historically melons) loom large in the agricultural picture of the Valley but acreage has remained constant for many years.

Methods and motives are similar to those in the Imperial, but the Coachella is concerned more with local (i.e., California) markets. There are lesser differences in kinds and emphasis, based upon local biologic and environmental factors . Lettuce, for example, is not important in the sandy soils of the Coachella, which specializes in sweet corn, carrots, summer squash and okra. In total, the Coachella produces about a score of different vegetables.

### One Big Feed Lot

Livestock are far more consequential in the Imperial Valley than in the Coachella.

Earlier, Southern California markets for feeds was expanding and water was available. But feed crops yield far lower return per acre. Hence there is a single cattle-feeding operation in the Valley; it is one of the nation's larger, able to handle 45, 000 cattle—in summer feeding begins at 3:30 a.m. (to avert the heat of "high noon.")

### Townscapes

Population density is higher (with smaller farms and greater per-acre output) in the Coachella than it is in the Imperial. Coachella residents are town dwellers.

Urbanization is favored by compactness of the farm area, close network of rural roads, importance of specialized shipping facilities and relatively high rural purchasing power. The four agricultural Coachella towns, established before much highway travel, are located along the railroad. Until recently the more northerly the town the more it was favored by new irrigation development and routing of main highways, which explains why only two towns, Indio and Coachella, have attained significant size.

**Indio** (32, 000), ranking commercial, governmental, farming, travel and shipping center of the Valley, is doubtless the most attractive "agricultural" city of the entire Colorado Desert.

Indio, while geographically "off center" for service to Valley farmers, has superior shipping facilities (as a rail-road and highway junction) that gave it an early advantage. Added impetus came from

**Figure 5-14.** Typical older street, Coachella. (dwl)

proximity to date groves (producers of relatively high incomes) and the need for elaborate date processing in Indio.

Properly self-styled as "Date Capital of America," Indio is astride the main Los Angeles-Phoenix corridor (I-10) at its junction with Ca. routes 111 and 86. Dozens of travel facilities, railroad shipping and truck traffic provide year-round activity.

While suggestive of El Centro socioeconomically, Indio has more white-collar employment, hence incomes are near state averages. Still a quarter of its housing (the only public housing for migrant workers in the Coachella) is "public assisted." But the eastside squalor which once typified Imperial towns has been absent.

There is considerably more emphasis upon trade volume and employment than in El Centro. The "sub-county seat" of Riverside County, it has hand-

some county and city civic complexes. Thus, in the governmental sector, it suggests El Centro.

The central district remains viable despite two shopping complexes. But there is local concern at the continued thrust of the city into farm lands.

The "ethnic capital" of the Colorado Desert, **Coachella** (13, 000) contrasts markedly with Indio. It is a residence place for farm workers.

"There is no way we can go but up," commented one city official in evaluation of the town in socioeconomic terms. Half the residents are poverty-level and half live in rented dwellings (90 per cent absentee-owned). Coachella is 80 per cent ethnic, with some of the worst residential crowding in rural California.

The Hispanic influence is evident. Many stores have bilingual signs; most of the city employees and most of the members of the city council are Hispanic. Despite frustration there is determination to improve housing. The city has commenced development of an industrial park.

---

### THE PALM SPRINGS DISTRICT
### (The northern Coachella Valley)

Recreational activities dominate the northwestern Coachella as singularly as agriculture does in the southeast. Despite the sweltering summer heat, the Colorado Desert has mild winters.

Thus with California population growth, improved transcontinental transportation (especially by air), an expanded leisure group (including many senior citizens) and technological developments

**Figure 5-15.** Palm Springs, the largest community in the Colorado Desert. (Palm Springs Convention and Visitors Bureau).

(especially air conditioning and swimming pools), the Desert has become one of the nation's smart winter playgrounds.

Activity is concentrated principally along the Piedmont at the base of the San Jacinto Range.

Assets for recreation here include proximity to the Los Angeles Basin via San Gorgonio Pass (I-10), absence of agricultural utilization, and the spectacular backdrop of the San Jacinto.

Staggered southward from Desert Hot Springs through Palm Springs to La Quinta is a strand of recreation-oriented communities.

The "permanent" population is almost twice that of the agricultural Coachella. Originally widely separated, these towns are coalescing along Ca. 111. Many of the remaining "open stretches" are occupied by golf courses—about 30 in total.*

Appropriately the area calls itself "America's winter golfing capital."

**Palm Springs** (31, 000), a renowned winter resort, has become the largest city of the Colorado Desert. Besides recreation, the residence function looms large. It is the luxury shopping, entertainment and air travel hub of the Valley.

A veritable transmogrification of Beverly Hills and Ventura Boulevard, Palm Springs is the composite production of wealth accumulated in Hollywood entertainment industries, the rise of the suntan fad, and nouveau West Coast and Midwest fortunes.

The Springs now ranks fifth (76 square miles) in area among California cities and has developed real "growth concerns." Partially because of tax pressures, a low key effort is being made to attract "clean" industry employing Ph.D.s—land has been set aside for such use.

While Palm Springs dates from the 1880's it languished until the 1920's, when it became a dreamland Hollywood "set, " complete with movie starlets, swimming pools and palms. National publicity has attracted many others, including numerous vacationists and retired well-to-do from all parts of America. The share of the resident population over age 65 is twice the California average. Many "poorer" (i.e. middle income) retirees live in the south end in mobile homes.

The principal thoroughfare, Palm Canyon Drive, has branches of smart New York and Los Angeles shops, nightclubs, and stock brokerage offices. Service facilities (including lodging, nightclubs and restaurants) exceed those of many larger cities.

Plans for a convention center have been dropped. While the Springs does attract conventions, efforts to attract others have stopped. Monies are being expended for parks and other recreational facilities to be enjoyed by residents and visitors (an an "average" weekend 50, 000 or more Angelinos come to see how the "other" five per cent lives). Construction of the aerial tramway to upper reaches of the San Jacinto Range helped attract additional visitors.

Like Beverly Hills, zoning is stricter than in most California cities. Early dispersal of the town was caused by the alternate square miles that form part of the Indian reservation (south of The Springs). Several decades ago federal approval allowed the Cahuilla to make long-time leases of their land—members of the small tribe have become wealthy and the "squares in the checkerboard" have filled in. Cahuilla desires to maximize their returns conflict with city planning.

Palm Springs is postdated by several nearby recreation-oriented communities.

Some are the haunts of the world famous while others are strictly middle-income. The conurbation is gradually securing a more complete array of city facilities.

**Desert Hot Springs** (9000), lacks opulence and suggests a "poor man's Palm Springs." Many of its upper-middle income residents are disinterested in the glamour of The Springs.

Located at the base of the Little San Bernardino Mountains, it is a bonafide mineral springs resort and tends to appeal to desert lovers rather than socialites.

**Cathedral City** (22,000), a southeasterly "extension" of Palm Springs, has shown much growth in the late twentieth century.

Appreciably less affluent than The Springs, its retail shops tend to be less "glamorous" than those of the neighboring city.

**Palm Desert** (11, 800)is trying to gain identity as an upper income community. It provides retail trade and services for nearby residential places.

Incomes tend to be lower and the city is less resort-related than Palm Springs. Income levels tend to rise "up-slope" (the town is on an alluvial fan).

---

*Over a decade ago the Coachella Water District began spreading Colorado River water, bought from the Metropolitan Water District into the Whitewater River bed, to maintain water levels for sprinkler irrigation of the golf courses. Temporarily, at least, the M.W.D. appears to have a water surplus, thanks to the California Aqueduct (see Chs. 9, 10 and Overview G).

Before its incorporation the city's growth tended to be haphazard.

Once listed on a national magazine's list of "play schools," College of the Desert is a relatively-typical community college which has strived to assist ethnic students.*

A trio of "guarded-gate" residential towns is expanding in the vicinity of Palm Desert.

**La Quinta** (8000), frequented by wealthy desert enthusiasts, is as uneffusive as Palm Springs is flamboyant. Before the 1980's it was little more than a golf course and a lodge.

Residents of **Rancho Mirage** (9000) tend to "look down" upon Palm Springs. Seemingly every house is adjacent to a golf green.

**Indian Wells** (2400) tends to have the wealthiest residents of any town in the Colorado Desert. Except locally and to golf enthusiasts, it is virtually unknown.

## COMPENDIUM

Agriculture and recreation dominate the economy of the Colorado Desert. The Desert's farm markets and resort clientele are closely tied to metropolitan Southern California. For time to come continued growth in Southern California will create expanded recreational use of the Palm Springs District (a local booster anticipates 100,000), Anza-Borrego Desert, the Salton Sea and the Colorado River. A local authority fears the Coachella Valley is in danger of becoming a "desert San Fernando Valley (Ch.6) with golf courses. A few small groups voice concern over urbanization. Unfortunately there are strong inter-community rivalries—some feel Palm Springs acts as if it had no neighboring towns.

Produce farming and livestock feeding can anticipate expanding markets (unless per capita consumption of beef drops dramatically). Future farm labor policies could have considerable social and economic impact—the problem of the illegal entrant remains unresolved. Perhaps unionization of farm labor is hastening more complete mechanization and a possible host of unemployed ex-field workers.

While the Desert appears to pose some limitations for added population, one wonders if settlement will not continue (in light of the growth that has occurred in environmentally-similar central Arizona. Large empty wastelands, *East Mesa* and *West Mesa* (Fig. 5–1), potentially arable, are adjacent to the cultivated Imperial Valley, but the 1964 decision of the Supreme Court relative to distribution of Colorado River water favored Arizona and negated prospects of additional consumption in California. This should stimulate more efficient water usage in the Imperial Valley. Through arrangements with the federal government the Imperial Irrigation District sublet a small tract on East Mesa for crop experimentation. Extremely porous soils, drifting sand, and crops that are voracious

---

\* Relative to the college and the community a local observer noted "We live in a rich man's community...many (of the affluent) are elderly, retired, childless, or children grown-and-gone, and seasonal residents. This very apparent class in our community has almost no contact with the college...They arrive in the desert after our fall semester starts and depart in the spring long before June...The rich barracade themselves behind walls which are privately patrolled and live in country clubs of unimaginable luxury. When they venture out it is in a large showy Cadillac or Rolls Royce."

**Figure 5-16.** A guarded-gate entrance to a Rancho Mirage subdivision. This is one of the costlier places for housing in California. (dwl)

**Figure 5-17.** Palm Springs, viewed from Mt. San Jacinto. (Palm Springs Convention and Visitors Bureau)

water consumers pose problems. So far one does not hear talk of seawater conversion as a possibility on the margins of the Imperial Valley.

The Department of the Interior once commenced steps to enforce its 160-acre limit on Imperial Valley ranchers. But in 1981 Congress expanded the limitation to 1280 acres.

The status of the Salton Sea is still problematic as regards its level, salinity and contamination. It has been proposed that its south end be diked to withhold

salts and wastes from the main body. Related also is increasing exploitation of minerals at its southern end. Morton Salt has had plans for construction of a plant near Niland to extract sodium and calcium chlorides from geothermal brines. Geothermal electric production is occurring.

How will continued urbanization in Southern California affect the Desert? Will lemon growers relocate in the Desert, even as orange farmers relocated in the San Joaquin Valley?

Although the San Jacinto Piedmont would seem a possible area, industrialization has not yet become momentous. Does the electronics industry of central Arizona provide a clue? Whether the Desert is an adequate location for lighter "high value added" manufacturing in terms of services, labor force, communications, and research facilities is still questioned. Nevertheless, the spectre of air pollution remains prevalent, largely as a result of air movement from the Los Angeles Basin through San Gorgonio Pass.

**Figure 5-18.** The Coachella Branch of the All-American Canal has permitted considerable agricultural expansion in the Coachella Valley. (Bureau of Reclamation, photo by R.C. Middleton)

PART TWO

THE
HEARTLAND

# THE HEARTLAND

The term **Heartland** has been conceived by the authors to identify a very important portion of California. For this is the Golden State that the world knows. It contains the second and fourth largest conurbations in the United States, the 100 largest cities in California and all of the score and four metropolitan areas (as identified by the Census Bureau). It has the closest ties with the Pacific Basin—and the world. "Everyone" who visits California comes to the Heartland. For Los Angeles is here—so too are San Diego and San Francisco. And also the Central Valley with its legendary productivity.

The Heartland, like the filling in a cream puff, is the piece de resistance. It is the focus of cultural attainment, industrial output and agricultural activity. Most of the social ferment is here, as are representatives of the many ethnic groups that so enrich the Golden State.

How many Californias are there? The authors find four in the Heartland. Many strangers would be hard pressed to identify the other seven portions of the Golden State discussed in this book. But though the world does not know the other Californias, their interrelationships are so overpowering as to make occasional twaddle about dividing the state ludicrous. Discussed previously, the California segments of the **Intermontane Region** provide some minerals, timber and wood, as well as recreation sites. And in the southeast, primarily, an impressive agricultural output. **The Northern Highlands**, to be discussed later contains much of California's vaunted mountain country. It provides the Heartland with water and timber, as well as natural loveliness—places for relaxation and outdoor recreation.

Residents of the Heartland furnish the other two major portions of California with foodstuff and industrial products and with support for their highway towns. Moreover, the Heartland provides backland Californians with shopping centers, urban amenities, health services and insurance and banking facilities.

But where is the Heartland—without explanation most Californians probably could not identify it on a map. It coincides, to a considerable extent, with the dry-summer subtropical (or Mediterranean) portions of the Golden State. It shares the Pacific strand with the Northwest. While its coastal fog belt is well known, of more importance is the Pacific air, which provides moisture for all of California. The strand affords an elongated playground, whose better known beach centers include Santa Cruz, Santa Barbara, Santa Monica, Newport and La Jolla. A number of the Heartland cities, including Long Beach, Morro Bay, Monterey and Sacramento, are seaports.

While much of California remains a one-story state, increasingly in the second half of the twentieth century, the Heartland has "three-dimensional" skylines, not only in San Francisco and Los Angeles, but also in San Mateo and Irvine too. Many evidences of transition from simpler livelihoods(such as farming, fishing and mining) can be seen from congested freeways and in industrial establishments of such cities as Cupertino, Vernon and Torrance.

Principal portions of the Heartland, to be discussed in successive chapters, are (1) **Southern California**, (2) the **Central Coast**, (3) the **San Francisco Bay Area**, and (4) the **Great Central Valley**. The percentage of the book devoted to these areas reflects their importance to the Golden State.

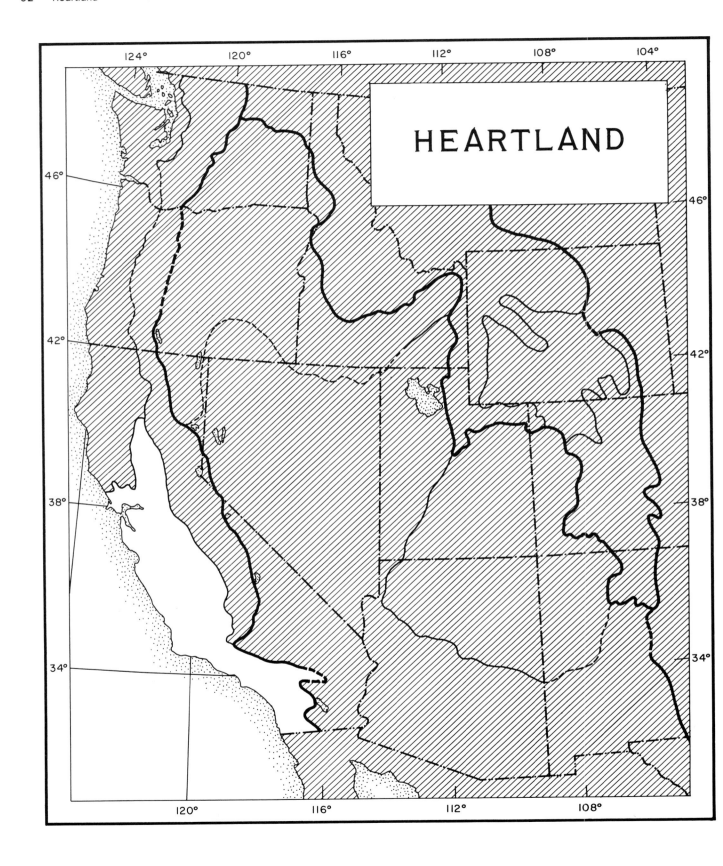

**Figure 6-1.** Street scene, downtown Los Angeles. The heterogenuous populace is obvious. Southern California's ethnic ties with the Pacific Rim have expanded markedly in the late twentieth century. (dwl)

Chapter Six

SOUTHERN CALIFORNIA

This chapter has been reviewed again by Richard Logan, University of California at Los Angeles. It was reviewed previously by the late John W. Reith, University of Southern California.

# SOUTHERN CALIFORNIA

Assuredly one of the world's unique geographical entities, Southern California lies south of the Tehachapi Mountains and west of California's southeastern deserts.*

This intricate land extends from the Mexican border (southeast) to Point Conception (northwest); it includes the Transverse Ranges, Peninsular Ranges and the Channel Islands. It presumably approached an American dream of terrestrial paradise until the mid-1900s.

Southern California is among the smaller subdivisions of the Golden State.

Only the Southern Cascade and the Colorado Desert have lesser extent (see Map, 6-1). With its area of approximately 12,000 square miles, Southern California approaches Belgium in size.

While it covers only eight per cent of the Golden State, Southern California is the residence of more than half of California's people.

It is crudely triangular in shape. And its heart is the Los Angeles Basin, a densely populated complex of coastal plain and intermontane basins.

Southern California presents many visages.

It has miles of sandy beaches, complex granitic mountains rising abruptly, groves of lemons and avocados, assorted Spanish missions, spots to bask in the sun—or to live out one's final years under a palm tree in a clime without a true winter. There are also Hollywood and its cinema legacy, the skyscrapers of Los Angeles, and San Diego with its beauteous bay and its military installations. To these in recent decades have been added a vast industrial complex, congested freeways and the problem of infamous smog. Growth has been so rapid and change so frequent as to suggest a temporary, unfinished landscape painting.

One muses—what makes Southern California different from other parts of the United States, even from the balance of California? More than anywhere else in America, Southern California is a transplanted landscape—literally so with respect to its ornamental and agricultural plants, nearly all of them imported. Much the same applies to the people, with their foods, religions and languages from "almost everywhere." Even essentials such as water, fuel and electric energy must be imported.

Southern California differs from the rest of the United States and even the rest of the Golden State in its long-deferred, then hasty transformation from cow counties to a seemingly perpetually booming urban-scape with high rises and equally-bustling rurban fringes. Societal evolution has been impressive and often abrupt, with a Native American populace yielding to Hispanics and then Anglos, to be followed by immigrants from around the world and currently from the Pacific Basin especially.

The juxtaposition of ocean, coastal plain and brushy slope in association with a mild summer-dry climate—an "American Riviera" once suggestive, in the minds of some, of a terrestrial paradise. The singular dependence of the economy upon a distinctive combination of aircraft, tourism, electronics, research, agriculture, military activities and motion pictures and television is unusual.

Apart from its particular arrays of natural and artificial landscapes, its assemblage of people and its economy, Southern California becomes more standardized as its nationwide linkages evolve. Despite an abundance of suitable relicts, local architecture is no longer as renowned as it was during the "mission revival" and "craftsman bungalow" periods. No longer are the visual arts, as once represented by the **Arroyo** and **Laguna** schools of landscape painters, nationally distinctive. The enlarging leadership that Southern California assumedly exerts, due to its energy and productivity, is chiefly a matter of larger dimensions or quicker technologic applications rather than true innovations based upon an unique regional status.

---

* Note the distinction between Southern California, a *specific* geographic subdivision, and the more ambiguous southern California, sometimes used to describe all of California south of the Tehachapi, including the deserts, as contrasted with northern California. Upon occasion the Los Angeles *Times* includes Fresno County and the High Sierra. Some geographers and others prefer South Coast to Southern California. And some, a bit facetiously, suggest "Greater Los Angeles."

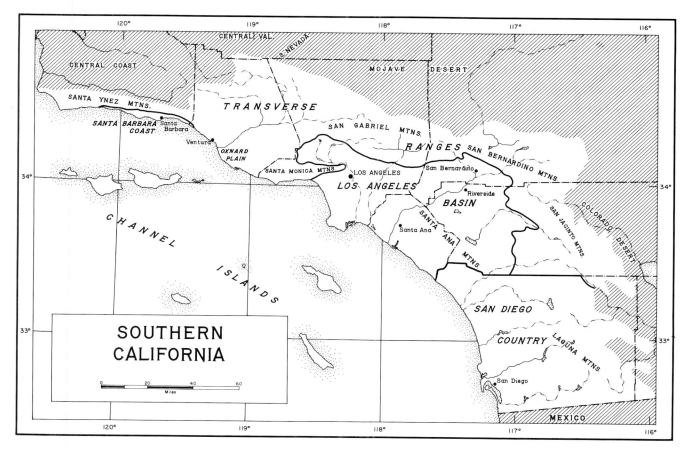

120°          119°          118°          117°          116°

**Map 6-1.** Southern California, a land of many millions. Map shows major areal subdivisions,
the seven county seats and principal mountain ranges.

More imagined or dated than real is the concept of Southern California as a lotus-land of exotic denizens who pioneer new and better lifestyles for less benign realms elsewhere.

### FROM HOKANS TO PACIFIC BASIN PEOPLES

In the past Southern California was occupied by two distinct cultures, American Indian and then Hispanic. More recently Southern California was populated by a representative cross section of American people. But since 1970 it has gained more of a Pacific Basin populace.

Although the earlier occupance stages were overwhelmed after 1848, place names, travel routes, historic sites and the few descendants of the Indian and colonial Hispanic groups remind us of yesteryear.

#### Hokans and Shoshones

If Southern California connoted a Garden of Eden,

its American Indians were surely "strangers in paradise."

These people and their possible predecessors resided here for thousands of years before the Spanish arrived yet they were technologically unable to utilize many resources the land provided.

The Indians depended upon food gathering, hunting and fishing. There was little incentive to store food against times of shortage or build elaborate shelters in a winterless land.

Two Indian families, the *Hokans* and the *Shoshones* occupied Southern California in late prehistoric times.

Desert and mountain barriers discouraged travel eastward; geographic isolation has helped explain limited contacts with people along the main lines of migration through the Americas.

The Hokans were represented by *Yuman* peoples of the San Diego Country and the the *Chumash* of the Santa Barbara Coast.

Between these Hokans and occupying the Los Angeles Lowlands and contiguous areas were

Shoshones, personified by the Serranos, Gabrielinos and Luisenos. Linguistic relationships between some of these people were as remote as those between Chinese and Greeks. Yet their basic economies, resource use, and lifestyles were remarkably similar.

## Hispanic Colonials

Permanent European settlement in Alta California began at San Diego in 1769. The Spanish established seven missions in Southern California between 1769 and 1797.

All have been preserved or restored—they afford museums of a bygone time and serve religious needs. They were linked by *El Camino Real,* a primitive trail now traced generally by Highway 101.

Half of Alta California's four presidios, San Diego (1769) and Santa Barbara (1782) were established in this area.

In contrast with the more successful missions the presidios were drab. Rather than these forts the missions formed the social and cultural centers of the colony. *Pueblos* (farm towns) were also planned as part of the settlement program. Thus Los Angeles was founded in 1781.

The dominant element on the landscape became the *rancho.*

The first three ranchos were granted in 1784. However, during the Spanish era (1769-1822) less than a score of private grants were assigned in all California (half were in Southern California). The choicest lands tended to be claimed by the missions.

During Mexican times (1822-1846) scores of land grants were distributed in Southern California upon petition to the governor. The preponderance was created after secularization of the missions began in 1834. Their boundaries, hastily ascertained with *metes and bounds,* often remain today as property lines, streets and even city limits.

## The Anglo Era

Even before the close of the Mexican period scores of Anglo-Americans became residents of Southern California.

Generally these aliens were seamen from whalers (or the hide-and-tallow schooners) or mountain men and horse traders who traveled overland. They often were naturalized and adopted the life of the province. A few became some of the wealthier early-day Californians, gaining their fortunes through marriage, business enterprise or ranching.

For two decades after statehood (in 1850) settlement in Southern California lagged far behind that in central California.

Relatively few Anglos migrated south of the Tehachapi during those years. Few new communities were organized and existing towns grew slowly. Although the Gold Rush markedly affected the Southern California economy, cattle ranching remained the way of life for over a decade. A cash system replaced barter. Earlier, beef carcasses had been almost worthless; then demands for meat in Sierran gold camps made the beef more valuable than tallow and hide.

Less than a decade after the start of the Gold Rush the wane of the mining brought changes that did much to alter Southern California.

Thousands of cattle perished during the drought of 1856— this added to the difficulties of the rancheros. Many landowners were heavily indebted and "Yankee" interest rates caused increasing insolvency. Taxation, all but unknown before 1847, became burdensome. Floods (in December 1861) followed by a "Great Drought" (1862-1865) and grasshopper plague (1863) virtually destroyed ranchero days and resulted in start of a new era.

With disintegration of the large estates, rural land was available for occupancy by Americans in Southern California.

Yet the homestead, important in settlement of the trans-Mississippi West, could not prevail here; most arable land was already privately held by the rancheros. But their bankruptcy frequently prompted rancho subdivision which permitted more landholders.

The 1860's and 1870's were decades of agricultural experimentation in Southern California.

Grapes gained speedy economic success. Experimentation with other items (such as cotton, flax, silkworms and tobacco) did not prove successful. After the Southern Pacific reached Los Angeles from central California (in 1876) a minor rush of health seekers began. New communities such as Pasadena were organized. Desert mine camps, especially Cerro Gordo (Ch.3) briefly provided additional income.

Following completion of two "transcontinental" rail routes in the 1880's a spectacular real estate boom occurred.

Rapid growth of the citrus industry began when straightforward refrigerated shipment became possible. More immigrants arrived from the Middle West than had previously come from the East Coast by ship.

Present-day patterns of urbanization and transportation were initiated; the Los Angeles Lowlands became the obvious economic and and social center of Southern California. The primary sources of support for more than a generation were provided by agriculture, fishing, petroleum and sunshine seeking.

## The Contemporary International Conurbation

In the twentieth century Southern California has attracted many entrepreneurs, artisans, technicians and other skilled individuals, including many "footloose" persons with worldwide connections, to create a large affluent populace. Semi-skilled clerical and blue-collar workers, while predominantly Anglo, include more ethnic people than the "elite" element, have migrated from around United States since 1940.

Even earlier, a still-larger supply of common labor had been attracted by Southern California's reputation as a developing realm.

Migrant Mexicans, Filipinos and Japanese gained many such positions early in the twentieth century. In contrast to eastern United States and central California, there never was a massive migration of Europeans directly to provide menial labor and create large groups of distinct "white" ethnic cultures. The 1930's and 1940's witnessed a considerable influx of Southern blacks and "dust bowler" Great Plains farmers. This marked the end of significant arrivals of retirees from eastern United States. The area had become too expensive and too urban. Thus the median age of the population began to approach national norms.

European refugees, some world-famed, began arriving in the 1930's.

Many of them augmented the sizable Jewish community already affiliated with the apparel and motion picture industries. Black migration continued, too, until the 1960's, then waned. Black numbers today remain below the national proportion and are increasingly subordinate to recent Southern Californians who have come from the "Third World."

Southern California has acquired sizable numbers of Pacific Basin people since the late 1960's.

These include many Hispanics, as well as Chinese of different nationalities, Middle Easterners, Vietnamese, Filipinos as well as people from various Pacific islands.

The considerable Japanese populace, which returned from World War II eviction and internment, has been augmented by a transient business-connected group from Japan.

The most numerous, and areally ubiquitous, component of Southern California's "global village" consists of immigrant Latin Americans.

In past decades they were mostly Mexican nationals. Now included are Cubans and other Central Americans as well as South Americans. The "Spanish language or surname" group consists of about twenty per cent of Southern Californians.

Completely disregarded in this brief summary have been the many people who have other ethnicities that would merit more attention if located in a less-populous realm. These include Armenians, Indonesian Dutch, "east" Indians, and several Indo-Chinese peoples such as the Hmong.

The total population of the Los Angeles conurbation approximates eleven million people.

The San Diego Country contains two million more while half a million Southern Californians live in the Oxnard Plain or along the Santa Barbara Coast. Residents tend to be essentially urban lowlanders. The highlands, except for view sites and resort areas, tend to contain limited populations.

Residentially, urban Southern California belies its rural Middle Western traditions.

Detached single-family houses are still dominant but overall population growth and social trends increasingly lead to multi-unit residences. Increasingly Southern Californians live in apartments and condominiums, both high-rise and low-rise. Today high-rise condominiums of 10 to 30 stories are becoming more common. Single-family units more and more are attached "town houses" or "common wall" units built on hillsides as well as lowlands.

## MARKET PERISHABLES, ELECTRONICS AND TOURISTS

The economic foundations of Southern California have been broadened appreciably in the twentieth century.

Increasingly, with resource depletion and environmental deterioration, the economy is reliant upon other enterprises. These include military operations, "artificial" tourist attractions, research facilities, assembly lines, and film and music industries. Intangible elements are important: transfer payments from other areas, and such hinterland services as engineering, health, recreation and education.

Southern Californians, to overcome the handicaps of late start and isolation from populous northeastern United States, have specialized in activities oriented towards specific local resources as well as those that can thrive without abundant raw materials, cheap labor or which have most of their customers locally.

Among the leading sources of livelihood, three (agriculture, defense and tourism) are sufficiently widespread in Southern California as to warrant general description here.

More constricted activities will be treated later in their respective localities.

### Eggs and Truck Crops

Despite urbanization agriculture remains a widespread economic pursuit; value of product exceeds that of any of two dozen states.

Southern California's farmland, as compared with the state generally, is more expensive, with smaller farms, fuller use of irrigation and other technologies and places more emphasis on high-value items.

Farm income is diverse. Despite urbanization, some commodities are destined for national as well as local markets.

Subtropical climate, coupled with alluvial soils and divergent inland and coastal temperatures, permits a genuine production advantage nationally. Orchards in particular have been favored because of their appeal as country residence places and for tax incentives. Truck gardens and flower fields make good interim use of future urban tracts despite spiraling land prices.

Production of perishable items, understandably, continues for local consumption. Thus San Diego and San Bernardino counties are among the state's leaders in output of eggs and San Bernardino in milk.

### Missiles and Submarines

Federal expenditures related to national defense and space exploration in Southern California provide economic support comparable to all other major economic bases combined.

Civilian ship and aircraft construction, as well as electronics manufacture, are largely the province of industries sustained by government contracts. "Think tanks" and other research enterprises likewise have an important defense component.

Military operations in Southern California are commonly operated by the Navy and the Marine Corps.

Sites earlier were situated mainly upon San Diego Bay and later at Los Angeles-Long Beach harbors. During World War II coastal facilities were added in Orange, Ventura and northern San Diego counties and several Channel Islands, particularly San Clemente.

Major Air Force installations in Southern California are maintained around Riverside and San Bernardino.

Defense-contracted research and manufacturing have had even greater economic impact than the military installations. This includes the bulk of the aircraft, ordnance (missiles) and electronic industries. While Los Angeles is the principal locale, plants are scattered widely about Southern California. Many are light industries needing only available building sites with freeway access and amenable working conditions for scientific and executive personnel. 'Tis said that the end-product of a Rand Corporation multi-million dollar contract has been delivered by hand in a single attache case.

### The Seashore—and Human-Made Lures

As a contributor to the economy of Southern California, tourism, which exceeds agricultural exports in value, is surpassed only by the defense sector. The impact of the tourist primarily affects retail trade and services; only a tenth of visitor income derives from recreation or formal entertainment. Hence tourism is far-reaching but often inconspicuous. Yet there is a need for identifiable attractions such as Disneyland or Sea World, combined with the seashore, the weather and the presence of resident relatives, to entice tourists initially.

Visitation has changed markedly since the era when affluent tourists arrived from the East by train for a lengthy winter stay at a resort hotel, seeking sunshine, dry air, and amenable seashores and orange groves and possibly a trip to a mission or a ride into local mountains for adventure. Tourists today come year-round although more often in summer. They arrive by automobile or aircraft, stay briefly, may represent all conceivable economic and social groups, places of origin and visitation motives.

Many "tourists" come to Southern California for business, conventions and other compelling but extraneous reasons, such as connecting air flights.

Central Los Angeles remains an important stop for corporate travelers and many ethnic visitors. Long Beach, like Los Angeles, Anaheim and San Diego, is a leading convention place. "Prime" destinations for traditional visitors include Santa Barbara, the southern San Fernando Valley, Hollywood and other westside Los Angeles districts, Orange County and San Diego. The San Gabriel and Inland valleys have not maintained their earlier vacation appeal. Ventura County too remains apart from the usual visitor itinerary, as do the mountains generally. These realms are popular however with Southern Californians themselves.

## LAND, SEA AND SKY

The Southern California landscape has been altered so dramatically as to warrant prior attention to the human factors summarized above. It is obvious from this discussion however that the earth—especially the seashore, the mountains and the weather—has much influenced the human role in Southern California.

### A Near-Winterless Land

Southern California's version of dry-summer subtropical climate is the impressive characteristic of the physical environment of this almost-winterless realm. There are two seasons: a lengthy dry period from May until November when temperatures over much of the area are modified considerably from the heat of the deserts to the east and a generally mild winter half-year when precipitation may occur.

Like other Mediterranean-type lands, Southern California has abundant sunshine but its most appealing feature is the lower-sun mildness.

It is sufficiently temperate to permit year-round plant growth in favored localities. Summer weather is transitional between the Fog Belt (Central Coast and Northwest) and the interior desert.

Though once pursued by health-seekers and still appreciated by many outdoor enthusiasts, the Southern California climate is oft-maligned, not without cause. Some regard it as too monotonous while others consider it too sunny, or too damp, hazy or smoggy. It has temporal variations of note.

The latitude (32-34 degrees) tends to minimize winter cyclonic activity. Often, when rain is falling in central California impressive cirrus cloud "signs" appear over Southern California but precipitation fails to materialize. In a "normal" year

half a dozen storms bring rain; the remainder of the lower-sun period tends to be clear (away from the coastal fog belt). The extraordinary rainfall of some winters has brought disastrous floods throughout Southern California— the most destructive occurred in 1938 and 1969.

The ocean off Southern California is warmer and the northwest winds less steady than beyond Point Conception where the coast assumes a more northerly trend. Still there is sufficient oceanic upwelling to create fog, especially along coastal fringes, in spring and summer. Thus the gray overcast on many a morning convinces some visitors from eastern United States that rain is imminent. The main result of the overcast is the screening of an otherwise-brilliant sunshine.

Winter fog is infrequent but it is more commonly at ground level and hence is more disruptive of sea, land and air travel than is the high summer stratus deck, especially along the immediate coast and in sheltered inland basins which have nocturnal air drainage.

Desert air seldom penetrates to the coast during the warm season. As the heavier cooled maritime air moves onshore in winter when the Pacific (Hawaiian) High is displaced southward and interior air pressure increases, occasional spells of clear dry weather or even modified "polar outbursts" with subfreezing temperatures describe most of Southern California.

Sometimes these desert "outbursts" are mild and welcome but in early autumn especially they bring

**Figure 6-2.** Smog over the San Gabriel Valley a few hours after a rainstorm. There are over six million automobiles in Los Angeles County. Auto exhausts are a major contributor to the worst smog in the United States. (dwl)

violent "Santa Ana" winds with much dustfall, considerable property damage and fire losses.

Air pollution is described later in association with the Los Angeles Basin where it receives worldwide notoriety.

Descending air from the Hawaiian High forms a warm "inversion layer" that holds pollutants near the ground where they are trapped between ocean breezes and interior mountains. Foothill areas are especially prone to smog conditions wherever excessive contaminants are generated.

Southern California has been described as "Mediterranean", "semiarid", "near desert" and "desert"—these labels all have validity, for considerable variation exists within different sections of the area.

Temperature becomes more extreme inland. There is a decided difference between the colder winter nights and hotter summer afternoons of San Bernardino (July average 76 degrees F.) for example and the milder temperatures of coastal Santa Monica (July average 66 degrees F.) or Ventura.

Littorals are generally mild-summer subtropical and interior areas predominantly hot-summer. A number of coastal areas are regarded to have some of the choicest "residential" climates in continental United States. But the damp breezy littorals are not universally favored. Persons with respiratory problems often seek the lower humidities and lesser pollution of the nearby mountains and deserts.

In the highlands temperatures decrease with altitude and precipitation increases to create a succession of vertical zones. Above 6000 feet winter storms are likely to yield snow. Places above 3000 feet are usually above the stratus level in summer and receive longer hours of sunshine. Thunderstorms storms from tropical inflow and invading smog from coastal lowlands are other warm-season phenomena in Southern California mountains.

## Land of Imported Water

Summer drought and water shortage are problems that confront all Mediterranean-type lands.

Short-term solution in Southern California has relied first upon mountain-fed streams, then lowland aquifers, and finally upon imported water from other climatic realms within the state and nation.

The stream flow is discharged primarily through river basins.

**Figure 6-3.** The San Gabriel Mountains, a double horst, is an important portion of nature's wall around Southern California. Antelope Valley (Mojave Desert) in rear. (dwl)

From northwest to southeast these include the Ventura, Santa Clara, Los Angeles, San Gabriel, Santa Ana, San Jacinto, Santa Margarita, San Luis Rey, San Dieguito and San Diego.

Within the mountains the rivers have steep gradients that naturally decrease near the coasts. There are marked variations in flow and all of these streams frequently have dry channels. Thus many visitors from humid lands are amused that the Los Angeles is called a river, except during brief episodes of flooding. A number of flood-control basins, usually on the plains, and storage reservoirs within the mountains have been constructed.

While underground water has been an important resource, too often excessive use has led to reduced extraction.

*Spreading grounds* have been developed along some streams so that much water percolates underground and contributes towards maintenance of subterranean water levels. Heavy pumping of underground reserves has lowered some water table so much that intrusion of salt (ocean) water has occurred, especially on the Oxnard Plain and the Los Angeles coastal plain. Both areas once formed valuable artesian basins and remain locally-crucial suppliers.

Importation from other areas now furnishes more than local supplies. The initial large-scale project was undertaken by the city of Los Angeles.

During the period 1905-1913 the 250-mile-long **Los Angeles Aqueduct** was constructed to transport water from east-slope Sierran streams that had previously fed Owens Lake (Ch. 3). In 1940 a northward extension of the Aqueduct was completed, and in the 1960's a second pipe to Los Angeles was built.

The **Colorado River Aqueduct** was completed in 1939 (Ch. 4).

Water is pumped from Lake Havasu behind Parker Dam and carried more than 240 miles into **Lake Mathews** near Riverside; then it is distributed widely to various Southern California communities by the **Metropolitan Water District**, as far south as San Diego's San Vicente reservoir.

Subsequently the Colorado and San Diego aqueducts have been enlarged and additional cities, including some in Ventura County, have joined the District. The Santa Barbara Coast has resolved its water shortages thrice by constructing tunnels through the Santa Ynez Mountains to tap the Santa Ynez River.

Additional water reached Southern California upon completion of the *California Aqueduct* in 1973 (see Overview G). The Aqueduct transports water southward from the Sacramento River basin to Lake Perris with distribution to San Diego and Ventura counties as well.

### Mountains and Plains

The three principal physiographic units of Southern California are the **Transverse Ranges** (north and west), the **Peninsular Ranges** (south and east) and the intricate **Los Angeles Basin**, which forms a connective lowlands between these two highland areas.*

Southern California seems better endowed in weather than it does in topography; as noted above half the subregion consists of rough hills and mountains.

These separate the Los Angeles Basin and other coastal lowlands from the remainder of California; mile-high elevations are common. Both the Transverse and Peninsular ranges increase in height inland; fortunately for the subregion most of their drainage is toward the Pacific, not into the Mojave and Colorado deserts.

There is extensive flat land only around Los Angeles and in southern Ventura County.

Low elevation, alluvial soils, ground water reserves and access to the Pacific make these areas prime sites for present-day occupance. The shoreline of Southern California is often fringed with sea cliffs backed by marine terraces, which are utilized for transport, agriculture and urban use.

**San Diego Bay** provides the single large natural harbor.

Coastal lagoons are frequent where river valleys reach the coast; several have been converted into ports and small-craft anchorages.

Despite some ancient rock formations, the contemporary terrain of Southern California is geologically young.

Predominantly sedimentary, coastal plains and hills include include both fluvial and marine deposits. East and south of Los Angeles most higher surfaces are underlain by subterranean granitoidal masses; in the Peninsular Ranges these are considered part of a great *batholith* which extends into Baja California.

Lowlands and highlands alike owe their existence to crustal movements: faulting, folding and warping.

Occasional destructive earthquakes are reminders that earth molding is continuing. The topography is aligned along major axes of crustal disturbance. Northward of Los Angeles the uplands and lowlands have a common east-west orientation; elsewhere they generally trend northwest-southeast.

The deep **San Andreas Fault** enters Southern California in the southeast near San Gorgonio Pass, crosses the Transverse Ranges near Cajon Pass and continues along the northern edge of the San Gabriel Mountains where its resultant landforms are especially evident.

Other significant faults include the *Elsinore*, which bisects the Peninsular Ranges, the *San Jacinto* through the eastern Peninsular Ranges, the *Newport-Inglewood* system near the coastal margin of the Los Angeles Basin, and the *Santa Ynez,* which extends the width of Santa Barbara and Ventura counties. Some fault zones are bordered by impressive scarps while others coincide with major gaps through the mountains that have become vital transport corridors such as San Gorgonio and Tejon passes, Cajon Canyon and Santa Ana River Canyon.

### Coastal Sage and Chaparral

Southern California's natural vegetation reflects the long summer drought season. Almost half the subregion, mostly the uplands, retains its native plant cover. Principal types include coastal sage,

---

* There is long-time confusion in terminology. The physiographic term *Los Angeles Basin* refers to the Hollywood-to-El Toro geosyncline. The public uses this same term for all five of the *Los Angeles Lowlands*. The authors have accepted the term reluctantly because of its widespread usage.

**Figure 6-2a.** Chaparral ablaze— a hazard of residence in Southern California. Highly resinous chaparral shrubs produce "hot" fires, especially in late summer and autumn. (Hazel Gehrum)

chaparral, oak woodland, grasslands and mountain forests.

*Coastal sage,* dominated by California sagebrush, white sage, purple sage and wild buckwheat, is mistaken by strangers for chaparral, with which it commonly merges inland. The sage formation, consisting of smaller evergreen shrubs seldom more than five feet high, flourishes on near-coast hillsides. It is an open cover that does not discourage passage afoot as chaparral often does. It is most attractive at the end of the wintry rain period when it appears more luxuriant with sages abloom.

*Chaparral* represents the typical Southern California vegetation. Essentially a thick mass of evergreen shrubs, sometimes 10 feet tall, it has been called "elfin forest." Oft-ravaged by fire, chaparral is well adapted to long summer droughts— and to post-fire reproduction. The smaller leathery leaves help plants conserve moisture. Angular branches and density discourage people from cross-country hikes. Composition of the formation varies locally; scrub oak is conspicuous in different habitats. At lower elevations chamise is frequently dominant. Farther upslope manzanita and various ceanothi become common. While chaparral, which appears dull and drab to strangers from wetter lands, is without grazing value it is an important asset on steep slopes where it protects surfaces from erosion.

*Oak woodland,* which might be described as an oak-grove grassland, occupies north-facing hillsides away from the coast. It is dominated by the evergreen live oak, the deciduous valley oak and black walnut. Seasonal contrasts are noticeable,

especially because of the change from seared to green grasslands beneath and around the trees.

Basically coniferous, *mountain forests* are limited to higher elevations and will be discussed later in the chapter.

The *grasslands,* generally of a bunch-grass nature, were more characteristic of the plains and deep-soiled hillsides. They have been much eradicated or thoroughly modified with the advent of farms, heavy grazing and urbanization.

### Soils: Both Coarse And Fine

Southern California possesses the usual statewide dichotomy of noncultivable slopes and productive plains. The juxtaposition of inhospitable lithosols with alluvial lowlands occurs frequently (Overview D).

Yet rounded coastal sedimentary hills and granitic Peninsular Ranges foothills have agricultural merit, as do undulating sandy marine terraces. Within broad limits, farming in highly capitalized Southern California is often more dependent upon land accessibility, water supply and human choice choice than upon inherent soil qualities.

Most lowlands do not have uniform surfaces; inland they tend to have more slope, coarse-textured soils and good drainage. Towards coastal fringes, soils become progressively denser and poorly drained—a significant transition for farming and initial urbanization. Older alluvial soils occupy flood-free terrace sites, both coastal and inland. These are widespread in Southern California and frequently have been preferred settings for orchards and for residence.

Although it includes portions of only seven of the Golden State's 58 counties Southern California is the most complex geographical division of the state. Accordingly six subdivisions (map 6-1) will be considered in succession: (1) **San Diego Country**; (2) the **Los Angeles Basin (Lowlands)**; (3) the **Oxnard Plain**; (4) the **Santa Barbara Coast**; (5) the **Transverse Ranges**; and (6) the **Channel Islands**.

---

### SAN DIEGO COUNTRY

San Diego Country* is the southernmost portion of

---

* San Diego Country was initially reviewed by Donald Eidemiller, San Diego State University and subsequently discussed with James Blick, SDSU. This review has been made by Philip Pryde and James Blick, SDSU and James Switzer, Southwestern College.

Southern California.

It adjoins the Los Angeles Lowlands (map 6-2). Climatically it is the mildest portion of Southern California yet the most drought-prone.

The Country languished through most of the nineteenth century.

During most of the Spanish and Mexican periods it remained inconsequential, despite a lengthier post-Indian history than other parts of Alta California.

Despite abortive, short-lived booms in the 1870's and 1880's it still dozed, under American control, throughout the nineteenth century. Yet even then many recognized a climatic appeal for retirement residence.

San Diego Country awakened, if somewhat drowsily before 1940, around 1900.

Subsequently, stimulated by the needs of national defense and by the steadier, less sensational growth of agriculture, retirement residence and tourism, San Diego has been the Golden State's second most-populous county since 1960.

## Seascapes and Granitic Knobs

Physiographically San Diego Country coincides generally with the Peninsular Ranges.

The lengthy segments of the Ranges within Mexico have been excluded, as have the San Jacinto and Santa Rosa ranges and the San Jacinto Basin.

The terrain is underlain by granitoidal rocks; countless outcrops impart a knobby character to many slopes. Inland, faulting has produced a series of separate mountain blocks.

Particularly important is the northwest-trending *Elsinore Fault* system, along which the Santa Ana, Palomar (Agua Tibia) and Laguna mountains have been thrust upward so that higher summits exceed 6000 feet. Their extensive tabular uplands facilitate agriculture and recreation but partially fault-scarped slopes are often too steep even for grazing.

Much of San Diego Country is uplands, sometimes steep and rocky; elsewhere with "mesas" that are surprisingly even and deep-soiled. Down-faulting and stream erosion (commonly dissected by fault zones) have produced a maze of small basins, distributed widely and irregularly. Soils, coupled with the water supply of these generally westward-draining depressions are precious assets amid a somewhat forbidding countryside.

With their eastern fault faces and west-tilted granitic blocks these Peninsular Ranges are structurally suggestive of the Sierra Nevada.

The highest point in San Diego Country, *Hot Springs Mountain* indicates why the spectacular glaciated summits and U-shaped canyons of the Sierra Nevada are absent. Since the Peninsular Ranges also descend to the ocean, the western peripheries of of the two highlands are different.

The coastal margins of the Peninsular Ranges consist of a series of "stair-step" levels—marine terraces created by sea level oscillations and crustal movement.

The terraces around San Diego, called "mesas", extend inland a dozen miles. The width of the terrace belt narrows irregularly to the north to less than a mile at Corona del Mar.

Farthest inland and highest in elevation, the oldest terraces are quite eroded, so that the landscape has more relief than is commonly associated with coastal plains. Stream valleys have been entrenched below mesa levels and their mouths have lagoons, beach bars and marsh vegetation.

Between stream valleys the terraces commonly meet the ocean with sea cliffs at whose bases are typically beaches of substantial width. The coastline is customarily smooth; San Diego Bay affords the only large sheltered anchorage. At two places—Point Loma and La Jolla—the shoreline has scenic coves and headlands, backed by hills prized for their marine vistas.

## Chaparral and Fogbanks

San Diego Country lies on the southern fringe of dry-summer subtropical North America. Some of its area is *semi-arid,* with warm summers and mild winters; the eastern part of the the political County, in the Colorado Desert, is arid.

The area displays the typical Southern California climatic transition from seashore to mountain summits that produces several climatic variations.

The coastal strand has a mild climate (San Diego averages 54 degrees in January and 70 degrees F. in August) with one of the lowest seasonal temperature ranges within the 48 conterminous states. Subfreezing temperatures occur approximately once in a decade and the thermometer has never dropped below 25 degrees F. (at the main San Diego weather station). Afternoon sea breeze and night and morning fog (stratus clouds) are prevalent in summer.

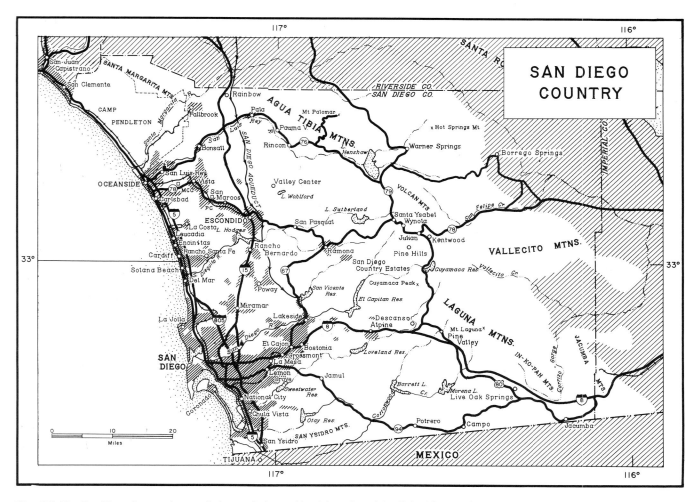

**Map 6-2.** The San Diego Country is regarded as a choice residential portion of the United States. Small wonder that San Diego is now one of the nation's eight largest cities.

Interior valleys and lower mountain slopes are more typically Mediterranean, with a wider seasonal temperature range. The annual picture remains prevailingly one of dryness and relative mildness. Precipitation is more copious on the highest summits. Crests of the Palomar and Laguna mountains average nearly 40 inches a year. Winters are relatively cold there and total snowfall averages three to four feet. By contrast summers are comfortably warm.

Over wide areas of the Country natural vegetation survives. Local variations rather faithfully reflect the climatic nuances just described.

Extensive stretches of uncultivated coastal terraces were once covered with coastal sage and associated semishrubs. Inland these formations merge with the heavier chaparral shrubs which still blanket much of the San Diego Country. Limited interior sectors support oak groves amid grasslands.

The highest elevations are dotted with conifer forests of open nature that include yellow pine, incense cedar and white fir as well as mesa oak. Larger stands are found upon the upper west slopes of the Palomar and Laguna mountains.

### Shoshones, Yumans and Hispanics

Numerically the Shoshonean and Yuman Indian groups occupied San Diego Country more successfully than the Spanish, Mexicans, or early Anglo Americans.

It was not until 1880 that the Country again contained as many residents as the pre-European population of 6000 to 12,000.

The arrival of the Spanish did not produce a flourishing economy.

The Indians remained hostile toward mission life

and semiaridity discouraged agricultural development. The small Spanish population was limited to the military and the missionaries.

Two widely-spaced missions were located in the Country, both within seven miles of the sea. San Diego (1769), first of the Alta California chain, suffered from erratic water supply so that foodstuff importation, generally from Mission San Gabriel, was sometimes necessitated. Grazing in the Back Country proved more successful. San Luis Rey (1798), in the best-watered valley of the San Diego Country, proved one of the more successful missions its yields of dry-farmed grains were often impressive.

The single nonecclesiastical establishment in Spanish times was the *presidio* at San Diego.

It consisted of a few squalid adobes, barracks and storerooms. The English voyager George Vancouver, a visitor in 1793, was understandably unimpressed.

During the Mexican period utilization of San Diego Country was altered somewhat.

Secularization permitted conversion of mission lands into ranchos; by the end of the era (1846) over thirty ranchos had been created. In aggregate, such lands included most of the suitable interior valleys as well as many of the coastal terraces.

Retired service personnel began constructing adobes near the presidio in 1825; thus the village of San Diego came into existence.

Now known as **Old Town** the village was better situated to obtain river water than for ship accessibility. Fear of Indian helped discouraged rural residence; therefore most Spanish-speaking resi-

**Figure 6-4.** Renaming of Market Street in honor of Martin L. King evoked so much controversy that the earlier name was restored. (dwl)

dents of the Country lived in the town despite despite the virtual absence of retail establishments or social activity.

## METROPOLITAN SAN DIEGO

**San Diego** (1.2 million) has become the second largest city in the Golden State (map 6-3) with a metropolitan population of around two and a quarter million. Though its setting has not elicited the praise lavished on San Francisco or Sydney, its setting is auspicious. San Diego Bay is one of the best harbors on the Pacific Coast of both Americas.

Limited tidal currents and natural protection from prevailing winds are physical advantages. Terraces ("mesas") rising gradually inland from the water's edge provide an ample easily-occupied metropolitan site. And the mild sunny weather has been appreciated by aircraft builder, farmer, retiree, sea captain and tourist alike.

The recency of San Diego's emergence is a paradox—this urban complex is almost wholly the product of the twentieth century despite its early start as California's first mission, presidio and seaport.

Several major disadvantages existed. Water shortage, the most critical, has been resolved through importation. A productive hinterland, such as those supporting San Francisco and Los Angeles, was lacking. The small basins and valleys of San Diego County are scattered. Unlike Los Angeles, San Diego did not have a direct low-elevation pass across the mountains. Thus competition with its larger "rival" to the north was hampered with the advent of transcontinental rail linkage, *especially* after improvement of the Los Angles Harbor.

San Diego's location in the nation's extreme southwest corner has been a commercial detriment. Hence relatively few of the the continuous flow of distinguished visitors who go to San Francisco or Los Angeles take a "side" trip to San Diego unless they specifically desire a vacation.

### Sleepy Village to Metropolis

For half a century San Diego was present-day **Old Town**.

It was a somnolent village for a generation after the end of the colonial era. Then in the 1860's enterprising Yankee developers created a separate community three miles to the south.

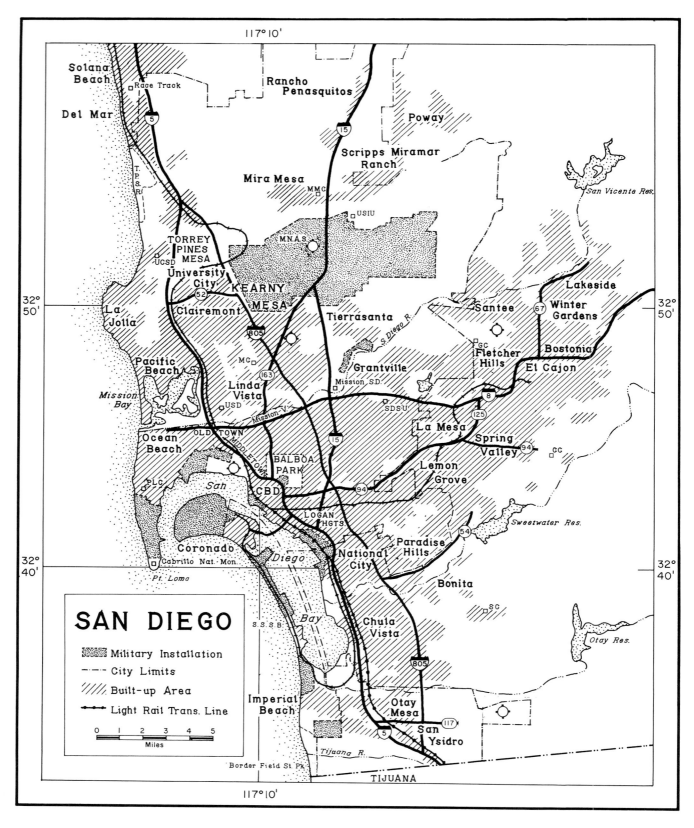

**Map 6-3.** Metropolitan San Diego has many ties with the Pacific Rim, especially Mexico.

Still the core of San Diego, this area was initially **New Town**. Unlike Old Town it has had good waterfront access.

Several outlying nuclei likewise appeared even before the Boom of the 1880's.

Most important of these were La Playa, erstwhile port for the original (Old Town) village, and National City, basically agricultural. Even in the 1870's some regarded San Diego as a place suitable for "rattlesnakes and tarantulas."

San Diego achieved its basic framework during the Boom of the 1880's.

Subdivisions, transportation facilities and waterworks were extended across a remarkable portion of the contemporary metropolis.

Connected by a citywide railway, nuclei appeared as distant from downtown San Diego as Chula Vista, Coronado, Imperial Beach, and La Jolla. But for several decades substantial growth was restricted to the periphery of New Town. Until the early 1900's the main urban frontier did not go around and beyond the close-in Balboa Park reserve.

## The Contemporary Metropolis

San Diego continues to gain metropolitan status although its functions differ significantly from those of some other larger centers in California and in United States.

San Diego lacks the industrial diversity of Los Angeles. And it does not have the financial significance of San Francisco. Unlike Sacramento it is not a major center of government although it is the county seat. As a seaport it lacks the significance of Oakland—its renown is based upon military and recreational use.

## "Navy Town"

Long a commonplace appellation for San Diego, this term has become less appropriate as the conurbation has grown.

Permanently, the Navy first arrived in 1907 but San Diego did not become a major military center until World War I. As a Naval base, advantages included availability of the Bay and its strand, climate, and closer proximity to the Panama Canal than any other Pacific port (in the United States).

Much evidence of military activity is visible around San Diego Bay.

This is the "home port" for approximately a fourth of the United States Naval fleet as well as head-

quarters for Naval operations (11th District) in Southern California.

Major installations include the Naval Station (southern San Diego), North Island Air Station (with dockage for Pacific Fleet aircraft carriers), the district supply depot (downtown waterfront), the electronics laboratory (on Point Loma), the Naval Amphibious Base along the Silver Strand, the spacious air base at Miramar and the Navy and Marine recruit training stations near San Diego International Airport.

Nearly half of the entire Bay frontage is used by the military. Destroyers, submarines, tenders and a "mothball" fleet are conspicuously anchored in the Bay. Transfer of Naval facilities from Long Beach and Pasadena (in the 1970's) increased the activity.

## By Land, By Air and By Sea

As befits a major urban center, San Diego has a variety of transportation facilities.

Yet its far-southwest corner location of the Golden State means that it is not a major subregional transit hub.

Despite its stellar embayment, non-military tonnage cannot compare with the ranking Pacific Coast seaports.

It is cheaper for a ship to visit Los Angeles and send San Diego cargo south by truck than to visit both ports.

As an air terminal too San Diego does not challenge Los Angeles or San Francisco.

While one can go almost "anywhere in the world" from San Diego, many of its flights are connector

**Figure 6-6.** Mission Valley, followed eastward from I-5 by I-8, has become the retail center of San Diego. In this view the junction of I-8 and I-15 are visible. (dwl)

**Figure 6-5.** The city of San Diego, with Mission Bay in the foreground. The political city alone covers 300 square miles. It spreads across marine terraces (locally called mesas) which ascend into the Peninsular Ranges. (Historical Collection, Title and Trust Company, Union Title Office, San Diego).

**Figure 6-7.** Downtown San Diego, with I-5 (diagonally) in the foreground (San Diego Fire Department, photograph by Dick McDowell).

flights via Los Angeles. Direct flights are possible to such destinations as San Francisco and Sacramento, Acapulco and Las Vegas, New York and Chicago.

Few American cities have such a comparably close-in terminal as International Airport (still called Lindbergh Field).In fact incoming planes glide between downtown high-rises.It has been the home base of an important West Coast line (now merged with another carrier) which has dominated employment at the airport.

Despite interstate highways north (I-5 and I-15) and east (I-8), San Diego tends to be a terminus rather than a crossroads.

It serves of course a major gateway to Tijuana and Baja California.

### Jets and Missiles

San Diego's defense-oriented manufacturing has frequently rivaled the military as the leading economic activity.

Reliance upon military contracts has produced severe fluctuations in employment and payrolls. Over two-thirds of all factory employment tends to be allied with the Department of Defense.

San Diego's aviation future was presaged early in the century.

Glenn Curtis established a flying school on North Island. By 1920 good "flying weather" had prompted the Navy to establish permanent air installations. A few years later Ryan Aeronautical Company (a local firm) built Lindbergh's Spirit of St.Louis. The municipal airport has honored the famed pioneer aviator in its name.

In 1935 Consolidated Aircraft Corporation, seeking an ice-free harbor and available land near its principal customer (the Navy) relocated its operations (construction of amphibious craft) from New York state to San Diego. During World War II thousands of heavier aircraft were constructed by the firm.

Its successor (General Dynamics Corporation) has been San Diego's principal civilian employer for decades. In recent years products have included military jets and missiles.

Other aerospace firms include Ryan (now Teledyne), Rohr (builder of the original cars for the Bay Area's B.A.R.T.), and and Solar (now part of International Harvester).

Other long-prominent industrial activities, less-successful of late, have included shipbuilding and seafood canning.

With aerospace these activities tended to dominate the industrial belt (along the eastern side of the Bay from the International Airport to Chula Vista).

In recent decades a single shipbuilding firm (National Steel and Shipbuilding Corporation) has survived only by dependence upon federal contracts.

Seafood canning collapsed in the middle-1980's but there is local optimism for high-tech research and development, especially in biomedicine.

## Opera and the Sciences

In past decades San Diego lacked its present recognition as a cultural center.

Perhaps one should not expect a Navy center, aircraft builder and retirement town to so be. A generation ago a local scholar still described San Diego as "a cultural wilderness peopled by sunworshippers."

Subsequently San Diego has had time to mature as a metropolis. While it may not rank with Los Angeles and San Francisco, neither is it "Norfolk West."

Thus the *Places Rated Almanac* gives it good scores in both education and the arts. Although not a corporate center like Chicago, San Diego physical appeal has attracted such influential "elite" as Scripps and Spreckels, who have given the metropolis civic leadership and tangible works. Thus the city takes pride in its opera, its civic theatres, its zoo, its fine arts galleries and its major league sports.

Cultural attractions include historic sites related to San Diego's early importance to Hispanic California.

Among these are the mission, **Old Town**. whose core is a state historic park with colonial memorabilia and popular *Bazaar del Mundo* and *Cabrillo National Monument* on Point Loma.

San Diego now has much stature as a center of higher education.

San Diego State University is generally regarded as about the best in the California State system. Other institutions include the University of California at San Diego, the University of San Diego, United States International University, National University, Point Loma College and five community colleges.

A full-fledged branch of the University of California, with medical school and known especially in mathematics and the sciences, has evolved from the once-specialized Scripps Institute of Oceanography.

## Visitors and Retirees

In the problems and bustle of defense-oriented activities, the traditional role of San Diego as an "amenities" place is sometimes underestimated.

Balmy weather, the seacoast and proximity to the international border, so important to the defense complex, attract the tourists and old folks too. Once military personnel became familiar with the area it became a popular retirement place.

*Balboa Park* brings justified recognition to San Diego. Urban San Diego's attenuated shoreline likewise provides a major attraction— for bathing, pleasure boating and sports fishing.

The one-time tidal flats of *Mission Bay* have been converted into more attractive settings with varied facilities for aquatic recreation (Fig. 6-5). Mission Bay and San Diego Bay together provide berths for several thousand pleasure craft. Coastal beaches include state parks at Silver Strand, Mission Bay and Ocean Beach.

Present-day San Diego is as far-flung as its most ambitious developers of the 1880's might have dreamed (map 6-3).

With annexations, even the political city reaches from Escondido to the Mexican border.

The contiguous urbanized complex extends inland to contain over 500 square miles. Despite considerable building space still within the city limits, the satellites (even waterbound Coronado) have grown rapidly. Over half of the total population lives outside the political city. After much "fill-in" of earlier subdivisions, growth has been mainly northward, especially Interstate 15. Interstate 8 has also a growth axis eastward with much expansion in such places as El Cajon.

The urban complex is much fragmented, partly because of an irregular shoreline, Balboa Park and military reservations. Another factor is terrain—terrace surfaces tend to be deeply dissected. The steep-sided canyons that crisscross San Diego effectively preclude urban continuity yet provide impressive view lot sites. Patterns of higher-income residence occur on some terrace edges, facing both seaward and inland.

### Along the Shore

The Pacific shore from La Jolla to Imperial Beach has long been a preferred-residence place. While its separate communities are quite individualistic, all have grown more costly and more densely occupied. The propriety of seafront high-rises has been keenly argued, especially in Coronado and La Jolla.

Affluent **La Jolla**, with many wealthy residents, prefers to consider itself a separate entity even though it has always been within San Diego city limits.

Its cove-and-cliff locale is esteemed by artists, tourists and higher-income residents. A little theatre, quality retail shops and careful landscaping add charm.*

Southward from La Jolla the strand is completely utilized. As in most of San Diego, single-family dwellings predominate although the number of apartments, more frequent than in some parts of the metropolis, is increasing.

Middle-income residents dwell in **Pacific Beach** and **Ocean Beach** where apartments are replacing single-family residences. By the Bayside is *Sea World*, a premier tourist attraction.

Mission and San Diego bays together provide berths for several thousand pleasure craft.

The north shore of San Diego Bay has been much altered too for public access and aquatic uses. *Harbor Island* and *Shelter Island* are both man-made peninsulas and contain lodging, a marina and eating facilities.

**Point Loma**, with superior marine vistas, affords San Diego's most extensive higher-income area, although its affluence is surpassed in parts of La Jolla and Grossmont.

**Coronado** (20 000) remains a favored place for residence by retired Navy officers (Fig. 6-9).

The town, with its old landmark hotel, has been a major sea resort for decades. Now connected with San Diego by bridge, it still depends considerably on nearby Naval bases. There is also a large, youthful, modest-income group and in some sectors apartment houses are conspicuous, including waterfront high-rise.

Much of the *Silver Strand*, the attenuated sand reef that forms the western border of San Diego Bay) is shared by a state beach and Naval installations.

Affluent *Coronado Cays* is a marina community along the Bay.

**Imperial Beach** (25,000) is a lower-income residence town, principally Anglo.

Inhabitants include many married Navy enlisted personnel. An otherwise fine strand has been marred by the flow of ill-treated sewage in the Tia Juana River from the south side of the border.

### North by East

Another traditional urban axis extends northeastward from downtown for about 15 miles. It has focused upon El Cajon Boulevard, the principal retail thoroughfare.

Names of individual neighborhoods, *University Heights, Normal Heights, City Heights, College Heights* and the city of **La Mesa** (52,000), bespeak the ascending terrace surfaces.

This section gained early favor with farmers for its soils and water supply and by health seekers for its drier, sunnier weather. Now the small avocado and citrus groves set on low hillsides and freeway access are added attractions for the prospective suburbanite.

The interior setting, like the seashore, has gained a certain residential prestige. **El Cajon** (83,000), locale of Grossmont College, is the leading city.

Other growing suburban areas in the northeast include **Lemon Grove** (22,000), **Spring Valley** (57,000), **Lakeside** (41,000), and **Santee** (51,000).

Urban expansion northward onto the mesas north of I-8 was delayed by topographic considerations as long as better-regarded sites were available.

---

* A high-rise seaside structure here, as well as several in Coronado, reinforced the need to give the coast additional protection (see Ch.7).

Before mid-century the southern edge of Kearney Mesa had been subdivided into the Clairemont and Linda Vista districts.

Subsequent growth has extended discontinuously beyond University City into the "North City West" area adjoining Del Mar. Three institutions here are Mesa College, sectarian University of San Diego and the University of California.

Offices, aerospace firms and other advanced technologic facilities, including Salk Institute for Biological Sciences, are scattered between Montgomery Airport and UCSD in a fast-developing node called the "Golden Triangle."

Farther north toward Escondido, a dramatic urbanization has occurred, "wedded" to San Diego by Interstate 15.

Miramar Naval Air Station, itself a major workplace, long created a barrier, along with other military land, which has shrunk. Campuses of Miramar College and United States International University are here.

The new city of **Poway** (40,000) has grown rapidly. New suburban districts, within the city limits of San Diego, include *Mira Mesa*, *Rancho Penasquitos*, and *Scripps Miramar Ranch*.

### South by East

Expansion southeastward has been recent.

The industrial Bayshore and dry interior slopes formerly held little development appeal. But with the interior portion gaining direct freeway downtown via I-805 new neighborhoods are interposed between the central district and the outskirts, especially in the vicinity of Southwestern College.

Immediately southeast of downtown San Diego is the principal ethnic group sector of the metropolis as well as the chief cluster of cemeteries.

Blacks and Hispanics are present in comparable numbers in the city (approximately six per cent of the populace). Sizable numbers of immigrants from southeast Asia have located in Kearney Mesa and east San Diego.

**National City** (55,000) is an older industrial satellite. There is shoreline manufacturing, warehousing and Naval activity yet half of its workers are employed in San Diego. A less-affluent population predominates.

**Chula Vista** (125,000), second largest city in San Diego County is the industrial leader.

It has a major aerospace firm; many of its workers commute from other parts of the conurbation. Its numerous upper-middle income residents help support the solitary country club in the southern metropolitan area. Southwestern College is here while a large shopping complex attracts many Baja Californians.

Metropolitan San Diego has never had a sizable ethnic orientation despite its massive federal employment base.

Even residents of Mexican descent are modest in comparison with Los Angeles. This is an apparent result of unfavorable employment structures combined with the proximity of Tijuana as a source of commuter labor.

The *San Diego* ("Tijuana") *Trolley*, opened in 1981, follows abandoned rail trackage much of the distance between the Amtrak station downtown and the San Ysidro border crossing. A line subsequently built eastward will ultimately use another abandoned right-of-way to El Cajon.

The Mexican segment of the conurbation, **Tijuana** (over a million inhabitants) warrants note.

There are in excess of 30 million border crossings annually. The socioeconomic contrasts are vivid despite the dozens of "twin" industrial plants. Numerous San Diego visitors retain memories of interminable weekend border delays, the matter of Mexican automobile insurance, concern about different foods and drinks, a strange language and another currency, souvenirs, the international border "fence", helicopter patrols, detention centers—nowhere else along the nation's borders is is a "foreign culture" more accessible to so many.

### Downtown

The **central district** extends eastward from the waterfront and is disproportionately small for the size of the metropolis. After the rise of shopping centers in Mission Valley it appeared that the downtown area would lose much of its retail function. But revitalization of the district has made it one of the nation's more attractive metropolitan cores.

Adding to the appearance are fountains, statues, trees and flowers. Downtown San Diego has a feeling of space absent in some central districts.

Now the C.B.D. has several multi-star hotels, including the renovated U.S. Grant, a long-time landmark.

Particularly noticeable is Horton Plaza, a regional-scale shopping mall with four department stores as well many specialty shops. The Gaslamp Quarter nearby has restored structures housing small retail establishments.

Construction of quality apartment complexes and

**Figure 6-8.** A segment of Horton Plaza, "revitalized" downtown San Diego. (dwl).

condominiums has prompted a gentrification trend that has occurred also in other metropolitan centers.

The downtown skyline has acquired a third dimension. In multi-story buildings are found financial and corporate offices as well as law offices and accounting firms.

The waterfront is the focus of varied activities.

These include hotels, Navy structures, Seaport Village visitor complex and civic buildings (police and county administration). There is also a convention center while the area is "dominated" by the towers of the waterfront Intercontinental Hotel.

Changes have taken place too on the periphery of the central district.

To the east once-fashionable mansions on Golden Hill now house elderly low-income residents.

Northwest of downtown **Middletown**, occupies the "heights" and "dropoffs" between Balboa Park and the airport. Despite heavy traffic on east and west fringe it remains a desired residential quarter, with view site highrises facing the Park while singlefamily dwellings and smaller apartments overlook the harbor. The district has become increasingly commercial and industrial.

Few American cities are so fortunate to possess open space comparable to **Balboa Park** on the fringe of the city center.

The Park, approximating two square miles, begins a few few blocks from the downtown district. It has been the site of two world's fairs (1915-1916 and 1935-1936). Although the land was fortunately reserved before the Boom of the 1880's, it was necessary to resist subsequent urban pressures

and to landscape the unpromising iron hardpan soil.

Among its varied attractions the park contains the foremost zoological garden in western United States, an art gallery, a natural history museum, a concert amphitheatre, a botanical garden and the usual park facilities. Considerable acreage has been utilized for a high school (with San Diego City College adjacent to the park) a Naval hospital and freeway crossings.

Some districts bordering Balboa Park have been stable.

However the increasingly older population here has led to more multiple dwellings. *Mission Hills*, the "classic" older district, is popular with the "modern rich."

**Mission Valley**, extending eastward along Interstate 8 (from Mission Bay and I-5), has become the retail heart of San Diego.

With much "free" parking, it contains several regional shopping centers. The many lodging places along *Motel Row* reflect the city's consequence as a highway terminus and visitor center. *Jack Murphy Stadium,* near the junction of I-8 and I-15, provides a focus for major league sports.

## NORTH COUNTY *

An attractive portion of Southern California, North County extends more than 20 miles between metropolitan San Diego (Del Mar) and southern Orange County.

It consists of several terrace levels, as previously noted, masquerading as a coastal plain along the western flanks of the Peninsular Ranges (map, Fig. 6-3) and extends eastward into the Back Country. Thus it has definite boundaries only on the west, south and north.

Prevalence of flat to rolling terrain, pleasant summers and mild winters and the Pacific shoreline favor farming, recreation, retirement residence, and commutation to San Diego and Orange County.

Such utilization, together with a large military installation and services for travelers, support a population of several hundred thousand. The Coast has become one of California's more coveted assemblages of real estate parcels though more intensive development has come recently.

---

*This section has been reviewed by Lawrence Thompson, retired geography instructor, Oceanside, and Patricia Karinen Hightman, geographer-planner, Oceanside.

**Figure 6-9.** North Island and downtown San Diego. In this view North Island (left) and Coronado (right) are in the foreground, then San Diego Bay and downtown San Diego (middle, right). (U.S. Navy photograph).

The existing cultural landscape has evolved in the past half century and the population continues to increase. Affluent retirees from less benign parts of California as well as the "snow belt" continue to move here. Much of the growth indicates the outward expansion of metropolitan San Diego as well as reduced availability of attractive locales in Orange County.

Until recent decades some of the original colonial rancho holdings in North County remained in consolidated ownership, reserved for agriculture.*

Most of these properties have succumbed to urbanization although their demise was sufficiently slow as to produce urban pressures on adjacent lands.

Much of the contemporary population resides on the portion of North County which was never awarded as colonial grants.

Occupance is either urban or rurban. High land and water costs have encouraged farmers to confine their operations to smaller holdings, thus creating a type of semiurban residence.

### Between Here and There

North County affords the transportation linkage between Los Angeles and San Diego.

Hence accessibility has influenced its utilization since colonial days. The original trail, El Camino Real, extended the length of the Coast. It pursued the wave-cut cliff at the inner edge of the second terrace level (i.e., the head of canyon erosion by present-day streams), inland from coastal lagoons.

Rail transport has followed this corridor for a century. And current Amtrak traffic volume ranks second nationally only to the nation's Northeast corridor.

The California Southern Railroad (Santa Fe) was constructed from the Los Angeles Lowlands to San Diego in the 1880's.

Highway travel reasserted its primacy along this route over half a century ago.

The southern section of U.S. 101 (now replaced by I-5) was completed as a paved highway in 1928.

The freeway (Interstate 5) between Los Angeles and San Diego was constructed in the 1960's. It follows a route inland from the coast at the behest of coastal communities.

A second freeway, Interstate 15, farther inland, provides an alternate travel corridor between the eastern Los Angeles Basin and San Diego.

---

* Estates here and in adjacent southern Orange County included the Irvine Ranch (between Laguna Beach and Corona del Mar, Niguel (south of Laguna Beach), Boco de la Playa (north of San Clemente) and Agua Hedionda (south of Carlsbad). Santa Margarita y Las Flores, though now coincident with Camp Pendleton, is suggestive of the same category.

**Figure 6-10.** The scalloped coast, the wave-splashed shore and the seaward slope of Mt. Soledad (a marine terrace) have provided La Jolla, San Diego's most-prestigious in-limits suburb, with a superlative setting. In the rear (left) is located the University of California campus. (San Diego Convention and Tourist Bureau).

East-west vehicular travel is less adequate, although Ca. 78 is a freeway between Oceanside and Escondido. The three freeways (I-5, I-15 and Ca. 78) form a triangle whose sides have been the principal growth belt of North County in late 20th century.

### Shrinking Farm Land

Farming evolved belatedly in North County and water shortage has been a persistent handicap.

Rivers flow intermittently while the underground supply for pumping is likewise limited. Some arable land remains in pasture or is devoted to dry-farming of barley or beans (especially blackeye, garbanzo or lima). The foggy summers, relatively cool, favor the beans but discourage crops such as olives or grapes, which also could be grown without irrigation.

Irrigation agriculture has been localized primarily where there is sufficient runoff from the higher Peninsular Ranges. Drip irrigation (especially effective on slopes) has been a response to rising water costs. In the second half of the twentieth century much farm land has been converted to urban uses.

The largest acreage centers upon the San Dieguito Valley, which has long had storage water from Lake Hodges. The district around Oceanside and Carlsbad has relied upon extensive pumping in the San Luis Rey Valley.

Terrace soils, often derived from sandy marine deposits, are a lesser consideration than water supply and frost-free environment.

Avocados, citrus, flowers, vegetables and nursery stock, the major irrigated products, require mild winters and bring sufficient returns to compensate for expensive land and water.

Valencia oranges are prominent around Rancho Santa Fe, which is far enough inland from the coast so that summers are warmer.

*Fuerte*, the principal avocado variety, does not yield best along the coastal strand. However, summer coolness retards ripening so that growers can harvest a crop at a period of lesser competition from interior districts. In some sites avocados have been raised so near the coast that wooden frames are used to shield them from see breeze damage.

Vegetable marketing is even more closely related to harvest schedules than the avocados.

Some varieties can be harvested at any time of year, but competition from other sources (in California and nationally), severely curtails the "economic season." Thus tomato harvest extends from May through January, snap beans from June through December and lettuce from December through January. San Luis Rey Valley, with its environs, has been the Coast's chief vegetable center.

Seasonal scheduling is also vital to flower growers. Thus carnation farmers of the Oceanside-Carlsbad-Encinitas district have strived to meet the peak demands at Easter, Mother's Day and Christmas.

Judicious use of lath, cloth and plastic shelters, coupled with air freight shipment, has permitted the carnation growers to compete with flowers grown in greenhouses nearer large eastern cities. But urbanization, high taxes and foreign import (even of market flowers) have prompted some flower growers to relocate in the Willamette Valley of Oregon.

The poinsettia, another major flower export, provides fields of crimson flowers in December. Some of the crop is sold nationwide as propagation stock. Cutbacks in availability of natural gas have sometimes posed problems for some growers.

## Camp Pendleton

Camp Pendleton is one of the Marine Corps' largest training areas with a complement that varies from 10,000 to 50,000.

It occupies Rancho Santa Margarita y Las Flores, which had previously been the largest Mexican rancho in San Diego County. The rancho had persisted as an agricultural operation until the federal government purchased much of it in 1942 for the Marine Corps facility.

With its Pacific frontage for amphibious landings, rolling (and rugged) terrain for maneuvers and proximity to the Recruit Depot in San Diego, the location has been ideal for the Corps. Permanent installations have been erected; each of the the several encampments forms a "complete" unit. The old rancho "casa" (one-time home of Gov. Pio Pico) provides headquarters for the commandant.

Several thousand acres have been leased to truck farmers "temporarily" for many years. The land has been coveted for other uses including a nuclear electric plant and a public campground. It has been proposed that an international jet port, serving

**Figure 6-11.** Surfing at San Clemente. (dwl)

**Figure 6-12.** Garden at Mission San Juan Capistrano. The mission (excluding the chapel) was rebuilt after earthquake destruction early in the nineteenth century. (dwl)

San Diego and Orange counties, be established here.

Travelers on I-5 are impressed with the open landscapes which which provide vistas with 18 miles of ocean front. This "rural" stretch becomes more evident as competition for recreational and residential sites increases in North County.

In San Diego County the Camp is referred to as "our *Maginot Line*" because it provides a barrier from expanding metropolitan Los Angeles.

## Leisure Land

As a subregional playground North County is popular with residents of San Diego Country, the Colorado Desert, the Los Angeles Angeles Lowlands and out-of-state visitors.

Until the 1920's it remained a local vacation land; subsequent improvement of the Coast Highway and population growth in Southern California have created wider patronage.

## Beach Places

The coastal towns tend to be atypical California communities, dependent upon resort trade and commuter and retiree residence.

They have attracted senior citizens from "everywhere." They are not primarily commercial centers but some industrial (especially along Ca. 78 and near Palomar airport) and retail influx is occurring. Hotels and motels, shopping malls, trailer parks and retirement complexes and real estate offices are much evident.

Where the settlement is sufficiently old, lush subtropical landscaping prevails; eucalyptus, avo-

**Figure 6-13.** Laguna Beach is one of California's choice coastal places. Its beach has been much narrowed by erosion in recent decades. (dwl)

cado, ice plant, bougainvillea and geraniums help give an illusion of higher population density.

Coastal towns originated during four periods.

A few, founded in the Mexican period, such as San Luis Rey (now part of Oceanside), have not grown too much. Nearly all of the beach towns originated during the Boom of the 1880's or in the 1920's. Whereas the Mexicans restricted their hamlets to the stream valleys, more recent towns invariably have had terrace sites.

Some beach towns were resorts from the start; others were at least partially agricultural. Virtually all of these communities extend in shoestring fashion parallel to the seacoast. Older and more built-up sections are commonly located near Ca.1 or the railroad and within half a mile of the seashore. Newer residences, ascending inland slopes, are conspicuous near Interstate 5.

**Oceanside** (105,000), the ranking city of the coastal belt, was transformed from a resort and farm town into the primary service point for Camp Pendleton during World War II.

Resident multi-ethnic service personnel, their dependents, tradespeople and retirees gave Oceanside a social composition rather unique among North County cities. In the 1980s a "yuppie invasion" from southern Orange County modified the city. Over the past generation many changes have occurred and there has been aggressive redevelopment with expenditure of scores of millions of dollars.

The lengthy beach, once-renowned for fishing and surfing, had been severely eroded after construction of military and civilian harbors "up coast" (to

the north). Subsequently there has been shoreline reconstruction and the pier has been rebuilt. Downtown deterioration had likewise occurred. More recently a multi-media transportation terminal (Amtrak, buses and taxis) and a new civic center have been constructed. A multi-star hotel has been erected.

Tracts of "affordable" residences east of "older town" have been constructed. Occupants represent a recent population influx (many retirees) that is less military-connected. Well inland are Mira Costa College, a country club and hospital; their locations near Ca. 78 freeway are accessible to nearby Vista and Carlsbad as well.

**Carlsbad** (62,000) to the south has grown as a choice residential place and retail center.

Many higher-income dwellings are found on hillsides. Located here is La Costa, a prominent resort development.

Carlsbad is the locale of North County's first "full service" regional shopping center, supported by Oceanside and Vista as well.

South of the town center former flower fields contain homes, light industry and a travel-service complex along I-5.

The **San Dieguito District** contains a quintet of bluff-top communities between **Leucadia** and **Del Mar**.

**Solana Beach** (25,000) is the largest of these coalescing shore towns. Tourism, retirement, farming and commutation to nearby cities prevail.

Inland is **Rancho Santa Fe**, a classic "society ranch"-community. The Santa Fe Railroad planted three million eucalyptus trees, only to find other wood more suitable for rail ties. It then constructed Lake Hodges to provide a water supply and sold small parcels which became country properties of wealthy city dwellers, including some famed entertainers.

### Inland Towns

Interior North County has experienced population upsurge later than the coastal belt and townscapes are less contiguous. An urban landscape continues to replace productive farmlands.

A populace of "real" farmers and modest retirees from distant places is yielding to more affluent emigrees from metropolitan Southern California, including both senior citizens and commuters.

In the countryside golf courses, residential "ranchettes" and viewsite dwellings are noticeable. Once-compact towns are spreading laterally.

Conspicuous shopping and other services include an abundance of real estate offices.

**Escondido** (92,000), with its specialty shops, fruit-packing plants and several dozen mobile home parks, is the principal interior city.

Served by commuter express buses to San Diego via I-15 and possessing two regional shopping centers, it has become a virtual suburb.

Adjacent **Rancho Bernardo** is a "new town", largely within the limits of San Diego, whose downtown is 22 miles distant. Also on the periphery of Escondido are **San Marcos** (30,000), locale of Palomar College, and **San Pasqual**, chaotic site of the *Wild Animal Park* and a proposed site for the North County campus of San Diego State University.

**Vista** (53,000) sprawls "out of control" among hillside avocado groves. Adjacent **Fallbrook** (20 000) too, is surrounded by small-acreage avocado orchards. It houses personnel employed at Camp Pendleton and the affiliated Naval Ammunition Depot as well as commuters to Riverside County.

## THE BACK COUNTRY

*Definitely* mountainous, the Back Country occupies higher portions of the Peninsular Ranges. Landscapes here are often lonesome, with knobby slopes, steep and half-wooded. Sometimes these loftier portions of the San Diego Country penetrate west of I-15, within view of the San Diego metropolis. The small, scattered towns and farms afford conspicuous contrast with the populous lowlands near the Pacific, reminding visitors of the tranquil California of yesteryear. Further distinctions of this realm include pine-forested mountaintops, a number of man-made lakes,

**Figure 6-14.** Many hundreds of acres of avocado groves occupy hillsides near Fallbrook. (dwl)

and the Golden State's largest group of Native American reservations.

Despite the maze of slopes, the granitic knobs and the canyons paved roads have made the Back Country more accessible.

Interstate 8 and Interstate 15 are the most traveled of the through routes; these are San Diego's main avenues of access to Imperial Valley (and Arizona) and the eastern Los Angeles Lowlands respectively. Even on these main highways, however, occasional long grades remind the traveler that the Back Country is mostly rough terrain devoid of sizable interconnected lowlands.

### Indians, Retirees and Commuters

Residents of the Back Country do not constitute a representative cross section of Golden State population.

This area is not a center for Hispanic people (despite the above statement about pre-California landscapes). Most of its habitants are of north European ancestry. Besides ranchers and tradesfolk in the towns, there is an expanding number of retirees from all parts of the United States. Included in this latter group are many whose incomes are modest and for whom climatic mildness is both healthful and economic. Meanwhile increasing numbers of exurbanite commuters are moving upslope, especially around **Ramona** (16,000) and **Alpine** (9000).

Perhaps 2000 Indians and a score of reservations in the Back Country testify to California's pre-European heritage.

The reservations are usually alongside roads and small "American-style" cottages prevail. Unlike the Indian lands of the Southwest one does not find hogans and rug or pottery sellers. Bingo, operated by outsiders with local Indian employees, is a recently-added source of income, here as among various other California Indians.

**Pala**, with its restored *asistencia* chapel and the area immediately to the southeast forms the major focus of Indian population.

Elsewhere, reservations are widely scattered over the Back Country, southward to the Mexican border, on relatively unproductive lands. Many Indians reside apart from the reservations, closer to places of cash employment. Sutton (see bibliography) notes that reservation occupance has become increasingly social; he states that "it is not possible in the long run to enclave a people from their destiny in another man's civilization."

## A Fading Market Basket

The diversity of product from the "blurred" North County-Back Country fringeland is impressive—leading items (approximate order of value) are tomatoes, poultry and eggs, citrus, market milk, avocados, and cattle. Additional "this and that", which would almost fill a grocery list, include grains, grapes, hay, honey, apples, potted flowers and kiwi fruit.

Water is a more critical factor than topography.

The number of reservoirs in the Back Country reflects the importance of irrigation for nearly all major commodities. Additional water is pumped from floodplains such as along the San Luis Rey River.

Higher elevation and dispersed location of many basins and mesas make import of water physically difficult. Thus the San Diego Aqueduct, although it carries Colorado River water as far south as Otay Reservoir, is best used by the lower-lying and wealthier districts toward the coast.

*Tomatoes* constitute a more recent addition in a succession of "Cinderella" crops that have enraptured San Diego County farmers.

Recently they have provided the most valuable commodity. Tomatoes are grown almost exclusively for fresh use, and production extends through much of the year. At times the Back Country and adjacent North County form California's principal source. Cultivation is laborious; it generally entails placement of a protective cap over each young plant and erection of poles to support the maturing tomatoes. The rolling topography from Fallbrook toward the Pacific has been the tomato center.

The *avocado* (map 6-4), indigenous to Middle America, is one of the most sensitive "tropical" plants (others would include macadamia nuts and limes) grown in the Back Country; it is distinctive in the area.

The tree cannot tolerate frost, aridity, or high temperature, thus locales where it can be grown in the United States are restricted to southern Florida, Hawaii and more favored spots in Southern California. San Diego County, particularly the Back Country around Fallbrook, Vista, and Escondido, accounts for a definite majority of California output. Demand has increased with greater public acceptance and avocado acreage has increased phenomenally since production began around 1920.

Output is approaching demand; there has been a noticeable decrease in the number of new orchards in the past two decades. Ownership of an avocado ranch has had appeal comparable to that which an orange grove held for an earlier Southern California generation.

**Figure 6-15.** Escondido is the largest city in interior North County. (Palomar Pictures).

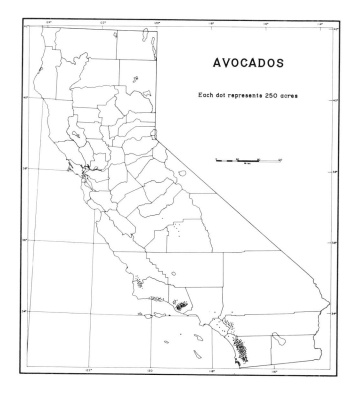

**Map 6-4.** Avocado production is limited primarily to the San Diego Country, the Oxnard Plain and the Santa Barbara Coast.

Relatively few can afford to become avocado growers. Land is unbelievably expensive in the select areas that are climatically suitable. The rancher needs sufficient capital for land preparation, nursery stock, and installation of a sprinkler or drip irrigation system, as well as subsistence during the non-bearing period after the orchard is planted!

*Citrus* was an earlier "glamour" crop of the Back Country. Valencia oranges and lemons occupy comparable acreage, usually on hillsides.

Navel oranges are more limited although orchards are expanding. Citrus and avocados, with broadly similar site needs, tend to coincide in areas of production. Their extent and value of output in the Back Country are comparable although, with respect to profit, avocados have been regarded with more enthusiasm for some decades. Thus avocado and citrus acreage shifts as subdivisions encroach upon some groves.

Milk, eggs, chickens and turkeys have been produced in response so the expanding metropolitan population of San Diego.

As additional land around San Diego is taken from cultivation Back Country foodstuffs should have greater consequence. Poultry farming tends to be especially widespread since initial costs for land and water are minimal.

Cattle ranching is the most widespread land use in the Back Country.

It is practiced on smoother uplands as well as in many unirrigated basins, often in conjunction with cultivation of winter grains.

There is a limited acreage of grassland in the Back Country. Pastures are nutritious only a few months each year. Supplemental feeding is based upon alfalfa imported from the Imperial Valley ("especially for dairy cattle in dry lots"). Consideration has been given to replacement of the widespread chaparral by substituting grasses. Some controlled burning has been effected. But because of limited rainfall most of the year and the threat of soil erosion during winter storms such a change has not been practical.

### Camping, Touring, hopefully Snowplay

Terrain and weather in the Back Country blend to provide a delightful countryside; many winding roads and diverse scenery beckon the urban dweller.

Landscapes vary with the season and the locale. The sycamore, cottonwood and oak turn golden in autumn; in winter greenness remains in the lower valleys while snow laces the higher country; spring brings flowering of the chaparral and hopefully, flowing streams; during summer the cooler higher forest country is sought after.

As the Southern California population increases, utilization of this hill-and-mountain land intensifies as a subregional playground.

The **Cleveland National Forest** contains many of the higher summits within the Back Country.

A score of improved campgrounds are maintained. On smaller private tracts numerous hamlets cater to vacationers or provide second homes for lowlanders from as far away as Los Angeles and Imperial Valley. Much of the brush-covered mountain area is closed to public use during the long fire-hazard season. Around Mt. Palomar attractions include the famed observatory and Agua Tibia Primitive Area.

The largest expanse of forest in the Back Country is found in the **Laguna Mountains**. Within easy access of San Diegans, this is the leading highland recreation area of the San Diego Country.

Snow is less common here than farther north in California. Yet this is the most likely locale afforded San Diegans to toss a snowball or possibly even ski crosscountry. Cuyamaca Lake (when it

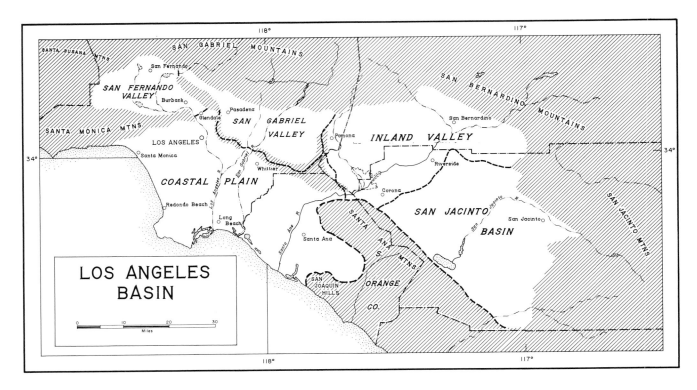

**Map 6-5.** The Los Angeles Basin (Lowlands) occupies the Los Angeles Coast Plain, the Santa Fernando Valley, San Gabriel Valley, the Inland Valley, the San Jacinto Basin. Orange County occupies the southeastern Coastal Plain and bordering uplands.

has sufficient water) and spectacular views of the Colorado Desert are among scenic attractions.

The village of **Julian** is the principal town. This one-time gold camp provides no pretense of boom growth. Its false-fronts suggest the "Old West" while white frame cottages are reminiscent of a New England hill town. Nearby, just enough apples and pears are grown to attract city folk during the spring blossoming and autumnal harvest.

Storage reservoirs in the Back Country are popular with anglers, especially since freshwater fishing spots are so limited in Southern California.

Low water level and restricted access are major handicaps but several of the lakes are widely patronized (two of the lakes are maintained with Colorado River water). Near Lake Henshaw is *Warner Springs,* a Back Country "institution", now privately visited on a "time-share" basis.

---

### THE LOS ANGELES BASIN (The Lowlands)

Heartland of Southern California and nerve center of an evolving megalopolis (San Diego to Santa Barbara), the Los Angeles Basin (Lowlands) has an areal extent of less than 3000 square miles, yet it contains over half of the population of California. Its several parts extend into both the Transverse Ranges and into the the Peninsular Ranges (map 6-5).

Groups of low hills and mountains subdivide the Lowlands into five distinct units: (1) the **Coastal Plain** (2) **San Fernando Valley** (3) **San Gabriel Valley** (4) **Inland Valley** and (5) **San Jacinto Basin**.

Each is physiographically independent, but all five are filled with alluvium that originated in the Transverse or Peninsular ranges. Surfaces are generally smooth, but inland margins of these lowlands have increasing slope.

The masses of rough country that separate the five lowlands rise from a hundred to several thousand feet.

The largest of these intervening uplands are the **Santa Monica**, **Santa Ana**, and **Verdugo** mountains. Each of the uplands creates an obstacle to travel and to conurbation; even some of them close to Los Angeles have remained conspicuously untouched by settlement. Collectively these hills help create climatic variations within the Lowlands and they form barriers to water runoff (both surface and underground).

The five Lowlands are interconnected with narrow low-level gaps.

Several appear to have resulted from rivers (antecedent) that were able to maintain their courses as intervening ridges were uplifted; others are fault-line depressions. **The Los Angeles-Glendale Narrows**, **Whittier Narrows**, and the **Santa Ana Canyon** constitute the major openings between the Coastal Plain and interior basins. These gaps have been utilized effectively for important highway and railroad routes; some are sites for flood-control dams and groundwater extraction as well.

The five Lowlands are described individually later in this chapter. However, the western three definitely lie within metropolitan Los Angeles, thus their geographic details are best understood if preceded by an account of the complex that has engulfed them.

## A SPRAWLING CONURBATION

Scoffed at in San Francisco, dismissed in Paris, envied in Moscow and joked about everywhere, Los Angeles is very much for real. Though people may call it "Smogville" and "50 suburbs looking for a city," Los Angeles appears destined to replace New York as the largest U.S. conurbation. It has been called the prototype twenty-first century metropolis and its more ardent boosters insist it will become the cultural center of the Americas, if not the world.

'Tis small wonder that Los Angeles is so difficult to comprehend. The *political city* alone spreads over 458 square miles to form the heart of the Lowlands.

It occupies much (but not all) of the western portion of the Coastal Plain and the San Fernando Valley. Within the city limits one can drive about 50 miles in a straight line southward from the base of the Ridge Route (Interstate 5) to San Pedro).

The *geographical city,* or *metropolis,* encompasses virtually all of the three western lowlands.

It includes scores of politically independent satellites, six of which exceed 100,000 inhabitants each. A few decades ago it could have been described as "All American." Now, with hundreds of socioeconomic neighborhoods, it is truly the ethnic core of a Pacific Basin state.

### Pueblo to Gargantua

Initially Los Angeles occupied the site of Yang-na, one of several Gabrielino Indian hamlets that were situated along the Los Angeles and San Gabriel rivers.

Founded in 1781, Los Angeles was the second of Alta California's three original Spanish pueblos. The townsite, encompassing 28 square miles, evolved around a central square (*approximately* the present-day plaza) and its limits had cardinal orientation.

The nucleus, typical of Spanish colonial towns, was a half mile west of the Los Angeles River.

It was on a terrace sufficiently high for protection from winter floods yet irrigable by means of a *zanja* (canal). The intake of the zanja was at the Los Angeles Narrows, where the river is confined by hills on the west and alluvium from Arroyo Seco on the east, thus easing diversion of irrigation water. River flow at this point was perennial (disappearing only in later years when the city began extracting water farther upriver).

In contrast to the site selected by the Spanish, an English or American community might instead have been situated at a place suitable for ocean commerce (as San Pedro, Santa Monica or Newport).

The location of Los Angeles, is not entirely propitious for the ranking metropolis of western United States but it does occupy the largest coastal lowland in California.

And it is insulated against the interior by the loftiest coastal mountains in the Golden State (which, however, are easily penetrated by such passes as **Cajon** and **San Gorgonio**).

But the city is away from the mid-point of the west coast and there is insufficient local water. Its "back country" is the sparsely populated Intermontane Region (Part One), not San Francisco's Central Valley hinterland.

An initial disadvantage was the absence of a good natural harbor. Distance from the industrial East was also a handicap. Originally the surrounding countryside was not productive and local mineral fuels long remained undeveloped.

### Before the Railroads Came

During the colonial periods Los Angeles did not flourish; by 1800 it had only 300 residents.

In the Mexican era, especially after mission secularization and establishment of ranchos nearby, it grew somewhat.

Los Angeles became the social and economic center of the Lowlands following the demise of Mission San Gabriel And until 1850 it was the single settlement of much substance in all Southern

California; the more prosperous rancheros established town houses in the village.

Rapid change was not prompted by American stewardship although the economy was stimulated by travel and such exports as wine and beef to Sierran gold camps.

The plaza remained the focal point although the residential district expanded upslope to the west. The flat-roofed adobe was still the typical structure and the earthen streets became quagmires during wintry rains. Orchards of apples, citrus, figs and peaches began to impart a suggestion of a "garden town." With division of ranchos a few outlying settlements appeared.

## Spasms of Growth

### The First Boom—and afterward—

The establishment of the Southern Pacific rail route into New Mexico and Texas, coupled with rising subregional prosperity and the start of winter tourism, helped inspire the *Boom of the Eighties* (the first boom).

Following establishment of a rail connection with northern California in 1876 significant growth commenced. But the land boom was triggered by opening a second direct transcontinental railroad (the Santa Fa) and a brief rail war in the mid-1880's.

Dominated by citrus, which benefited from eastern markets by rail, agriculture remained the leading economic mainstay into the twentieth century.

In the 1870's small farm communities had been founded on the inner Coastal Plain and in the San Gabriel and San Fernando valleys. As well drilling became commonplace, settlement was liberated from location near springs and perennial streams.

Some seaports and coastal resorts were also established but neither the outer Coastal Plain nor most of the San Fernando Valley was favored for settlement before the twentieth century.

By 1890 Los Angeles alone had a population of 50,000, but many localities suffered from poor drainage, excessive depth to water, inadequate transportation or climatic conditions unsuitable for citrus.

Los Angeles doubled in population during the 1890's.

Orange groves were expanded and a petroleum industry was developed. Before 1900 four oilfields were producing. They were located along the inner margin of the Coastal Plain (between Elysian Park and Santa Ana Canyon) and began to supplement

tourism and agriculture as mainstays of the Los Angeles economy. The first field, the *Los Angeles City Field* "came in" in 1892.

### Turn of the Century

As its population tripled during the *second boom* (1901-1914) Los Angeles became a small metropolis.

Rapid growth of the city and its environs occurred as agriculture, oil and tourism were further developed and the motion picture industry was established.

With confirmation of San Pedro (in 1899) as the principal seaport and completion of a third transcontinental rail link (now part of the Union Pacific), via Whittier Narrows in 1905, southeast Los Angeles, with its flat terrain and maze of rail lines, was assured status as the primary wholesale and industrial district.

On a small scale, manufacturing, mostly for local needs, was beginning, with food processing dominant. Distance prevented shipment east of ordinary consumer goods but also "protected" local industries from Eastern competition.

The downtown district expanded southward from the old plaza as its importance was magnified with extension of the Pacific Electric interurban network to outlying districts on the periphery of the Lowlands.

Affluent citizens sought the western fringes of Los Angeles, apart from commerce and industry. Centrally located Bunker Hill and Boyle Heights lost status as choice residential districts.

Completion of the *Los Angeles Aqueduct* from the eastern slopes of the Sierra Nevada (Ch. 3) in 1913 finally eliminated dependence of Los Angeles upon its own river.

A surplus water supply enabled the city to absorb many outlying districts whose supplies were inadequate. In the decades that followed aqueduct completion the area of the city quadrupled in extent through annexations.

The second boom ended with World War I and brief curtailment of the tourist trade.

The war briefly stimulated a few industries, such as steel fabrication and shipbuilding. Thus by 1920 Los Angeles, with a population of 580,000 had become the nation's tenth largest city.

### A Third Boom: Autos and Oil

During the 1920's Los Angeles experienced its third boom when the absolute population increase within the city limits established an all-time record.

**Figure 6-16.** Segment of the Burbank Studios (jointly operated by Warner Brothers and Columbia), one of six motion picture and television complexes in the southeastern sector of the San Fernando Valley (dwl).

By 1930, with a population of 1.23 million after a decade of major economic change, it was the nation's fifth city.

Yet Los Angeles began to have a lessening share of the metropolitan population as expanded automobile usage increased and political annexations decreased (this trend still continues). Petroleum and effects of the automobile especially sparked the growth.

Fifteen new oilfields were discovered in the Los Angeles Basin between 1917 and 1929. The newly-opened Panama Canal enabled petroleum export to the East Coast as nation-wide consumption mounted with automotive use. Considerable oil revenue was reinvested around Los Angeles; many landowners, producing companies and tool manufacturers considered their attachment to Southern California permanent.

Oil production in the 1920's shifted from the inner margin of the Coastal Plain to new fields along the *Newport-Inglewood Uplift* and along the *Santa Monica littoral.*

Major oil refineries were constructed on the Outer Plain between El Segundo and Wilmington (Fig.6-34), convenient locations for supply of crude oil and ocean export. At the time the abundance of space necessary for such sprawling facilities was available.

The oil fields themselves tended to repel residential construction yet adjacent communities which housed oil workers spiraled. Impressive petroleum office buildings were erected in downtown Los Angeles and ample local fuel was assured a coal-less, automobile-oriented society.

By this decade the population of Los Angeles was sufficiently large to stimulate new market-oriented industries.

Most notable were automobile assembly plants and rubber processsors, which developed rapidly during the 1920's. Already Los Angeles County led the nation in total number of autos in use, thus assuring a sizable market for cars and tires.

The cost of transporting such items from Eastern factories favored local production. For decades all of the nation's leading rubber tire and automobile manufacturers were represented in metropolitan Los Angeles. Most firms constructed plants in the primary industrial belt though decentralization of auto assembly occurred.

Aircraft and motion-picture production, which commenced early in the twentieth century, expanded considerably during the 1920's.

These two radically different industries paralleled each other in their "creative, foot-loose" nature, their timing and their westside location toward Santa Monica Bay. In the late 1920's and during the 1930's Hollywood used the glamorous airplane both as subject matter and personal avocation.

*Semi-Depression: The 1930's*

The metropolitan area gained over half a million new residents during the 1930's even though the growth of Los Angeles was slowed.

Expansion of the motion picture industry, which capitalized on newly introduced sound and color techniques, softened a bit the effects of nationwide depression. Between 1933 and 1937 employment in movie making increased by half.

Urbanization was particularly vigorous on the western Coastal Plain and in the southern San Fernando Valley (locations favored by the motion-picture industry). Radio broadcasting and recording gained recognition at this time as important Hollywood enterprises. It was logical, with the talent in drama, literature and music assembled by the motion-picture industry, that the district should have become a major program center when major radio (and later television) networks materialized.

Several other Los Angeles industries based partly upon uniqueness of design gained prominence before 1940.

In addition to apparel and furniture, these included ceramics, carpeting, playshoes and cosmetics; thus Los Angeles has become one of the world's foremost fashion centers.

Wearing apparel is the leading fashion industry.

Los Angeles is a leader in creation of playclothes and sportswear and ranks second nationally to New York in total garment output.

Attire created in Hollywood by costume designers for motion pictures exerted strong influence. There also was the increasing emphasis upon "styled in California" sportswear. Focal point of clothing manufacture became the downtown wholesale district with its building lofts although there has been less concentration than in New York's famed "garment district." Establishments have been scattered around the Lowlands — cheaper land and labor supply were often important site considerations.

Like garment making and radio broadcasting, furniture manufacture originated earlier but did not become a major "export" industry until the 1930's.

The Los Angeles Furniture Mart is visited by thousands of buyers. Initially the industry was based upon availability of low-wage Mexican craftsmen and imported wood. Distribution of furniture manufacturers is complex; many firms are located southeast of downtown Los Angeles in the primary wholesale-industrial district.

*Aerospace Era*

World War II triggered the fourth boom, which lasted until 1969.

It was marked by much industrial expansion, particularly in aircraft and allied activities.

After the war, population increase continued at an accelerated rate. By 1950 the political city had replaced Philadelphia as the nation's third city. By the end of the boom the metropolitan population exceeded that of metropolitan Chicago.

The boom witnessed the construction of vast housing tracts and suburban shopping centers on former agricultural lands. Construction of a freeway network managed to keep pace with increased vehicular flow (after a fashion). In a quarter of a century the number of automobiles in Los Angeles County increased five-fold, to reach five million.

A major contributor to the fourth boom was the growth of aerospace industries.

Evolution of aircraft manufacture was affected by early popularity of flying in Southern California (doubtless encouraged by superior flying weather). Glenn Martin built California's first airplane in Santa Ana in 1906 and Donald Douglas, who had been Martin's chief engineer, formed his own company in Santa Monica in 1920 while the Lock-heed organization had been founded even earlier in Santa Barbara.

The expansion of aircraft manufacture was aided by a nucleus of experienced personnel.

In fact, it depended upon residence of skilled designers, availability of financing and early start more than upon labor, market or raw materials (once this industry could be highly flexible in its site location).

As western terminus of commercial transcontinental air service in the late 1920's, Los Angeles was ideal for aircraft builders. Government military and airmail contracts provided major incentives.

With concentration of the aircraft industry in Southern California it became the major assembly center of the United States.

Plant maintenance costs, as opposed to "snowbelt" locations, could be reduced because the climate allowed year-round work outdoors. Also, the military expansion during World War II was facilitated by availability of land in proximity to parts manufacturers and labor supply.

The larger plants were situated apart from the primary industrial belt; many were originally on the urban fringe where ample airport space was available.

Los Angeles International Airport became the chief focus; other major facilities were located around airports in Burbank, Santa Monica, Hawthorne, Downey and Long Beach. Lesser assembly plants and parts makers have been scattered widely through the metropolis.

Aerospace concerns attempted to convert or diversify in the postwar years.

Newer products included radios, television sets, industrial controls and X-ray apparatus. Largely however the industry has depended upon defense contracts (thus, like aircraft, it has been vulnerable to defense changes).

There has been an evolution of research and development, as well as to smaller-scale manufacturing. Thus aerospace-electronics installations have spread widely across the metropolitan area.

They have occupied spacious "campus-style" plants whose quiet, airportless nature has permitted much freedom in location—communities have eagerly sought their tax revenues and educated and skilled personnel.

Once short of scientists, planners and other professional personnel, the industry sought location near attractive residential sectors as well as open space. Orange County, ignored by the airplane manufacturers, became particularly favored. There was lesser focus upon the San Fernando and San Gabriel valleys.

Population growth during the fourth boom ("aerospace era") warranted a multitude of service industries.

The "local" metropolitan market has permitted the manufacture of everything from adzes to zithers on a scale that increasingly made Los Angeles products competitive in distant locales.

Many non-manufacturing activities, including entertainment and professional services (such as engineering and medical) also enjoyed patronage from distant populations.

Thus the economy of Los Angeles was widened and the population boosted.

Conversely such long-established, resource-oriented industries as citrus-packing, petroleum refining, and fish canning became less important as the economy matured. Subsequently, since 1970, in common with the eastern "rust belt", such industries as steel, rubber and auto assembly largely vanished. Only the influx of low-wage illegal immigrants kept the garment industry alive.

*A Brief Interlude*

As the fourth boom ended it seemed that metropolitan Los Angeles might be entering a period of stagnation. The problems that growth had fostered had made the area less attractive for migrants. Jobs lessened with the slowdown at the end of the Viet Nam era.

*The Trans-Pacific Boom*

Towards the end of the 1970's it became apparent that another spurt of population growth was occurring in metropolitan Los Angeles.

The new migrants were not Anglos from "back east" but non-Americans, seeking refuge from economic, social and political problems in Latin America and Asia.

"Almost overnight," the political city of Los Angeles was no longer "all-American" but rather, an Anglo-minority city. Anglos sought new locales on the metropolitan periphery as the area acquired districts like Little Seoul and Little Saigon.

Much economic energy for this boom came from the huge national defense build-up. Other contributions came from the migrants themselves as well as foreign-based investors.

Nowhere else in America was the impact greater than in metropolitan Los Angeles.

**A More Worldly Metropolis**

Until the past several decades, metropolitan Los Angeles had the image of an "All-American City," despite a sizable Hispanic and Japanese population. Subsequently a large influx of Asians (Chinese, Vietnamese, Filipinos and others) and Hispanics (not only from Mexico but from Central America and South America as well) has prompted the appellation of "America's new Ellis Island." Some ethnic groups have established themselves in definite "pockets" while others are more widely scattered. This influx includes a large but indeterminate number of illegal entrants.

**Contemporary Urban Patterns**

Metropolitan Los Angeles sprawls ever more widely, confusing the visitor if not the local resident!

Its population exceeds thirteen million and appears to be overtaking greater New York.

There are more than 19,000 factories and 840,000 industrial workers. While the large establishment (electronics plant or oil refinery) is conspicuous on the landscape, the thousands of small factories are less easily discernable.

The primary industrial belt extends southeastward from the downtown fringe to Pico-Rivera, with extensions along rail lines into San Fernando and San Gabriel valleys, Orange County and to the Harbor.

Scattered locations of aircraft factories, electronics plants, motion picture studios and oil refineries partly reflects the availability of land at the time of construction.

The Coastal Plain, the San Fernando and the San Gabriel valleys and appreciable portions of the Inland Valley have been filled by urbanization.

The contiguous built-up metropolis extends more than 20 miles from downtown Los Angeles wherever level land has allowed.

Industrial dispersion and freeway development (almost wholly since 1950) have facilitated and seemingly accelerated centrifugal movement. Along the Ventura, San Bernardino, Santa Ana and Golden State freeways the urban fringe now lies more than 40 miles from the Central District.

The metropolitan area continues to reach outward.

At the base of the San Gabriel Mountains, where slopes and federal land ownership have been unyielding, metropolitan Los Angeles has nearly attained its physical limits.

Along 30 of 50 miles of Pacific shore to the southwest it has contiguity. Hence greatest expansion is now directed to the northwest-southeast corridor between the ocean and mountain barriers. Recent urbanization has focused on eastern Ventura and southern Orange counties and in the Inland Valley.

In 1910 the "political city" of Los Angeles contained almost 60 per cent of the metropolitan residents. Now, with nearly three million inhabitants, it has only 30 per cent; outlying areas have filled rapidly.

After Colorado River water became available through the Metropolitan Water District, surrounding cities were no longer forced to merge into Los Angeles to obtain water. The last last major merger into the city occurred half a century ago.

Thus the metropolis has marked municipal fragmentation. Except on distant travels, residents of scores of independent satellites do not look upon themselves as Angelenos and many resent being so labeled.

Several communities in both counties have incorporated to preserve special functions, such as high-quality residence and industry.

Rising land values coupled with population growth have encouraged a vertical aspect to the metropolis.

While the downtown skyline has changed dramatically, tall office and residential buildings have appeared in many satellite centers as well.

To meet the needs of young working couples as well as elderly people, apartment construction accelerated. These units are mostly two-story and often frame an outdoor courtyard swimming pool. They tend to be especially common in older neighborhoods formerly occupied by single-family dwellings as well as outlying districts where there is freeway access.

But two-story townhouses and high-rise condominiums have become commonplace also, apparently engendered as much by social preference as by land costs.

Sizable tracts of semirural land persist within the metropolitan complex.

These include the aforementioned uplands, oilfields and surfaces reserved for flood control. "Dead land" is still apparent, especially in potential industrial zones. Some of it finds temporary use for intensive truck farming, as do flood control lands and the rights-of-way for power transmission lines.

## An Expanding Cultural Center

Los Angeles is beginning to challenge New York as *the* American cultural center.

While urban dispersal and rapid expansion have somewhat limited cohesion, there is evidence that Los Angeles is gaining inclusion with New York, London and Paris in cultural centripetency.

Its "major league" status in sports is widely recognized. The metropolis warrants more recognition in architecture, art, engineering, literature, medicine and music than it has sometimes gotten.

For over a half century its theatrical arts, including motion pictures, radio and television, have much influenced American (and worldwide) customs, tastes and mores. An influx of educated and cultured individuals continues, attracted by the opportunities in this spiraling money market. Their cultural tastes tend to be obscured by the fascination with casual living the climate permits.

Los Angeles and its Lowlands have acquired widespread educational recognition.

The University of California maintains three campuses and the California State University system has seven. There are more than half a dozen private colleges and universities, including the University of Southern California and the internationally-known California Institute of Technology. Creation of impressive art galleries and theatres has reflected determined leadership and a civic spirit once deemed impoverished and hopelessly decentralized.

## Problems: Both Physical and Cultural

All conurbations have problems—those of Los Angeles have been compounded by the rapid, rambling and disorganized growth of its metropolis.

*Air pollution,* a major problem for half a century, has evoked world-wide interest, partly because it is developing elsewhere.

While Los Angeles is still regarded as the world's "smog capital" higher maximum readings of certain individual pollutants occur in Mexico City, New York, Tokyo and elsewhere.

Although weather is a cherished Southern California asset, the area becomes inherently smog-prone when sufficient industrial, automotive and domestic gases are present. Sunshine reacts with these gases to create complex chemicals and a "dirty yellow haze."

Pollutants in the Los Angeles Basin accumulate as result of the interior mountain wall, an "inversion layer" in the settling marine air from the Hawaiian High and the inland movement of sea breezes.

Controls are exerted over smoke emission from factories although electric generating plants may not have access to sufficient low-sulfur oil indefinitely. The automotive exhaust, a major source of pollutants is now rigidly controlled—one possible solution may be to require electric cars. Obviously this would not be a short-time solution!

Los Angeles has been more fortunate than some of its urban neighbors in obtaining a *water supply*. And it is less flood or water pollution prone than many American metropolises.

Yet delivery systems are expensive and the specter of water famine seems ever-imminent; because of this circumstance inhabitants have endeavored to provide themselves with a steadier supply.

Despite many dams, levees and storm drains constructed since the "great flood of 1938", storm runoff has posed difficulties in low-lying locales. Long-range programs in several counties have attempted to minimize this problem.

Rapid growth has placed heavy loads upon the sewage system despite the proximity of the ocean (sewage must be treated to avert beach contamination). Conveniences such as garbage-disposal units and automatic washers discharge additional water per family; attempts have been made to reclaim waste.

Hazardous waste disposal is still unresolved while solid-waste landfills pose problems. Despite smog, additional incineration developments have occurred.

Metropolitan Los Angeles suffers from inadequate public transportation.

This is an unfortunate development, since for the first half of the twentieth century the *Pacific Electric* interurban system was one of the world's best. Relatively low population density, dependence upon the private automobile (in part because of absence of common destination and strong personal preference have discouraged use of public buses). Still, patronage is increasing as a consequence of subsidized fares and rising costs of auto travel.

An extensive freeway network no longer eases vehicular movement, especially during rush hours; there are just too many million cars (map 6-7, Fig. 6-18).

Belatedly, by many years, construction finally commenced on a rapid transit rail system (i.e., light-rail from downtown Los Angeles to Long Beach and the subway westward from central Los Angeles) despite its disapproval by voters and by the federal government.

Urban blight occurred more rapidly in Los Angeles than in many metropolitan areas.

Housing decay rapidly extended out from central Los Angeles. Submarginal neighborhoods tend to differ physically from those in eastern cities; the "slums" often consist of single frame houses on 30- to 50–foot lots rather than the usual tightly-packed multi-story brick tenements. With better upkeep and more attractive landscaping many of these dwellings would still be appealing. Although some older houses are being replaced by multi-family apartments or non-residential land use, peripheral blighting continues. Fears that many thousands of the hastily-constructed tract dwellings built after World War II would become slums are so far unfounded.

In the past several decades Los Angeles and San Francisco have become two of the more crime-ridden cities in America.

Poverty, unemployment (and idle time), drugs and broken families are among major causes. Scores of juvenile gangs roam parts of the metropolis. Muggings and rape have increased. Particularly dangerous areas have included Compton and Watts, the county strip between Carson and Torrance and Lafayette Park, a center for many convicts released from Cuban jails.

There are a number of other problems as well.

These include the high costs of housing and health, wildfire hazards, loss of beaches, destruction of older homes and buildings that should have been saved, the earthquake hazard (and the necessity of evicting thousands of residents to mitigate it), overcrowded airspaces, shortages of elementary schools and teachers, immigrant acculturation (including family breakups as the "new" generation becomes Americanized), overdependence on a military-based economy, care services for the elderly and the children of single parents, the homeless and many others.

As in any metropolitan area there are problems of social anger and the social pressure resultant from millions of people.

Some, of course, do not seem troubled by the hordes of people but others find it difficult. It is hard to find quiet. And the metropolis is infamous for blatant advertising (such as billboards).

## THE LOS ANGELES COASTAL PLAIN *

Most intensively utilized of the five Lowlands, the Los Angeles Coastal Plain (map 6-5) is the heart of the Los Angeles Basin.

During the Spanish colonial era, however, the San Gabriel Valley with its mission had this role. Subsequently the degree to which the Coastal Plain has been urbanized is impressive. One senses, from a promontory in the Santa Monica Mountains, that the metropolis encompasses the entire surface.

Sizable portions of Los Angeles and Orange counties lie within the Coastal Plain.

Along its inner margin it is bounded by the *Santa Monica Mountains, San Rafael Hills, Montebello Hills, Puente Hills, Santa Ana Mountains,* and *San Joaquin Hills.* It fronts along the sea from *Malibu* to *Newport Bay,* with miles of sandy beaches interrupted only by the Palos Verdes Hills and the Harbor Area.

Sedimentary rocks underlie the Plain to a depth of 20,000 feet beneath the extensive alluvial cover; deeper still are old hard rock blocks.

Faulting of these blocks has been responsible for rippling of the sediments to form the anticlinal *Newport-Inglewood Uplift* with its line of low hills and domes.

*The Palos Verdes Hills,* one-time island that now forms the southwestern edge of the Plain, has been uplifted, faulted and folded. It ascends to 1500 feet with marine terraces and cliffs along its seaward side.

The southern half of the city of Los Angeles and a score of municipalities of more than 50,000 each lie on the Coastal Plain.

It is crisscrossed by a network of rectangular streets; many streets have cardinal orientation to section lines, whereas others were laid out irregularly according to old rancho boundaries or local topography.

---

* This section has been reviewed by Roderick McKenzie, University of Southern California.

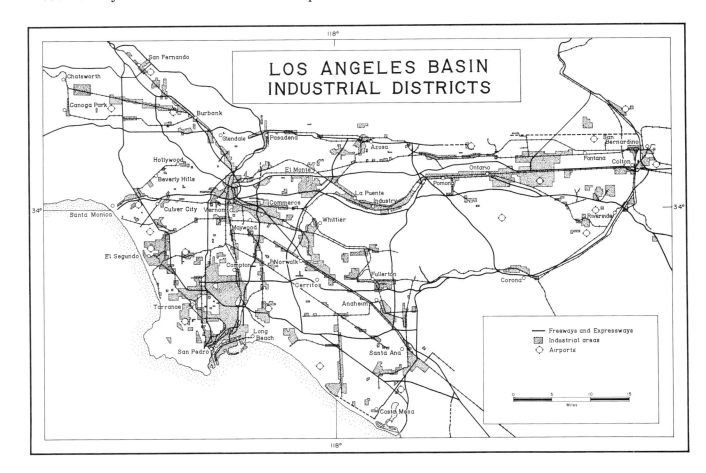

**Map 6-6.** Industrial areas in the Los Angeles Lowlands are commonly located along rail lines, around airports, and at the Los Angeles-Long Beach Harbors. Electronics firms tend to be located where there was still space after 1950.

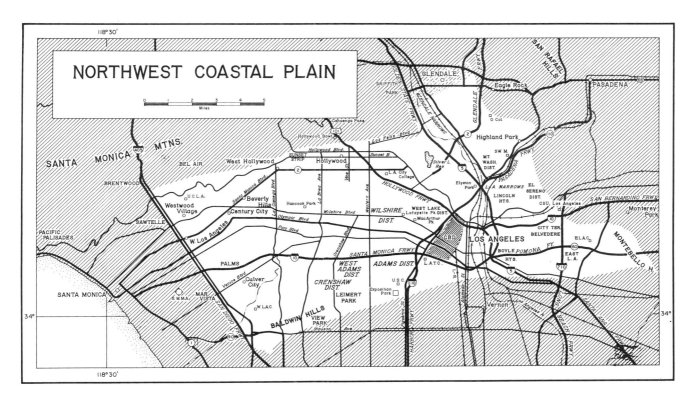

**Map 6-7.** The Northwest Coastal Plain, between downtown Los Angeles and Santa Monica, has some of the most elaborate land use in the American West. Much of it is within the political limits of Los Angeles.

**Figure 6-17.** The Los Angeles Civic Center, viewed from Union Station. City Hall (to left), Federal Building (center) and the Hall of Justice (right) are seen. This is the locale of colonial Los Angeles. (Los Angeles Chamber of Commerce)

**Figure 6-18.** Downtown Los Angeles, the northwestern edge, viewed to southeast. At The Interchange, four freeways (Pasadena, Harbor, Hollywood and Santa Ana) converge. On left margin is western fringe of Los Angeles Civic Center. In upper middle of view, use of Bunker Hill has changed markedly since this photo taken (Caltrans).

Selected arteries that radiate from central Los Angeles follow old Indian paths, colonial oxcart trails or former lines of the Pacific Electric interurban. Many older thoroughfares are lined for miles with miscellaneous retail shops. Such "string streets" along with the newer suburban shopping centers and miles of housing tracts, reflect the influence of the automobile (street cars and interurban lines were discontinued in the 1960's).

Generally urban skylines remain low (despite high-rise clusters); across the Plain trees (frequently rows of palms) vie with buildings for the visitor's attention. Oil fields add a distinctive touch to the scene along the inner and coastal edges of the Plain. Agricultural tracts, much decimated, remain in Orange County.

Urbanization and level terrain give the Plain superficial uniformity.

Its many localities, with their differences in natural setting, age of occupance, and economic evolution, create a bewildering mosaic.

For a better perspective, the Coastal Plain has been divided into these parts: the **Northwest** (which includes central Los Angeles), the **Outer Plain**, the **Central Plain**, and the **Southeast** (Orange County).

## THE NORTHWEST

With the possible exception of the city of San Francisco, the Northwest section of the Coastal Plain contains the greatest cultural complexity in western North America.

There are scores of neighborhoods, with wealth and poverty, mansions and shanties and some of the newest and some of the oldest dwellings in California; it also includes central Los Angeles.

## Downtown
## (the Central Business District)

The site of the Spanish pueblo is now downtown Los Angeles, near the emergence of the Los Angeles River upon the coastal plain.

Its street grid has northeast-southwest alignment (an orientation related to terrain and colonial flow of irrigation water). Its older portions (east of Main Street) display the imperfectly rectangular blocks laid out before 1848.

Several vestiges of the original community remain.

These include the much-altered *Plaza* with a tiny park with adjacent Olvera Street and other nearby structures "restored" as tourist attractions. "Old" *Chinatown* too has largely disappeared, as has the early Mexican settlement *(Sonora Town)*.

Business blocks of the nineteenth century have been replaced by the *Civic Center*.

Its buildings, mostly of contemporary design, are flanked by multiacre parking lots (Fig. 6-17). The Civic Center has encroached westward upon Bunker Hill, once occupied by the city's wealthier residents. The Center now contains the Los Angeles Music Center. Farther south on the Hill are office towers and the recently-opened *Museum of Con-*

**Figure 6-19.** Downtown Los Angeles. View to northeast with Santa Monica Freeway in foreground. (dwl)

*temporary Art,* parking structures and multi-story apartments for higher income come residents and senior citizens (*Angelus Plaza).*

Meanwhile **Little Tokyo** *t*o the east has experienced expansion.

While its significance as a Japanese center has become somewhat symbolic (since the Japanese have scattered across the Lowlands) it provides shopping, worship and senior housing. With its multistar hotel it provides a meeting place for visiting Japanese business people as well as a tourist attraction.

Downtown (C.B.D.) has migrated, first southward along Broadway and then in the 1920's westward, focusing on Seventh Street.

Originally its pivotal point was the Plaza. Presently most skyscrapers are located within a 20-block area bounded by the Harbor Freeway, Grand Avenue, and Third and Eighth streets.

Small for the area of Los Angeles and its metropolitan population, Downtown contains scarcely 200 city blocks.

Los Angeles is so completely the product of the automobile that rapid vehicular traffic has al-

lowed much dispersal of urban functions in divers parts of the Basin. The nightlife of midtown Manhattan or Chicago's Loop is largely absent in the city center. Many Angelenos never go downtown to shop—they make their purchases, eat, are entertained and attend to administrative matters in their own parts of the megalopolis.

In recent decades the skyline has acquired the third dimension characteristic of large Occidental cities yet a feeling of spaciousness remains.

Previously a 150-foot limitation had prevailed for many decades. This restriction, coupled with parking lots (which have covered half of the space) tended to give the district an openness absent in many larger cities. Downtown is ringed by four freeways which provide good vistas of the area. A big issue has been the "recycling" of older office buildings —some have been converted to residential use. Examples of commendable restoration should include the Bradbury, Oviat, Eastern Columbia, Barker Brothers and Bullock's buildings.

The functions of Downtown seem less diversified than those of some central districts.

Increasingly C.B.D. has become a daytime work

**6-20.** Seventh and Broadway during 5 p.m. rush hour. This is the principal Hispanic shopping district of the metropolis. (dwl)

**6-22.** The Japanese community of Little Tokyo, with city hall and the New Otani Hotel in the background. (dwl)

**6-21.** Seventh and Grand at noon. This is the heart of the white-collar office district. (dwl)

**6-23.** Downtown Los Angeles is expanding west of the Harbor Freeway. View northeast from Sixth St. (dwl)

place, with corporate offices and financial institutions. Gargantuan legal and accounting firms occupy many floors in the high-rise structures. Although there are a few multi-star hotels (some relatively new), the number of quality restaurants tends to be limited. Headquarters of large petroleum corporations and major public utilities are found here.

Essentially Downtown has become a bipolar-bilingual area.

The older eastern portion, devoid of the new high-rises, is essentially Hispanic. So complete is the Latin influence that one almost feels there should be window signs "English is spoken here." On its western edge, centered on Hill Street, Asian immigrants have made the C.B.D. an important wholesale and retail jewelry center. The grand old theatres on Broadway now show Latin pictures. Another vestige of the past is the Grand Central Market.

The western portion, reduced in size (due to land taken for the Harbor Freeway) is essentially Anglo, with the luxury hotels, quality shops, relocated department stores and corporate offices. Although financial services are important, there has been much relocation westward. especially along Wilshire Boulevard and even away from central Los Angeles.

Downtown, and its periphery, retains residential importance, especially with older, cheaper hotels, apartments and other multiple housing units.

Latinos pack all available spaces—aged hotels are no longer torn down. Thus population is probably increasing. "Skid row" remains conspicuous and in the late 1980's the homeless too have received much publicity.

*New Chinatown,* on the northern fringe of the Central District, affords a focal point for the Chinese community (approximately 170,000) and is strongly tourist-oriented.

## The East Side

The East Side is crisscrossed by freeways (including I-5 and I-10), as well as main rail lines. Hence large numbers of people drive across the East Side daily. Lying to the east of Downtown,it is bisected too by the Los Angeles River. Complex, both topographically and in socioeconomic aspects, the East Side is generally unknown except to its residents and those whose occupations take them there.

This is an area of small plains, terraces and valleys, backed by a broad belt of low hills that separates the Coast Plain from the San Gabriel Valley. Several railroads have their classification yards here and along the rail lines are warehouses and factories. Here has been the eastern extension of the principal (north-south) industrial belt of the Lowlands. The many factories, of small to medium size, in the past produced diversified goods (such as flour, beer, pottery, machinery and furniture), often for local markets. But in recent decades manufacturing has lessened.

In days bygone some of the prestigious neighborhoods of Los Angeles were here; now there is considerable lower-income housing and a large ethnic population.

Proximity to industry favored rather early evolution into workers' neighborhoods, especially *Lincoln Heights, Boyle Heights* and East Los Angeles.

The greatest concentration of Mexicans in California centers on the East Side, with **East Los Angeles** (unincorporated; 105,000) as its core.

Despite the nodal position of "East L.A.". Lincoln Park's *Plaza de Raza* is the cultural center and Boyle Height's *Mercado* and Broadway (downtown) the shopping centers and the Plaza Church and St.Vibianes the *religious* centers.

East L.A., with a strip commercial sector extending some distance along Whittier Boulevard, is to some suggestive of an Americanized Tijuana. "Everyone" seems to speak Spanish although bilingualism prevails among the commercial signs.

Only Mexico City contains more Mexicans than metropolitan Los Angeles. Statewide, Hispanics represent the fastest-growing ethnic group. Though less segregated than some ethnic groups, the Mexicans are the largest underprivileged assemblage in California. Although centered on the East Side, with a numerical majority through a ten-square mile belt, the Mexicans (and other Hispanics) are conspicuous not only in a zone extending from Glendale through El Monte into Orange County but elsewhere in the metropolis (including the principal black sector)and around the state. As will be noted later, there has been a recent Hispanic increase on the Central Plain.

The Hispanic population tends to be youthful, with large families and strong commitment to industrial and service jobs where they are well-regarded as workers.

Increasingly Hispanics have entered white-collar and professional fields but many (especially more recent arrivals) are hampered by inadequate command of English and too little formal education.

Many Hispanics are second or third generation Angelenos, although recent migration from "south of the border"is large.*

Central location in the metropolis coupled with early settlement led to establishment of such community institutions as cemeteries, detention homes, hospitals and schools.

Higher education is well represented here, as evidenced by California State University, Los Angeles, Occidental College, and East Los Angeles College. CSU, Los Angeles was located on its present small site, necessitating high-rise structures, after much dispute over its location. Here too is the vast County-U.S.C. Medical Center. Also located in this area are Southwest Museum and Heritage Square with its preserved homes.

## Southwestern Los Angeles

Southwest of Downtown is an extensive area south of the Santa Monica Freeway and west of the Harbor Freeway (Map, 6-7) that reaches westward into the Baldwin Hills.

Located here are several locales that earlier in the 20th century were among the most fashionable in Los Angeles (*especially* the Adams District).

The Southwest has an important cultural concentration that includes the University of Southern California, Shrine Auditorium, Exposition Park and Clark Library.

Belatedly the University, oldest and largest private institution in the subregion, discovered its campus was too small— it has been enlarged by destruction of surrounding residential blocks. Between the University and nearby Downtown are several prominent churches, hospitals and other institutions including Los Angeles Trade Technical College.

Exposition Park contains the Coliseum, site of two Olympic Games, college and professional football and other sports, the Sports Arena as well as the County Museum and the State Exposition Building.

Despite its many institutions the Southwest deteriorated "years ago" especially the West Adams District, into which blacks expanded after the 1950's.

Some of the shabbier housing within the city of Los Angeles is found here, where the Anglos abandoned their aging neighborhoods. There are higher crime pockets (drugs and robbery). Besides blacks, the Southwest houses lower-income groups including Hispanics and such Asians as Thais, Cambodians, Vietnamese, Malaysians and others.

In recent decades more affluent blacks have expanded westward into the Baldwin Hills. Near the Southwest there are middle-income blacks in Inglewood and more recently, in Culver City.

## The West Side

An intricate, wholly-urbanized landscape exists between Downtown Los Angeles and Santa Monica. Besides political segments of Los Angeles it includes the independent communities of Culver City, West Hollywood and Beverly Hills. Primarily residential there is heavy commutation from the Westside to Downtown and elsewhere. Along the southern base of the Santa Monica Mountains, from the Los Angeles River to the Pacific, is a higher income belt with many high-rise apartments and condominiums.

Hospitals, entertainment places, country clubs and quality hotels and specialty shops north of Santa Monica Freeway reflect the presence here of a sizable affluent populace.

On the eastern fringe, near Downtown, there is a higher population density and housing deterioration. This area has become increasingly ethnic, especially Filipino and Korean.

In the past Filipinos in California tended to be single men. Recent arrivals tend to be younger families; there are many illegal entrants...and many professional people. The Filipino community is centered west of Downtown near the several hospitals which provide a major source of employment. Salvadorans and Guatemalans are also found here.

A long-established Korean populace has resided west of the University of Southern California.

In recent decades it has been augmented by a new wave which has created *Koreatown* between Hollywood and the Filipino/Salvadoran/Guatemalan area. During the 1970's the Korean community was much expanded and infusion of overseas capital led to a major commercial and cultural district centered near Western and Olympic boulevards. The Korean sector has extended westward along Olympic.

To the world the ***Hollywood District*** has long been a synonym for motion pictures. But the real Hollywood today is much different, with a variety of supportive functions.

---

* Lamentably there is too little inter-communication between Hispanics and Anglos. An expanding literature deals with Spanish-speaking frustrations. For example, see Ch.10, "The Mexican Factor", pp. 245-272 in P.Wiley and R. Gottlieb, *Empires in the Sun*, and novels by R.Vasquez, *Chicano* and J. Michener, *Texas*, Ch. 14, pp. 993-1096.

**Figure 6-24.** East Los Angeles meat market in the heart of the barrio. (dwl)

**Figure 6-25.** The Hollywood District with Hollywood Hills, a segment of the Santa Monica Mountains (middle) and San Gabriel Mountains (skyline, rear). Wilshire Boulevard crosses photo in the foreground. (Hollywood Chamber of Commerce)

Although some miles of older residential neighborhoods separate Hollywood from Downtown, it is easily reached by the Hollywood Freeway, one of the world's most-traveled arteries.

Functions of present-day Hollywood include entertainment, tourism, retail trade, higher education and residence (Fig.6-25).

The District remains a tourist mecca—still the first spot in the Lowlands visited by some strangers. Retail trade, especially along the "old" Hollywood Boulevard core, has suffered of late.

Hollywood, as a residential area, has become poorer, more densely populated and more ethnic.

Some areas are not considered "safe." And in stores more clerks seem to be Central American than Anglo. In part because of employment in motion pictures, there has long been a Jewish populace. Possibly no other portion of California has a "richer" intermix of peoples, including Mandarin Chinese, Vietnamese, Bulgarian, Russian, Armenian, Palestinian, and Thai. Residential density is higher than the metropolitan average with many small courts, multiplexes and high-rise complexes as well as standard two-story apartment houses.

The *motion picture* industry has had a long and varied history in Hollywood.

Initially, independent studios sought refuge in Los Angeles from law suits instigated by the Edison-organized "trust" in the East. After the advantages of landscape and climate in Southern California became apparent, the initial firm, Selig, moved to Edendale (northwest of downtown Los Angeles) in 1909. Movie-making soon shifted westward into more spacious Hollywood, which became the focal point of casting offices and allied activities.

Hollywood, a temperance center in the 1880's and a pleasant orange-grove town, acquired its first studio in 1911. Water shortage had cost the community its political independence the previous year. By the 1920's this District was the center of a billion-dollar industry, whose "stars" were world known. Much production now occurs elsewhere but the district remains the headquarters for one major studio and smaller firms which make advertising, religious and specialty films. There are also many associated activities (casting offices and photographic equipment) and cosmetics, costume and lingerie houses.

The motion picture industry spawned radio programs and later television, in part a testimony to the reluctance of local talent accumulation to relocate in New York.

Traditionally Hollywood has been a "good address" for divorce lawyers, psychiatrists, beauty specialists and travel agents.

It has been assailed as the prostitution and pornographic capital of America. Although Hollywood Boulevard became seedy and tawdry, considerable money was being spent in the late 1980's for rehabilitation—appreciable renewal has occurred.

Many tourists (and others) often overlook other significance of Hollywood.

On its eastern margin is Los Angeles City College, which was long the nation's largest community college. Its small campus was the ancestral site of U.C.L.A. (which began as Los Angeles Normal School). Within the Santa Monica Mountains are the Ford Theatre, Hollywood Bowl and *Griffith Park,* one of the nation's largest in-limits reserves,

**Figure 6-26.** Quadrangle, Los Angeles City College. This was the ancestral home of U.C.L.A., initially called Los Angeles Normal School. (dwl)

with its planetarium, Greek Theatre, the Los Angeles Zoo, and other facilities (soon to be included is the Gene Autry Western Heritage Museum).

***West Hollywood*** (38,000) was finally incorporated as a city in the 1980's by elderly "straight" tenants (who wanted rent control) and homosexuals.

"Hints" remain of the "glory years" along the Sunset Strip before the rise of Las Vegas as the night life capital of Los Angeles and western America.

Now the Pacific Design Center, fittingly nicknamed the "blue whale" and serving the decorating and furnishings industry, is the landmark of West Hollywood. On the southern border of the city is the *Cedars-Sinai* medical complex

The western portion of the West Side has been the focus of one of Southern California's vital ethnic clusters, the nation's *second-largest* Jewish community.

There are, of course, many Jews elsewhere, as in Beverly Hills and Tarzana. But it was here that extensive settlement occurred in the 1930's, concurrent with emigration from Europe and expansion in the film industry, affording divers employment for newcomers. Now many residents are elderly. Multiple residences, including many small apartments, are much evident. One observes synogogues and temples, a major Jewish community center, hospital and specialty shops.

The population of the West Side overall approximates county means in such traits as incomes and educational attainment.

But ages tend to be higher and family units smaller. From Hollywood westward there is a progressive increase in wealth.

The West Side has a myriad of tourist and cultural attractions, including art galleries, smart bou-

tiques, restaurants and nightclubs.

South of Hollywood, the ***Wilshire Corridor*** focuses upon Wilshire Boulevard, along which it has long been proposed to run a rapid transit route.* This fabulous multi-lane street, extending from Downtown through Beverly Hills and Santa Monica to the Pacific, is a counterpart of the Champs Elysees in Paris or Michigan Boulevard in Chicago.

Wilshire, younger than some of the world's great boulevards, is given a tropical look by files of palms. Construction, on-going for many years, has created a file of skyscrapers visible from a distance.

The Corridor provides a series of fashionable residential locales, clusters of high-rise office buildings, large churches, expensive apartment and condominium towers and several shopping centers.

Near its eastern end (in the C.B.D) Wilshire crosses locales with low to medium income. It bisects MacArthur Park, an apartment-house neighborhood with many aged poor and increasing numbers of recent ethnic arrivals, including Cubans. Business blocks include offices of many physicians and some fraternal offices. Farther west have long existed some of the smarter department stores and specialty shops in the nation, as well as several first-class hotels. There are also older prestige mansion neighborhoods like *Fremont Place, Hancock Park* and *the Wilshire Country Club* area.

Site of dramatic post-World War II growth, the *Miracle Mile* was one of the nation's early shopping centers with sizable off-street parking lots. On its western edge, Wilshire passes the converted **La Brea tar pits**, where Los Angeles has created Hancock Park, site of the *County Art* and *Page Prehistoric* museums. *Park La Brea,* a high-rise/low-rise apartment complex, is north of the park. For much of its 16-mile length the Boulevard traverses neighborhoods of high middle-income to upper income. Nearby is a Hollywood outlier, *Television City* (C.B.S.).

The prestigious place of the Northwest is ***Beverly Hills*** (34,000), the costliest city in the nation for median-house purchase. This sumptuous residential satellite, despite its municipal independence and village government, gains much sustenance from employment outside its limits.

---

*Many sojourners now avoid Wilshire, using the speedier Santa Monica Freeway.

**Figure 6-27.** A segment of Rodeo Drive, Beverly Hills. This is one of the world's renowned shopping streets. (dwl)

**Figure 6-27a.** "Typical" residence, middle level (between Wilshire and Sunset boulevards, Beverly Hills. (dwl)

Yet the triangular central district includes three internationally-known hotels, department stores, and expensive specialty shops as well as corporate offices and financial institutions.

Careful planning and strict zoning has prevailed in this slum-free city. Utility poles are placed unobtrusively along alleys and thousands of curbside trees are city-planted. Apartment houses (over half of the units in the community are multiple family) and business blocks help screen traffic noises from individual dwellings.

High-salaried movie stars began building mansions on the slopes of the Santa Monica Mountains in the "golden twenties." Through the decades the city has drawn the urbane sophisticates, sometimes the new-rich, enchanted having theatrical personalities as neighbors. Jews have always been well represented. Recent additions to the polyglot populace include such ethnic groups as Koreans, Arabs and Iranians (including one of out every five school children).

West of Beverly Hills and surrounding the separate city of Santa Monica are a near-dozen districts within "political" Los Angeles that form some of the most residentially-attractive segments of the nation's second city (map 6-8).

The physical appeal increases westward (milder temperatures, winter and summer—and less smog) and northward (more relief into the Santa Monica Mountains), where streets wind. Lots tend to be more spacious and dwellings larger than in eastern parts of the city.

***Century City*** has become a "city within a city" on the former back lot of a motion-picture studio (Twentieth Century Fox).

Its high-rise structures, a virtual appendage of Beverly Hills, house affluent residents as well as entertainment and shopping services for both occupants and visitors—patronage comes from afar. Besides a prestigious hotel and a theatrical playhouse, there are many corporate offices.

**Westwood Village**, with a major university and fashionable shopping "downtown", provides one of the better addresses in Los Angeles.* It is a center of youthful activity, with 20 cinemas showing first-run and foreign films, foreign, fast and junk foods, boutiques with funky and freaky clothes. On Friday and Saturday it attracts milling crowds of under-twenty year-olds.

This district is truly a favored portion of Los Angeles. Some of the costliest high-rise condominiums and office structures in the Lowlands line its portion of Wilshire Boulevard.

Late partition of a colonial rancho allowed space for a 400-acre campus for the University of California at Los Angeles (U.C.L.A.), now handsomely landscaped with much statuary. As the institution has grown it has added professional schools and has achieved academic excellence.

A considerable portion of ***Bel Air,*** most expensive residential area in the city of Los Angeles, is within the Santa Monica Mountains.

It is wholly residential—retail needs are provided in Westwood and Beverly Hills. The social focus is provided by a small hostelry and the country club.

---

* Except for dormitories and crowded nearby apartments, many students or faculty cannot afford to live can afford to live in Westwood. Most institutions of higher education in the Lowlands, including U.C.L.A. and U.S.C., tend to be commuter schools— student, staff and visitor parking has become a difficult problem.

The luxury of the district cannot be appreciated fully from the streets. While the chaparral-covered slopes do not have the beauty of expensive suburbs in more humid lands, and the threat of brushfire can be severe (a fire in 1961 destroyed homes valued at the time at $24,000,000), views of metropolitan lights and the Pacific are rewarding. Shrubbery often obscures the low rambling structures with walls of glass, the sometimes-ornate gardens and the many swimming pools.

While a bit less costly than Bel Air or Beverly Hills, *Brentwood* too is a choice part of Los Angeles.

Districts to the south and west (of Westwood), while sometimes attractive, are considered less prestigious.

Lots are smaller, the terrain is flatter, streets usually follow the grid pattern and houses smaller and more modest. This portion of the Northwest includes middle-income **West Los Angeles**, **Cheviot Hills** and **Mar Vista**.

West Los Angeles has an old business district plus homes that range from expensive to modest. *Sawtelle,* a small county enclave, contains a Veterans Hospital, one of the largest institutions of its type, and veterans' housing. Cheviot Hills, partly on dissected terraces, has winding streets and is well regarded—it has had a significant Japanese population.

*Culver City* (41,000), politically independent, is an industrial-residential suburb.

Low tax rates helped it entice motion picture studios (chiefly M.G.M.) from Hollywood in the 1920's. More recently it has been affected by aircraft and electronics (especially GM's Hughes). There are miscellaneous industrial plants, a shopping mall (Fox Hills), hotels along I-405 and West Los Angeles College. Recently it has gained a significant Asian population (chiefly Japanese and Chinese).

## THE OUTER PLAIN

South of the Santa Monica Mountains, especially seaward from the San Diego Freeway, coastal Los Angeles County is more Pacific-oriented, climatically as well as in terms of human utilization, than most of the Lowlands. Moreover, it displays a more uneven topography.

In addition to residence and strand recreation, oil and aerospace have consequence. This is also the water and air transport centrum of Southern California.

There are six airports plus rail lines crossing the Outer Plain to the coast. These form sites of extensive industrialization (map 6-6).

Long after Los Angeles had become a leading American city much of the Outer Plain remained rural.

Large tracts were utilized for grain and beans because of water and soil impediments. Early citrus growers considered the climatic coolness unsuitable for orchards. Where conditions were favorable, and properties smaller, dairies, vegetables, strawberries and market flowers were important. Even after World War II Japanese and Mexicans were involved in specialty farming; numbers of both groups remain in nonfarm occupations.

Now the population exceeds 1.5 million and open space on the Plain has essentially disappeared.

Still, on parts of the Plain density remains less than in some portions of the Lowlands.

More intensive utilization is evidenced by shoreline high-rise structures, hillside subdivisions, two-story tract houses adjacent to oil refineries and aerospace plants.

Much of the Santa Monica Bay strand as well as the **Palos Verdes Hills**, remains largely Anglo in habitation.

Attractive seafrontages or view lots in place like Pacific Palisades, **Marina del Rey**, Manhattan Beach, Palos Verdes and Verdes and Naples have become some of the nation's more costly real estate. Elsewhere the Outer Plain is ethnically di-

**Map 6-8.** Numerous districts and several politically-separate cities comprise the west side of Los Angeles, between Downtown Los Angeles and Santa Monica.

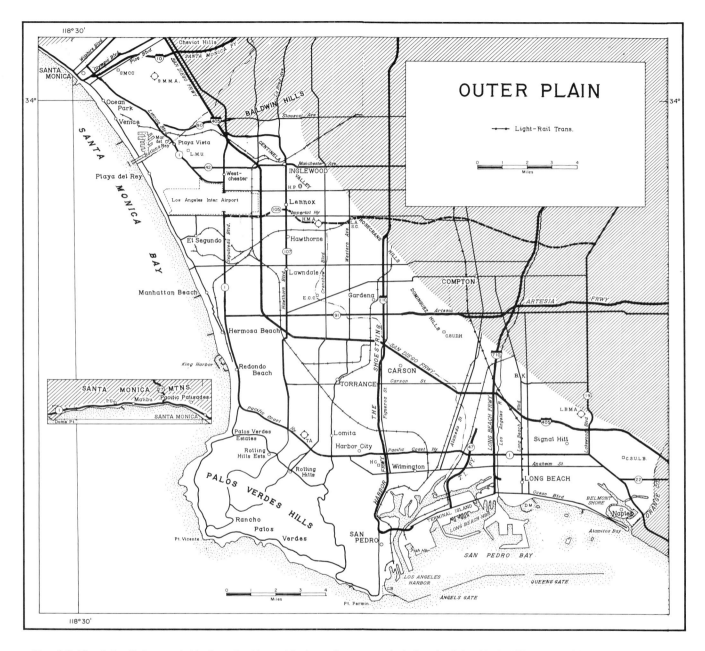

**Map 6-9.** The Outer Plain, coastwide from the Newport-Inglewood structure, includes the Palos Verde Hills, a prestigious residential sector.

verse with neighborhoods adjoining south-central Los Angeles having a sizable black population while the Harbor area houses Hispanics, Asians and others in low-profile houses and apartments.

Nineteen individual cities, some rather small, have absorbed almost the entirety of the Outer Plain. The most prominent unincorporated districts are Malibu, Marina del Rey and Lennox. The city of Los Angeles reaches the Pacific north and south of Santa Monica and at San Pedro and Wilmington.

For its age and cumulated wealth, the Plain could be labeled somewhat "underdeveloped" in number of colleges, symphony orchestras, museums and other cultural facilities...perhaps a consequence of civic fragmentation and dependence upon Los Angeles.

Blurred identity now occurs. Politically-separate towns coalesce; "locals" commute knowingly, strangers are bewildered.

Overall, the Outer Plain is a net importer of workers including many from Orange County and the San Fernando Valley. The principal employment centers include Santa Monica, the the Harbor area, the periphery of Los Angeles Airport and Carson-Torrance. Areas such as the Palos Verdes Hills are largely residential.

Travel to work in central Los Angeles is limited. Freeway connections, relatively few, came later than in some parts of the Lowlands.

Santa Monica, Torrance, and Long Beach are the prime shopping and office centers. Many shoreline attractions await the visitor but only around Los Angeles Airport and at Long Beach are there major commercial traveler and conference facilities.

### Hills, Flat Lands and Sea Cliffs

Flatness is disrupted by many minor undulations in topography. The northwest-southeast trend of the *Newport-Inglewood Uplift,* separating the Outer Coastal Plain from the geologic Los Angeles Basin, forms a prominent feature.

Here crustal uplift has produced low rises and hills, marking the cleavage between contrasting rock blocks hidden beneath coastal plain deposits. Stream courses have penetrated the Uplift sparingly to create low "watergaps" (Ballona, Centinella, Dominguez and Alamitos) that provide foci of transport routes and industrial sites.

Oilfields are associated with the Uplift, which tends to be the locale of golf courses and more expensive homes. Yet other than Signal Hill, no town nucleus has formed along the Uplift and considerable acreage remains unincorporated. Broadly the southwestern city limits of Los Angeles coincide with the Uplift, from the Baldwin Hills to the Rosecrans Hills.

Highest segment along the Uplift is the *Baldwin Hills,* which encompasses five square miles, mostly unincorporated.

Much of the western half of the Hills, coinciding with an extensive oilfield, remains undeveloped. The sloping flanks are dotted with expensive "view lot" residences, including the dwellings of some of California's more affluent blacks. Also here is the campus of West Los Angeles College.

A parallel line of level basins, westward from the Uplift, forms the locales for West Los Angeles, Inglewood, Lennox, Hawthorne and Gardena.

Higher terrain to the west encourages most drainage southeastward to the Harbor via Dominguez Channel. Ballona Creek Plain, a former outlet of the Los Angeles River, drains most of northwest Los Angeles (i.e., south of the Santa Monica Mountains) piercing the Uplift at Culver City.

**Figure 6-28** A continuous strand of beach "cottages," extending for miles along the Malibu Coast, helped inspire a coastal conservation movement. (dwl)

The contemporary plain of the Los Angeles River crosses the Uplift northwest of Long Beach at Dominguez Gap. Marshlands at Wilmington and Playa del Rey, into which the Los Angeles River once flowed, have been transformed through harbor development.

A higher, undulating terrace surface borders much of the coastline.

The communities of Santa Monica, Westchester, Torrance, Wilmington and Long Beach are situated on this surface.

Between Playa del Rey and Palos Verdes, low sand "hills", now semi-consolidated and stable, form a rolling landscape that provides higher-value housing sites.

A former sea mount, the *Palos Verdes Hills* (circa 90,000), rises a thousand feet above the Pacific to provide attractive housing sites, give the Outer Plain a vertical skyline, and afford San Pedro Bay wind and wave protection.

The Hills is much terraced, which facilitates urban occupance as it once did truck gardeners. Locally there are problems of landslides and other hazards. Higher elevations provide views of the Pacific as well as the nocturnal sparkle of the brightly-lighted Coastal Plain. Residents tend to be well-to-do and there are many horse "ranchettes."

There are four communities within the Palos Verdes Hills.

*Palos Verdes Estates* (15,000), the oldest of the four, tends to have many multi-story residences.
*Rancho Palos Verdes* (46 000), largest in population and area, has as a visitor attraction the *Way-*

*farers Chapel*. **Rolling Hills** (2100) is mostly low-density, equestrian with street names like *Pinto* and *Roundup*. **Rolling Hills Estates** (7800) is the major shopping place and has the *South Bay Botanical Gardens*.

### Los Angeles-Long Beach Harbors

The world's largest artificial harbor, consisting of the twin ports of Los Angeles and Long Beach, evolved in the lee of Palos Verde Hills in the twentieth century from a former open roadstead with marshy shores.

Although a railroad from Los Angeles had been constructed early (1868) the main breakwater was delayed until 1899 (the Southern Pacific desired Santa Monica as its harbor). To become a coastal city Los Angeles extended its boundaries to the sea, absorbing the existing towns of Wilmington and San Pedro, which were attached to Los Angeles along *The Shoestring,* a strip of land nine miles long and half a mile wide. The Shoestring tends to be residential but at the junction of the Harbor and San Diego freeways is an industrial zone, the Ascot auto raceway and with office towers nearby.

State-owned tidelands were ceded to Los Angeles and Long Beach in 1911. Including docks and buildings most of the water front belongs to the two municipalities.

The joint Harbor has two segments (map 6-9): **Outer Harbor** provides commercial and Naval anchorages; **Inner Harbor,** with a deep channel, has double entrances. Man-made **Terminal Island** lies between the two and is divided between the two ports.

Earlier docks were concentrated on Inner Harbor. Newer facilities, including the Navy Base and supertanker terminals, came later, often on landfill. Collectively, Long Beach, Los Angeles and the federal government have expended hundreds of millions on facilities which extend along 40 miles of waterfront; space for expansion remains.

Los Angeles-Long Beach ranks among the nation's leading ports in cargo and tonnage value.

Despite competitive transport media, commerce continues to rise. Ship clearances have declined since the peak year (1930) but tonnage has expanded.

Petroleum dominates heavy bulk-transport items. Other high-tonnage commodities include gypsum, copra, various minerals (such as potash), foodstuffs and automobiles.

Less bulky, general cargos shipped mostly in containers, are likewise important. Both city ports provide vast facilities for handling containers, with additional ones anticipated. Truck trailers, another transport mode, take further space; a ter-

**Figure 6-29.** The Port of Los Angeles with Terminal Island (left) and San Pedro (right), linked by the Vincent Thomas Bridge across Main Channel. (The Port of Los Angeles).

minal to handle trailers between trucks and rail flatcars opened in Wilmington in 1987.

*Fish Harbor* on Terminal Island was long the nation's ranking fishing port with a dozen canneries. Depleted supplies of fish, and more importantly, costlier production in California, have led to establishment of American-owned canneries in Puerto Rico, Peru and Samoa. Imports from foreign companies have also increased. The Harbor remains the state's leading freshfish terminal (in San Pedro) some fish is even trucked north to San Francisco.

The primary industrial belt of the Lowlands reaches south to the Harbor where port-type activities are important.

These include lumber milling, oil refining, copra conversion into supplemental dairy foods, margarine and soap, borax processing, and production of gypsum wallboard.

Still considered a strategic industry worthy of conduct, the shipbuilding and repair industry, is dependent on federal contracts. Peak activity occurred during World War II. Subsequently, shipbuilding has suffered from lower-cost domestic and foreign competition. Several private facilities, a Naval base and shipyard still employ thousands!

Extending outward under San Pedro Bay, the **Wilmington Oil Field** has been a leading producer for many years.

Petroleum withdrawal produced subsidence in the Harbor area for many years (until 1959). Subsequently, salt-water injection has proved remedial although subsidence to depths of 25 feet necessitated sea wall and much rebuilding in Long Beach Harbor.

Long Beach has utilized oilfield monies to construct elaborate waterfront facilities and to expand its share of twin-port commerce.

Inter-city rivalry has promoted modernization of both ports, but at the cost of duplicate facilities. The two ports cooperated to obtain a joint federal customs house and occasionally in other respects.

The Harbor area became a populous segment of the Outer Plain early.

Nevertheless many employed residents find employment inland. Automation in shipping and declining industrial workforces have been chronic. Incomes tend to be significantly lower than in some parts of metropolis.

Space for additional housing close-in has been a long-time problem. Much housing is older and there tend to be more multiple units than is usual in Southern California.

Although the Hispanic population is sizable, other ethnic groups create a rich diversity although some neighborhoods display monoethnic clusters.

*San Pedro* (50,000), *another* political district of Los Angeles, is a community of several parts. Maritime activity includes container and cruise ship ter-

**Figure 6-30.** The expanding Port of Long Beach and the city of Long Beach with the Central Coastal Plain in the rear. (The Port of Long Beach).

minals.

Nautical equipage firms, sailors' accommodations and the Los Angeles Harbor Commission are there. Also present are branch city offices, reflecting the areal extent of the political city. Surrounding the central district (near the waterfront) there are dwellings of such sundry ethnic groups as Mexicans, Italians, blacks, Norwegians and Yugoslavians.

The recreational function is important. Adjacent to *Fisherman's Dock,* where fresh fish are landed for metropolitan markets, is Ports o'Call, the Los Angeles version of Fisherman's Wharf in San Francisco. Maritime history and marine life museums are augmented by Cabrillo Beach outside the breakwater and by a recreational boat facility and public fishing pier.

Historically, San Pedro was the colonial leader in the hide-and-tallow trade.

*Wilmington* (41,000) too is a district of Los Angeles which has considerable port activity.

This includes cargo terminals, industrial plants, shippers' associations and longshoremen's dispatch halls. Oil wells and refineries are conspicuous. Residents tend to be lower-income Hispanics.

Wilmington is the site of Los Angeles Harbor College, adjacent to a regional park fashioned from a marshland.

Closer to Los Angeles than San Pedro, Wilmington flourished in stagecoach days. With the arrival of the railhead at San Pedro and the rise of the fishing industry, San Pedro became more important.

In the second half of the twentieth century, as open space in more favored locales vanished, several towns evolved north and west of Wilmington. These include *Lomita* (20,000), Carson,and the Los Angeles *district* of *Harbor City* (20,000).

*Carson* (88,000), the largest of this trio, has grown rapidly and is buoyed by several activities. Moreover it occupies a larger area than most communities in the Outer Plain.

On its northern edge is California State University, Dominguez Hills, the youngest institution in the 19 university system.

Carson has a strong industrial base, concerned especially with petroleum and chemicals. Activity is favored by the several rail lines that cross it; it is also bisected east-west by the San Diego Freeway (map 6-9) and bordered by three other freeways.

In addition to a regional shopping center, it has a handsome civic center, adjacent community center and multi-star hotel.

**Figures 6-31.** Aircraft plant (McDonnell Douglas) at Long Beach Airport. This plant is one of many aerospace factories in the Los Angeles Basin. (dwl)

Strongly ethnic, Carson has a sizable Hispanic population, as well as blacks, Filipinos and Samoans.The latter group has trebled in Los Angeles County in the past several decades.

*Long Beach* (410,000), California's fifth most-populous city, is the leading amusement, shopping, educational and medical center of the southern coastal plain.

Long Beach might be likened to the plain younger half-sister of a vibrant, international famous sibling (i.e., Los Angeles). As was hinted earlier, had Long Beach been founded by English or Americans before 1850 it might have become the dominant city of Southern California.

Founded during the boom of the 1880's, Long Beach was still small early in 20th century when Los Angeles had become the largest city in western United States and its port development had commenced at San Pedro. For decades Long Beach was a favorite with retired Middlewesterners who formed the largest segment of its population.

Once allegedly there were more ex-Iowans than any community in Iowa except Des Moines. Conservative Protestants, they made the city renowned for a multitude of organizations supported by "joiners;" picnics were characteristic.

Social stratification of Long Beach began to change in the 1920's with Navy installations, an oil boom and port development. McDonnell-Douglas' aircraft plant, largest employer in the city, attracted many working families after 1940. Ever more workers currently commute daily out of the city than into Long Beach.

Reflecting the size of Long Beach, there are a number of important institutions.

These include military and civilian hospitals, California State University and Long Beach City College, the Queen Mary tourist complex and shoreside convention and theatre facilities Airport expansion has encouraged high-rise hotels and offices to the northeast quadrant of the city.

Hemmed in by the ocean, oilfields and refineries, Long Beach has expanded northward and eastward from its nucleus, which adjoins the mouth of the Los Angeles River (Figure 6-30).

Wealthy neighborhoods occur where the city spreads across "mesas" along the Newport-Inglewood Uplift and also the eastern bayshore (locale of prestigious *Naples*—with its aquatic setting it should be called Venice!). Pretentious mansion estates are lacking.

Southwest of Signal Hill, around the city core, are found numerous low-income inhabitants including many ethnics. A number are Harbor workers or Navy enlisted personnel. Many blocks north of the C.B.D. house lower-income blacks; more affluent blacks tend to reside in West Long Beach tract dwellings as do various other ethnic groups. In many older neighborhoods apartments are replacing individual residences.

Downtown is small for the total population reflecting competition from Los Angeles and neighboring communities, limited purchasing power of nearby residents and absence of urbanization on two sides. In an effort to maintain the central district as a shopping center a regional shopping mall has been built.

The appeal of Long Beach, and some of its present-day attractions, results from the appeal of coastal residence and visitation.

There is a resemblance to Santa Monica in placement of the central district (on bluffs overlooking the bay), shoreline apartments, many retirees and the tourist and convention trade.

The considerable seaside appeal of Long Beach is jeopardized by such things as crime, poverty, congestion, downtown obsolescence and deteriorating qualities of San Pedro Bay with large oil-drilling towers close offshore. But lavish oil revenues have been expended to build waterfront visitor facilities. Newer shoreline high-rise structures (for hotels, residences, offices and government agencies) are conspicuous.

## Surf and Sand

Surf-spanked by the Pacific, miles of sandy beaches lie broadside Santa Monica Bay as well as eastern San Pedro Bay—there is considerable residential appeal.

Yet this is not quite paradise due to fog and cooler summers. But coastal towns are relatively smog-free and experience the narrowest temperature range in the Lowlands. Truly these are choice Lowland locales and chiefly-Anglo occupants tend to be affluent.

The strand has provided aquatic frolic places for decades; some communities were founded as early as the 1880's. Now more beach frontage is occupied by its satellites than by the city of Los Angeles. Thousands of homes, often of pastel stucco and handsomely landscaped, plus an increasing number of multi-storied buildings, have produced a nearly continuous urban landscape.

Though acreage, parking and maintenance are not always sufficient for the needs of metropolitan millions, most beaches are publicly accessible. Still, there are other problems.

Shore erosion is a pressing problem; dammed streams no longer supply sand, while jetties and breakwaters interfere with its deposition.

Proximity of the petroleum industry creates problems too; at El Segundo and Venice, recreation and oil have at times been incompatible. More widely, oil slicks (spilled from ships and offshore drilling) and "beach tar" are nuisances.

Beach devotees also face competition from electric generating facilities, harbors, and sewage disposal plants. Polluted air is sometimes carried inland by sea breezes.

*The Malibu Coast,* which extends westward from Santa Monica for 22 miles, has long been cluttered with files of beach cottages, private clubs, public beaches, parking lots and a diversity of other uses.

Probably, as nowhere else along the California coast, the "Malibu" demonstrates the need for shoreline "protection." For miles the travelers' views of the Pacific are minimal.

Uses include Will Rogers Beach State Park, Getty Museum, motels and restaurants. At sheltered Las Trancas and Malibu beach colonies, affluent Angelenos maintain seaside "cottages" (i.e., mansions) protected by private guards and fences. Recreation has been augmented by aerospace research laboratories, a second Pepperdine University campus and a county governmental complex.

Long ago there were three Mexican ranchos. Then much of this foreshore and its mountainous back country was purchased (in 1887) by Frederick Rindge. Although this wealthy Bostonian died before he could convert it into an American Riviera his widow stubbornly kept the property intact and thus prohibited the Southern Pacific Railroad from following the shore with its Coast Line. The State of California, by obtaining court approval in 1925, was finally able to construct a segment of *Coast Highway* (now Route 1) here.

An imaginative, future-looking effort to "save" the Malibu and much of the adjacent Santa Monica Mountains is the ***Santa Monica Mountains National Recreation Area***, a cooperative federal-state-county and city venture. Approved by Congress (1978) and by the State of California (1979) it involves much of the Santa Monica Mountains, encompassing 150,000 acres. The National Park Service is the supervisory agency; unfortunately the limited land acquisitions in the Area's first decade have hardly kept pace with new housing developments.

***Santa Monica*** (91,000) is one of California's more attractive beach towns; it affords a combination sea resort, residential bedroom (whose homes vary from mansions near Sunset Boulevard in the north to modest cottages), and industrial city.

It has an assemblage of seaside hotels, a fishing pier and a yacht basin, as well as a viable central area. Municipal pride is demonstrated in Palisades Park, Santa Monica City College, and the civic center (Figure 6-32). Nearby is a "think factory", the RAND Corporation research center, which employs scores of Ph.D.s.

Santa Monica was platted in 1875, intended to be the seaport for Los Angeles and environs. In the early 1900's Ocean Park on its southern fringe was acclaimed the "Coney Island of the Pacific." The city grew rapidly in the 1920's, a period when movie stars erected beach estates (which became clubs after Malibu Colony became more fashionable). Establishment of Douglas Aircraft adjacent to the municipal airport stimulated industrial growth. Apartment houses have subsequently become characteristic—Santa Monica has received much publicity as one of California's strongest enclaves of rent-controlled legislation.

Approximately half the ocean frontage along Santa Monica Bay is within the political limits of Los Angeles. ***Pacific Palisades*** (circa 12,000), lies near the western end of the expensive-residence belt at the base of the Santa Monica Mountains (which continues eastward through Brentwood, Bel Air and Beverly Hills).

Its terrace setting is one of the most appealing in the metropolitan area but there is a severe landslide problem. Yet its seaward edge contains multiple-story dwellings and beach clubs. Nearby the Getty Museum has one of the world's stellar art collections.

***Venice*** (33,000), has a diverse population including well-to-do and poor. Dwellings vary from little cottages to large multiunit dwellings. Its municipal beach is much frequented by devotees of surfing, sunbathing, physical fitness and athletics.

Its founder tried to convert a marshland into a New World replica of the Italian city, with canals,

**Figure 6-32.** Western Santa Monica, including the downtown area, Malibu Coast in the rear. RAND Corporation, a "think tank", occupies the waffle-shaped building (lower left). (Santa Monica Chamber of Commerce, photo by Tom Carroll of Photographic International).

gondolas and cultural activities. The image vanished early with establishment of an amusement park. Then, in 1930, an oil boom brought a "forest" of "town-lot" derricks. Many residents today, including writers and artists in modest canalside abodes, oppose "upgrading" of Venice.

***Marina del Rey*** (10,000), one of Southern California's principal yacht anchorages, was formed from the western portion of the Ballona coastal marsh in the 1960's.

Its man-made peninsulas are occupied by expensive multi-unit dwellings and leisure-oriented services. It has created an impact for improvement of nearby Venice neighborhoods.

Plans have been advanced for the little-used inland part of the Ballona marsh. These include restoration of some natural wetland coupled with intensive multiple-use urbanization to form a new community, *Playa Vista,* still in unincorporated territory.

A wide beach and proximity to Marina del Rey provide "pluses" for ***Playa del Rey*** (5000).

With proximity to the runways of Los Angeles International Airport, oil fields and the major Los Angeles sewage disposal plant, this seems an unlikely spot for an attractive town.

"South (Santa Monica) Bay" consists of a trio (plus a segment of Torrance) of attractive beach towns, Manhattan Beach, Hermosa Beach and Redondo Beach. Basically these are residential places, whose sand dunes provide a third dimension.

Land values have spiraled and the strand now has many multi-story apartments. Basically, residents are white-collar Anglos and many are upper middle-income. There is much commutation to nearby aerospace and airline employment; retirees tend to be long-time residents.

***Manhattan Beach*** (35,000), one of California's costlier cities in which to purchase housing, has lost a bit of its "nice little town" reputation (a legacy of its temperance-colony origins).

Its beach has gained week-end popularity with affluent singles. Land values are high and costlier dwellings have replaced many of yesteryear's cottages. A fringe of the El Segundo "tank farm" has become an attractive regional shopping mall.

Hermosa Beach (19,000) has many retirees and a considerable number of apartment units.

***Redondo Beach*** (65,000) is larger and more socially complex than its two neighbors to the north. Recreation is important, focusing on the *King Harbor* marina, as are the residential, service and industrial functions.

Once proposed as a site for Los Angeles harbor, Redondo for decades was a leading beach resort of the Lowlands. Despite its marina, it has become primarily residential. Its once-blighted central core has been extensively rebuilt. Inland, there is a regional shopping center (much supported by residents of Palos Verdes) and much of the sprawling TRW aerospace-electronics complex, one of California's largest.

### Whiffs of Oil

The Newport-Inglewood Uplift and the Outer Coastal Plain contain two of the three principal oil-field belts of the Los Angeles Basin.

Generally widening southward and extending beneath the ocean offshore from Long Beach (and Orange County), fields have a southeast-northwest trend. After its beginnings (in 1948), oil exploitation in San Pedro Bay expanded. Santa Monica Bay remained "out-of-bounds" for drillers into the 1980's.

Between El Segundo and Wilmington petrochemical plants, refineries and tank farms are ever-visible.

With juxtaposition of major fields and refineries, the Outer Plain is the state's leading oil center. Nocturnally, a "touch" is provided by flickering flares, decoratively lighted towers and condensing steam clouds. Visibly as well as aromatically, the petroleum industry "dominates" much of the southern Plain, despite heavy outlays to curb air pollution.

Refinery construction came in the first three decades of this century.

Abundant space for sprawling facilities was available and the Outer Plain offered access to crude oil

**Figure 6-33.** Downtown shopping mall, Santa Monica. Nearby is a newer enclosed multi-story mall. (dwl)

and port facilities. With rising in-state consumption, refineries have been enlarged to draw increasingly upon crude oil imported in super tankers. Spectacular ruptures, sometimes within residential neighborhoods, have revealed the invisible maze of pipelines which link tanker terminals, fields and refineries.

Despite residential repellance the petroleum industry no longer has much of the Outer Plain to itself. In places it destroyed residential neighborhoods as it expanded. But as urban growth has continued, there are instances of costlier residential developments vicinal to oil fields and refineries. As urbanization has advanced on once-lonesome refineries and oil fields, not too many garden patches, once consequential, remain.

An oil town "orphan" of the recreational-residential Santa Monica coast, *El Segundo* (15,500) is also a surprisingly-tidy dwelling place.

When Chevron (then Standard Oil) established its 1000-acre refinery (now the largest in Southern California) in 1910, the locale was "open" pastoral land. For many years oil came from nearby fields. The Bay afforded tanker anchorage as well as cheap coolant while the sand dunes furnished a good storage site from which gravity flow was possible into the tankers. Unused land, long leased to farmers for beans and truck crops, has become an office and industrial area adjacent to the International Airport (and a handsome shopping center in Manhattan Beach).

Diminutive *Signal Hill* (8500), surrounded by Long Beach, is experiencing its third transition.

Before 1921, and a wasteful "town-lot" oilboom that made its name internationally-known, Signal Hill was an attractive village whose view lots hinted at exclusive residence. Long Beach too was much influenced as thousands of oil workers arrived. Oil tool, refinery and other service establishments appeared although much of the refining was nearby.

An incredible wealth has been removed from under the town's 1400 acres. It has continued in the 1980's through employment of an unitized water injection-oil removal system.

Now there are many vacant lots. The forest of derricks has vanished and oil operators were compelled to remove superfluous equipment. While Signal Hill remains a lower middle-income town there are viewsite condominiums and parts of the town have become a more expensive residential place.

**Aircraft and Missilry**

An early center, the Outer Plain remains the aerospace leader of California.

One of the nation's earliest air shows (in 1910), residence of Donald Douglas in Santa Monica (where he founded Douglas Aircraft, now McDonnell Douglas, in 1920) and the National Air Races (held at Los Angeles International Airport, 1928-

**Figure 6-34.** Southern California's largest oil refinery at El Segundo has its own tanker-loading facility. (Chevron Corporation).

1936) helped trigger the rise of the industry.

Despite coastal fog, open countryside away from the mountains, climatic mildness (including vigorous sea breezes) and proximity to shipping were environmental assets. Vast airplane factories evolved during World War II at Santa Monica, Los Angeles International Airport, Hawthorne and Long Beach, as well as elsewhere in Southern California, adjacent to airfields, publicly provided.

Additional aerospace expansion (1950-1969) found existing airport sites nearly saturated. Evolution of "think factories" permitted more flexible location than was possible in aircraft assembly. New plants, such as those at Malibu, Redondo Beach and Palos Verdes, were established, indicating the rising importance as amenable settings and freedom from traditional industrial sites. Many smaller companies, scattered about the Outer Plain, produce small parts, often electrical, for use in producing space hardware and surface military equipment.

Aerospace, the leading employer in the Outer Plain for nearly half a century, has been a major stimulant to urbanization, affecting location, extent and timing.

The largest impact has occurred in the triangular area between Gardena, Redondo Beach and Westchester (map 6-9).

A framework of middle- and upper-middle income tracts, primarily single-family houses, Anglo-occupied, has been fostered by aerospace. Manhattan Beach, Hermosa Beach, Lawndale and **Lakewood** (76,000) are good examples of residential cities with minimal "home industry" which depend considerably upon nearby manufacturing plants.

**Westchester** (50,000), a residential district of Los Angeles, occupies a "mesa" between the Baldwin Hills and the Pacific.

Residents, mostly upper middle-income and strongly Anglo, include many employed around the International Airport and at Hughes Aircraft. On its northern edge, Loyola Marymount University, a large sectarian institution, occupies a spacious campus with a commanding view.

**Inglewood** (102,000), despite other functions, is basically residential, with more multi-unit dwellings than most Outer Plain cities.

From the 1880's until 1940 Inglewood was the service center for the agriculturally-prospering Centinela Valley. Then came wartime boom, followed by surface congestion and "flight-path" degradation

accompanying Airport enlargement. The westward expansion of "black Los Angeles" then engulfed much of the city; by the 1970's Inglewood joined Compton as a black-majority municipality.

Inglewood has an oil field, horse racing track (Hollywood Park), sports arena (The Forum) and Northrop University, an engineering college. Many residents are employed at the nearby Airport.

**Los Angeles International Airport** ("LAX") leading terminal in western United States, exceeds its planned saturation capacity of 40,000,000 passengers annually. The volume of freight has continued to increase as well.

It began as a flying field in 1925 and became a municipal airport in 1928 although it did not become the principal commercial airport until 1946. The leading port in the Lowlands in the 1920's was in East Los Angeles. It was succeeded by Grand Central (in Glendale) and then by Lockheed (now Burbank-Glendale-Pasadena). Timely establishment while vacant land was available was negated by growth of surrounding cities. Then Los Angeles embarked upon extensive urban demolition to establish north runways.

In 1936 North American Aviation opened a plant on its southern edge. Now scores of industrial establishments, concerned principally with electronics and aerospace, fringe the airport in addition to 40,000 persons employed at the facility.

In recent decades impressive accommodations for travelers have been constructed around the port. In preparation for the Olympic Games in 1984 the *Thomas Bradley International Terminal* was

**Figure 6-35.** The Los Angeles Basin has many miles of sandy beach as this one in Santa Monica. Hundreds of thousands go to the beaches when the temperature rises into the 70's or above. (dwl)

added and the encircling access roadway was double decked. Nevertheless auto and aircraft congestion persists, along with environmental damage litigation. Alternative airport sites have been much-discussed but are unlikely to be found within the Los Angeles Basin now.

*Hawthorne* (62,000), with much industrial activity (especially aerospace plants and Mattel, one of the nation's leading toymakers, houses many factory workers, including Hispanics.

*Gardena* (51,000) is principally an industrial bedroom with an interesting ethnic mix.

Residents include many Anglos, Japanese, blacks, and Mexicans. Its Japanese community, a legacy of a home gardener, agricultural worker and nursery trade past, is the largest in Southern California. This ethnic group is widely dispersed across the Lowlands and intermarries extensively in contrast to earlier generations. The Japanese have gained a wide range of employment and have relatively-high income status.

*Lawndale* (25,000) is a "misfit" community in this area. Like Lomita and Signal Hill, it is a diminutive compact town. The town is largely residential with a lower middle-income populace including considerable Mexicans.

In a sense its name is appropriate, for spacious Alondra County Park and El Camino College, one of the larger two-year institutions in California, supported by nine communities, are in adjacent county territory.

*Torrance* (139,000) has a variety of functions. Space-wise it is a residential city whose residents have a wide income range. The "hub" city for the southwestern Coast Plain, it has a large regional shopping and office center (Del Amo) as well as medical and branch county services. A busy general aircraft port has become a nucleus for industrial plants adjoining oilfields near its southern fringe.

Somewhat unique among California cities, Torrance was laid out as a planned industrial city (in 1911)—it had workers' bungalows around a central district and a peripheral industrial zone. Such heavy industries as steel, chemicals, aluminum processing and oil refining were once dominant, along with spacious oil fields and tank farms.

About half of Torrance's area is residential. Houses range from luxury level along the Pacific shore to workers cottages around factories. Its populace includes many Japanese and Mexicans, groups once employed on nearby truck farms.

Much of its growth occurred during the 1950's with a "fill-in" of open space.

## THE CENTRAL PLAIN

Hastening along a major boulevard or a freeway, the wayfarer probably finds little in the Central Plain (map 6-10) to titilate the senses. If one happens to observe "city limits" signs one is aware of its numerous political units.

Verily this is not the Los Angeles that the tourist seeks. Converted decades ago from farming to a multiplicity of urban uses there is no longer much newness in this landscape. Neither terrain, lofty buildings nor tall trees interrupt the general flatness. Like various other portions of the Lowlands this area is perhaps best viewed at night, when the eyes are mesmerized by countless lights.

Between the Newport-Inglewood Uplift and the low *Puente-Montebello* hills, the Central Plain occupies the middle of the synclinal "Los Angeles Basin" (i.e.,the geologic unit). The Plain extends from south-central Los Angeles to the Orange County line.

The Los Angeles and San Gabriel rivers have wandered widely across the Central Plain in the geologic past, depositing their sandy debris. Drainage seaward became more sluggish, soils heavier and more alkaline and water tables higher. Early settlements were given such names as Artesia, Clearwater and Green Meadows.

Peopled by conservative Anglo Protestants, dispersed farm villages evolved in the late 1800's after railroads improved access.

Thus the northwest fringe of the Central Plain was urbanized by the early 1900's. Still, as late as 1950, broad expanses of rural landscape persisted.

Many towns remain politically independent of Los Angeles.

Earlier, they were surrounded by "ranches" (small, intensively tilled farms). There were flowers and nursery stock at Montebello, citrus groves around Downey and Whittier, and into the 1960's, truck gardens and dairies farther east, toward Orange County. Since mid-century, however, the Central Plain has become part of a gargantuan metropolis.

Most of the Plain and its peoples are compartmented into nearly two-dozen politically-separate cities. However, a quarter of the inhabitants of the Plain live within Los Angeles and another 10 per cent reside in unincorporated patches.

Despite much local manufacturing, there is heavy reliance upon employment in Los Angeles. In half a dozen cities there is more industrial employment

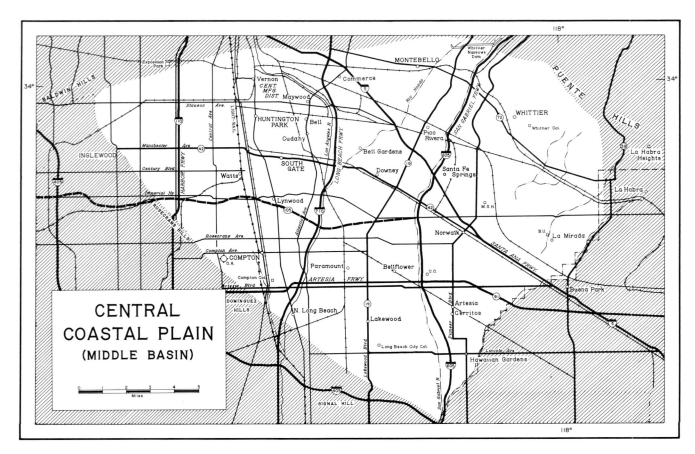

**Map 6-10.** The Central Coastal Plain houses many blacks and Hispanics as well as Anglos and others. Except for north Long Beach and Watts (a district within Los Angeles), all listed communities are incorporated.

than resident workers; the remaining communities are primarily residential. The medium to lower income residents do not support many corporate offices, shopping centers, colleges, museums or similar institutions.

### The Muted Hum of Machines

The Central Plain is more industrially-oriented than most of of the Lowlands. A fifth of the Plain has been utilized by (or reserved for) factories and related functions.

Industry has been favored by contiguity to the original manufacturing belt of Los Angeles, by level sites and by the rail net that has diverged widely over the Plain from Vernon. It has afforded direct connections with out-of-state points and with the Harbor. Industrial districts tend to coincide with rail routes (map 6-6). Products tend to be market-oriented; much of the food, metal and machinery output of Southern California is located here. There are only a few aerospace firms. Trucking headquarters and warehousing estab-

lishments are important.

Machinery, and other metal-using industries of the Central Plain have been adjusting for several decades to a lengthy decline in nearby oilfields. More recently manufactural cutbacks have occurred too in the automobile assembly and rubber plants that were major employers in the sector between south central Los Angeles and Pico Rivera. Many newer wholesale-distributive facilities also have been located outside the Central Plain, in Orange County and City of Industry, where "rents" are cheaper and access almost as good.

Three cities (Commerce, Vernon and Santa Fe Springs) were incorporated principally for industrial use. **Commerce** (10,000), in addition to factories, has two of the three major rail classification yards for Los Angeles.

It *also* has "business" hotels, a casino and a quartet of small cemeteries!

**Vernon** contains a railroad-promoted manufacturing belt.

Its *Central Industrial District* employs 80,000 yet

this "city" has fewer than 100 residents, limited municipal services and the lowest tax rate among all incorporated California cities.

***Santa Fe Springs*** (15,500), the locale of heavier manufacturing including earthenware and and oil refining, sprawls along its "namesake" railroad trackage for six miles.

In the past it had the state's leading oilfield, with wooden derricks "everywhere". Now natural gas is stored underground. Open space for additional manufacturing remains.

## Western Black Block *

Beginning with the 1920's, the western segment of the Central Plain has experienced the southward and westward advance of the principal Los Angeles ghetto. The black area, which evolved over some decades, was largely ignored by Anglos until social frustrations precipitated the *Watts riots* of 1965.

The western quarter of the Central Plain represents the largest black concentration in California (circa 500,000), although expansion has tended to be westward beyond this area.

Earlier the black community expanded southward along Central Avenue (south of downtown Los Angeles), thence southward and westward to the Newport-Inglewood Uplift. It houses a majority of the county's blacks.

Once the east edge of black Los Angeles was sharply defined along much of its length by Alameda Street, where a wide railroad-track right of way and bordering factories formed a gray "cotton curtain."

In the 1970's significant black occupance "crossed the tracks" in Lynwood, Compton and Long Beach.

Meanwhile older ghetto segments in and around Watts began to experience a Hispanic intrusion.

In other directions, black residence extends generally north to Pico Boulevard and west to Culver City.

Three fourths of the black community resides within the political limits of Los Angeles; the remainder lives primarily in unincorporated territory. Bordering cities (except Compton) remained "all white" until the 1960's when blacks found residence in Lynwood, Inglewood, Carson and northern Long Beach.

The black belt, mostly residential, has had a dearth of industrial and shopping facilities.

Commutation is common, with greater reliance upon public transit than is typical in Los Angeles. Personal and domestic services downtown and in more affluent areas of the Northwest Coastal Plain, have provided much employment but industrial jobs have been too limited. An increasing number of blacks have employment in white-collar positions.

There is an appreciable social gradient within the several nuclei of black population.

The old *Central Avenue* area is no longer the core. Now the "real" heart is west of the Harbor Freeway where influential church pastors and black businessmen prevail. There is even a shopping center (Crenshaw) shared with Asians. *West Adams* has deteriorated considerably in recent decades. Even so, the "worst" looks good in comparison with black slums in eastern United States.

The *southern area*, focusing on Watts and Compton, looks a bit less dilapidated than several decades ago. ***Southwest Los Angeles*** and Inglewood, which became increasingly black after the mid-1950's, is more affluent. Overall too much black housing is shabby and much in need of renovation. The real problems include jobs and work ethic, crime (worst "pockets" in the metropolis), drugs, one-parent families, poor role models and such.

The small ***Watts District*** (35,000), politically within Los Angeles, symbolizes the "black belt."

Since the late 1960,s Watts has been the focus of determined civic efforts to improve job opportunities, services, transit. A third of a century later, despite such additions as the King-Drew Medical Center and Southwestern Community College, subsidized housing and a small shopping center

---

* This section was reviewed by Robert Sherrard, political science professor, C.S.U., Chico.

**Figure 6-37.** Martin Luther King Medical Center serves Watts and nearby areas. (dwl)

community problems remain. Meanwhile Hispanics are replacing the blacks.

For several decades **Compton** (94,000) has been a black majority city. Considerable social foment has taken place within the black community and between it and other peoples.

An early Central Plain (1869) farm town, Compton was proud of its long established community college and major shopping district.

As the black population doubled in the 1960's there was a hasty exodus of Anglos. Nonwhite incomes average above those in Los Angeles but civic leaders have been concerned with the trend toward a mostly black city and with lower incomes and high crime.

Helped by the tax base from a warehouse and factory corridor along Artesia Freeway, with a high-rise county court building, a new library and a renovated central district, Compton gives an appearance of having checked decline.

Incomes tend to increase westward into the *golden ghettos* of *View Park* and *Leimert Park* where live many blacks with business and professional positions elsewhere.

Blacks replaced Anglos in the larger homes of this area from mid-century.

### The North-Central Hispanic Block *

*All* cities in the Central Plain have a sizable Hispanic populace, *even* Compton and the Watts district.

Hispanics have gained majority status through a zone extending halfway across the Plain from East Los Angeles between Alameda Street on the west and Santa Fe Springs on the east. This *barrio* zone is extending presently into the cities of Lynwood, Paramount and Norwalk and surrounding but not including Downey.

Even in older, completely "built-out" areas the Hispanic influx has created net population increase. More apartment houses and burgeoning school enrollments are indicative.

Other changes in the cityscape include additional Spanish language signs and different kinds of store merchandise and services, churches and other institutions.

Income levels have apparently declined in some districts but risen in others but remaining low average. Several cities, like **Bell Gardens** and **Paramount**, show recent civic rejuvenation.

***Huntington Park*** (51,000) has limited industry but houses many who work in adjacent Vernon.

There is a substantial older string-type shopping

**Figure 6-38.** The Central Manufacturing District in Vernon in includes 750 industrial establishments. In rear Los Angeles River runs diagonally across the picture. (Central Manufacturing District, Inc., photo by Howard Kelly).

nucleus.

***South Gate*** (78,000) contains several square miles of dwellings including numerous multifamily units, placed between industrial plants on its eastern and western sides.

Despite closure of its large Firestone and General Motors plants the population has increased. Black migration from adjacent Watts has not penetrated the city.

***Lynwood*** (55,000), long known for its major hospital and its tent revival meetings, contains factories (within the Alameda Street corridor) but is principally residential.

Its southern sector, bordering Compton, received an influx of black residents in the 1970's. Hispanics however form the largest ethnic group.

***Montebello*** (60,000) has oil fields on its hilly northern margin (the Puente Hills) and truck terminals on the southern "flats".

Its extensive residential districts vary from upper middle incomes (in the Hills) to low middle income on the Central Plain.

Bisected by rail lines, ***Pico Rivera*** (61,000) is now chiefly residential.

Less land was zoned for industrial use than for water infiltration grounds (along the bordering Rio Hondo and San Gabriel rivers). Closing of its Ford assembly plant hurt the city economically.

---

* This portion has been reviewed by Jaime Raigosa, sociology professor, C.S.U., Chico.

**Figure 6-39.** Pico Rivera, view westward. The former Ford Motor Company plant, closed in 1980, became an aerospace facility. (dwl)

*Norwalk* (88,0000) became the largest Central Plain city in midcentury. It has a diversity of governmental payrolls.

After construction of the Santa Ana freeway Norwalk grew rapidly. Although it is largely residential there is a branch county government complex, Metropolitan State Hospital and highrise offices.

### The Southeastern Anglo Block

The crescentric belt of the Central Plain that lies fartherest from downtown Los Angeles has not become a sector of strong Hispanic impact. Anglos still dominate in all but exceptional locales like south Whittier and Artesia. Dwellings tend to be newer and more spacious and there are more shopping centers, colleges and features usually associated with middle income segments of metropolitan Los Angeles. The impact of the Artesia Freeway (Ca. 91) was suggestive of that of the Santa Ana Freeway (I-5) on Orange County somewhat earlier.

Despite location between Hispanic Paramount and Norwalk, *Bellflower* (58,000) remains more ethnically diverse. Commutation to jobs elsewhere is important.

Besides the Anglo majority and Hispanic minority there are assorted Asian peoples. It does have a retail district as well as branch county civic center.

*Downey* (87,000) remains an Anglo isle in an ethnic lake. It is bolstered economically by an aerospace plant.

With many spacious homes, once bordered by orange groves, considerably high land values seemingly have discouraged an ethnic influx.

Downey has one of two large aerospace plants in the Central Plain and large attractive shopping fa-

cilities. There is a a considerable number of newer multi-housing units as well as a newer landmark hotel that looks Victorian in age.

*Whittier* (73,000) has persisted as an attractive Anglo residence place for many decades, in part because of the Quaker influence and the college, and despite its oilfield.

Founded during the boom of the 1880's at the base of the Puente Hills it remained relatively small until the post-World War II boom years, when orange groves in south Whittier became housing tracts and and diversified light industry materialized.

*La Mirada* (44,000), a much younger community, is also well-regarded as a residence place.

This commuter community evolved with Santa Ana Freeway construction in the 1950's. It is home for many white-collar workers and is the site of sectarian Biola College, relocated from downtown Los Angeles.

*Cerritos* (58,000) is essentially an above-average income residential city.

Initially it was incorporated as the "city" of Dairy Valley to protect its dairy farms from urban encroachment. With rising land prices, the land became too valuable and the dairies were relocated around Chino or in the San Joaquin Valley.

Features of the community include detached homes, one of the state's largest auto sales malls, a regional shopping center adjacent to I-605 and Cerritos College. Blacks and different Asian groups form important ethnic peoples.

### ORANGE COUNTY *

Less than half a century ago Orange County, with a population of 200,000, had a series of farm towns surrounded by thousands of acres of orange groves and other crops. Subsequent growth has created an urban mosaic of over two million which has more people than metropolitan Seattle or St. Louis.

Since it occupies a county apart from Los Angeles, the Southeast (Los Angeles) Coast Plain has long been accepted as an alien lowland. Once it was known as the Santa Ana Plain; now it is popularly referred to as Orange County. It includes portions of the northern Peninsular Ranges (i.e., "South County.")

* This section has been reviewed by Ray Young, CSU, Fullerton and Steven Herman, CSU, Chico. Previously it had been reviewed by Gertrude Reith, CSU, Fullerton.

Physically, bases for separation of this portion of the Coast Plain result from the relationship of soils, drainage and water supply to the Santa Ana River *rather* than to the Los Angeles or San Gabriel rivers.

For a century, since partition of the Plain into two counties in 1889, strong separationist attitudes have existed in Orange County. One evidence was successful agitation for Census Bureau acceptance of a distinct metropolitan area apart from Los Angeles.

Commutation across the county boundary as well as urban coalescence tend to obscure the traditional distinction. Yet population supports new institutions and services that impart to Orange County more independence than ever. With deconcentration of work centers in Orange County commutation to Los Angeles has declined relatively.

Reticence to accept the county as a completely independent metropolis is reflected in the names of the professional sports teams, the Los Angeles Rams and the California (nee Los Angeles) Angels. Still, there is an "Orange County mentality—one that connotes, overall, greater political conservatism favored by dominance of pro-growth segments of the society. Also, Orange County is much less complex ethnically than southern Los Angeles County.

The Southeast Plain merges inland with the Santa Ana Mountains and lower-elevation prongs, the Chino and Coyote hills (map 6-11). In the south it abuts against the San Joaquin Hills.

The Plain remained primarily agrarian until the 1950's. Then, with construction of the Santa Ana Freeway (I-5) from downtown Los Angeles (map 6-11) rapid metamorphosis occurred and it began to fuse into the vast conurbation.

As residential space "closer in" to Los Angeles filled, thousands of dwellings materialized farther to the southeast.

A powerful energizer for urbanization came from industries seeking space for expansion, supplemented by petroleum, recreation enterprises and military bases. While there is commutation to Los Angeles it is exceeded by commutation into Orange County, especially from western Riverside and San Bernardino counties.

### The Santa Ana Plain

Seemingly featureless, the Santa Ana is an alluvial surface which has been built mainly by deposits of the Santa Ana River.

Prior to construction of dikes downstream and flood-control structures upstream, the river wan-

**Figure 6-40.** Most of the growth of Huntington Beach has occurred on the flatlands that are a distance inland from its center. (dwl)

dered widely during flood stages (and might again, with "200 Year" floods).

There are slight variations in surface. North of Fullerton the low oil-bearing Coyote Hills separate the Plain from a higher basin in which Brea and La Habra are located. Along the coast the Newport-Inglewood Uplift is seen in low rises and wells tapping rich petroleum deposits.

### Cattle...Grapes.. Valencias...Specialty Crops

While the Spanish made slight use of the Santa Ana Plain, change came with Mexican rule.

Ten ranchos, some extending beyond the Coastal Plain, were awarded during the Mexican period. Grain farming and grazing remained as the basic activities during the second half of the nineteenth century.

The change to town development and cultivated fields came with Americanization.

Anaheim, the first post-Mexican colony in the entire Los Angeles Lowlands, was established in 1857 by a group of Germans from San Francisco. Until disease ended viticulture in the 1880's it was the principal wine producer of the Lowlands.

Another new agricultural phase commenced with the sudden shift from vineyards to orange groves and walnut orchards.

West of the citrus groves, where soils were heavier and the water table higher, alfalfa, beans, sugar beets and truck crops were grown extensively. Avocados were added, on south-facing slopes of the Chino and Puente hills, in the 1930's.

Farm products achieved their peak values in 1959 although the maximum orange acreage was attained a decade earlier.

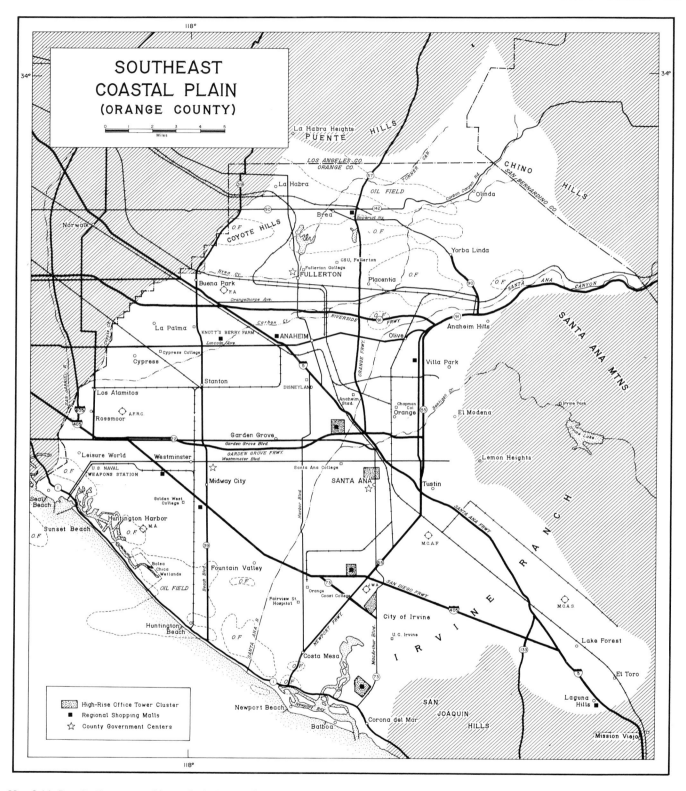

**SOUTHEAST COASTAL PLAIN (ORANGE COUNTY)**

High-Rise Office Tower Cluster
Regional Shopping Malls
County Government Centers

**Map 6-11.** Despite the topographic continuity (much of the county is part of the Los Angeles Coastal Plain) it has long been recognized as a separate political entity.

Contrariwise, dairying expanded in the mid-1950's, only to vanish in the 1970's. Remaining agriculture, largely limited to space under power lines or land reserved for future urban use, was stabilized by the 1980s, emphasizing high-value (especially perishable) items such as strawberries, nursery stock and vegetables.

## People, Electronics and Mickey Mouse

With its multi-million people, Orange County achieved urban maturity rapidly. Hurried expansion of a score of municipalities has created city boundaries about as irregular as jigsaw puzzle pieces.

Three activities, manufacturing, services and tourism, have fostered urbanization. All three have been motivated by metropolitan growth and improved highway linkage within the Los Angeles conurbation.

Nearly a third of Orange County employment is dependent upon manufacturing.

Many establishments satisfy numerous wants; output includes such diverse items as chemicals, containers, auto parts and foods. "Older" industries are based upon food or petroleum production.

Petroleum, particularly significant since the l920's, has been concentrated in two belts.

One is the coastal zone from Newport Beach to Seal Beach—it includes Huntington Beach, one of the state's leading producers (see table, petroleum section, Chapter 9). The other is inland; oil is pumped in the vicinity of Brea, Olinda and Fullerton. Here there are oil company research laboratories and a related synthetic fertilizer plant. Output of minerals in Orange County now considerably exceeds value of agricultural products.

Industrialization was long paced by aerospace developments; defense and aerospace have accounted for more than half of the county's factory employment.

Although Orange County lacked traditional aircraft plants, its open space attracted "parent" aircraft companies in Los Angeles County when new facilities were needed during the electronics era. Hence Hughes, Northrop, North American Rockwell and McDonnell Douglas erected factories in Orange County while some some smaller firms transferred their entire operations from Los Angeles. Other corporations are either indigenous to the Southeast Plain, or like Ford Motor Company's Aeronutronics, represent an influx of outside manufacturers.

Most aerospace development is unattached to airports.

**Figure 6-41.** Landscape near John Wayne Airport. Orange County has much high-tech industry. (dwl)

Factories that emphasize heavy production have been erected on level tracts adjacent to railroad lines. Where research and lighter production dominate, site requirements have been less restricted. Hence rougher lands around Fullerton and Newport Beach have been utilized. Industrial zones are widely dispersed on the Southeast Plain. Usually they form ribbons parallel to established rail lines and freeways or around oil fields.

Recreation achieved significance in the 1920's with increased automobiles and improvement of Newport Bay and Coast Highway.

Beach patronage has continued to expand while several large-scale retirement communities have been erected.

The greatest impact followed creation of Disneyland in Anaheim (early 1950's). This has fostered one of the state's largest entertainment and tourist-serving complexes, including a convention center. Knott's Berry Farm, like Disneyland, has had on-going success. Other ventures have proved short-lived.

## The One-Time Orange Belt

Orange groves have essentially vanished from the interior portion of the Southeast Plain—the erstwhile citrus belt remains the County's focus of population and influence.

In part this is the result of established communities, as well as freeway and through railroad location. Now these fertile flatlands are occupied by single-family homes, apartments, condominiums, attached townhouses and mobile homes of white-collar or factory workers. Here and there are an in-

**Figure 6-42.** California State University, Fullerton has one of the few high-rise campuses in the Golden State. (dwl)

creasing number of high-rises or campus-like industrial parks.

On the average there is slightly greater affluence, with a lesser range of incomes, than in Los Angeles County. Socioeconomic districts tend to be fragmented although the total population is more Anglo and less representative of the Asian and American rims of the Pacific Basin.

This landscape once suggested one vast orchard with a few residential-shipping towns carefully deposited so as not to disturb a single tree. In those days social stratification between relatively prosperous Middle Western immigrants and Mexican laborers was rigid.

*Anaheim* (238,000), due to its recreational and industrial activities, is distinctive. Although it is the largest city in Orange County (and the ninth largest in California), its growth rate began to slow in the 1960s. Renovation of its downtown, decimated by shopping center competition, has been sluggish. Much growth has occurred in Anaheim Hills, site of large-scale planned development.

It owed much of its dramatic growth over three decades (1950-1980) to closer-location to Los Angeles than Santa Ana and to civic aggressiveness. Remaining open space is reserved principally for industry.

Within its 12-mile breadth are large housing tracts and major shopping centers. Aerospace and other factories draw employees from many towns (some outside the County).

Disneyland has attracted many allied facilities (motels and restaurants especially). Nearby are a large convention hall and Anaheim Stadium, used by major-league football and baseball teams.

*Santa Ana* (228,000), the seat of Orange County, also has importance for industry, transportation and residence.

Its boom-decades growth has been slightly slower than that of Anaheim. Although it is comparable in size, in-limits, to Dayton or Richmond (Va.), this is not obvious in the central district (other than the imposing city-county civic center).

The several shopping centers and variety of specialty shops reflect county growth. Recent renovation of a shopping center indicates rising interest in commercial revitalization.

Its cultural attractions include Santa Ana College and the Bowers Museum. Santa Ana is the leading city for communication media in the county; there is also a sizable transportation facility (serving Amtrak, intercity and county transit buses). Industrial activity is diversified and there are two nearby military bases of consequence.

In a county identified with residence of conservative Anglos, Santa Ana's ethnic make-up is unique.

The old C.B.D. and the south side is conspicuously Hispanic. Much of the small black populace of the county resides here.

*Garden Grove* (135,000) epitomizes an inconsequential farm village that boomed into a commuter residence place. There is modest retailing and manufacturing.

The fourth-largest city of Orange County, it gained a "spillover" of hotels and other tourist-related services from Disneyland along Harbor Boulevard, locale of widely-publicized *Crystal Cathedral*.

Housing is less expensive than in some Orange County cities and a sizable Latino expansion has occurred from the barrios of Santa Ana. East-west Garden Grove Freeway (Ca. 22) promotes ease of traveling to work. The city has also become a des-

**Figure 6-43.** Holiday throng at Disneyland. The Asian and Hispanic patrons may be foreign tourists—or more likely local residents. (dwl).

tination for recent Korean immigrants.

***Fullerton*** (112,000) is more diverse in functions (residence, higher education, manufacturing) than some cities in the County.

Founded during the boom of the 1880's, Fullerton experienced growth from oil (1920's). The city benefited from the post-1950 movement of aerospace firms into Orange County. It is favored by good transport facilities, including freeways and three rail lines. To its food processing, petrochemicals and other industries, aerospace has been added.

Fullerton has an extension of the "higher income-higher education" belt extending eastward from Whittier and La Mirada. Residences of the affluent occupy hillsides in the northern part of the city. Nearby are campuses of Fullerton College and California State University, distinguished by high-rise structures.

***Orange*** (104,000), at quick glance may appear largely residential but is diversified in function.

Downtown Orange still epitomizes the classic Middlewest-in-California, with brick business blocks around a town square.

Educational facilities include the large U.C. Irvine and St. Joseph's Children's Hospital medical complexes as well as Chapman College and Culver Loyola-Marymount University.

The considerable retail facilities include *The City*, an office-retailing development and Mall of Orange and Town and Country (fancy retail shops). There is also a trackside mixed industrial belt.

***Buena Park*** (66,000), important as a commuter residence town, has large tourist attractions as well

as manufacturing and warehousing.

Adjacent to the Los Angeles/Orange county line and crossed by two freeways (including the Santa Ana), Buena Park provides a logical home for industrial commuters. Through the years, *Knott's Berry Farm* has become more popular as a tourist attraction. It has prompted development of lesser attractions.

## The Flatlands

Inland from the Inglewood-Newport Uplift and seaward from the erstwhile citrus belt, the Flatlands was long utilized for vegetables and truck crops. Subsequently farming has been replaced by urbanization.

In days past the Flatlands displayed a disinteresting landscape. Without orchards and windbreaks it was less attractive than the citrus belt to the northeast. The few villages were drab.

Housing developments appeared later (1960's) than in much of Orange County. Land scarcity elsewhere, freeway access and provision for drainage compelled urbanization of this less-attractive poorly-drained quadrant with its heavier soils.

***Westminster*** (73,000) still has older dwellings in its core, but it is chiefly an assemblage of middle-income dwellings often occupied by commuters. It has the ranking "west county" mall and civic center and motels and retail offices along freeways.

The city has a definite Vietnamese group, centered in *Little Saigon* along Bolsa Avenue. Despite its Asian architecture, it has not become a tourist attraction comparable to San Francisco's Chinatown, as some have expected.

**Figure 6-44.** Knott's Berry Farm in Buena Park preceded and inspired the creation of Disneyland not far "down the road." The Farm remains a leading visitor attraction. (dwl)

These Vietnamese are actually *Chinese,* even though they may have lived in Vietnam for several generations. A number have developed a sizable addition to Los Angeles Chinatown, to which they commute daily. One commented, "I used to commute three blocks by boat on the canal. Now I drive 50 miles on the freeway. American-born Chinese ("ABC's") refer to the new-comers as the "FOB's" (fresh off the boat) in contrast to the "JOJ's" (just off jets), a term used to describe the businessmen from Taipei and Hong Kong who have established an electronics plant with a multi-million dollar investment.

## The Bay and the Beach

From Newport Bay to Seal Beach the Orange County shore forms an almost unbroken continuum of public beaches.

Low terraces provide sites for most urban nuclei; intervening marshy strips (former mouths of the Santa Ana River) have been gradually converted into harbor usage or residential sites.
There is a diversity of shoreline uses.
Seafood restaurants, transient accommodations, sportsfishing piers, surfboard shops and other shore-oriented enterprises proliferate.
Contrary, and sometimes opposing, activities include oil fields, a weapons depot, sewage disposal and electric generating plants.
Both neighborhoods and residents are varied—they include well-to-do retirees at shoreside, commuters in tract houses and the "beach set" in crowded, albeit expensive, rental units. The Shore population tends to be transient or fairly recent with ties that are northward toward Los Angeles as much as towards the "old citrus belt." So far the

**Figure 6-45a.** This main north-south boulevard in Santa Ana is more suggestive of a larger city than is much of the original city core. (dwl)

coastal area is not so populous, so cohesive or so determined as to challenge the dominance of the county's inland and southern cores.

*Seal Beach* (29,000), a popular waterside suburb of Long Beach, has varied activities.

Once it was the roadstead for Anaheim's 19th century winegrowers. Now there are Naval installations and aerospace research and developments facilities. Upper middle-income residences and a Leisure World planned-retirement community augment the densely-settled original townsite along the beach.

In the later twentieth century *Huntington Beach* (192,000), with varied functions, has been one of the more rapidly-growing cities in the Lowlands. After filling-in elsewhere it still had space!

In the past it was known for its oilfield, its sandy seacoast (popular with surfers) and its sports pier. The oil boom began in 1923; later, *whipstocking* (non-vertical drilling) permitted the tapping of offshore tideland pools. Oil remains important, evidenced by recently-erected offshore platforms.

Aggressive annexation has subsequently extended the city limits four miles inland and discontinuously along the shore from Seal Beach to Newport Beach. Adjacent to Seal Beach manmade *Huntington Harbour* has become a marina. Higher-income residences and apartments have been erected. Housing tracts and shopping centers have replaced beanfields. Considerable land, marshy or within oilfields, has not been developed. While basically residential, Huntington Beach also has some aerospace, oil-related industries and shoreline tourism.

**Figure 6-45.** Orange County governmental center, Santa Ana. (dwl)

*Bolsa Chica Wetland,* long known as a "battle-ground" between developers and preservationists, is being apportioned for continuing oil output, urbanization and wetland maintenance.

Four communities surround Newport Bay: *Balboa, Costa Mesa, Corona del Mar* and *Newport Beach.* They constitute the principal "watering spot" for the entire Los Angeles Basin.

The Bay was once a silt-clogged inlet at the terminus of the Santa Ana River (until a new mouth was dredged upcoast to the northwest). Resort activity, inaugurated in the 1890's, expanded after construction of the Pacific Electric interurban and then through highway connections and extensive harbor improvement.

While summer visitation to this resort area is considerable, the year-round population has expanded considerably.

***Costa Mesa*** (90,000), principally on terraces away from the Bay shore, is a misfit community. It is sustained by a variety of supports and has the widest income range and ethnic mix (including many Mexicans).

Politically, Balboa and Corona del Mar are portions of Costa Mesa which prefer to downplay the connection.

Elsewhere, Costa Mesa is less affluent and despite its country clubs, less involved with aquatic activity and with retirement. It does have a residential "overflow" from Newport Beach.

Reaching along the west side of *John Wayne,* the county's commercial airport, the oddly-shaped city does have considerable industrial activity.

Other supports include two colleges (Orange Coast and Southern California), a state hospital (Fairview) and South Coast Plaza, a huge office-shopping-hotel complex near the crossing of I-405, Ca. 73 and Ca.55 freeways. It is the largest development of its type in Southern California. Some shops are comparable to those in Beverly Hills. The Plaza is now the site of the County's two leading performing-arts theatres. It may be the cultural hub of Orange County.

The original town on the Bay, ***Newport Beach*** (67,000) is one of California's plushiest communities, dependent upon recreation, residence and retail trade.

Merged with Balboa (since 1902) and Corona del Mar, it completely surrounds the Bay and includes some artificial islands. Hundreds of pleasure craft are anchored in the Bay (it is the self-acclaimed "yachting capital of the Pacific," and the city has many expensive homes. In Orange County only Laguna Beach has a higher per cent of retirees. *Fashion Island,* surrounded by high-rise office structures, hotels, and civic facilities, approaches Beverly Hills in smart shops.

## Irvine Ranch

The Ranch, assembled over a century ago over a century ago by James Irvine and his partners from Mexican land grants, is beginning to disappear through planned urbanization.

Decades ago choice waterfront lots adjacent to Newport Bay were made available, under long-time lease, for residential use. Since sale of the family-held Irvine Corporation in 1977 complete urbanization of the 84,000-acre barony seems inevitable. Although there are still several thousand head of cattle and thousands of acres of farmland, orderly urbanization is underway.

**Figfre 6-46.** Balboa Peninsula and Newport Beach. (dwl)

**Figure 6-47.** A street of handsome homes near the University of California, Irvine campus. (dwl)

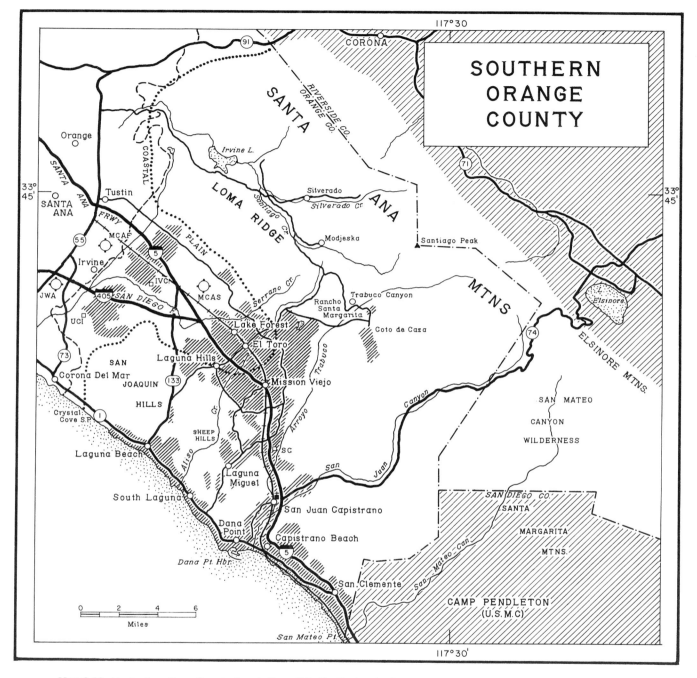

**Map 6-12.** Much of southern Orange County lies within the Peninsular Ranges southeast of the Los Angeles Coastal Plain.

*Irvine* (115,000), a planned city on the northern portion of the former Ranch holdings, is sustained by diverse functions including industry, higher education and residence.

*John Wayne Airport,* the commercial terminal for Orange County, is adjacent to the city. Despite its modest passenger terminal, there are flights to sundry California destinations and elsewhere. It is surrounded by many industrial plants. Aerospace, as well as other manufacturing, takes place in plants which often are attractively designed and landscaped.

The *55 Freeway Corridor,* extending from Costa Mesa into Tustin, has become a major employment area.

The spacious University of California (founded

1960) campus, on donated Ranch land, is well designed. It has grown rapidly and still has much space for expansion. Other institutions include Irvine Valley College and sectarian Christ College. Larger dwellings house affluent residents, concerning those citizens who hoped Orange County would achieve a broader income and ethnic balance.

## South County

Occupying the lower western portion of the northern Peninsular Ranges, southern Orange County differs considerably from the Santa Ana Plain to the northwest.

Between the Pacific Ocean and Cleveland National Forest (to the east) this was a near-empty land, used principally for grazing, until the 1960's.

In the past several decades, since construction of Interstate 5 between metropolitan Los Angeles and San Diego, South County has increased dramatically in population as several unincorporated higher-income communities have appeared.

In part this resulted from the breakup of several large ranches, coupled with disappearance of attractive open space "closer in" to San Diego and Los Angeles.

This is an Anglo realm, occupied by affluent business and professional people, many of whom commute, as well as higher income retirees. Most towns have one or more country clubs which reflects the lifestyles of residents. In some instances, gate houses and security guards screen out "unwelcome" visitors.

There are two principal foci, the coastal strip, occupying terraces along the path of old Coast Highway (now Rt. l) and the inland route, partly in Oso Creek valley, traversed now by Interstate 5.

Although a few older villages now serve as urban cores, a number of the communities, developed since 1960, have opposed incorporation.

**Laguna Beach** (19,000), one of the more attractive resorts along the nation's Pacific Coast, has endeavored not to expand.

Originally a summer refuge for residents of Orange County, it had become an artists' colony by 1920—its abrupt headlands and craggy coves attracted painters. The community is proud of its heritage, with attractive facades and quaint shops. It has strived to be a cultural center despite youthful visitors who might prefer it to be another Venice. Permanent residents tend to be affluent and elderly. *Three Arch Bay,* on its southern pe-

riphery, is an "exclusive" beach place with security guards, as is *Emerald Bay* on the northern edge. Socially the two contrast with *South Laguna* and *Laguna Canyon.*

**Dana Point** (16,000), a hamlet before the 1960's, remains unincorporated despite much growth in recent decades.

Newer residences have been built into the San Joaquin Hills; there is also a yacht basin serving South County.

**San Clemente** (36,000), although founded in the 1920's, remained a small village until post-1960 growth.

Belatedly residents realized how much hillside growth had occurred. Of late there has been strong opposition to further growth. During the presidency of Richard Nixon, the city was often in the news as the site of the "western White House."

Most of the communities along Oso Creek valley are newer and still unincorporated. An exception is **San Juan Capistrano** (24,000) which retained its California atmosphere as a mission village until the late 20th century. Catering to mission visitors is evident here.

**Mission Viejo** (70,000), largest of South County towns, is essentially residential.

Part of the city, unincorporated by choice, focuses on a natural-looking reservoir. Saddleback College, one of the newer (and larger) California community colleges is here. Adjacent **Laguna Niguel** (25,000) to the southwest, is basically residential, as is **El Toro** (60,000) to the north.

On the northeast fringe of Mission Viejo is *Rancho Santa Margarita,* intended to have multiple-unit dwellings and a business park.

**Laguna Hills** (52,000), now larger than the beach community to the west, is unique in several aspects.

It has in *Leisure World* one of the nation's largest senior citizens' complexes (circa 22, 000), where the "average" age is 76, plus a shopping mall with associated high-rise office structures.

---

## THE SAN FERNANDO VALLEY *

In the city of Los Angeles there is *only* one valley—the San Fernando Valley. For knowledgeable Americans the Valley has conjured the "good life" in the Golden State—that is, for affluent Anglos.

---

* This section has been reviewed by John Carthew, Pierce College.

The San Fernando, northwestern Lowland in the Los Angeles Basin, is now completely urbanized (maps 6-5 and 6-13). Its population of 1.8 million includes almost half the people of Los Angeles—it is exceeded by only five cities in the nation.

The San Fernando experienced a multitudinous population gain, 1940-1980. Much of the Los Angeles increase of those decades occurred here.

Eighty per cent of the Valley consists of seventeen political *districts* within Los Angeles; the remainder lies within four independent satellites, Glendale, Burbank, San Fernando and Universal City.

Until recently the Valley was Anglo land; populace-wise, like the Coast Plain south of the Santa Monica Mountains, it is becoming more of a trans-Pacific Basin realm.

Despite increases in numbers of Jewish, Hispanics, Arab, and other ethnic peoples, an Anglo majority continues.

While there are pockets of lower incomes, about half of the Valleyites still have superior living standards. In few places in the world do so many live so well.

"The good life" is reflected in such things as houses, swimming pools, educational attainment and per capita ownership of automobiles. There are sometimes three or more cars per family and two is deemed as *essential* (yet approximately half of the families do not have two cars) in the San Fernando, where public transportation is inadequate. Although the number of apartments is increasing, especially near freeways, the San Fernando remains a realm of single family homes.

The San Fernando provides an important entryway into central Los Angeles from the west and north.

Freeways, Golden State (I-5), Ventura (U.S. 101), Hollywood (Ca. 170), San Diego (I-405) and Simi Valley (Ca. 118) carry heavy vehicular flow. Despite the freeways and a system of intersecting boulevards, rush-hour traffic becomes congested at many points. Partly this results from the local deficit of employment. Despite a sizable influx of industries into the Valley which account for a third of local employment, there is much commutation to other parts of the Los Angeles Lowlands as well as movement into the Valley, particularly for employment in service positions.

Airports have formed a conspicuous aspect of San Fernando landscapes, despite the height of bordering mountains, for as long as flying has been important.

In the historic succession of chief commercial airports for metropolitan Los Angeles, the second and third, have been located here. Now much-expanded airports, the tri-city *Burbank-Glendale-Pasadena Airport* (formerly the Lockheed) and *Van Nuys* (general aircraft) serve jet planes, while another Valley field helps accommodate the Lowlands' large number of light private planes.

The Valley has served as a rail corridor for over a hundred years.

Southern Pacific tracks enter the basin through the *Glendale* (Los Angeles) *Narrows* from central Los Angeles. Rail routes bifurcate in Burbank (map 6-13); the Coast Line crosses the Valley northwestward through Chatsworth, then continues toward the Oxnard Plain via tunnels while the Central Valley Line extends northward and leaves the San Fernando through a tunnel beneath San Fernando Pass to proceed into the Mojave Desert. Spur lines of the Southern Pacific allow freight movement to industrial zones within the basin.

### An Intermont Basin, With Hot Summer Afternoons

The mountain-girt San Fernando Valley is separated from the Los Angeles Coastal Plain by the Santa Monica Mountains (see map 6-13).

To the north rise the Santa Susana Mountains and to the west the Simi Hills. On the east are the Verdugo and San Rafael hills, backed by the loftier San Gabriel Range beyond the rift known as La Canada Corridor.

An intermontane basin, the San Fernando, covering more than 200 square miles, is covered with alluvial debris transported by streams flowing out of the surrounding highlands. A southward sloping plain without apparent relief, the Valley rises from 500 feet along the Los Angeles River to 1500 feet elevation in the north. Alluvial fans spread out from surrounding uplands, especially in the northeast.

The Los Angeles River provides the single exit for external drainage.

During some winter storms excessive runoff from surrounding canyons has caused serious flooding which prompted the large *Hansen* and *Sepulveda* flood control basins. The channel of the Los Angeles River, with considerable subterranean flow, is heavily pumped by Los Angeles in the vicinity of the Glendale Narrows.

The Valley has more variable weather than does the Coastal Plain. It approaches the *semiarid* modification of the dry-summer subtropical climate and is characterized by hot summer afternoons but generally pleasant nocturnal temperatures.

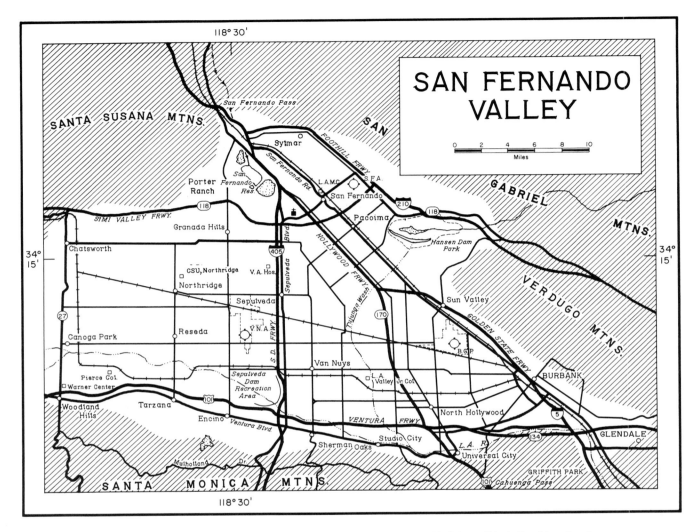

**Map 6-13.** Most of the San Fernando Valley constitutes the northern half of the political city of Los Angeles.

Whereas Santa Monica has an average July temperature of 66 degrees F., that of San Fernando is 73.5 degrees F.

While winters tend to be mild for the latitude, minimal temperatures are usually lower than on the Coastal Plain (sub-freezing temperatures *do* occur). Especially in early summer, thick banks of advection fog move over the low summits of the Santa Monica Mountains, creating a "high overcast" that commonly "burns off" before mid-day.

The San Fernando receives limited benefit from sea breezes, although sometimes cooler ocean air flows inland across Cahuenga Pass. Seasonally, particularly in spring and autumn, hot dry (and sometimes dusty) winds from the Mojave Desert blow into the Valley via San Fernando Pass.

**From Mission to High Rises**

Little evidence of Indian occupance of the Valley remains.

There are a few modified place names, a few settlement "sites," and some romantic lore.

Mission San Fernando Rey, established in 1797, was among the more prosperous California missions.

Fields were irrigated and it was known for its grapes and its wheat. Thousands of cattle and sheep were pastured. Hides and tallow were hauled to San Pedro in oxcarts.

Even before the Mission, the Spanish had awarded two early grants in the Valley; these were Rancho San Rafael (1784) and extensive Rancho Encino (1795).

During the ensuing decade after secularization (in 1834) the mission was divided into five ranchos.

These were El Escorpion (southwest), Providencia (northeast), El Encino (south). Tujunga (northeast) and Ex-Mission San Fernando, much the largest.

Activity during early American decades was similar to that elsewhere in California where there had been a rancho livestock economy.

The southern portion of Ex-Mission San Fernando became the property, in 1869, of a San Francisco group which formed the San Fernando Homestead Association, soon reorganized as a sheep company. By 1873 the company's lands were supporting 40,000 head of sheep. After drought in 1877 the firm divided its property into a series of large wheat farms.

Use of the northern portion of ex-Mission was acquired by another San Francisco group. Here the town of San Fernando was founded along the new trackage of the Southern Pacific near the southern approach to San Fernando Pass. Remaining land was planted in barley and wheat. But disagreement on farm policy prompted a three-way division; each partner received about 20,000 acres.

Until construction of the Los Angeles Aqueduct (see Chapter 3) grains remained the chief products.

Fruit raising, employing subirrigation, was tried around North Hollywood, without much success, for the city of Los Angeles, with prior water rights, prevented widespread pump irrigation. Sufficient pumping did occur in San Fernando, Burbank and Glendale to permit continued political independence. Until 1913 the static Valley hamlets remained farm towns.

In anticipation of Owens River water, a Los Angeles syndicate began purchasing Valley properties in 1905. Four new towns were established: Marian (Reseda), Owensmouth (Canoga Park), Van Nuys and Zelzah (Northridge). Two were located along the coast line of the Southern Pacific Railroad.

In 1915 Los Angeles absorbed 170 square miles of the Valley into its corporate limits.

Since the city was not consuming all the water the Aqueduct provided, this expansion permitted it to sell the surplus for irrigation in the Valley and *still*, through return flow, recover a third through return flow seepage into the Los Angeles River.

The sudden availability of water for irrigation prompted a rapid shift in land-use to orchards, truck gardens and vineyards. While only 30,000 acres were irrigated in 1917, within three years 50,000 acres were receiving water.

Most Valley towns did not elect to join Los Angeles immediately.

But within a decade *insufficient* water forced most of them to merge into the city: Canoga Park (1917), Chatsworth (1920) and North Hollywood (1923).

During the boom of the 1920's towns in the southern Valley gained rapidly in population.

With automotive transportation the lure of a "country home" was inviting and rurban advance spread westward from Glendale through Van Nuys. Impetus was given by the making of motion pictures at Universal City.

Population doubled in the San Fernando Valley between 1930 and 1940.

The film industry expanded its activities and the aircraft industry in Burbank likewise gained momentum. With urban expansion, agricultural decline in the southeast led to the disappearance of dairies, poultry farms, fruit-packing plants and nurseries.

In the northwestern Valley, however, agriculture remained. In the northwestern corner, 10,000 acres in the Northridge district were converted into "gentlemen" ranches as Hollywood stars and

**Figure 6-48.** Cahuenga Pass with Hollywood Freeway (U.S. 101) during morning rush. View southeast toward Hollywood. (Caltrans)

**Figure 6-49.** "The Valley", view southeast toward smog-laden Glendale Narrows. A railroad, a freeway (I-5) and the Los Angeles Aqueduct utilize San Fernando Pass (lower left). The Los Angeles Lakes, storage units for the Aqueduct, were reduced in size after an earthquake in 1971. (Caltrans)

other affluent Anglos established residence. Such development inspired the popular song of 1941, *San Fernando Valley*. Meanwhile, with industrial expansion under way late in the 1930's, the population of Glendale and Burbank was accelerated more than elsewhere in the Valley.

For several decades after World War II the San Fernando continued to be a major center of population growth in the metropolis.

Scores of housing tracts were built, ranging from modest dwellings (as in Panorama City) to luxurious hillside homes along the north slope of the Santa Monica Mountains. A number of regional shopping centers were constructed. Final vestiges of sizable open spaces, around Chatsworth and Porter Ranch, became housing tracts and huge industrial parks.

With the disappearance of open space the Valley has lost its impression of newness although change continues to occur.

Impressive high-rise clusters have appeared at several places along Ventura Boulevard, as in Woodland Hills, Tarzana and Sherman Oaks, in downtown Glendale and southwestern Burbank near Universal City. Expensive new dwellings have been built on the slopes of the Verdugo Hills in Glendale and Burbank and along the southern base of the Santa Susana Mountains.

Today the stranger flying across the Valley towards Los Angeles International Airport or speeding along a San Fernando freeway probably does not appreciate the attractiveness of the Valley—he sees only the sprawling metropolis.

## The Outsiders

The three cities of Glendale, Burbank and San Fernando, politically independent of Los Angeles, extend along the eastern periphery of the "independent" San Fernando Valley.

They straddle "California's Main Street", the Golden State Freeway (I-5), and the Valley line of the Santa Fe Southern.

They tend to be considerably older than many of the districts of Los Angeles in the Valley. And, in detail, each is considerably different.

*Glendale* (156,000), one of the oldest Valley cities, has diversified functions including industry, retail trade and residence.

The central district looks like a city. Recently-constructed high-rises house financial, medical, accounting, legal and other professional services. The district was one of the first in the Lowlands to acquire a downtown mall (The Galleria).

Commonly considered a residential town, Glendale has considerable industrial activity near I-5 and rail lines. Products of its 300 factories include pharmaceuticals, foods (including pet foods), electronics, and house trailers.

Glendale is a a pleasant residential place, particularly its northeastern periphery nestled along canyons within the San Rafael Hills. Most residences are modest, of frame or stucco construction. Apartment units, however, continue to replace single-family homes. Basically Anglo, the city is becoming more representative of the Pacific Basin, with Hispanics and Asians, as well as Arabs.

During the boom of the 1880's Glendale was a citrus town. With construction of its Pacific Electric interurban link (in 1904) it grew as a "close-in" suburb of downtown Los Angeles, especially during the Boom of the 1920's. By 1940 little vacant land remained. Subsequently annexations have extended the city through wooded Verdugo Canyon and into the La Canada Corridor.

Cultural aspects include Glendale College, hillside Brand Park and Forest Lawn Memorial Cemetery, devoid of tombstones and renowned for its several churches and reproductions of art works.

*Burbank* (90,000), like Glendale a pleasant residential place, has other activities as entertainment facilities, considerable industrial output and a tri-city airport.

It is a legacy of the boom of the 1880's—but more distant from Los Angeles than Glendale, it remained a slow-growing village until the 1920's. Then transformation from an agricultural town and residential suburb began, quickened during World War II and reached a crest in Valley urbanization after 1945. Now there is little vacant land except for steep hillsides.

The downtown area is smaller than that of Glendale but there is a *second* center in the southwest, the locale of television (N.B.C.) and motion picture studios (Disney, Columbia and the former Warner Brothers), ancillary offices and a major hospital.

As the location of Lockheed Aircraft, whose World War II expansion prompted much growth, Burbank has much allied aerospace manufacturing. Adjacent to the aircraft plants is *Burbank-Glendale-Pasadena Airport,* a *secondary* passenger terminal for the Lowlands.

*San Fernando* (20,000) is much smaller than Burbank, more ethnic, less industrial, and has lower-income residents.

The original Anglo settlement in the Valley was sufficiently distant from Los Angeles to develop as an independent farm center with packing and shipping plants for olives, citrus and truck crops. Once it was an important pass city, at the southern approach to San Fernando Pass and the Ridge Route. Although it grew somewhat after surrounding farmlands within the city of Los Angeles received water from Owens Valley but overall the third boom (1920's) had limited effect.

Functions of San Fernando changed in the 1950's as the mushrooming suburban growth of metropolitan Los Angeles finally reached the community. Tract homes replaced orange and olive groves; packing houses closed down. With population growth in the north Valley, San Fernando has gained some retail trade and rebuilt its central core with a "mission" theme. But it is considered a Mexican town (nearly three-fourths of the population is Hispanic). The barrio continues into neighboring **Pacoima**, within Los Angeles limits, which also has the Valley's single black community.

## Seventeen Districts, And A Central Place (of sorts)

Seventeen erstwhile hamlets rapidly coalesced into one conurbation in less than two generations after World War II. And all of it is within the city limits of Los Angeles.

They tend to be oriented with principal six-lane boulevards, laid out with a grid pattern, and paralleling abandoned Pacific Electric interurban lines. Skylines are low and files of palm trees are conspicuous. Variety to large housing tracts and flat terrain is afforded by luxuriant plantings. Despite en masse construction, residences have often been designed for an upper middle-income business and professional Anglo market.

Original town cores can often be identified by on-street parking meters, small retail areas and post-offices. Individual communities retain such identifying nomenclature as high schools, service clubs and chambers of commerce.

Districts tend primarily to be residential. There is manufacturing, but it is not common in all communities. Public schools tend to be large with sizable playgrounds. Parks are much too limited for the total area and population. Ventura Boulevard, pre-freeway U.S.101, serves as an east-west main street for the southern Valley.

*North Hollywood* (120,000), immediately west of Burbank, is an "older" district which had considerable pre-World War II growth. Although it is near movie studios and houses many theatrical employees, it has never been a second Hollywood.

Like other Valley districts it was once a farm village which is still evidenced by many relict walnut trees retained for residential landscaping as well as the headquarters of the nation's largest independent egg-packing firm.

The district is essentially a lower-middle income community (except for the upper-middle income

**Figure 6-50.** Dwellings on terraced slopes, north side of Santa Monica Mountains, Sherman Oaks. I-405 in rear. (dwl)

area of *Toluca Lake),* a superior residential enclave on the Burbank boundary. This segment became "fashionable" when film personalities established homes here in the 1930's. North Hollywood is about a fourth Hispanic.

With a broader diversity of functions than other Los Angeles districts, **Van Nuys** (150,000) forms a central place for some of the Valley.

Like San Pedro, it has an outlying "city" administrative center. As in North Hollywood, its central core focuses along an attenuated north-south "shoestring" which extends along a single boulevard. Los Angeles Valley College is located in the

district. Apartment-house neighborhoods are becoming conspicuous.

Portions of north Van Nuys along Southern Pacific trackage and around much-enlarged Van Nuys Airport, a national leader for general aircraft, have industrial usage. Factories include an automobile assembly plant, missile producers, several large breweries and electronics firms.

**Sherman Oaks** (southern Van Nuys) forms a "spill-over" across the Santa Monica Mountains of the luxury-level dwellings of Beverly Hills and Westwood.

It is linked with the Coastal Plain by two canyon boulevards (Beverly Glen and Coldwater Canyon). The belt of expensive homes reaching along the entire northern slopes of the Hollywood Hills (Santa Monica Mountains) was noted previously. On its western edge multi-story Sherman Oaks Galleria is known for quality retail shops.

In the western San Fernando the farm villages became sizable communities later than the districts farther east. The period of major growth occurred between 1955 and 1980.

Essentially these are residence places.

The belt of higher-income residence continues westward from Sherman Oaks through **Encino, Tarzana**, and **Woodland Hills**. At the far southwest corner of the Valley Hidden Hills and Calabasas are now part of the urban complex.

Each district has a country club. While the popu-

**Figure 6-51.** The western San Fernando Valley, view southeast from Canoga Park. Topanga Plaza, one of the Valley's large large shopping centers, in foreground. The "open" space in rear (right) is now the locale of the Warner Center complex (industrial-retail shopping-office). (Caltrans)

lace is strongly Anglo, Tarzana is a Jewish center and the "hidden" Mexican community in Woodland Hills is a legacy of the agricultural past.

In addition to its residential function, **Woodland Hills** (36,000) also has Pierce College and other activities.

These include a high-rise office complex (Warner Ranch) and two adjacent shopping centers (Topanga Plaza and Promenade Mall). There is also a crossing of the Santa Monica Mountains (Ca. 27) leading to the east end of the Malibu Coast.

Districts to the north are slightly less affluent. Regional shopping centers and country clubs tend to be absent. Among these are **Reseda** (75,000), and **Canoga Park** (85,000). Recently a segment of the latter district has gained identity as *West Hills*.

Northwestern districts were filled-in later than most parts of the Valley. The course of the Southern Pacific's Coast Line prompted industrial zoning in advance of urban growth.

*Northridge* (30,000), which retains a bit of its "city-money" ranch atmosphere, has the only university in the Valley.

California State University, on a somewhat more spacious campus than some its sister institutions, was "spun off" from C.S.U., Los Angeles in 1956. A large mall (Fashion Center) also serves affluent *Grenada Hills* and *Porter Ranch* to the north.

*Chatsworth* (40,000), besides its residential function, has electronics and other industrial plants along the Southern Pacific trackage.

*Ventura Boulevard* is the Valley's counterpart of Wilshire Boulevard.

For four decades, until it lost its highway status to the Ventura Freeway (U.S.101), it was the principal east-west thoroughfare leading westward from Los Angeles toward San Francisco.

For along its 15 miles of commercial activity, between Studio City and Calabasas, it has been a magnet for offices, retail shops, restaurants and many other enterprises, catering to the well-to-do clientele nearby, especially along the northern flanks of the Santa Monica Mountains. Besides shopping and entertainment establishments, the Boulevard has connections with the film colony, which includes two nearby studios and the Motion Picture Country Home for theatrical retirees.

**The Future**

The rapid fill-in of the San Fernando, coupled with public apathy, made the achievement of the "planned" basin anticipated by a City zoning study, impossible.

For example, portions of the Valley were zoned for industrial use but residents were not enthusiastic about many types of manufacturing plants. And sometimes speculation made land too expensive for such use. It is possible that some of the earlier, more hastily constructed tracts will become "bungalow slums". A public rapid-transit system has been suggested but population density may not justify it. And yet the number of apartment units is increasing. The ethnic make-up of the San Fernando is changing also. And despite much-used Hansen and Sepulveda flood-control basins for recreation, too little land was set aside for parks.

### THE SAN GABRIEL VALLEY *

Original site of colonial settlement in the Los Angeles Basin, the San Gabriel Valley was well-known for decades as a garden spot. Even as the Coastal Plain and the San Fernando Valley, in the second half of the twentieth century it has experienced almost complete urbanization.

But the San Gabriel, unlike the two lowlands already discussed , is politically independent of Los Angeles. Economically, however, it is closely allied to the central city, partly because there is somewhat less industrial employment in the San Gabriel than in the San Fernando or in Orange County and hence much commutation.

* This section was reviewed by Thomas Best, geographer-travel agent, Covina and Pamela Herman, C.S.U., Chico. Earlier it had been reviewed by the late Delmas Bugelli, Pasadena City College.

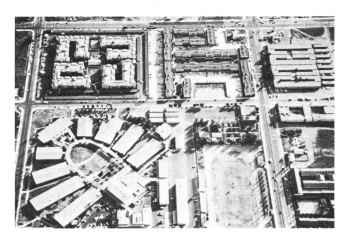

**Figure 6-52.** Apartments, Chatsworth. Increasingly the San Fernando is an area with multi-unit housing. (dwl)

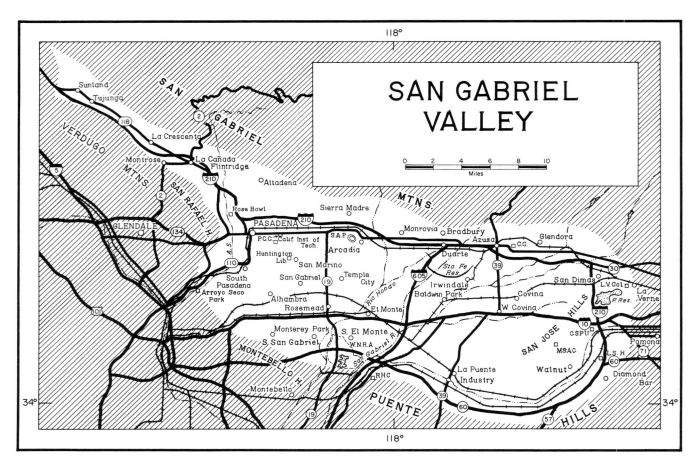

**Map 6-14.** Alsewhere in the Los Angeles Basin, the visistor is bewildered by the number of politically separate cities in the Los Angeles Basin (there are more than 80!).

Like the San Fernando, the San Gabriel Valley is an intermont basin of structural origin within the Transverse ranges (map 6-14).

The hilly uplands of the San Rafael Hills and the Verdugo Mountains separate the two basins. Between the San Gabriel and the Coastal Plain to the south rise the low Montebello and Puente hills. The San Jose Hills provide separation from the Inland Valley on the east. A definitive northern boundary is formed by the abruptly-rising southern block (Sierra Madre) of the San Gabriel Mountains.

The Arroyo Seco, the San Gabriel and smaller streams have transported alluvium to fill the Valley floor to considerable depth. Alluvial fans slope up more steeply north of Interstate 210. Within this basin, Santa Fe and Whittier Narrows flood-control basins have been constructed across the San Gabriel River.

### Friars, Orange Growers and Commuters

Founded in 1771, Mission San Gabriel was the fourth mission in Alta California. Prior to secularization it dominated much of the Los Angeles Lowlands—a million and a half acres from the San Gabriel Mountains to the Pacific.

When the original site proved susceptible to flooding the present location was selected (in 1776). One of the more prosperous missions, San Gabriel was the first on whose lands grapes and oranges were planted.

Following secularization (in the early 1830's) seven ranchos and a number of lesser tracts near the mission were parceled out by the Mexican government. These ranchos experienced the customary rise of cattle herds and eventual subdivision.

Anglo agricultural colonies were established in the 1880's as the Valley became an early "proving ground" for irrigation advances in the Los Angeles Lowlands.

The San Gabriel, the first major commercial source of oranges in Southern California, remained an important agricultural area through the 1940's.

The citrus belt extended eastward from Pasadena along the foothills through Glendora into the Inland Valley. The southern portion of the San Gabriel was extensively devoted to alfalfa, dairying, flowers, poultry, truck crops and walnuts.

Urbanization tended to move eastward from Los Angeles until the Fourth Boom (post-1945).

Then a surge of housing tracts transformed the basin, focusing particularly along the San Bernardino Freeway (I-10)

There are more than two dozen cities in the San Gabriel Valley yet unincorporated territory is unusually large and contains a fifth of the million-plus inhabitants of the basin.

The San Gabriel remains preponderantly an area of single-family dwellings, despite a boom in construction of apartments, condominiums and townhouses, especially in the older (western) portion of the Valley. There is considerable socioeconomic diversity, which affords sharp neighborhood contrasts within within short distances. Increasingly it is a Pacific Basin population, now including Asians as well as Anglos, Hispanics and blacks.

## Pasadena and Environs

Urbanization took place in the western San Gabriel many years before eastern portions of the Lowland.

The Pasadena (initially *Arroyo Seco*) Freeway was the only expressway in the Lowlands for a decade; it promoted much commuting. More recently, growth has slowed. There are greater extremes of wealth and economic diversity in the western Valley, as well as a richer variety of cultural institutions, than elsewhere in the San Gabriel.

***Pasadena*** (131,000), chief residential, retail, and manufacturing center of the Valley, was renowned for decades for its high-income "gracious living."

The city had its inception in the *California Colony of Indiana* in 1872. Similar to Riverside it developed as an orange grove town peopled by prosperous, often conservative, business and professional people. *Millionaire's Row* developed along Orange Grove Avenue before 1900 and several large resort hotels were erected. The renowned Tournament of Roses was inaugurated in 1890.

Pasadena gained international renown as a winter playground as a wintering place and the home of affluent senior citizens.

It was known for its resort hotels, especially the Huntington and the Green (recently a senior-citizen co-op, currently closed for "earthquake-proofing"). Sometimes retired industrialists joined the Chamber of Commerce to oppose industrial development. But not all residents were wealthy. A sizable number of permanent and many temporary residents lived in blocks of small frame cottages apart from the exclusive residential area. Like most cities even Pasadena acquired a depressed sector.

This is the single San Gabriel community which

**Figure 6-53.** Downtown Pasadena, view northeast with San Gabriel Mountains. The domed city hall (left) reflects a traditional civic opulence. The former Green Hotel (lower right), now a retirement center, was one of the grand hotels of earlier-day Pasadena. (Pasadena Chamber of Commerce, photo by J. Allen Hawkins).

presents the "feel" of a larger city, *including* rail passenger service.

This is reflected in its department stores, banks and high-rise structures. Lake Avenue is known for its stylish shops. Offsetting a lengthy decline of its western C.B.D. is Pasadena Plaza (an enclosed downtown regional shopping center of moderate size).

The impact of Pasadena as a cultural center has long been recognized.

Its academic institutions include California Institute of Technology, Pasadena City College (two year) and private Ambassador College. Norton Simon Museum contributes to the cultural atmosphere as does Huntington Art Gallery and Library "nearby" in San Marino.

In recent decades Pasadena has become more of a middle-income community.

Costs of maintenance, smog, and industrialization prompted the wealthy to abandon Orange Grove Avenue. Some large homes became apartments while others were replaced by multi-family units. In south Pasadena additional condominiums have been erected. Elsewhere, many younger professional couples are buying and renovating older dwellings in the north central area.

In the northwestern sector social decay is quite dramatic. Here, and in contiguous western *Altadena* (41,000) is the largest "outlying" black center of the Lowlands. This group originated with servants of the wealthy. High unemployment among its youth compounds the problem. There is a conspicuous contrast in Altadena between white affluence (east) and black poverty (west).

Location of precision instruments plants (to sup-

**Figure 6-54.** San Marino, a community of higher-income business and professional people. (dwl)

ply Southern California's aerospace industry) is partly due to presence of California Institute of Technology. Operation of the large Jet Propulsion Laboratory is supervised by "Cal Tech."

Districts with upper-middle to high income residents fringe Pasadena. These include the Foothill belt from La Canada through Altadena and Sierra Madre, the *exclusive* San Rafael Hills and the subtly undulating oak-dappled "rise" extending from South Pasadena through San Marino and Arcadia.

**South Pasadena** (24,000) is regarded now as one of the "better" residential addresses in the Los Angeles Lowlands.

Politically aloof from Pasadena, although also established in the 1880's, it was long considered less prestigious. Now it houses many business and professional people employed in Los Angeles or Pasadena. In recent years it has attracted many affluent Asian business and professional migrants. Upper-slope *Altos de Monterey* (1960's), with "cow-path" street patterns, is suggestive of San Francisco's Diamond Heights (Ch.8). The city's southern edge is crossed by three transcontinental rail lines hence it shares in the primary industrial complex of the Lowlands.

**San Marino** (14,000) exemplifies the "good life" of the wealthy.

This restricted and conservative southeastern Pasadena outlier suggests a smaller, less flamboyant Beverly Hills devoid of its shopping center. It was founded in 1903 by Henry Huntington, whose mansion today is Huntington Art Gallery and adjacent Library. The spacious homes and beautifully landscaped gardens reflect the high per capita incomes of its residents.

A stable albeit aging residential town, **Sierra Madre** (11,000) has residents with a range of incomes.

Essentially Anglo, it houses however increasing numbers of ethnic professionals. Residents in the north (Sierra Madre Canyon) tend to be upper middle-income. There tend to be blue collar workers and numerous artists in the southwest.

**Arcadia** (48,500) constitutes one of the Golden State's higher-income communities.

"Lucky" Baldwin established the city on his Rancho Santa Anita to legally conduct horse racing (the present race track is indirectly his legacy). This is another northside (costlier lots, upwards of a million dollars)-southside town with older couples and childless singles in condominiums. Its quality regional shopping center is one of

California's most attractive Here also an influx of Asian business and professional people is occurring.

The southwestern San Gabriel (south of Huntington Drive) contains several middle-income communities with much commutation as well as appreciable industry.

Residential-industrial *Alhambra* (73,000) is already more of a Pacific Basin city than many Los Angeles satellites.

It is experiencing *second-generation* urbanization as condominiums replace single-family houses. There is a pronounced ethnic (Mexican and Chinese) representation. Alhambra is becoming the Taiwanese "capital" of the Los Angeles Lowlands. Initially this was more evident from names in the telephone directory but now there are bilingual signs and Chinese architecture is more visible. In the metropolis there tends to be antagonism between long-established Cantonese and the newer "Mandarin" arrivals from north China via Taiwan and Hong Kong. This same old-timer-newcomer schism prevails in San Francisco (Ch.8). In the late 1980's it was argued that English should be used in signs so as to aid protective forces in identification of shop contents in case of emergency.

Bisected by a rail corridor (although much of the trackage is below street level) Alhambra shares in the main Los Angeles industrial belt. Offices (Braun Engineering and Sears Roebuck) have provided employment.

Less industrialized than Alhambra, *Monterey Park* (62,000) is also strongly ethnic. Locally it is sometimes referred to as *Little Asia*.

This is a long-established part of "Mexican" Los Angeles—a third of the residents have Spanish surnames. A number are second or third generation in the community; incomes tend to be higher than in East Los Angeles. A Chinese influx has taken place.

There is also industry in *San Gabriel* (33,000) but it is essentially a commuter residence place with considerable Hispanic populace.

Beginning with adobe huts around the mission (*still* a focal point for the civic center), the town evolved haphazardly. Its highly-irregular street pattern dates from small "lot-size" ranchos.

San Gabriel languished, like Monterey (Ch. 7), for decades. Gradually the mission and the adjoining Playhouse attracted tourists.

Industrial plants, as in Alhambra, reflect eastward expansion of the *primary* industrial belt of

the metropolis along a transcontinental rail line, lamentably near the old mission.

## La Canada Corridor

Between the Verdugo Hills and the San Gabriel Mountains the La Canada Corridor is an elongated rift. It links the San Gabriel and San Fernando valleys and has considerable residential appeal.

Flat land is limited along the Corridor, which formerly had citrus orchards, olive groves and vineyards.

Popular as a residential area, the Corridor contains many custom-built homes. Approximately half of it remains in unincorporated county territory. Sloping terrain facilitates imaginative landscaping as well as providing vistas; its higher elevation attracted many health seekers, as had the northern edge of the San Gabriel Valley farther to the east.

Luxury-level homes distinguish the southeast half of the Corridor, especially in **La Canada-Flintridge** (22,000). Dwellings tend to be more modest in the Sunland-Tujunga district of Los Angeles at the northwest end of the Corridor on the edge of the San Fernando Valley.

## The Middle Valley

Cutting a wide swath across the middle Valley, the San Gabriel River and its distributary Rio Hondo have prompted a different cultural landscape, one with lower-income residents.

Historically there has been flooding; soils and drainage have been less suitable for citrus.

Occupants have tended to be lower middle-income while industrialization reaches its maximum, accounting for a third or more of the employment in most towns. In the 1960's these cities were among the most rapidly-growing in the San Gabriel as choicer residential sites elsewhere were occupied, as flood control improved and as industry expanded locally. Subsequently growth has slowed.

An older city (founded in 1852) *El Monte* (95,000) has diversified functions. Predominantly it is both blue-collar and Hispanic.

It is one of earliest towns in the Lowlands. Once the western terminus of the *Old Spanish Trail*, it provided a way station important for its water supply between interior western America and Los Angeles. Early beginnings and crossroads location favored development of a sizable shopping district while rail lines and available land have attracted a broad range of industrial establishments. The Valley's major general aircraft port is here. However the downtown core has deteriorated markedly; El Monte's downtown mall did not prove successful.

Adjacent **South El Monte** (20,000)and **Rosemead** (47,000) were incorporated in the late 1950's—the latter was principally residential prior to relocation of two large offices from downtown Los Angeles. South El Monte gained fame locally in a national "cleanest town" contest despite "13 junkyards and 40 dog kennels."

*Temple City* (31,500) is basically a middle-income Anglo residence town with a tidy C.B.D. and an aging population.

*Azusa* (38,000) has become an industrial city.

The broad gravel-covered floodplain of the San Gabriel River on its western edge has provided a major source of Southern California sand and gravel. This barren surface, unsuitable for orchards, yet accessible to rail and highway transport, has been converted to industrial use with such products as beer, missile motors and chemicals. A fourth of the populace is Mexican, a legacy of the citrus era with employment of low-cost labor.

*Irwindale,* extending along the river bed for half of the San Gabriel's course across the Valley, was incorporated solely to facilitate sand and gravel mining. Like several other "cities" incorporated for industrial use, its population has declined. Construction of a stadium for the Los Angeles Raiders has been considered.

Adjacent *Baldwin Park* (62,000), tardily incorporated, appealed for years to Mexican farm workers because of cheaper land.

There is still a Hispanic majority. It is likely that industrial development may take place since there is open land.

*Monrovia* (33,000) has a broader socioeconomic variance than its neighbors.

Principally residential, in the past there was agricultural processing; more recently there has been some light industry. Besides its sizable group of senior citizens, Monrovia is the only San Gabriel town, other than Pasadena and Altadena, to have a black group; it began with servants of wealthy Arcadians.

Several communities were incorporated to prevent their absorption into Azusa. One of these, Irwindale, has been noted.

Upslope to the east of Monrovia is *Bradbury,* the "Bel Air" of the San Gabriel Valley. Behind locked

**Figure 6-55.** A segment of Walnut, in Puente Valley. (dwl)

gates it is a hillside estate complex. A brush fire (in 1981) caused much property loss.

Nearby *Duarte* (22,000) is an upgrading bedroomplace with considerable residential redevelopment. The large *City of Hope Medical Center* is here.

### The Eastern Valley

The eastern portion of the San Gabriel Valley contains several white-collar residence places.

Thousands of acres of citrus orchards and other agricultural activities remained in the 1950's. Following construction of the San Bernardino Freeway (I-10) this "open space" prompted much urban growth as vacant land disappeared farther west. There are several regional shopping centers and a possible excess of commercial development.

The old citrus towns (two were founded more than a century ago) retain their individuality and residents associate themselves with individual communities. Foothill areas have particular residential appeal.

Two-story Victorian houses and rows of palms stand as anachronisms amidst blocks of newer mass-constructed houses. Downtown areas cultivate "western" themes with varying success. Light industries, distribution facilities, several major medical centers and a surfeit of commercial activities vie with expanding number of multi-unit housing for available space.

The oldest of these towns is *Glendora* (43,000). It has become a "higher-income" blue-collar community which additionally has two colleges.

Its northern fringe is the east end of the Valley's affluent residential belt at the base of the San Gabriel Mountains.

Through much of its past (it was founded during the first boom in the 1880's) Glendora was known for its citrus shipping sheds and surrounding groves. Production of nursery stock persisted here into the late twentieth century. The city is also unique among Valley communities in having two colleges, Azusa and Azusa Pacific. Industrial activity includes irrigation equipment (Rain Bird).

*Covina* (42,000) lost considerable community cohesion with urban expansion.

Its downtown area has suffered much blight. In fact, its regional shopping center, as in many communities, is beyond city limits (there was in-limits opposition to growth at the time of its construction). There is however a distinctive office park.

Essentially *West Covina* (93,000) has evolved as a post-freeway commuter town.

Astride I-10, which allows a quarter of its working populace to commute to Los Angeles, it has become the wealthiest and largest of the east Valley towns. It has a sizable regional shopping and entertainment complex. Around the attractively-landscaped hillslopes around the eastern Valley are several country clubs and an assortment of small institutions including colleges, academies, seminaries and religious retreats.

### Puente Valley

Drained by intermittent San Jose Creek, the southeastern San Gabriel Valley is known as Puente Valley.

The San Jose Hills have given it some separation from the remainder of the San Gabriel. Its fertile bottomlands formerly produced cut flowers, nursery stock, truck crops and walnuts.

The Puente Valley is traversed by the tracks of the Union Pacific and the Santa Fe Southern. Prior to urbanization the Regional Planning Commission zoned considerable acreage for manufacturing to provide local employment for a segment of the San Gabriel populace and thus reduce rush-hour commutation.

Zoned for manufacturing, *Industry* (600), a mile wide and 14 miles long, extends along railroad tracks.

Besides diversified industry, there is much warehousing. City services tend to be minimal; for example city planning is provided by a consulting firm.

The largest community, *La Puente* (34,000) is primarily a middle-income residence town.

Many industrially-employed residents commute

elsewhere—a third drive to Los Angeles. Mexicans (a carry-over from the agricultural past), compose a third of the population. Also a legacy of the past and sheepherding is a Basque group, which explains a "landmark" restaurant in the central area.

*Walnut* (25,000) is the most appealing residence place.

With its hilly areas, adjacent country club, multi-star hotel and conference center and large two-year college (Mt. San Antonio), Walnut has acquired considerable upper middle-income residents.

### THE INLAND VALLEY *

Sometimes referred to locally as the "Inland Empire", the Inland Valley is a triangular-shaped intermontane basin.

It is sometimes referred to as the Pomona-San Bernardino-Riverside valleys and at one time was more charmingly called "the Valley of the South."

On the southwest it is bounded by the San Jose and Chino hills, on the north by the San Gabriel Mountains and on the northeast by the San Bernardino Mountains and on the southeast by the ill-defined hilly uplands that separate it from the San Jacinto Basin (Map, 6-15).

Although the Valley remains more rurban than the Lowlands previously discussed, eventual urbanization seems probable.

Already it is the nation's 25th most-populous metropolitan area, with more people than Milwaukee, Cincinnati or Kansas City—but no "big league" ball teams! While there are few multi-story buildings there are three separate nuclei of urbanization.

### Alluvial Fans and Santa Anas, Too

Topographically the Inland Valley is one of the more complex Lowlands of the Los Angeles Basin even though alluvial surfaces largely obscure underlying structures.

Physiographically this intermontane basin is filled to depth with alluvium from the San Bernar-

* Initially this section was reviewed by Homer Aschmann, University of California, and W.J.Thomas. Jr.. California State University, Hayward. Subsequently it was reviewed by Crane Miller, California State Polytechnic University, Pomona. This review was made by Ray Young, C.S.U., Fullerton.

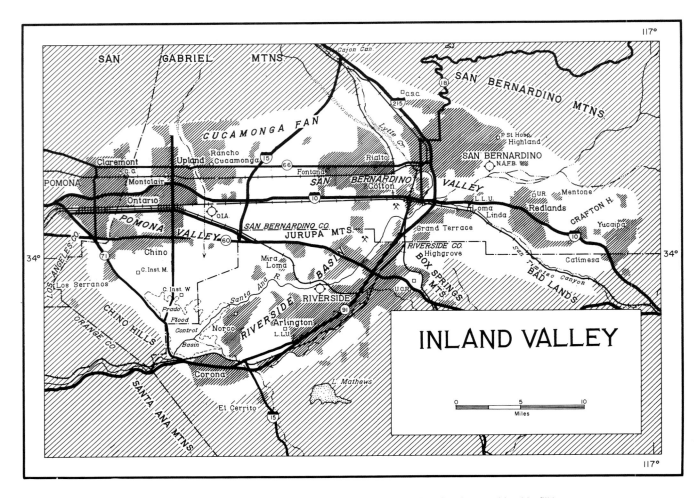

**Map 6-15.** There is *still* some open space in the Inland Valley despite considerable fill-in.

dino and San Gabriel mountains. Several low granitic uplands have been buried by this debris, although the *Jurupa Mountains* rise above it near the Valley center.

Alluvial fans, especially prominent along its northern flanks, include the extensive *Cucamonga Fan.*

Prior to irrigation, low spots in the Pomona Valley contained marshes. External drainage of the entire basin is limited to the Santa Ana River Canyon west of Corona. The San Jacinto Fault, crossing the Valley southeastward between San Bernardino and Colton, significantly constricts both surface and ground-water runoff at that point.

Climatically, there is less residential appeal than some parts of the Los Angeles Lowlands. The Valley has the hot summer ( interior) phase of dry-summer sub-tropical type (much area is *even* semi-arid.

Polar outbursts sometimes can bring subfreezing temperatures, as interior air flows seaward from

the Mojave Desert. The desiccating *Santa Ana* wind, resulting from higher pressure over the Mojave, sometimes stirs up much dust and brings enervating heat across the Valley.

Summer afternoons tend to be hot and skies are often smoggy. While humidity is lower than coastal areas it is not as dry as the Mojave Desert.

Slight evidence of the natural vegetation cover remains.

In the early nineteenth century. it consisted of marshland, chaparral, and native grasses (and sage shrub)

### Indians, Mormons and Others

Small numbers of hunter-gatherer Indians (*Serrano, Cahuilla* and *Gabrielino*) who inhabited the Valley utilized the basin floor and the surrounding slopes.

The Valley remained on the fringe of colonial Spanish settlement, a condition that continued during much of the Mexican era.

It formed part of Mission San Gabriel for decades and afforded pasturage. Rancho San Jose was finally awarded in 1837. The Serrano Indians, who lingered in the nearby highlands, raided cattle even after the Mexican War.

Anglo occupance commenced soon after United States gained control of California.

Mormons and others soon began settling, sometimes as squatters , along the *Old Spanish Trail* westward from San Bernardino through Pomona.

Significant agricultural settlement was delayed until the 1870's, when the arrival of the railroad and the irrigation works of Chaffey and others prompted citrus colonies and appreciable settlement in the 1880's.

**Figure 6-56.** This scene near Chino becomes increasingly-dated as agriculture is displaced by urbanization. (dwl)

### "Vanishing" Eggs, Milk and Oranges

Despite urban encroachment, some portions of the Valley may retain agricultural importance for a decade or so. However, continuing population growth and increasing land prices are strong "push" factors that will tend to eliminate agriculture.

As farming continues to decline in Southern California, the Valley remains a leading area. Its several agricultural pockets are related to such factors as climatic variations (as frost threat) and soil conditions. Zones include (1) citrus, (2) vineyards (3) pastoral and (4) truck crops, poultry and dairying.

Once Southern California's major "orange empire" extended from Hollywood into the Inland Valley.

Within the Valley it formed a crescent around the upper Santa Ana floodplain and then continued southwestward past Riverside and Corona into Orange County.

The orange was the most valuable farm commodity of the entire Lowlands between 1890 and 1938—it was a major factor in permitting Los Angeles County to rank first nationally in farm output for 40 years. A guided tour of this area on the Pacific Electric interurban coaches was once a highlight of many visits to Southern California.

Agricultural colonies at Riverside (1870), Pasadena, Santa Ana and others, were based upon oranges.

Citrus production in the late twentieth century has fast-retreated to relict groves of Navel oranges around Redlands, though output of lemons has continued at Etiwanda and Corona. Air pollution and competition from other areas were less serious than high production costs and the march of ur-

banization.

Southern California's principal grape-growing district long occupied a triangular area on the Cucamonga alluvial fan.

This sandy surface was not suitable for citrus because of soils, absence of irrigation and seasonally hot or cold air descending from Cajon Pass.

Founded by immigrant Secundo Guasti in 1902, the Brookside (ex-Garrett) vineyard near Ontario became one of the nation's largest wine producers.

Now the firm trucks in many of its grapes from newer vineyards near Temecula. A few wine-tasting establishments remain in the former vineyard belt, specializing in high-sugar "sweet wine" varieties.

Farming "inside" the encircling horseshoe of citrus on alluvial fans, has appreciably exceeded the value of the more conspicuous citrus groves.

In this more frost-prone belt, a triangle bounded by Chino, Corona and Rialto, poultry, milk, alfalfa, eggs and truck crops have been important.

The Chino-Ontario dairy belt, which expanded its output considerably after dairymen forsook the urbanizing Coastal Plain in the 1950's, is in turn now experiencing urbanization.

Dairymen of Danish, Dutch or Portuguese descent have been moving to the San Joaquin Valley. There have also been thoroughbred horse farms around Chino.

The Fontana-Rialto district, farther east, was long an important center for production of chickens and rabbits.

The demands of the Los Angeles market made this the leading egg producer in the nation. The dozens of grandpa-and-grandma farms have been re-

**Figure 6-57.** A historic landmark, the steel mill in Fontana. A foreign-owned consortion now uses part of the plant to make fabricated steel products. (Kaiser Steel Company)

placed by a limited number of "egg factories." Eggs are still a ranking agricultural commodity of the Inland Valley.

### The Western Valley

Communities surrounding Pomona and Ontario have evolved into a single metropolis that is "over the hill" (i.e., San Jose Hills) from the San Gabriel Valley.

The heterogeneous population includes many lower-middle or middle-income people, with a substantial Hispanic group and some blacks and Asians. Higher housing costs in Orange County prompted many workers employed in Orange County or "elsewhere" farther west to locate here.

Some of these towns originated as nineteenth century orange colonies—they tended to be staid, conservative and flourishing (apart from the farm laborers' neighborhoods). Functions included residence, agricultural processing and shipping and and local trade. A "prosperity gradient" remains from the flatland railsides into the foothills that flank the San Gabriel Mountains.

In recent decades the population surge of metropolitan Los Angeles has fostered extensive housing tracts, especially to the south and east of the old town cores as freeways eased automotive transport.

**Pomona** (115,000) is supported by such functions as industry, public services, higher education and retail trade.

Pomona (founded in 1874 after a right-of-way across Rancho San Jose was acquired by the Southern Pacific) was named for the Roman goddess of fruit. Until the mid-twentieth century

Pomona was a handsome little city whose prosperity was related to the thousands of acres of surrounding orange groves. Pomona is still the site of the Los Angeles County Fair.

Following freeway construction in the 1960's overbuilding of low-interest Federally-supported housing occurred. After the Watts riots, many blacks from southeast Los Angeles moved in and many affluent whites left Pomona. Meanwhile, local aerospace employment declined. Despite a good industrial base and attractive civic center, Pomona is viewed negatively in surrounding communities and downtown shopping has declined despite its mall.

Industries include the nation's first guided-missile plant, glass containers, paper, perfumes, plastics, soap and tile.

Hilly western sectors, especially *Phillips Ranch* are more affluent. California State Polytechnic University and a state hospital are located on the western outskirts.

**Montclair** (26,000) is a conservative blue collar community. Montclair Center, one of two regional shopping mall in the Pomona-Ontario conurbation, has pulled much trade from Pomona. After a brief spurt of housing construction, little vacant land remains.

**Claremont** (36,000), distinguished by the presence of Claremont Colleges, is a pleasant residence place at the base of the San Gabriel Mountains.

It is noted for high median incomes including a number of professional retirees. Understandably it has attractive retail specialty shops and tourist-conference facilities.

**Figure 6-58.** Ontario International Airport, view west toward Ontario. An expanded array of allied activities (such as restaurants and hotels) has appeared in the environs. (dwl)

Founded during the Boom of the 1880's amidst orange groves it has long been known for its colleges. Besides Claremont Colleges, an Oxonian group of small private institutions, noted for scholarship and well endowed, there are two theological schools (relocated from Los Angeles).

While the academic atmosphere has given Claremont residential preference for senior citizens (a trait shared with some Middlewestern towns), high taxes (resulting from a narrow economic base) and smog detract from "the image."

Padua Hills Theatre, presenting Mexican players, is located north of town. Nearby also is Rancho Santa Ana Botanical Garden, with 80 acres of California shrubs.

*Ontario* (115,000) long the second largest city of the Pomona Valley, began as a farm colony in 1882. Agriculture has been supplanted by industrial and residential development.

*Ontario International Airport* serves the entire Inland Valley.

It handles more than 12 million passages annually and features an utilities terminal and aircraft repair services. There is a sizable surrounding industrial zone, airport-oriented as well as hotel and offices. If sound-proofed, multiple housing is allowed nearby. Since the facility is owned and operated by the City of Los Angeles Department of Airports, local officials have limited control.

*Upland* (57,000), a handsome residence place, was formerly a citrus-shipping point.

Homes are attractive, streets (*especially* broad Euclid Avenue with its rows of pepper trees) well shaded and the civic spirit strong.

Despite the physical attractiveness, Upland has been acclaimed "California's smoggiest city." The smog, drifting east from Los Angeles, plagues all of the Inland Valley.

*San Antonio Heights,* upslope and unincorporated is a residential hodgepodge with septic tanks, residual orange groves and limited public services, circumstances its populace seems to prefer.

***Rancho Cucamonga*** (90,000), incorporated in 1977, encompasses all the vineyard land between Upland and Fontana. It is one of California's new towns, and there is still much open space in the eastern portion of the city.

It houses many upper middle-income business and professional commuters (a number are refugees from Pomona!). It is basically single-family residential and has a large regional shopping center. It encompasses the planned community of **Victoria**. The spacious campus of Chaffey College is here.

***Chino*** (52,000) with lower-income residents and a sizable Mexican population, differs from other western valley cities.

Apart from rail lines and long plagued by water shortage, it provided residence for many farm workers. Lower incomes and proximity to Pomona and Montclair help explain its small central district and absence of quality specialty shops. Payrolls at state correctional institutions (for both men and women) are substantial.

With its cheaper housing and improved freeway access many blue-collar workers have moved to Chino, anticipating a small-town atmosphere and pleasant life. The surrounding dairy belt (in county territory) is also experiencing urbanization.

### The Northeastern Valley

San Bernardino, second-largest city in the Inland Valley, is a nucleus for half a dozen lesser cities that form a single population cluster. Oft-times attractive residential districts extend in a "broken" half circle on higher terrain from Rialto past southeast San Bernardino southward to Redlands. But more modest flatland settlements, which are in the majority, indicate dominance of farm, industrial and other labor forces.

***Fontana*** (60,000).in the path of Mojavan winds via Cajon Pass, has been one of the shabbier towns in the Los Angeles Basin.

Its appearance in part reflects the presence of a steel mill that operated for four decades. Even near the town center there is much vacant land but in-

**Figure 6-59.** Pomona, with a northward view to San Gabriel Mountains. High summit on right is Mt. San Antonio. (United States National Bank of San Diego)

**Figure 6-60.** Diamond Bar, a still-evolving community southwest of Pomona. (dwl).

**Figure 6-61.** California State Polytechnic University, Pomona. (dwl)

filling is now occurring. Fontana has a conspicuous ethnic population (more Hispanic than black) and less-expensive housing tracts are being built. Spacious, newly-annexed areas with rail service await industrial or other usage.

**San Bernardino** (141,000), with newer high-rises downtown (mostly occupied by financial institutions and local, state and federal agencies), is beginning to look like a larger city. Never the typical orange belt town, it has varied supports, including transportation, public institutions, commuter residence, higher education, retail trade and the military.

"San Berdoo", seat of the largest U.S. county, is one of the oldest Anglo towns in the Lowlands. In 1851 a Mormon group purchased Rancho San Bernardino and fashioned a townsite, including broad streets, in the manner of Salt Lake City. Brigham Young recalled his "saints" to Utah in 1857; San Bernardino experienced wild years as an outfitting point for Mojave Desert mines. Following construction of rail and highway lines through Cajon Pass, it gained importance as a "pass city."

Industrial employment, now diminished, focused on railroad shops, cement plants and the Fontana steel mill. Norton Air Force Base (supply, repair and missile defense for the Lowlands) and Patton State Hospital persist as major employers.

The largest ethnic groups (Mexicans and blacks) of the Inland Valley occupy the west side. The prominent central district, with a *mall* and *free* parking, has gained a third dimension. Although it is accessible from two freeways, it is increasingly eccentric. As the city expands to the northeast Highland Avenue has become a major commercial strip. Many residents of the Mojave undertake "major" purchases here. Hampered by a number of county enclaves, San Bernardino strives for orderly growth.

As an educational center, San Bernardino has California State University and San Bernardino Valley College. There are decreasing orange groves to the east but the National Orange Show is still held here.

**Colton** (31,000) is a Mexican-majority town oriented to its railroad (Southern Pacific) facilities. A line from Colton to Palmdale via Cajon Pass, opened in 1967, allows transcontinental traffic destined for central California to bypass congested terminals in Los Angeles.

Colton's large laboring group has included many employees of the cement plant. Many residences are modest while the small central district reflects retail trade conducted in nearby San Bernardino or Riverside.

**Rialto** (60,000) is largely residential. It occupies a low terrace along the west bank of a wide wash. Neighborhoods grade from the affluent country club area to small dwellings near the city center. Mexican and black groups are prominent.

Probably more than any city in the Lowlands, **Redlands** (54,000) still personifies the "prim and proper" orange belt town.

Retaining many acres of surrounding groves, it is the principal center in Southern California for packing and shipping navel oranges.

Less affected by recent boom periods than many Lowlands cities, it has a substantial central district and adjoining mall. It does have small industrial firms, however, including an aerospace plant. Redlands has been regarded well for its homes and gardens for decades. Its hillside section has impressive views of the San Bernardino Mountains (when not obscured by smog) as does the appealing campus of the University of Redlands.

**Yucaipa Valley** (28,000), in the past the center for the single apple-producing district in the Los Angeles Basin, has become primarily an area of senior-citizen residence.

Retiree incomes are often modest and there are several score of mobile-home parks. Like Paradise (Ch. 10) and Clearlake (Ch. 12), Yucaipa has problems as a city. Mesa-top Crafton Hills College serves the Yucaipa and Redlands areas.

**Loma Linda** (13,000), a Seventh Day Adventist community near Redlands, is known for its medically-oriented university and its Veterans Administration

**Figure 6-62.** Southwesterly view of Riverside with Ca.60 freeway and industrial area in foreground. (dwl)

hospital.

Surrounding orange groves are vanishing as houses are making it an extension of Redlands.

### The Southern Valley

Along the southeastern side of the Santa Ana River, a continuous urban corridor is emerging along a freeway (Ca. 91) which links Orange County with the southeastern deserts of California and points east.

Developed early for irrigation, Santa Ana River water permitted the largest canal system in the Los Angeles Lowlands to evolve in western Riverside County. While a decreasing acreage of citrus groves persists, the landscape is essentially urban. Many of the additional homes house commuters to Orange County and elsewhere.

*Riverside* (200,000), through annexation, has become the largest city in the Inland Valley. Varied economic supports include government services, retail trade. services, transportation, higher education and manufacturing.

Its central district, while it has lost retail shoppers to malls on the city's southwestern outskirts (and in San Bernardino) has been sustained by civic offices in high rise structures which provide more of a feeling of a metropolitan center than in some California cities.

The once-famed Mission Inn hints of days bygone when Riverside was regarded as one of the charming places of the Golden State. There is also a convention center, performing arts center and weekly open-air market.

As an agricultural colony, where the navel orange groves began, (commemorated by the Citrus Heritage State Park), Riverside was once a "jewel" of the citrus belt.

It was a trim residential community with well-maintained gardens and homes. In its downtown district specialty shops reflected the prosperity of the surrounding countryside. The city has lost some of its once-gilded charm with urban growth. Still Riverside is sustained by varied functions.

As an eastern gateway into the Lowlands (on Ca. 60 freeway), the city has importance as a waystop.

It is also the seat of one of the nation's larger counties and has importance as a center of higher education in the Los Angeles Basin, a University of California campus, Riverside City College, La Sierra campus of Loma Linda University, California Baptist College, Sherman Institute, and a state school for the deaf. Federal offices serve farmers, Indians and management of public domain lands for much of interior southern California.

Sundry manufacturing, including aerospace firms and a cement plant, as well as military installations, are scattered around the fringes of this "elbow-shaped" metropolis.

Growth has brought varied changes to Riverside. Expansive housing tracts, influenced by March Air Force Base and economic activities noted above, have replaced orchards.The ethnic make-up has become more varied. Many residents have more-restricted incomes than the citrus orchardists of the past. Thirty years too late, voters approved *Referendum R,* establishing a five-acre greenbelt.

*Corona* (46,000), although it has become increasingly a commuter residence town, like Redlands has retained some of its citrus-belt atmosphere.

Founded in the 1880's Corona was the center of a now-declining lemon-growing area. The city has a handsome civic center and strong community spirit. But the agricultural base has been superseded as more and more residents are commuters, to Pomona, Riverside, and especially to Orange County.

---

### THE SAN JACINTO BASIN *

The most isolated and least populous of five Los Angeles Lowlands, the San Jacinto Basin is structur-

---

\* The phrase *San Jacinto Basin* does not have common local acceptance. It is used in absence of a widely-accepted proper name. Geomorphologists have termed it the *Perris Block.*

**Figure 6-63.** An aquatic recreation area, Lake Elsinore is maintained with water from pump wells. (dwl)

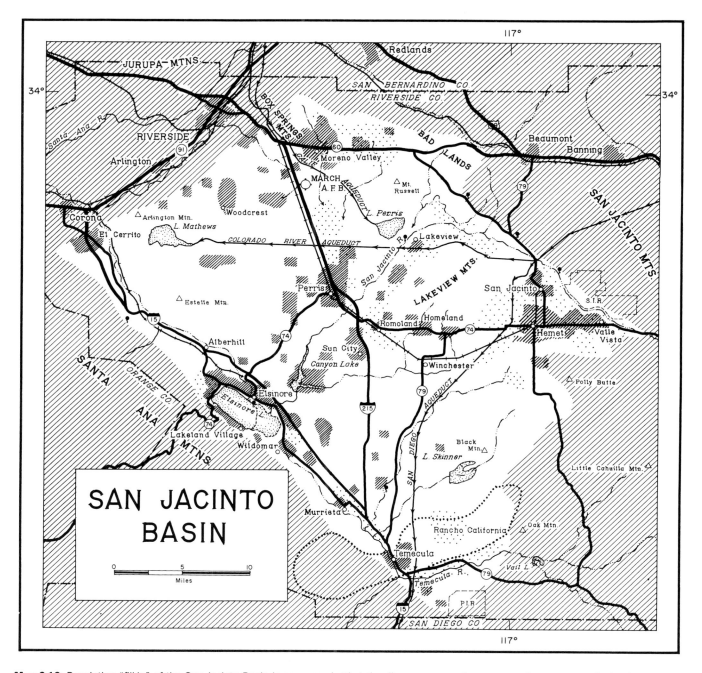

**Map 6-16.** Population "fill-in" of the San Jacinto Basin is now occuring but the disappearance of open space is many years in the future. Stippled pattern indicates irrigated areas.

ally part of Peninsular Ranges. It lies south of the Inland Valley with the Santa Ana Mountains to the west and the San Jacinto Mountains to the east (map 6-16). There is still much rural land in this least-visited of the Lowlands although it is now experiencing increased urbanization as open countryside vanishes elsewhere.

## Drier, Hotter, and Rockier

Overall the Basin has had less physical attraction than some of the Lowlands. Rather than Mediterranean, it is semi-arid.

Not only is it farther south than the other lowlands but it also lies in the lee of the Santa Ana Mountains. Precipitation is too limited to consider it as "Mediterranean."

With its interior location, without the benefit of sea breezes, summer afternoons in the Basin can feel torrid. Winter temperatures are noticeably lower than coastal areas while the eight-months growing season is short by Southern California standards. Air pollution in summer, while less intense than in the Inland Valley, is present and is worsening.

The San Jacinto Basin, a granitic block, is more rugged than the other Lowlands.

Its bordering faults, the *Elsinore* to the southwest and the *San Jacinto* to the northeast, are two of the most impressive cracks on the face of Southern California—activity along these ruptures explains hot springs that have been used commercially.

Irregular terrain results from an earlier period of mountain building.

The Basin was not uplifted when the Peninsular Ranges were most recently elevated. Scattered about the surface are small granitic knobs whose rocky outcrops and thin soils minimize agricultural use (but may make future sites for view lots!) The most prominent of these uplands is the *Lakeview Mountains*.

The area is about equally divided between the knobby hills, which rise to elevations around 2500 feet above sea level, and small valleys. The latter, about a thousand feet lower than the knobs, provide smooth alluvial surfaces.

Most of the sparse natural runoff drains into Lake Elsinore via the San Jacinto River.

The San Jacinto rises on the upper slopes of the San Jacinto Range. Since irrigation development, its channel is generally dry. Historically Lake Elsinore has spilled over northwestward into the Santa Ana River but drainage in most years is internal.

### From Acorn Gatherers to Thermal Resorts

Devoid of some of the attractiveness of some portions of Southern California, the San Jacinto has held less appeal to humans. This condition was reflected in its modest *Luiseno* population.

Perhaps several thousand of these hill-dwelling Shoshones focused their attention on the periphery of the Basin where their usual diet (acorns, small game, and seeds) could be obtained. Since their lands held slight appeal for Hispanic colonials, the Luiseno have persisted into the twentieth century.

The colonial Spanish *almost* ignored the Basin.

There was neither sufficient water nor Indian neophytes to prompt the Spanish padres to establish a mission.

An interior travel route connecting missions San Diego and San Gabriel traversed the western periphery. Later it became a link in the *Old Emigrant Trail* from Ft. Yuma to Los Angeles, followed by many gold seekers; it also formed a segment of the route of the Butterfield Stage.

At the close of the Mexican period four land grants were finally awarded in the San Jacinto.

They encompassed only marginal western and eastern lands where water was available. The usual patterns of livestock and then grains were developed. Land was still available for homesteading in the 1870's. During the boom of the 1880's several hot springs became the sites of thermal resorts, particularly around Lake Elsinore. Most irrigation development came rather late.

### Grains, Truck Crops—even Citrus

Extensive irrigation agriculture, so widespread in some parts of the Los Angeles Lowlands, has been limited in the San Jacinto.

The Basin had the double curse of limited water and thin rocky slopes. Thousands of acres of grain, usually barley, have been cultivated. Still, many steeper slopes remain covered with chaparral. Livestock, both beef and dairy cattle, have become increasingly important. Potatoes (both spring and fall) form the most valuable crop although grapefruit and oranges are both consequential.

In the second half of the twentieth century imported water has been available.

Colorado River water was obtained in 1952 through affiliation with the Metropolitan Water District. Then in 1973 water from northern California arrived at Lake Perris, the southern terminus of the California Aqueduct. With aqueduct water many wells are not needed but imported water is sufficiently expensive to restrict some uses; for example, only larger barley fields are given supplemental sprinkler irrigation.

West of the Lakeview Mountains, **Perris Valley** has benefited especially from imported water.

This area contains the largest cultivated acreage in the Basin. Its output includes potatoes, truck crops, winter barley and milk, which is largely consumed locally.

East of the Lakeview Mountains the San Jacinto Valley rivals Perris Valley agriculturally.

It receives water chiefly from the San Jacinto River, much of it groundwater; there is also storage in Hemet Lake in the San Jacinto Mountains.

**Figure 6-64.** Hemet, view eastward, with Hemet Valley and snow-capped Mt. San Jacinto (10,831 ft.). Hemet is conspicuously westside (retiree mobile-home parks) and eastside (the established "working" community). (Hemet Chamber of Commerce, photo by Aerial Enterprises, San Bernardino).

In the foothills, where there is good air drainage, citrus is grown. Downvalley, Hemet is a center for potatoes, apricots, walnuts and poultry.

Farther north, west of San Jacinto, is the "last refuge" of dairymen in the Los Angeles Lowlands. Breeding of horses ( especially riding animals) has suggested to several writers a dubious image of the Kentucky Bluegrass.

Agriculture in Elsinore Valley followed division of Rancho Laguna in the 1880's. Water shortage has always hampered productivity.

Grain farming followed early cattle ranching; in turn suitable arable land was converted into orchards. Much land, especially around Temecula, is still used for dry-farmed grains. Irrigated orchards have been restricted to sites with suitable soils and available water, especially northwest of Lake Elsinore.

### Retirees and Commuters

Dramatic increase in population is finally occurring in the San Jacinto Basin. Much of the open land elsewhere in the Los Angeles Lowlands is now urbanized. Much growth represents a "spill-over" from high-priced Orange County.

Hot springs encouraged retirement residence even before 1900 and a military "presence" has been significant locally for over half a century. Lately many more retirees, often with modest incomes, are residing here, especially in Hemet, San Jac-

into, Perris, and Sun City. An expanding commuter belt has evolved along U.S. 60 east of Riverside. New tracts and "land for sale" signs seem to be "everywhere." Mobile home parks too are much in evidence.

Despite origin in the 19th century, most San Jacinto towns grew slowly for decades. Hence reminders of a somnolent past lingered into the 1970's.

*Perris* (8900), a lower middle-income community, had its start as a boom town of the 1880's, on the former main line of the Santa Fe Railroad to San Diego.

It has provided a local retail center and shipping point for surrounding farms, and residence place for Mexican farm workers. An appreciable black population moved here from Los Angeles. More recently, many younger Anglo blue-collar families have located here because of "affordable" housing.

*San Jacinto* (12,000) eclipsed commercially by nearby Hemet, long remained a sleepy village serving the dairy belt along the San Jacinto River. More recently it has attracted lower-income retirees, many residing in mobile homes.

*Hemet* (32,000), long the largest and most viable town in the Basin, has served as the center (trade, residence, shipping) for the irrigated district along the upper San Jacinto River.

Much recent growth is due to retiree residence, especially on the west side. Hemet serves as a pass town at the base of the of the Pines-to-Palms

Highway and shares a community college with San Jacinto. Many Lowlands residents of the Los Angeles Basin know it for its spring-time Ramona Pageant.

The economy of **Lake Elsinore** (13,000) has been related to use of its intermittent lake, to agriculture and retiree residence.

For a while recreational use of the hot springs and the lake increased with population growth in Southern California and with automotive travel, the town grew. But fluctuations in the lake level continue to hamper aquatic activity and detract from shoreline appeal.

The ethnic composition that includes middle-income Jewish retirees from Eastern cities, blacks and Mexicans is unique in semi-rural Southern California. Lesser diversity is found in the outlying communities of *Lakeland Village* and *Lake Sedco Hills*. which together rival "old" Lake Elsinore in population. The same is true of **Canyon Lake** (circa 2500) in bare hills to the east which contains many second homes for weekenders from the Los Angeles Basin.

With recent population growth (representing an in-migration of commuters and retirees), several "new towns" have developed and "clustering" suggests that others may develop.

**Moreno Valley** (75,000) represents recent suburban residential expansion eastward from Riverside along highways 215 and 60.

Tract housing here is more affordable than in many parts of the Lowlands. A majority of the residents are Anglos and many commute long distances to work. Military employment (March Air Force Base) and retirement residence are contributing to growth. Lake Perris reservoir to the southeast is a state recreation area with much visitor usage.

**March Air Force Base** (3600) extends for several miles along I-15 south of Moreno Valley.

Initially a training field (World War I) it became more important during World War II. It now accommodates Strategic Air Command craft. The base sustains commuting workers, including blacks and other ethnic groups, who reside throughout the San Jacinto Basin.

**Sun City** (8900) is a planned retirement center without schools.

It has evolved around two golf courses. "Effective" shade trees are too limited and there are many green-painted gravel "lawns." In such a community activities tend to involve couples —unin-

tended social ostracism of widows can be acute. Sun City has reached the limits of its "sphere of influence" but several new "clusters" of people are appearing nearby.

Growth of **Rancho California** reflects a massive corporate "selling" of open space and a profitable tax shelter for lesser investors.

Development of the large Vail Ranch surrounding Temecula began in the late 1960's and accelerated after completion of I-15. An ultimate planned city of 250,000 is anticipated.

West of I-15 former grazing land has become avocado orchards. Farther east fruit, dairying, truck farming and other uses more intensive than pasturage have been promoted as rapidly as irrigation water, agronomic research and well-financed operators has allowed. Vineyards are now supplying wineries locally and more distant.

Several developers are constructing housing tracts. Prior to complete fill-in a "leapfrog" landscape exists.

Adjacent to Rancho California *Rancho Joaquin*, founded more recently, shows hints becoming a sizable community as well.

## THE OXNARD PLAIN *

When urbanization of the Oxnard Plain is completed, there will be no major farming areas of consequence remaining in Southern California. Northwest of the Santa Monica Mountains, the Plain lies beyond the Malibu Coast (map 6-17). Facing the Pacific Ocean at the mouth of the Santa Clara River, it is the economic core of Ventura County as well as the ranking agricultural area of Southern California.

* This section was reviewed initially by the late Rex Brittingham, Ventura College.

**Figure 6-65.** Rancho California. (dwl)

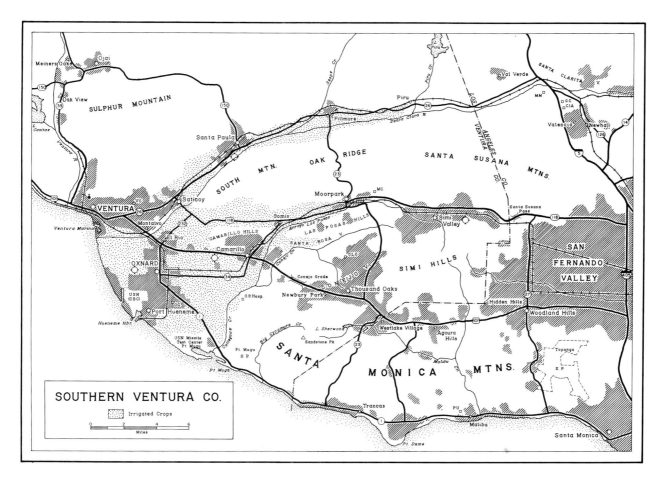

**Map 6-17.** Population "spill-over" from the Los Angeles Lowlands is altering land use in Southern Ventura County.

The Oxnard, on its interior edges, is bounded by units of the Transverse Ranges: Santa Monica Mountains to the southeast, South Mountain to the northeast and Sulphur Mountain to the north (map 6-17).

**Figure 6-66.** The eastern fringe of the Oxnard Plain and lemon groves. Ventura County is the nation's lemon "capital." (dwl)

While the Plain is considerably smaller than the Los Angeles Coastal Plain, it forms one of the Golden State's more important coastal lowlands. Now the Ventura Freeway (U.S. 101) allows speedier access into the Los Angeles Lowlands and population increase has hastened. Local planners anticipate 730,000 people by the year 2000 with increased industrialization (despite considerable opposition).

## A BOUNTIFUL DOMAIN

A delta-like surface, the Oxnard is underlain by several hundred feet of horizontal-strata alluvium, deposited at its mouth by the Santa Clara River (and lesser sources).

Surface irregularities are slight and apart from the Mugu Lagoon, the natural shoreline is straight.

The Plain is well insulated against interior cold or heat (except for occasional outflow of continental air from the Mojave Desert). Marine-influenced, it has a mild-summer modification of dry-summer subtropical climate.

Soils and water resources are related to the Santa Clara River.

Groundwater is carried by the Santa Clara and other streams from interior mountains. Soils are mostly loamy or sandy, with patches of clay near the coast and gravelly soils adjacent to the mountains.

### Ranchos Become Truck Gardens

For the Chumash the Oxnard Plain afforded one of California's better habitats. Yet these Indians did not practice agriculture. Like many other senior Californians they were hunter-gatherers who *also* fished.

The Spanish padres established Mission San Buenaventura near the mouth of the Ventura River, on the west edge of the Oxnard in 1782.

Local Chumash were recruited for several decades as neophytes and the mission prospered. For a time it held more cattle than other missions. The Chumash, however, retained the Plain through the Spanish period and no land grants were awarded.

During the final decade of Mexican control, following mission secularization, eight ranchos were awarded. Much of the Plain became *Rio de Santa Clara o La Colonia*, a 45,000-acre tract. An even larger property, ex-Mission Rancho, included a portion of the Plain as well as considerable mountainous terrain.

After the drought of 1862 large Anglo grain farms were established and persisted here much longer than in most arable portions of Southern California. Construction of the Southern Pacific "Coast Line" from Los Angeles through Ventura to Santa Barbara in 1887 did not prompt town growth on a scale comparable to boom activity around Los Angeles.

Conversion of the Plain into a landscape characterized by irrigation agriculture has occurred almost wholly since 1900.

Because of a water table too deep for primitive drilling machinery and the difficulty of draining the coastal fringe, widespread irrigation was long delayed.

Over much of the Plain soil drainage was necessary, largely to reduce the salt content. This necessitated master ditches to dispose of the water and tiles buried below plow depth to drain wastes into the ditches. It was then necessary to flush the soil with fresh water to carry away residual salts.

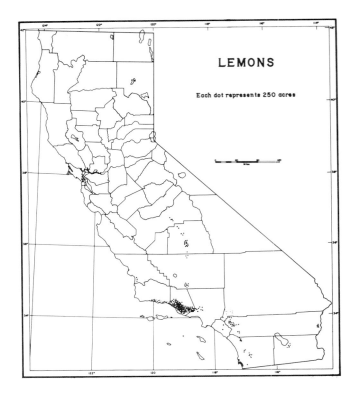

**Map 6-18.** Urbanization may force relocation of lemon groves, perhaps to the Colorado Desert or the Palo Verde Valley.

As the century began, sugar-beet cultivation was established and a sugar factory was erected. A generation later, lima beans became important. Subsequently citrus groves were established. Finally, national demands coupled with improved production and shipping methods contributed to a marked expansion of acreage devoted to vegetables. In the latter twentieth century urbanization is resulting in a decrease in farm land.

### The Fruitful Land

Contemporary agriculture, intensive in nature, brings a high return per acre. Hence little Ventura ranks eleventh among California counties in output.

There is much use of machinery as well as considerable hand labor. The mild climate permits some commodities to be marketed every month of the year. Avocados and citrus have importance in the interior portions of the Plain; lemons especially can tolerate the cool summer weather.

But much of the Oxnard tends to be too cool in summer, or too poorly drained for optimum orchard production. Shallow-rooted plants adapted to mild temperatures tend to be more widely grown than tree crops.

During the winter "half-year" specialty crops are cultivated carefully for off-season harvest in fall or spring, so as to reduce market competition. Celery however is marketed much of the year (except in summer).

Important crop shifts have occurred with rising land prices. Thus acreage of field crops has declined while that of truck crops has doubled. Strawberries, market flowers, and turf for "instant lawns" have increased greatly. The Oxnard has become a ranking producer of strawberries.

### Lemons

Southern California has a near-national monopoly in production of lemons (Figure 6-18).

The lemon, an evergreen that bears repeatedly through the year, requires nearly frost free conditions but needs less summer heat than other citrus.

The Oxnard, combined with the contiguous Santa Clara River Valley, is the nation's leading lemon producer.* Additional production comes from the Inland Valley of the Los Angeles Lowlands, the Santa Barbara Coast and the San Diego Country. Despite tariff against foreign imports, overseas production is making the the lemon an *endangered* Southern California crop.

### Large Lima Beans

Once the Oxnard was the world's leading commercial producer of large lima beans.

More sensitive to summer heat and drought than baby limas, the large varieties in Southern California are grown only along the fog-belt coast.

The lima no longer competes with such commodities as lemons, truck crops and strawberries hence it has essentially disappeared.

### A Matter of Water

Water depletion on the Plain has dramatized the limitation of local water supply in Southern California even better than do the Los Angeles Basin and the San Diego Country.

The Oxnard did not receive Colorado River water (from the Metropolitan Water District) until the 1960's. Now it gets water from the Feather River (California Aqueduct) as well, primarily for urban use.

Marked expansion of pump irrigation coupled with urban growth necessitated water importation.

The water situation became acute. Ventura, formerly dependent upon water from the Ventura River, now has pump wells near the mouth of the Santa Clara River. But increased pumping on the Plain lowered the water table so much that salt-water incursion is a continuing problem around the outer edge of the Oxnard.

Spreading grounds have been constructed along the tributary streams of the Santa Clara River and a storage reservoir exists on Piru Creek.

In decades past local drainage basins were not used with maximum effectiveness. But discord among water users in the various parts of the Santa Clara drainage basin were resolved and a water conservancy district was established. Unfortunately erosion of beach sand along the coast (*especially* east of Port Hueneme) has worsened since reservoir construction.

## A SOURCE OF OIL

Ventura County has been a longtime source of petroleum. Most of its output has come from surrounding mountainsides, *not* the Oxnard Plain.

**South Mountain**, along the south side of the Santa Clara River Valley, and **Sulphur Mountain**, south of Ojai, have produced oil since the nineteenth century. South Mountain production stimulated the establishment of Unocal. More recently three fields have been developed northeast of Oxnard as well as increased output from offshore platforms.

On the northwestern periphery of Ventura the **Ventura Avenue** oilfield, one of the richest in the state, has been one of California's three leading petroleum sources (see table, Chapter 9).

Production began in 1916 and high output has been made possible by *multiple-deck sandwiching* as a result of multiple faulting) within an elongated anticlinal ridge with east-west orientation. However depletion has caused a slow decline in production.

## AUTOS, TRAINS AND OIL TANKERS

Sundry types of transportation contribute to the economy of the Oxnard Plain.

This is understandable with its location athwart the coastal corridor between Los Angeles and San

---

* While the Ojai Valley and the Santa Clara River Valley are inland extensions of the Oxnard, they will be considered later as part of the Transverse Ranges because of their intermont location.

**Figure 6-67.** The southeastern edge of the Oxnard Plain and the western edge of the Santa Monica Mountains. Pacific Missile Range facility is in center of picture. (official U.S. Navy photo).

**Figure 6-68.** Junction of U.S. 101 and Ca.126 freeways on the outskirts of Ventura. Most of the crop land seen in photo has been urbanized. (Caltrans)

Francisco, with its agricultural output and the adjacent oilfields and with its expanding population.

The Plain is a focus of highways leading outward to the north, west and east.

U.S. 101 crosses the width of the Plain as Ventura Freeway; at El Rio it meets the Coast Highway (Route 1) which follows the Malibu Coast to Santa Monica. Farther to the northwest it meets the Santa Paula Freeway (Ca. 126) which connects the Oxnard with I-5 via the Santa Clara River Valley. From U.S. 101 at Ventura little-used Ca.33 begins its tortuous path across the Transverse Ranges

into the San Joaquin Valley. Highway-related facilities are evident on the Plain.

The Oxnard has both airline and railroad facilities.

Both freight and passenger (Amtrak) service is provided by Santa Fe Pacific between the Bay Area and Los Angeles. There is a freight line extension to Port Hueneme.

"Feeder" airline service is available at County Airport (in Oxnard).

Ocean transportation focuses upon Ventura and Port Hueneme.

Although Ventura has no harbor, oil shipping has

given it some moment as a seaport. Tankers, infrequently seen now, have anchored close off-shore and received their cargo by flexible pipeline.

Port Hueneme was founded in 1870; in time a citrus packing plant and a fish cannery were located beside this swampy natural harbor. In the late 1930's the harbor was dredged; an offshore submarine canyon eases entry of larger vessels. Since World War II Hueneme has been a military harbor. It is the locale of the major *Naval Construction Battalion* ("Seabees") base on the Pacific Coast—it has been an important supply depot for shipment of material to Pacific bases. The port also allows commercial and sports fishing as well as berthage for pleasure craft.

## THE SEASIDE

The Oxnard shore is a damp and windblown strip. Still, it has good (albeit erosion-prone) beaches and several low-lying sites where ports and marinas have been established. A lengthening urban ribbon has developed so that open space has lessened.

Military installations and other seashore uses occupy the littoral of the Oxnard Plain.

The two military installations along this coast are operated by the Navy—Port Hueneme, already noted, and the Naval Air Missile Center. In the past as many as a fifth of all employed persons in Ventura County worked at the installations.

*Point Mugu Naval Air Missile Test Center* was created after World War II with the evolution of the military missile (Figure 6-67).

In the late twentieth century the strand has gained increased residential and recreational importance.

Although the coast is often foggy, distance from metropolitan Los Angeles primarily discouraged more utilization earlier. More recently, as the population of the Oxnard has increased and other Southern California shores have been taxed this coast has assumed more importance.

Pierpont Pier at Ventura and San Buenaventura State Beach Park have been improved considerably and small-boat harbors have been developed. Part of the program has included groin construction and beach rebuilding.

Seaside villages adjacent to Oxnard and Port Hueneme, which once principaly housed military personnel, attract increasing numbers of seashore enthusiasts.

## MEGALOPOLITAN INFRINGEMENT

Merger of the Oxnard Plain into the Southern California megalopolis is occurring, yet this may not too obvious to many travelers; U.S. 101 does not reveal the scope of urban expansion well.

Except in southeastern Ventura, most urban growth has been compact by Southern California "standards." Commonly intensive farming borders the backyards of urban fringes. Sizable blocks of farmland still exist.

A preponderance of the Plain's residents are city dwellers (half of them reside in Oxnard and Ventura).

There has appeared to be stronger desire to be "bigger and better" in Oxnard than in Ventura. Yet neither city *seems* as large as it is, except for sprawl, because of low vertical profile.

The old mission town (its *official* name is still *San Buenaventura*) of **Ventura** (88,000) is supported by such activities as commercial and public services, tourism, retail trade and petroleum output. It is also the seat of Ventura County.

Ventura's elongated pattern relates to topographic restriction (map 6-17); *older* Ventura occupies a narrow shelf between the outer wall of the Transverse Ranges and the Pacific . This site has squeezed its downtown district with narrow streets and congestion.

One residential arm of the city extends northward upward the Ventura River Valley past the oilfield. But primary growth has occurred eastward onto the widening Oxnard Plain.

Here one finds Ventura College, the County Government Center, a regional shopping center (Buenaventura Fashion Center), the public golf course, hospitals and much of residential Ventura. Along the coast is a yacht harbor with visitor center and the the newer growth has been eastward, tributary to Santa Paula Freeway (Ca.126). Many commuters come from inland residences along the Ventura Valley and Ojai.

**Oxnard** (126,000), a century younger than Ventura, has always been strongly attached to agriculture (residence, processing,shipping).

It fails to impart the concept of a central place of its size. Truly it does not suggest another Modesto or Visalia. In part this reflects a sharing of functions with Ventura. It has however acquired a community college.

In heavily residential Oxnard incomes tend to be significantly lower than those in Ventura. As in

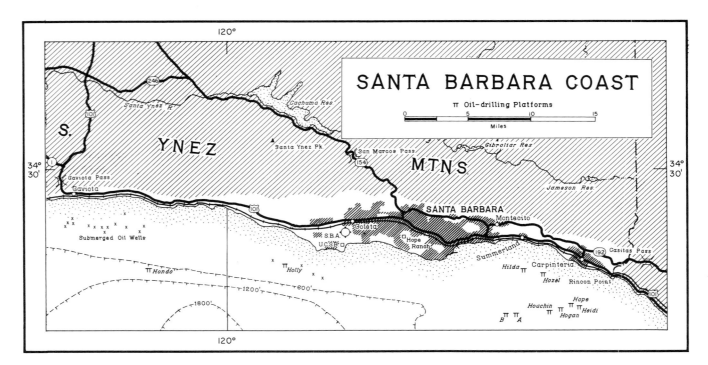

**Map 6-19.** Open space is disappearing along the Santa Barbara Coast as urbanization continues. Goleta now approximates Santa Barbara in population.

many California agriculturally-related communities, there is noticeable demarcation between the expanding west side, strongly Anglo, and the persisting "little Mexico", with its farm worker heritage, on the east side. An expanding number of Hispanics reside in south Oxnard. A third of the population has Hispanic surnames. There is also an appreciable black and Asian component.

The small central district has suffered with development of north end and west side shopping centers. Retail trade approximates that of smaller Ventura. An emerging "county downtown" has evolved along U.S. 101 between the two cities. It has a shopping mall as well as high-rise office towers and a hotel.

Oxnard remains a center for such agriculturally-related activities as processing (and shipping) facilities. Fresh freezing and vegetable shipping plants adjoin the rail line. There is also canning of chili peppers.

**Port Hueneme** (21,000), contiguous on the south with Oxnard, is nearly surrounded by its larger neighbor.

Its population has become less military-oriented. It is a lower middle-income town, occupied principally by families of military personnel as well as civilians employed at the big Naval base.

Much of the growth of **Camarillo** (48,000) represents housing for commuters to metropolitan Los Angeles (via U.S.101).

Its diminutive central district has been augmented by outlying shopping plazas. Some industrial development has also taken place but agriculture remains important.

On Camarillo's fringes are a county airport, a seminary and Camarillo State Hospital. Strip developments along U.S. 101, including "g.e.m." services, are producing a narrow urban belt between Camarillo and Oxnard.

---

### THE SANTA BARBARA COAST *

The Santa Barbara Coast is a very inviting portion of Southern California—indeed, this provides the North American counterpart of France's *Cote d'Azur* (the Riviera).**

With the dull hues of the swiftly-rising wall of the Santa Ynez Mountains as a backdrop, the richer blue of the Pacific, and the charm of imaginatively-

---

* This section has been reviewed by David Lawson, the University of California, Santa Barbara. It had been reviewed earlier by John Estes, also UCSB.

** News media are now using the term "Gold Coast", long associated with the Miami area in Florida and the Chicago fringe of Lake Michigan north of the Loop.

landscaped dwellings this narrow lowland has much appeal.

The east-west trend of the Coast and its mountain wall inland produce more equable weather than is found in most of California. Yet it does not quite duplicate the Riviera; for example the cool Pacific is less attractive for surf bathing than the warmer Mediterranean.

### The American Riviera

Never as wide as 10 miles, the Santa Barbara Coast extends for more than 50 miles, from *Point Rincon* westward to *Point Concepcion* (map 6-19).

The Santa Ynez Mountains rises so suddenly from the Pacific between Ventura and Point Rincon that the Santa Barbara Coast is physically separated from the Oxnard Plain. In olden days before automobiles and the Coast Highway the wagon trail in places followed the narrow sandy beach—thus a trip by horses and coach required timing of sea and tide.

This constricted alluvial lowland has extensive terrace remnants as well as the foreslopes of the Santa Ynez Mountains.

Faulting has been extensive; the city of Santa Barbara lies in a small structural depression *(graben)* between parallel faults with a southeast-northwest trend. Shifts along these ruptures have produced several disastrous earthquakes.

East of Santa Barbara the Carpinteria Plain also is fault-bound on its inner margin (i.e., the base of the Santa Ynez). This Plain has more abrupt edges and is oriented more east-west than the Goleta Valley to the west.

Climatically the Santa Barbara Coast is similar to the Oxnard Plain. They share a mild-summer phase of the dry-summer subtropical climate (see Overview A).

However the Santa Barbara is spared the outbursts of interior air from the Mojave that upon occasion plague the Oxnard. Nor does the Santa Barbara, with its east-west expanse, experience the fog-laden Pacific winds from the west. Understandably the Coast is regarded quite favorably as a place of residence.

### How Much Water?

Local water resources are understandably limited—the Santa Barbara Coast has no rivers comparable to the Santa Ana, Los Angeles or Santa Clara. And the Santa Ynez Range is too low and too narrow to prompt much orographic rise.

Thus irrigation agriculture was long dependent upon pumped groundwater. Like part of the Oxnard Plain, the Coast has not had access to imported water.

Urban growth coupled with increasing rural demands has depleted underground supplies.

In 1947 severe water rationing was necessitated in Santa Barbara and there was threat of saltwater intrusion. Congress authorized the *Cachuma Project* the following year; it has provided additional water from the Santa Ynez Valley for the Carpinteria Plain, Santa Barbara, Montecito and the Goleta Valley.

By the late 1970's the water situation had again become acute. In 1973 *Friends of Santa Barbara* (i.e., outside developers) proposed water importation from the California Aqueduct (Ch.9) but this was not approved by the voters. Other proposals have included recycling and sea-water conversion.

North of the Santa Ynez Range the small arable acreage within the drainage basin of the Santa Ynez River has a better water supply (see Ch. 7). This has been the source of "outside" water for the Santa Barbara Coast.

For years water stored in Santa Barbara Reservoir on the Santa Ynez was delivered to the Coast. However, silting of the reservoir reduced its storage capacity. The Cachuma Project included a larger storage facility, *Lake Cachuma* downriver from the older unit. Six mile-long *Tecolote Tunnel* carries water through the Santa Ynez Mountains to *South Coast Aqueduct* which distributes it along the Coast.

**Figure 6-69.** Lemon processing, Carpinteria. (dwl)

**Figure 6-70.** There are obviously too few public facilities along the coast of Southern California. This is Carpinteria State Beach Park. (dwl)

## Indians, Spanish and Anglos

Even as it is a choice spot for contemporary Americans, the Coast was a favored area for earlier peoples.

It was occupied by the *Chumash* and supported perhaps the densest pre-European population in Southern California. Considered superior to other Indians in the subregion by the Spanish the Chumash were skilled mariners as well as food gatherers. In addition to the mainland they utilized the adjacent Channel Islands where the Spanish named them the *Canalenos*.

The Spanish discovered the Coast early when Cabrillo visited it in 1542.

Yet Mission Santa Barbara was not founded until 1782. Acclaimed the "queen of the missions" it has been maintained continuously by the Franciscans since its founding. The mission prospered for some decades and its pastures supported many cattle.

With secularization of mission lands the era of Mexican ranchos began.

Changing economic conditions and the drought of the early 1860, led to the division of the ranchos and the evolution of Anglo farming.

Rural land-use changes came more slowly to the Coast than to portions of the Los Angeles Lowlands around Los Angeles.

Until the Coast Line of the Southern Pacific arrived in 1887 transportation facilities were meager.

The through railroad to San Francisco, followed by the Coast Highway (now U.S. 101) did not evolve until the twentieth century. Walnuts then became an agricultural mainstay, followed by avocados and lemons. With good frost protection, lemon

yields are high. And the orchards add to the esthetic appeal of the Coast. Many groves are maintained by gentlemen farmers, as in the estate areas of Montecito and Hope Ranch, and on the western edges of Goleta.

## Oil—Under the Ocean

An important *petroleum-bearing belt* trends westward from Newhall (in Los Angeles County) through Ventura County (already noted) and thence along the the Santa Barbara Coast.

Extent beneath the Santa Barbara Channel (see map 6-19) is not fully known although oil companies have explored beyond the Channel Islands through waters as deep as 1000 feet. For decades petroleum has been recovered from the sea floor off Summerland and several nearby locales. Here wells are near-shore and yields have been modest.

The state began awarding offshore drilling rights in the late 1950's.

Cash bonuses and royalty payments were accepted from the oil companies. For esthetic reasons, such leases were not allowed in an eight-mile area, fronting on Santa Barbara.

The federal government awarded the first exploratory lease for drilling in the Santa Barbara Channel *beyond the three-mile limit* near Carpinteria (in 1966).

Subsequently a series of giant drilling platforms became visible on the Channel horizon. In 1969 a well on a submerged federal area "blew" out of control. Petroleum poured widely into the Chan-

**Figure 6-71.** The beach at Goleta near the University of California at Santa Barbara campus. Small wonder there are hints of a "play school" despite high academic standards. (dwl)

nel, killing wildlife and coating beaches from Ventura to Santa Barbara with oily scum. Yet an increased number of platforms is visible (when the thick marine layer allows!) offshore.

The county's voters approved shoreside processing facilities to serve offshore processing facilities despite determined opposition from *Goo* (Get Oil Out) and other groups. Seemingly the oil spill (and future threats) have not permanently impacted tourism and retirement residence along the Santa Barbara Coast. Newer offshore and near-shore facilities have been confined to the segment of the Coast west of Goleta beyond urban realms.

### The Carpinteria Plain

East of Santa Barbara the Carpinteria Plain is agriculturally the most productive portion of the Coast. But its farming is in jeopardy, threatened by suburbanization.

For decades the rural economy was dominated by lemons. Perhaps unwisely many growers have replaced their lemons with avocados. Market flower production has also expanded.

Dutch growers have raised fresh-market chrysanthemum plants under plastic for a generation. The plantings are scheduled so that shipment contin-

ues throughout the year.

***Carpinteria*** (13,000) has been a "growth" town of the Coast several decades. Besides its agricultural activity (including processing) it is a residence town with a popular state beach park.

Carpinteria has sufficient water that the population curb in Santa Barbara prompted growth here—there is strong boosterism. Besides homes of long-established farm workers, there are now condominiums (mostly housing commuters to Ventura and Santa Barbara) plus retirees in mobile homes. The county has not discouraged fringe-area growth and an industrial park has been established.

### The Goleta Valley

West of Santa Barbara the Goleta Valley has had more diversified land use than the Carpinteria Plain.

The gentler upward slope of the Santa Ynez Mountains has permitted grazing not possible on the steeper fault face east of Santa Barbara. Variations in soils and drainage conditions partially explained varied crop patterns that included lemon and avocado orchards, field crops, and nursery stock, as well as small vegetable plots. But in the late twentieth century little agriculture re-

**Figure 6-72.** University of California, Santa Barbara, occupies an attractive coastal site on the edge of Goleta Valley. (Goleta Valley Chamber of Commerce)

**Figure 6-73.** The northwestern edge of Southern California—Point Arguello. While the Coast Line of the Santa Fe Southern follows the shore, U.S. 101 goes inland at Goleta Pass, farther to the east. (Official U.S. Navy photograph).

mains, chiefly along the base of the Santa Ynez Mountains.

Transformation into the Southern California megalopolis is underway.

Research facilities, small warehouses and industrial plants have appeared beside the freeway (U.S.101). During some years in the 1980's defense-related research firms (including Santa Barbara Research, Delco and Raytheon), "brought" more money into the county than did the University or the one-time leader, incomes from the trusts and pensions of the wealthy. The Santa Barbara Airport (inside the city limits due to a narrow strip within the ocean) is used by scheduled carriers.

The big transitions, of course, have resulted from the expansion of the university campus and the growth of *unincorporated* Goleta.

The population of **Goleta** (80,000) is approaching that of Santa Barbara. The community experienced an almost Cinderella-like transformation from unattractive village (mostly housing farm workers) to an university town and commuter place.

Unfortunately, unlike Irvine (Orange County) or Davis, Goleta was not incorporated and has suffered from insufficient planning. In a more modest way, Goleta suggests the metamorphosis in the Santa Clara Valley (Ch. 8). It is not a continuous urban area but a series of clusters. Portions may

become an incorporated city and other segments may be merged into Santa Barbara.

Rapid change followed the relocation of the University of California campus from an earlier site in Santa Barbara. Unfortunately the University did not officially recognize soon enough the impending growth. No University coordination of enrollment policies with off-campus planning has occurred.

Despite its high academic standards, the seaside setting of the University invites students (and their friends) looking for a playplace. Such is *Isla Vista* (circa 10,000), which local youth called *sin city* in the 1960's. Surrounded by the campus and unincorporated partially because of University opposition, Isla Vista became one of America's "incredible student ghettos" during the Viet Nam years. Acute social problems included high rentals (and many absentee landlords including some UCSB faculty and administrators). Conditions are somewhat better now; alcohol appears to have become the "drug" of choice.

### The Western Terraces

Width of the Santa Barbara Coast narrows west of Goleta Valley with a series of dissected terraces cut by a series of small parallel streams which flow southward from the Santa Ynez Range in gullies.

Much land is devoted to beef cattle pasturage or dry-farmed grains because of water limitation. Expansion of avocado and lemon groves has occurred with use of drip irrigation. Other uses include a large orchid "ranch", oil processing facilities (from offshore sources) and a succession of state beach parks. "Hints" of impending change exist in the planned *Sandpiper World* resort.

**Figure 6-74.** Handsomely-landscaped State Street, downtown Santa Barbara. (dwl)

**Figure 6-75.** Santa Barbara is sited in one of California's most attractive settings. The Santa Ynez Mountains forms a backdrop. The principal downtown street, State, extends northward from the pier. (Santa Barbara Chamber of Commerce, photo by Randle Photography)

## Santa Barbara and Environs

The city (85,000) has long been recognized as one of California's choice seaside communities (Figure 6–75).

Its appeals include scenic setting, agreeable climate, and many well-maintained homes with landscaped gardens.

Few aircraft echoes or train whistles are heard and there are no expansive military or aerospace installations. Santa Barbara has *nearly* avoided the disruptions that plague many locales in Southern California today. But one wonders: "For how much longer?"

*Officially* Santa Barbara hopes to curb its population at 85,000 (in the *political* city). Beyond that level changes in zoning will be necessary to allow more multiple units. Already population expansion in a physically-confined townsite has notably added to traffic (although conversion of U.S. 101 to full freeway status through the city by 1990 will help), housing and recreational congestion.

Despite much affluence on northern slopes, Santa Barbara, within its *political* limits, is not one of California's wealthier communities.

Median incomes are much lower than those of Beverly Hills, La Jolla or Manhattan Beach. A modest-income populace (retirees, service personnel, ethnic groups and college students) increasingly fills Santa Barbara proper.

On the less-taxed fringes the barely-wealthy have replaced yesteryears' multi-millionaires who so conscientiously endowed their city. One now senses an aversion to philanthropy.

Some obsolescence is inherent in a city where so many civic and private facilities were constructed long ago—or most recently rebuilt following the earthquake of 1925.

Once Santa Barbara, where industry was long discouraged, could be described as the home of the wealthy and those who served the wealthy.

Evidences of the Hispanic colonial legacy are widespread in Santa Barbara.

Some, like the mission (despite a replaced facade) and such street names as Cabrillo and Micheltorena, are genuine. Others, like the widespread employment of synthetic mission architecture, blend with the landscape and the historic tradition. The county courthouse is an outstanding example—damage in the 1925 earthquake prompted restoration in the mission style. Each August the spirit of the Spanish heritage is revived with a

**Figure 6-76.** "Downtown" Montecito, The Village. (dwl)

fiesta. It contrasts with the counter-cultural celebration of the summer solstice in June!

Economic patterns of Santa Barbara differ somewhat from those of other California cities of comparable size.

They include tourism, investment income, attendance upon a leisure group, pensions, county government, higher education, local trade, limited manufacturing and defense-related research.

Winter once brought fewer visitors who, as in Pasadena, remained much of the season, frequenting the exclusive hotels or maintaining their own residences, now motels advertise "off-season" rates in winter). Summer brings the "great American public" in family automobiles. Metropolitan Santa Barbara's monied "coupon clippers" have included representatives of some of the nation's most prominent families. For many visitors, attractions have included the shore with its historic Stearns Wharf and historic buildings from the Hispanic and early American eras.

The city proper houses a surprising number of retired couples with modest pensions—many reside in the southwestern section of the city. Also, there is a considerable Hispanic population.

Although Santa Barbara serves as the retail center of the Coast the luxury items in its specialty shops especially along State Street are found in quantity unusual for its population.

The number of brokerage houses is another reflection of high per capita incomes in the metropolitan area. The city denied the proposal of its consultants to develop a second regional shopping center on the western periphery of the central district. But a major mall is now planned for lower State Street. The chief corridor of urban expansion is northwestward paralleling U.S. 101 into Goleta Valley. This strip, with its elongated shopping center rather than downtown, is now the retail core.

The metropolitan area is understandably one of California's important cultural centers, especially for its size.

Besides activities related to the state university and city and private colleges, there is a community playhouse, a museum, zoo, parks and organizations related to the arts. The city has crafts shops as well as designers' studios. Many artists, actors, musicians, and writers make the city their home; clubs related to music, drama and art flourish.

Santa Barbara is fringed by attractive suburban residential districts.

To the west is Hope Ranch and to the east Montecito. On the north homes ascend the lower slopes of the Santa Ynez Mountains.

West of Santa Barbara **Hope Ranch** is an exclusive residential area of 2000 acres developed on rolling terrain amidst lemon groves.

There are no retail shops—its social center is La Cumbre Country Club. It provides the appeals of a private beach (Laguna Blanca), 25 miles of bridle paths, view lots affording vistas of the Santa Ynez Mountains and the Pacific, and an absence of commercialism.

Likewise politically separate, **Montecito** (6000) has been described as the "home of American trademarks."

Residents have included families of American industrialists whose products are widely known. Centers of this long-time millionaires' retreat are the Montecito Country Club and *The Village* (retail shops), not the retail strip along U.S. 101. Homes are sequestered by lemon groves and signposts, "private" or "no trespassing" along the winding lanes. But clearly the era of great wealth is waning here. A younger, less affluent, family-rearing populace has increased. Newer dwellings, on smaller lots, have replaced some former estates. Yet realtors report that six-figure incomes are necessary to buy property here.

---

## THE TRANSVERSE RANGES

Because of their proximity to the millions who inhabit the Los Angeles Basin, the Transverse Ranges have been much frequented and widely publicized.

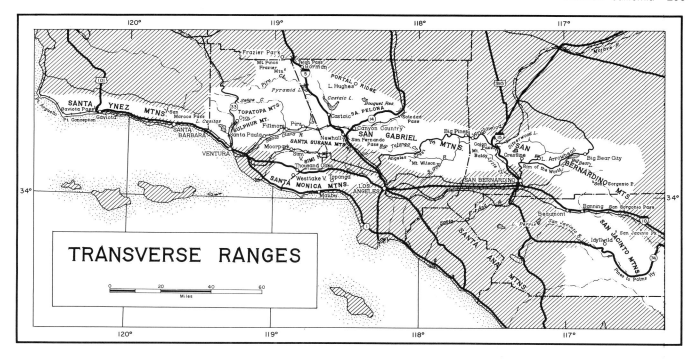

**Map 6-20.** Within the Transverse Ranges land use is complex. An impressive population resides in many small basins.

They are accessible but they are not of exhilarating grandeur. Still the Transverse Ranges upon occasion provide snow in winter and they are cooler than the Lowlands in summer. And they afford appealing vistas when there is not too much smog. The snowy crowns, almost perpetual, of the Cascade Range, the glaciated canyons of the Sierra Nevada, the serrated summits of the Rocky Mountains and the hardwood forests of the Appalachian Highlands—all these are absent.

Some have entitled these ranges the Southern California Mountains while others have designated them as the Los Angeles Ranges, or less accurately, the Coast Range.

The Transverse Ranges have an east-west orientation whereas the adjoining Coast Ranges trend more north-south. From east to west they include the *San Bernardino, San Gabriel, Santa Monica, Santa Susana, Topatopa* and *Santa Ynez.* The *San Jacinto* and *Santa Rosa* mountains are discussed herein because of location and utilization (by residents of the Los Angeles Basin). *Physiographically* they are parts of the Peninsular Ranges.

The Transverse Ranges provide important physical influences in utilization of Southern California.

They "shut out" much of the interior desert heat in summer and interior cold in winter. They also wrench considerable moisture from Pacific maritime air masses.

The barrier function has not been restricted to air movement alone—the mountains have tended to curtail plant migrations as well. They have also

**Figure 6-83.** Nearing the summit of "Old Baldy" (Mt. San Antonio) (10,064 feet). Contrast with side view (Fig. 6 59). (dwl)

hampered the movements of traffic which must focus upon only a few favored crossings.

## MOUNTAIN BLOCKS AND CHAPARRAL
### Fault Blocks and Upfolds

The Transverse Ranges differ considerably in elevation, structure, size, and surface expression. Generally the eastern ranges, particularly the San Gabriel, San Bernardino and San Jacinto, are loftier.

Highest summits include *Mt. San Antonio* (10,064 feet), *San Gorgonio* (11,384 feet) and *San Jacinto* (10,805 feet). Farther west the local relief is sometimes insufficient to classify the highlands accurately as true mountains. Thus it is fitting that the segment of the Santa Monica Mountains between the Los Angeles Coastal Plain and the San Fernando Valley is called the *Hollywood Hills*. Within these heights are a number of intermontane basins, of which the Santa Clara River Valley is the most prominent apart from the interior Los Angeles Lowlands (i.e., the San Fernando and San Gabriel valleys).

The ranges represent several periods of mountain building.

Present-day topography results largely from diastrophism during the Pleistocene—recent earthquakes suggest that some development continues. Erosion has been dominant between periods of uplift and deep narrow canyons are commonplace. In the west, where slopes rise from the Pacific, narrow marine terraces exist.

Collectively the Ranges might be described as a group of "uplifted" blocks bordered and bisected by such great faults as the San Andreas, and much dissected by erosion.

But the western ranges show tilted and folded sedimentary structures. These include the Santa Ynez, Santa Monica and Santa Susana ranges. The San Gabriel (a compound horst), San Bernardino and San Jacinto are conspicuous for their granitic cores and impressively steep fault-scarp faces. They possess flattish summit areas where erosion has not yet worked its way back from the mountain margins.

### Summer Heat and Severe Winters

The greatest climatic variation in Southern California is found within the Transverse Ranges. The general rhythm follows the usual subregional pattern of hot dry summers and mild winters with occasional cyclonic activity.

A multitude of diverse *microclimates* results from elevation differences, distinctions between *sunny* and *shady* slopes and location with respect to the Pacific Ocean and the interior deserts.

Below about 3000 feet coastal slopes are exposed to considerable maritime air and cloud cover. Thus the Santa Ynez and Santa Monica mountains and the Santa Clara River Valley tend to have milder temperatures than the more eastern ranges. Interior slopes, especially eastward from the Ridge Route on Interstate 5, are exposed more to dry continental air and their summer and winter temperatures are somewhat extreme.

Hot-summer Mediterranean aspects do not prevail much higher than a mile above sea level because of temperature decrease with altitude. A milder-summer Mediterranean phase (too small to be shown on map A-5) occurs still higher—it is suggestive of the cool coastline localities.

Higher summits display middle-latitude severe-winter conditions atypical of the subtropics at lower elevations. Extreme interior slopes are recognized as semi-arid. Winter precipitation tends to increase with altitude; some highland stations in the San Gabriel and San Bernardino mountains receive in excess of 40 inches. Winter snowfall is common enough to sustain ski resorts (after a fashion). Summer cloudbursts and lightning strikes are not unusual on higher inland (desert facing) slopes.

**Figure 6-78.** The Ridge Route down Grapevine Canyon. This portion of I-5 is an eight-lane thoroughfare with six per cent grades. Divided-lane construction has lessened the accident rate on this heavily-used freeway. (Caltrans)

## Evergreens: Shrubs and Trees

Natural vegetation has understandable variations with semblance of vertical zonation.

The most widespread association is *chaparral*— stands tend to be less dense on south-facing slopes. Although hues vary seasonally its shrubs are evergreens. It consists of numerous species adapted to the long rainless months—thus leaves are often small and sometimes leathery. On lower south slopes the chamise or coastal sage subdivisions prevail. Chaparral covers steep slopes and checks erosion but it generally has no grazing value and is fire-susceptible during the drought season.

Desert-facing slopes of the eastern ranges reflect arid influences.

They commonly support a *pinyon-juniper* woodland in which yucca is sometimes prominent.

Forests, somewhat restricted in the Transverse Ranges, are being damaged by smog.

A *yellow pine* association, prevalent above 6000 feet, has thicker stands on north slopes and best development around 8000 to 9500 feet. There are several pines in this forest. Along streams a canyon-floodplain assemblage of oak, sycamore, alder, maple and willow is common; it tends to form groves rather than true forests. The oaks are widespread on south-facing slopes at 4000 to 6000 feet and reach much lower elevations on shady slopes where evaporation is reduced.

## THE ROLE OF PEOPLE

Few of the world's mountain areas are utilized by so many people in so many ways as are the Transverse Ranges. Easy access to these highlands by approximately half of the people of California makes their location especially meaningful. Significant uses include residence, recreation, transportation, water sources, mining and ranching.

## Water Conservation

A water-short land, Southern California must salvage as much of its local highland precipitation as possible.

The slope of canyon walls and steep stream gradients accelerates runoff. Snowpack in some locales is important *(Big Bear Dam* averages 124 inches— more than 20 inches monthly, December through March.

In a few localities storage reservoirs have been constructed but the nature of the precipitation, sometimes torrential, and the stream gradients and dangerously-faulted rock structures do not favor large units. Some Transverse canyons are also used to store "imported" water notably at Pyramid, Castaic and Silverwood lakes along the California Aqueduct system. They incidentally provide recreational opportunities.

The lowly chaparral is highly regarded as ground cover. Its protection is particularly vital to densely-populated lowlands that adjoin the Transverse Ranges—this was evidenced by the tragic flood of 1934 in *La Canada Corridor* and more widely in the winter of 1969.

Unfortunately chaparral is a voracious consumer of moisture; canyon-bottom forests also absorb great volumes of streamflow that is much needed for human use.

Thus riparian forest removal has been practiced in selected locations and efforts are underway to find satisfactory substitutes for chaparral. The "brush problem" is intensified by the flammability of this vegetation most of the year—an increasingly-serious menace the longer chaparral is saved from fire. Sizable sums are allocated annually to prevent and extinguish fires in the Ranges. To reduce the hazard, extensive tracts within the national forests are withdrawn from public entry during the long "fire season."

## Entryways

All land routes into Southern California from the east and north must cross or skirt the Ranges. These offer relatively easy high-speed automobile passage except in storms, but the requisite extra mileages and gradients are still formidable.

Rail routes from the north reach the San Fernando Valley only after passage through tunnels. Paucity of services within the Ranges has always given economic support to "pass towns" at or near the base of the several highlands.

Among the passageways *Tejon Pass, Cajon Pass* and *San Gorgonio Pass* have particular importance.

The latter two (Cajon and San Gorgonio) are used by both highways and railroads. Other passes are also important. *

---

* Major passes from west to east include Gaviota (950 feet) crossed by the Coast Highway (U.S. 101) and San Marcos (2224 ft.) in the Santa Ynez. Farther east, across Pine Mountain Summit Ca. 33 follows

**Figure 6-79.** Cajon Pass. Two railroads and Interstate 15 cross the famed passage between the Los Angeles Lowlands and Mojave Desert. Substitution of the name "Amtrak" would update this picture. (Union Pacific Railroad).

There are also utility crossings of the Transverse Ranges to deliver electricity, natural gas, petroleum, telephone messages, and water to Southern California. The above passes provide routes for them also. But power and telephone lines especially are less restricted by terrain and tend to follow the shortest routes.

**Resorts—Even Hikers Too**

The Transverse Ranges may seem to be a "desperation fringe" to many outsiders. But the handicaps tend to be offset by proximity to large metropolitan populations.

The San Bernardino Mountains *alone* have twice as many visits annually as the most popular of the nation's national parks. Visits of a few hours, a

day, or a weekend are typical. Habitues are generally Southern Californians rather than out-of-staters.

Scenic drives, some with inviting names and spectacular views, lead across several of the highlands.

Major examples are *Mulholland Drive,* along "the spine" of the eastern Santa Monica Mountains, *Angeles Crest Highway* (Ca. 2) in the San Gabriel, *Rim of the World* in the San Bernardino and *Pines-to-Palms Highway* (Ca. 74) in the San Jacinto.

Such roads become more congested than many city streets, especially on weekends. Still, they are extremely well built for such rough terrain—construction has often been justified for the need of fire-fighting access alone.

Much of this mountain country is included within three national forests.

---

a lengthy winding course north of Ojai. Interstate 5 crosses Tejon Pass (4239 ft.) on the Ridge Route across the Knot. This limited-access highway, with eight-lane stretches, is a very different road than it was in past decades (Figure 6-78). Decelerated movement of heavy trucks reflects the six per cent grades, the maximum permitted on federal highways. Farther south, the Coast Line of the Santa Fe Pacific employs tunnels beneath the low Santa Susana Pass, enroute from the San Fernando Valley to Ventura. The San Fernando-Simi Valley Freeway (Ca. 118), a short distance to the north, uses the same crossing.

From the northern tip of the San Fernando Valley **San Fernando** (or Fremont) **Pass** and **Soledad Pass** farther to to the northeast provide the Valley Line of the Santa Fe Southern egress from the Los Angeles

Basin. Beyond the Transverse Ranges, farther north, the rail crosses the Tehachapi Mountains to reach San Joaquin Valley (Figure10-11). Between the San Gabriel and San Bernardino ranges **Cajon Pass** (4260 ft.) is a famed crossing. A freeway (Interstate 15) leads to the central Mojave. It is vastly improved from the crude trail that was used by early travelers travelers in the late Mexican colonial years. The Santa Fe Southern trackage across this pass is also used by the Union Pacific Railroad (Figure 6-79) at a slightly lower elevation (3800 ft.).

Farther to the southeast is another extremely important entry into Southern California, **San Gorgonio** (2559 ft.). The freeway here (Interstate 10) leads to Palm Springs and on to Phoenix. This crossing is also used by the main line of the Santa Fe Southern to Phoenix and eastward.

These are Los Padres in Santa Barbara and Ventura counties, Angeles in Los Angeles County and San Bernardino in San Bernardino and Riverside counties. Angeles was created to provide Los Angeles with a mountain playground—forests are not common.

In the national forests, campsites, "recreation areas" and hiking trails have been developed.

Sites for cabins and even ski lifts are leased though these are at a premium. Fishing and hunting are too popular for the limited resources.

Within the forests are several wilderness and primitive areas (see Ch.2) containing nearly 200,000 acres. These allow the limited number who are willing to abandon their automobiles for long hikes to visit some of Southern California's most rugged terrain.

Resort and residence places (with much commutation) are frequent although they occupy only minute portions of the Transverse Ranges.

The Santa Monica is much favored because of its proximity to both Los Angeles and the seacoast. Before 1980 plans were underway to establish a national park. Under the Reagan administration this was "down-graded" into *Santa Monica Mountains National Recreation Area*.

The San Bernardino Mountains has the largest resorts, which benefit from an unique combination of moderately-level topography and higher elevation. Here is Southern California's largest expanse of forest, lake and winter snow country, which became known to millions of movie-goers as the "Rocky Mountains" and the "Canadian North Woods" (Figure 6-81). Its permanent population

**Figure 6-80.** The Santa Clarita (i.e., upper Santa Clara River) Valley is the locale of fast-growing Valencia and a dozen other unincorporated communities. (dwl)

(Crestline, Lake Arrowhead and around Big Bear Lake) exceeds 20,000.

### Specks of Gold

Except for petroleum, sand and gravel, mining has had limited importance in the Transverse Ranges.

Small amounts of gold were recovered from Placerita Canyon north of San Fernando Valley even before the Gold Rush commenced in the Sierra Nevada. As late as the 1930's gold panning took place in the San Bernardino and San Gabriel mountains. Holcomb Valley in the former range was important enough in the "early days" that it was considered as the seat of San Bernardino County.

**Figure 6-81.** A mile above sea level in the San Bernardino Mountains, Lake Arrowhead is a much-frequented playground for residents of the Los Angeles Basin (U.S. Forest Service).

The extensive oil-bearing zone which extends along both sides of the Santa Clara River Valley has been noted (see Oxnard Plain and Santa Barbara Coast).

This belt, generally called the **Ventura Basin**, has ranked after the San Joaquin Valley and the Los Angeles Basin as a source of petroleum in California.

## Nocturnal Dreamland

Particularly within and adjacent to metropolitan Los Angeles sections of the Transverse Ranges have much residential utilization.

Development largely has taken place since 1920 with evolution of the automobile and better roads. "View lots" where residents can enjoy metropolitan lights, have become expensive—a choice, relatively-flat half-acre lot now costs hundreds of thousands of dollars in the more "exclusive" settings. Some of the most luxurious homes around Los Angeles are found on such hillsides. More prominent localities include **Flintridge** (between Pasadena and Glendale), northern Beverly Hills, much of Sherman Oaks, Bel Air and Brentwood.

Construction economics, building codes, and personal whims have resulted in lot leveling, which results initially in a savage disfigurement of the earth. Nor do such changes always produce scenic or safe occupance settings. Environmental protection movements in recent decades have decreased somewhat the pace of hillside transformation, notably in the western Santa Monica Mountains, which earlier seemed destined for complete urbanization. The National Recreation Area has been noted.

**Figure 6-82.** Onion harvest in January, Santa Clara River Valley, west of I-5. (dwl)

## Basin Urbanization

Within the Ranges small valleys and intermont basins provide many small pockets of arable land— the larger basins (San Fernando and San Gabriel valleys) were discussed separately.

While chaparral-covered hillsides have not provided pasturage, some unirrigated areas allow dry-farmed winter barley or seasonal agriculture. But urbanization is proceeding rapidly. The hill country of southern Ventura County has been particularly attractive for ranching as well as town development.

### The Santa Clara River Valley

The Santa Clara River Valley* has provided an exceptional example of the diversity of Southern California agriculture. Only a low divide (Soledad Pass) separates its upper end from the Mojave Desert while on the west it widens into the Oxnard Plain near the ocean.

In colonial days a series of Mexican ranchos were awarded along the Valley. Several large properties remain: the Newhall, Sespe, Camulos and Limoneira. The vast Limoneira, near Santa Paula, assembled in the 1870's and later, contains the world's largest single lemon acreage.

Upriver farming, always handicapped by wind and frost, is vanishing (see Figure 6-82) with continued urbanization.

On irrigated bottomlands not yet urbanized, alfalfa, carrots, and various other crops have been grown.

Around Piru, farther west, walnut groves appear and on well-drained lower slopes, oranges.

From Fillmore westward, citrus groves are more widespread. Below Santa Paula air-drained slopes, almost frost-free, are planted in avocados and lemons.

Seed flowers and various field crops are found on lower sites where the water table may be high. In the bed of the River (made doubly broad by the siltation from the St. Francis Dam failure in 1928) and adjacent sideslopes grazing of beef takes place.

The towns of the "downstream" Valley serve as local trade centers and afford shipping points. They also provide residence for agricultural and petroleum

---

* It is simply called the *Santa Clara Valley* or *Santa Clara River Valley* herein to avoid confusion with the better-known lowland south of San Francisco. This problem is lessening since the portion in Los Angeles County is now called *Canyon Country* or *Santa Clarita Valley*.

**Figure 6-85.** Ojai Valley, a favored intermontane basin at the base of the Topatopa Mountains north of Ventura. (dwl).

workers. In "upstream" towns there tends to be increasing commutation to metropolitan Los Angeles along with expanding local urban activities.

The principal farm center and shipping point of the Valley is **Santa Paula** (25,000).

It houses commuters to the Oxnard Plain and has been an oil town (Unocal was founded here).

Many visitors remember it as a pleasant residence place, especially upslope on the north side (dwellings are more expensive). The conspicuous socio-economic cleavage of the past has lessened; traditionally, farm workers resided south of the central district. Present-day Hispanics reside more widely than in the traditional south-side barrio and participate more in community affairs.

**Fillmore** (12,000) is a smaller, albeit growing semi-replica of Santa Paula.

It has less retail trade and fewer commuting residents. Well-maintained packing sheds reflect the output of surrounding citrus groves. Commutation, as in Santa Paula, to the Oxnard Plain is favored by nearby freeway access.

Urbanization in **Canyon Country** (Santa Clarita Valley) increasingly reflects the outward thrust of metropolitan Los Angeles along main freeway corridors (map 6-20).

There are also such diverse employment sources as the county prison farm, an aerospace research facility and manufacture of glass and explosives.

Long established **Newhall** (20,000) provides a local center.

With growth the number of commuter residents has increased.

The "new town" of **Valencia** (30,000) seems destined to become the the major city of Canyon Country. It has been designed for an eventual population of 250,000.

It occupies the site of *Newhall Ranch* on which sizable tracts have been set aside for such diverse uses as industry and residence (including expensive houses, less-costly tract dwellings and high-density apartments).

Already a diversity of institutions has appeared. These include *Magic Mountain* (an amusement park), California Institute of the Arts (Disney-sponsored) and College of the Canyons. Along Interstate 5 there are a number of travelers' services.

**Figure 6-84.** The "new town" of Westlake Village "straddles the line" (i.e., the Los Angeles -Ventura county border). (dwl)

## The Ojai Valley

One of California's more pleasing rural settings is provided by the Ojai Valley (Figure 6-85). It has appeal for both residents and visitors.

There are fruit orchards (citrus and deciduous), stock ranches as well as groves of sycamore and oak. Of the Valley's 25,000 residents, many have nonagricultural interests.

*Ojai* (7900) is a combination resort, farm and retirement town. Here and in nearby hamlets many commuters reside.

The Ojai supports varied activities besides farming and residence.

It is noted for its private schools, several resorts, annual music festival and spring tennis tournament and an apple harvest. Nearby Lake Casitas was used for Olympic rowing races in 1984. Many visitors come from metropolitan Southern California. Among residents there are many Anglo white-collar commuters to the Santa Barbara Coast or Ventura as well as retirees.

### Eastern Ventura County

The fringes of metropolitan Los Angeles now reach westward beyond the San Fernando Valley into several little basins (especially the *Conejo* and *Simi*) freeway-accessible (U.S. 101 and Ca. 118).

Within the folds of the Santa Susana and Santa Monica mountains, these lowlands were earlier associated with cattle and ranching and the making of motion pictures. In the past few decades some of the most rapid growth in Los Angeles and Ventura counties has been occurring here. While there is some local employment but much commutation of Anglo white-collar workers despite an appalling absence of public transit facilities. There is much van-pooling.

*Thousand Oaks* (110,000), an erstwhile agrarian village, now ranks high among cities of Ventura County in median income.

Rolling terrain, oak groves and attractive landscaping lend appeal to this growing city.

This one-time *strassendorf* hamlet along U.S. 101 was once known for its "farm" of exotic animals used in motion pictures. Now, with a number of housing tracts and several regional shopping malls with "high-fashion" shops it is a hub for the area between the San Fernando Valley and the Oxnard Plain. It is the site of private California Lutheran College.

*Westlake Village* ( 7,000) is a planned "new town" developed by an insurance company adjacent to Thousand Oaks.

Amidst oak groves, with its artificial lake and peninsulas, it has social prestige and has attracted many upper middle-income Anglo professional workers (such as engineers and and accountants) from industrial plants and offices in metropolitan Los Angeles who seem willing to commute considerable distances to live in a new community without appreciable numbers of ethnics.

*Simi Valley* (105,000) represents urban engulfment of an agricultural basin, including absorption of several once-sleepy farm hamlets. Rapid growth was favored by "spillover" access from the northern San Fernando Valley via freeway (Ca. 118).

Earlier citification in the 1960's and 1970's included poorly-planned tracts for blue-collar commuters. Both husbands and wives tended to commute to metropolitan Los Angeles. More recently Simi Valley has become a higher-income white-collar community. The number of swimming pools is impressive. The transformation is faintly suggestive of Concord (Ch. 8) in the San Francisco Bay Area. There is no well-defined "downtown" but rather several shopping centers. Areas have been set aside for retirement complexes as well as industrial development, which is taking place.

*Moorpark* (20,000), farther west, is a farm town experiencing disorderly transition into a commuter bedroom.

For decades it served principally as a residence place for Hispanic farm workers. Recently less-expensive tract homes have been constructed and many residents are commuting to the Oxnard Plain or to metropolitan Los Angeles (via Ca.118 and 23 freeways). It is an important center for poultry eggs. One "ranch", *Egg City,* has over a

**Figure 6-83.** Simi Valley.

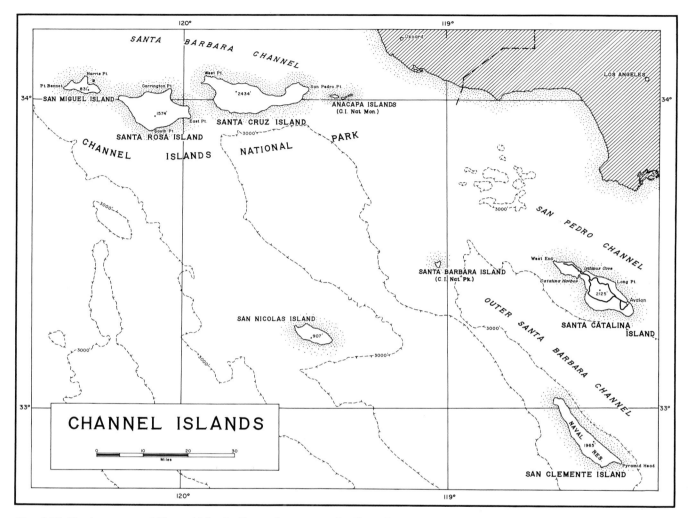

**Map 6-21.** The two groups of Channel Islands. The northern group plus Santa Barbara Island comprises the Channel Islands National Park.

million hens. A somewhat smaller plant is nearby.* A community college serves adjacent communities as well as Moorpark.

### San Gorgonio Pass

San Gorgonio Pass affords the single transmontane corridor into metropolitan Southern California where agriculture has consequence.

Farming began over a century ago. Winds that seem to blow almost constantly, plus elevation of half a mile, has discouraged raising of some subtropical crops. Most of the cultivated acreage is used for barley.

Cherries are the best known fruit along the Pass, although acreage of plums and peaches are larger. Spring-time blossoms and summer "pick your own" attracts city dwellers.

Wind constancy has favored establishment of "wind farms", covering considerable acreage, with thousands of whirling generators, in the eastern portion of the Pass. Electricity goes to Southern California Edison.

***Banning*** (18,000) and ***Beaumont*** (8000) are lower-income residential towns that serve as highway gateways into Southern California.

There is reliance in both communities upon local agriculture as well as highway trade. Both communities have sizable commuter and retirement populations, attracted by the higher elevation (hence cooler weather) and dramatic mountain scenery on both edges of the Pass.

---

* California, the nation's most populous state, understandably leads the United States in egg production. In recent decades the outdated idea of a small flock as "spending money" for a farm wife or a source of supplemental income for a retired couple has been replaced by "assembly-line" plants like Egg City with good access to urban markets.

## THE CHANNEL ISLANDS

The two groups of Channel Islands, Santa Catalina and Santa Barbara, are the least visited and most sparsely populated portions of Southern California.*

Except for much-visited Santa Catalina (map 6-21), few Californians have ever been ashore on any of these islands.

While the islands are all within 70 miles of the mainland, scheduled public transportation is available frequently only to Santa Catalina, and less frequently, to the Channel Islands National Park, especially Anacapa.

Except to government personnel and yachters, most of the other islands might as well be in the Indian Ocean—they are nigh inaccessible.

The *Santa Barbara* group forms a "close-together" east-west chain separated from the mainland by *Santa Barbara Channel*.

The group consists of Anacapa, Santa Cruz, Santa Rosa and San Miguel.

The *Santa Catalina* group, with more southeasterly alignment, is more scattered.

Santa Catalina is separated from the mainland by *San Pedro Channel*. The other three, San Clemente, Santa Barbara and San Nicolas, are beyond *Outer Santa Barbara Channel,* southwest of Santa Catalina.

## A LAND APART

### Anticlines and Grabens

Between the Southern California coastline and the continental slope the sea floor has an extent of more than 30,000 square miles. Rising above the floor there appear to be two general types of islands.

The Santa Barbara group is a continuation of the Santa Monica Mountains—a granitic ridge capped by complex anticlinal structures and containing assorted sedimentary and volcanic rocks.

The Catalina group is perhaps a continuation of the Peninsular Ranges in structure but without their granitic core. The structure south of the Santa Barbara group seems to be a series of parallel horsts and grabens. The grabens form *sea troughs,* reaching depths of as much as 6000 feet below sea level. The higher horsts form the Catalina islands; those which do not rise above sea level are *banks.*

Rough terrain is extensive and the narrow stream-dissected valleys have steep gradients.

Lower portions of some valleys are drowned. Wavecut terraces extend as high as 1500 feet above sea level. Some islands, such as Anacapa and Catalina, have surprisingly-level summit uplands. There are prominent fault scarps, such as the southwestern face of Santa Catalina.

### Cool Air and Fogs

Climatically the Channel Islands have a drier, cool-summer phase of the Mediterranean type.

Elevations are insufficient to produce much orographic effect during winter storms. Water deficiency has been a major deterrent of greater utilization. Because of oceanic location, seasonal temperature ranges are low for the latitude. The outer islands tend to be chilly and windy, particularly in winter and experience considerably more summer fog than Santa Cruz or Catalina.

### Coast Sage and Chaparral

*Chamise* chaparral and coastal sage form the characteristic vegetative cover on these dry, rocky isles.

Summit uplands, in some instances, are covered with wild grasses. The best wooded is Santa Cruz, with excellent stands of manzanita and some pines. Scores of flowering plants are peculiar to the islands. The most spectacular is the Giant Coreoposis. On Catalina and Santa Cruz eucalyptus and other types of trees have been planted.

### Albacore and Wild Sheep

The islands support a rich fauna despite their rocky slopes and their dryness.

Such animals as Catalina's bison herd, the wild goats of San Clemente (now removed), the wild boar, Santa Rosa's deer and elk, and the wild sheep and rabbits on several islands are descendants of creatures brought from the mainland.

Other species, such as skunk and fox, are indigenous. There are numerous birds, including eagles, hawks and ravens and meadowlarks. Western gulls are the dominant nesting bird on Santa Barbara and brown pelicans on Anacapa. There are also larks and sea gulls.

Life in surrounding waters is abundant; sea lions are found along several coasts, particularly Santa

---

* Authorities use the term *Channel Islands* differently. Gudde, in *California Place Names,* uses the term only for the Santa Barbara group. Drury, in *California, An Intimate Guide,* includes both groups but suggests they should be called *Cabrillo Islands* after the early explorer.

**Figure 6-86.** Santa Catalina Island has a "block" structure. (Lane Magazine and Book Company, photo by Martin Litton).

Barbara and San Nicolas, which also has a sea elephant colony. Sea otters also find refuge here. The cool waters contain such types of fish as albacore, bonita, sea bass, mackerel, perch, sword-fish and whitefish—and also sharks.

## THE OLDEN DAYS

With some modifications, occupance of the Channel Islands has followed the characteristic Southern California "pattern."

The Islands supported hundreds of *Canalenos* prior to European European colonial times.

Doubtless the largest populations subsisted upon Santa Cruz and Santa Catalina. These people were hunter-gatherers and especially, fisherfolk. Builders of planked canoes, they were adept navigators. The sea provided them with food; they also fashioned bone and shell into implements and tools.

A mere half century after the first voyage of Columbus, Juan Cabrillo "discovered" the Channel Islands.

While landing on San Miguel, Cabrillo was fatally injured and was buried in the islands.

The Spanish considered location of a mission on Catalina; investigations indicated that there was not sufficient water for irrigation.

Accordingly many Canalenos were taken to mainland missions. Presumably Russian and Aleut seal hunters killed most of the rest.

In the colonial Mexican period three islands, Santa Cruz, Santa Rosa and Santa Catalina became land grants.

During that brief era the Islands had slight economic value.

## THE ISLANDS TODAY

The Islands remain sparsely populated with relatively little economic importance—Avalon on Catalina is the single incorporated town.

Environmental restrictions, governmental use and private ownership have limited utilization. The major physical handicap seems to be limited water. However fog, kelp beds, rough seas, shoals and absence of suitable landings hamper navigation.

The Islands have been used in divers ways, in addition to Catalina's recreational importance.

Insular waters have considerable importance as commercial fishing grounds and for sports fishing. Livestock ranching has been conducted on most of the Islands. Military usage has been made of San Miguel, San Nicolas and San Clemente, as well as locally elsewhere.

Creation of Channel Islands National Park, discussed below, has recognized the uniqueness of the islands.

### The Catalina Group

*Santa Catalina* has had more extensive utilization than the other seven islands.

In 1921, except for the town of Avalon, the island

was acquired by the Wrigley family, who discouraged exploitation. In the mid-1970's the family prevailed upon Los Angeles County (in which the island is located) to establish a 50-year designation of "open space." Most of the island was then acquired by the "Santa Catalina Island Conservancy" which is preserving the environment.

Gentler surfaces have provided pasturage and feed grain but much of the terrain has steep slope.

Catalina is much frequented in summer; activities include fishing, sightseeing tours, biking, hiking and camping. Planes and cruise ships make scheduled crossings from mainland points. The Island is the weekend destination of many yachters with anchorages available at Avalon and The Isthmus. Skin diving is done near the shore while surrounding waters attract sports fisherfolk.

The center of public activity is *Avalon* (2400).

Visitors cannot bring their automobiles but walking, bicycling and golf-cart drives are popular as well as bus touring. There are restaurants and hotels. Many of the residents live in hillside homes. The waterfront Boardwalk, the beach, and inspection of marine life through glass-bottomed boats are popular.

***San Clemente***, south of Catalina, is held by the United States Navy.

This attenuated island is dry and lacks all-weather harbors. It was formerly used for sheep ranching but was overrun by wild goats. For a time grass provided forage for a few thousand wild goats. The goats have been moved to the mainland to halt landscape deterioration.

The Navy has maintained an airfield and its vessels have used the south end of the island for a target range. Another activity has been missile testing.

***Santa Barbara***, sometimes called *Santa Barbara Rock,* is the smallest of the group—it is part of the national park.

The island is uninhabited; its most conspicuous use has been the two flashing navigation lights, unattended, at either end of the "rock."

***San Nicolas***, the most remote of the Catalina group, is also held by the Navy.

The island has served as a radar station and for monitoring missile tests.

Some of its Canaleno occupants were killed by Russian and Aleut sea-otter hunters; the remaining Indians were removed to Mission Santa Barbara.

During the Boom of the 1880's a townsite was laid out but little pre-Navy utilization materialized except the raising of sheep.

### The Santa Barbara Group

Establishment of ***Channel Islands National Park*** has changed the utilization of several islands. Before 1980 only Anacapa and Santa Barbara (in the

**Figure 6-88.** Visitors watching seals and sea lions, Point Bennett, San Miguel Island, Channel Islands National Park (National Park Service, photo by M. Hill).

Catalina group) had gained protection (with national monument status). Subsequently San Miguel and Santa Rosa have been added and Santa Cruz has been "designated."

Various individuals (including the president of the United States) and groups had supported the Park concept for nearly half a century. Pressure from environmental groups, coupled with the threat of residential construction (on Santa Cruz) and oil exploitation hastened Park creation. A *National Marine Sanctuary,* jointly maintained by the Park Service and the National Oceanic and Atmospheric Administration, extends six nautical miles outward from each of the Park islands. More than 25 species of marine mammals, notably seals and sea lions, are found here.

A mainland visitor center (at the Park headquarters) has been been established at the Ventura Marina. Adjacent to the facility a private concessionaire provides charter boats operating to all five islands within the Park.

The Park Service has built trails and has provided sites for primitive camping on some islands but visitation, other than viewing the islands from shipboard has been limited.

Barren, windswept **San Miguel**, westernmost of the islands, can now be visited (including camping) despite former Navy use as a bombing range.

A marker indicates the grave of explorer Juan Cabrillo. Prior to 1942 the island has used for a sheep ranch and overgrazing had occurred. Subsequently the Navy used it for a bombing range. The surrounding waters provide a habitat for the once almost-extinct sea elephant.

**Santa Rosa**, one of the larger and better watered of the islands, has had a small Air Force station. But its principal use has been livestock ranching since colonial rancho days.

Once the island was owned by the Carrillo family of Santa Barbara. More recently it had been a 53,000-acre cattle ranch. Cattle were barged to and from the mainland from a wharf on the northeast side of the island. Grass has been well maintained. Santa Rosa became part of the National Park in 1987 and has been opened to visitation.

Comparable in size to Catalina, **Santa Cruz** is perhaps the choice Channel Island. Most of it is now set aside for research and for environmental preservation.

The island has had a colorful history. For a time it was used as a penal colony. Later it was obtained by Justinian Caire, who had a hundred retainers

and maintained an Old World barony in its central valley. Before Prohibition, the ranch was renowned for its excellent wines. More recently, much of it has been one of the largest cattle ranches in California. Since 1949 the Navy has operated a hilltop communications facility.

*Nature Conservancy,* a private non-profit society, has owned most of the island since 1978.

Although all of Santa Cruz is within the designated National Park no public facilities are planned in the tenth of the island that is public domain. A limited number of supervised *educational* trips are conducted annually.

Little **Anacapa** is actually three separate blocks whose walls rise steeply from the ocean. Since establishment of the National Park, it has been the most frequently visited of the group.

Coast Guard personnel, who formerly manned the lighthouse at the east end of Anacapa, have been the only "permanent" residents. Steps lead to the flattish summit where there is a visitor center, primitive campgrounds (permits needed) and usually a Park Service ranger.

## IN RETROSPECT

Southern California and the San Francisco Bay Area, among the subdivisions of the Golden State, have the closest connections, overall, with the Pacific Basin.

There is more travel to western Canada and Alaska, the Hawaiian Islands, Asia, New Zealand and Australia, to Mexico and South America. And of course there are more immigrants from Latin America and Asia.

"All" the world knows about Southern California.

To many, of course, it is merely names like Hollywood and Disneyland. Among many who have visited this land, too many have gotten only fleeting glimpses—and too often the impressions have not been too favorable.

Half of the people of the Golden State reside in this small portion of California.

But because so much of the terrain, in the Peninsular and Transverse ranges, is steep-sloped, much of Southern California remains unoccupied.

Yet in this still-evolving megalopolis, there seem to be people, *hordes* of people, everywhere along with their vehicles, noise, waste, and not-always virtuous ways.

Over an increasing portion of the occupied landscape, the newness has vanished as buildings and ornamental plantings have provided a more settled appearance.

Still, maturity has not always conferred beauty and grace. Many deplore the changes that time has brought. Some neighborhoods look tired and shabby. Escape from noise and traffic seems impossible.

Natural resources, on and beneath the earth, in the Pacific and in the skies above, have been depleted.

Land has become expensive and multistory residence more common.

Air is too-often polluted.

Despite a broad array of economic activities, there is probably too much reliance on federal "defense-related" industries.

Yet today Southern California continues to attract newcomers although more come from the rim of the Pacific and fewer from those many states east of the Sierra-Cascade.

What *is* the magnet of Southern California?

Part of it has to be the climate. And for many it has continued to be economic opportunity. And this land still offers so much, physically and culturally. Within this small bit of the earth there is a mystique, a vibrancy—Southern California is exciting and stimulating... and frustrating and bewildering.

**Figure 6-87.** Tidal pool, Anacapa Island. This is the most-visited island in Channel Islands National Park. (National Park Service).

**Figure 7-1.** The ridge-and-valley "reach" of the southern Coast Ranges, viewed westward from Diablo-Mt. Hamilton Range with Santa Lucia Range on skyline. Human activity is centered along the coast or in the structural basins. (dwl).

Chapter Seven

THE CENTRAL
COAST

This chapter has been reviewed by George Suchand and his colleagues at California Polytechnic University, San Luis Obispo. Previously it was was reviewed by Richard Ellefsen, Michael McIntyre and Raymond Stanley, all of San Jose State University.

# THE CENTRAL COAST

Waves pounding against the San Simeon Coast, camping at Lake Nacimiento, retirement residence at Atascadero, wine grape harvest near King City, beef cattle grazing on verdant slopes —this is California's Central Coast. So too are the beaches at Carmel and Santa Cruz, attending a lecture in San Luis Obispo; a walk through the garden at Mission San Miguel; golf at Cypress Point; eating a Danish pastry in Solvang; watching marine life in Monterey, a hike at Pinnacles Monument—and grain harvest in the Carrizo Plain. Most assuredly this delightful land that extends 200 miles from Davenport southward to Point Arguello has appeal.

Between San Francisco and Los Angeles, this land is comparable in size to Southern California and affords a major transit corridor.

The old Spanish cart trail *El Camino Real* is approximated today by the Coast Route (Santa Fe Southern) and U.S. 101, a major north-south California thoroughfare. The influence of travel between the two great metropolitan centers, and of tourism, is evident in the concentration of motels, restaurants, service stations and garages.

Basically the Central Coast is hilly and its dominant land use is pastoral. Yet human activity is centered in its lowlands— inland valleys or narrow coastal terraces.

No city dominates the Central Coast.

There is, in fact, no community larger than 100,000. One might consider what differences there might be in this subregion today had Monterey remained the capital of California.

## HILLS, VALES AND OAK GRASSLANDS

Three tiers deep, the Southern Coast Ranges form the backbone for this part of the Golden State—they lie *en echelon.*

Commonly summits rise to elevations of 2000 to 4000 feet; however a few higher peaks in the extreme southeast exceed 8000 feet elevation. But almost everywhere the local relief is such that the subregion qualifies as hilly rather than mountainous. Much of the upland is cultivated.

The trend of the ranges, relative to air mass movement, imparts a definite climatic contrast between seacoast, exposed summits and interior basins.

Accordingly the Central Coast possesses a multitude of intricate "small landscapes," more suggestive of New England than most parts of California.

### Ridges and Valleys

The Southern Coast Ranges, northward from the Santa Ynez Valley into the Bay Area (Napa and Sonoma counties, map 7-1) form the California counterpart of the folded Appalachian country of eastern United States.

However they are much newer geologically, consisting of Jurassic or younger sediments which arose from a geosyncline. Metamorphism is evident too and has effected especially the *Franciscan-Knoxville* group in which shales, sandstone and conglomerate are conspicuous. Geologic history has been complex (see Overview B) with repeated submergence, uplift and erosion. Contemporary terrain is the product of uplift that has occurred since the middle Pleistocene, accompanied by considerable folding and faulting; formation of stream and marine terraces took place late.

The Central Coast consists of three rows of ranges, en echelon, separated by two parallel files of narrow longitudinal basins.*

The entire area suggests a corrugated tin roof (chart 7-1) with numerous sharp ridges and steep-

---

* The three groups do not form straight-edge rows; seemingly each range is offset from its neighbors; thus there are really no continuous ridges or valleys as the Great Appalachian Valley of eastern America. Accordingly there are "low" passes between lowlands: Cuesta Grade with its famed Southern Pacific horseshoe curve and the now straighter route of U.S.101; Pacheco and Panoche passes in the Diablo Range; and La Panza Summit. The wayfarer who travels only the main highways cannot truly grasp the nature of the southern Coast Ranges!

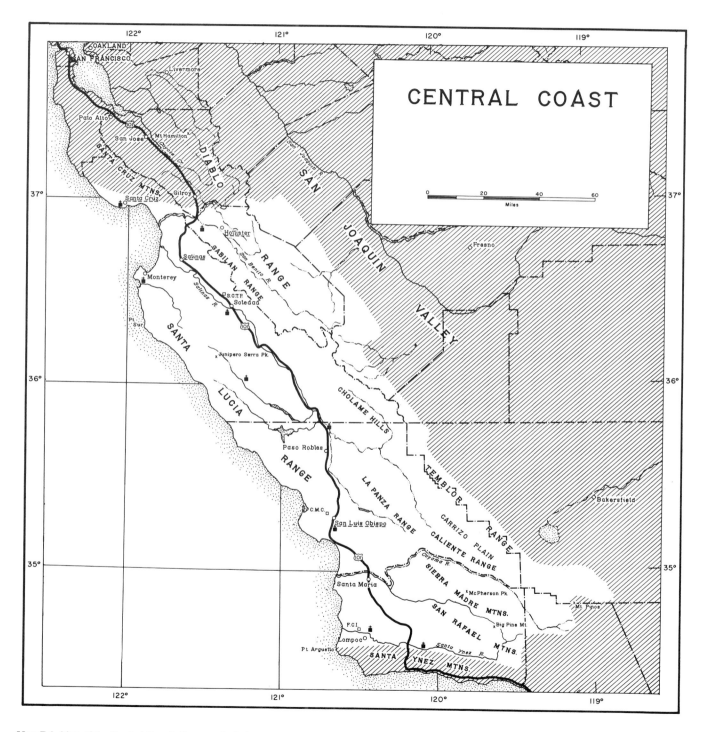

**Map 7-1.** Map of the Central Coast. The area includes *most* but not all of the southern Coast Ranges, which extend northward into the San Francisco Bay Area.

sloped canyons. Most famous of the many faults, the *San Andreas,* extends the length of the southern Coast Ranges; this rupture has been estimated to extend 20 miles into the crust.

The surface often rises immediately from the Pacific; coastal lowlands are narrow except where valleys meet the sea. At such places one finds small harbors (like Moss Landing). Marine terraces, often rising like stair steps, are prominent as are sand dunes (around Fort Ord and Pismo Beach).

The outer group of ranges consists of the *Santa Lucia* and **San Rafael.**

The San Lucia ascends abruptly from the ocean edge and contains some of the genuine wilderness country of the Central Coast. The San Rafael forms a series of southwest-facing cuestas. *Big Pine Mountain* rises to 6828 feet.

The middle group includes the *Santa Cruz* and *Gabilan* ranges.

The Santa Cruz, once a continuous mass with the Marin Hills of the Bay Area, has been separated by the submerged water gap of the Sacramento River (the Golden Gate). The Gabilan contains *Pinnacles,* an ancient volcanic mass now a national monument. Again the high summit is in the south.

The inner group, which begins in the north with the *Diablo* complex, includes the *Hamilton, Call* and *Temblor* ranges.

The *Diablo-Mt. Hamilton* is essentially one range. It culminates in *The Knot* where the Sierra Nevada (i.e., the Tehachapi), southern Coast Ranges and Transverse Ranges converge. *Mt. Pinos* (8826 ft.) is the highest peak in this area.

The two parallel rows of basins of course have much more consequence for humans than do the ranges.

While they are called valleys, these lowlands are products of diastrophism, both faulting and folding. Their alluvial fill, often of considerable depth, affords parent material for fertile soils. Often too the alluvium provides a storage reservoir for quantities of groundwater; the Salinas Valley is an outstanding example.

The outer line of lowlands, more valuable to humankind, includes *San Francisco Bay* and the *Santa Clara* of the Bay Area farther north as well as the *Salinas, Pajaro, Santa Maria* and *Lompoc* valleys.

Irrigation agriculture is important in these outer basins.

The inner basins, which have less importance, include the *San Ramon-Livermore* (in the Bay Area), *San Benito, Carrizo, Cuyama* and *Santa Ynez.*

Because of their rain-shadow position and lesser supply of moisture, they are generally used for winter grains and livestock pasturage.

### Cool Coasts and Interior Heat

Climatic variations in the Central Coast include *fog-belt, mild summer* and *hot summer* phases of dry-summer subtropical (or Mediterranean), as well as considerable interior areas with semiarid subtropical and even desert (see Overview A).

Coupled with mountain barriers, the direction of air flow and cool ocean waters offshore are especially significant considerations.

Much of the coastal strand (west of the first sum-

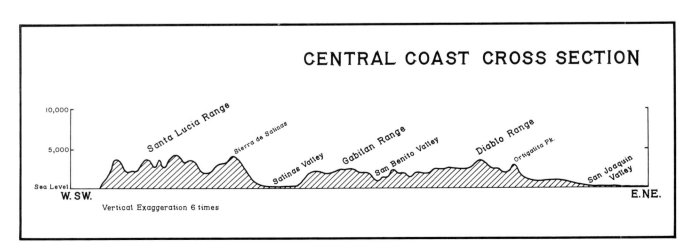

**Chart 7-1.** The Central Coast, topographically, consists of three en echelon files of southern Coast Ranges, separated by two files of structural basins.

mits) is characterized by "fog-belt" climate.

Effects of maritime air are visible as far inland as Santa Maria, San Luis Obispo and Hollister. Fog appears frequently during the year—but especially in summer. Banks, which often reach depths of 1500 feet, are prone to move against the coast during late afternoon and evening hours (ofttimes the fog deck "burns off" during the forenoon so that afternoon periods tend to be clear). Because of fog in early summer the highest temperatures are commonly recorded during August and September.

The influence of the Pacific (Hawaiian) High diminishes northward, so that much of the western portion of the Central Coast receives somewhat more precipitation than does Southern California.

Rainfall totals at Lompoc and Santa Maria are comparable to Los Angeles but precipitation increases northward, especially on exposed western slopes. Rainshadow areas like the San Benito Valley and the Carrizo Plain, however, are markedly drier.

A narrow strip of "mild summer" Mediterranean (which is much more extensive in the San Francisco Bay Area) extends into the northern periphery of the Central Coast.

In this environment maritime influence remains strong with some fog and afternoon sea breezes often prevailing. The low interior ranges, affected less by such conditions, can be described as "hot summer" phases.

Much of the Central Coast inland from the outer ranges has dry climate.

Over much of this surface a classification of semi-arid subtropics is indicated. In the southeast interior, Cuyama Valley and Carrizo Plain have weather conditions that approximates the southwestern San Joaquin Valley and are thus designated as *arid subtropics.*

Precipitation is appreciably higher in the upper portions of exposed ranges, particularly the Santa Lucia and the Santa Cruz. This is reflected in forest cover, including redwood groves in some canyons.

## Oak Parkland and Chaparral

The natural vegetation of the Central Coast reflects variations in climate and terrain.

As elsewhere in the Golden State, seasonal change is significant—spring is the season of wildflowers, with entire hillsides of lupines and California poppies, a time when even the coast sage and the chaparral bursts into bloom.

The "trademark" of the Central Coast countryside is a park-like cover with groves of oaks set in grasslands.

Such woodland association typifies interior valleys and many of the slopes. The deciduous valley oak, a graceful tree known to the early Spanish as *"roble"* is widespread on many basin floors, whereas the more stumpy coast live oak, or *"encina"* is more typical of the slopes. Soils occupied by these parklands tend to be moderately deep and rich. Grasses , which perhaps have the highest carrying capacity of all the major vegetation types within California, warrant praise.

The dominant vegetation over more southerly ranges and drier leeward slopes is *chaparral.*

Such *elfin forest,* so difficult to penetrate, can grow too tall to be considered shrubs. This intricate flora, an important watershed protector, changes aspects with the seasons. In spring when ceanothus and other species are abloom, it is especially attractive.

The Central Coast has the southern limits of coast redwood in the central portion of the central Santa Lucia Mountains, on the seaward side.

More extensive stands are found farther north, of course, in the Santa Cruz Mountains and in the Northwest (Ch. 12).

## INDIANS, SPANIARDS AND ANGLOS

The Central Coast has been an important portion of the state since its Native American occupance. The Spanish padres located nine of their twenty-one missions in this subregion.

**Figure 7-2.** Coast sage in bloom, Big Sur Coast. (dwl)

Monterey ranked among the five leading communities of the province in Mexican days and served as capital of Alta California. The fertile fields of Central Coast valleys have provided some of the major foci under American domination.

Two American Indian families resided in the Central Coast—the Penutians and the Hokans.

Their habitats included half of California: portions of Southern California, the Sierra Nevada and the Great Central Valley. In the Central Coast the Penutians were represented by a single group (Costanoans) and the Hokans by three.

The *Costanoans* (Spanish for "coastal folk") lived in scattered villages and their numbers may have reached 7000.

Seemingly they braved the open ocean in tule rafts. Salmon and mussels were important in their diet; acorns were also a staple.

The *Hokan* were represented by three groups (Esselen, Salinan and Chumash).

The *Esselen* lived south of the Costanoans in limited numbers. Hill folk of the San Lucia Mountains, these were the first California Indians to become extinct. The *Salinans* of the upper Salinas Valley and adjacent Coast Ranges did not occupy an ideal habitat. They ate about everything that their land afforded, including fish, reptiles, acorns, berries and bulbs. The *Chumash* (Ch. 6) were apparently limited in numbers north of the Santa Ynez Mountains. Interestingly the subregion has a single reservation and few rural Indians today, a reflection of early and complete occupance by Europeans.

The Spanish expended considerable effort along the Central Coast.

Activity began early with discovery of Monterey Bay by Vizcaino in 1602. His enthusiasm for this water body led to much eighteenth century activity. In 1769 Gaspar de Portola took a party overland in quest of the bay. Enroute northward he missed it and continued northward to "find" San Francisco Bay, then retraced his path to San Diego. The following year he traveled north again, leading the clerics and settlers. A presidio was established at Monterey and Mission San Carlos (moved to Carmel a few years later) was founded.

Captain Juan Anza "opened" the trail in 1776 that became *El Camino Real* and selected the site of San Francisco in the fall of that year.

One of Alta California's four presidios, Monterey (1770) and one of its three pueblos (Branciforte, 1797—now Santa Cruz) were established in the subregion.

The Franciscan fathers also located 7 missions between between Santa Cruz and Santa Ynez. Three were constructed within the Salinas Valley.

The Spanish never achieved more than a tenuous hold on the Central Coast.

Most of the Spanish were located at the presidios and the pueblos. The few land awards included a small rancho near Mission San Carlos in 1775—this was the first concession in Alta California. At the close of the Spanish era Governor Pablo Sala made several awards, including (in 1822) the two earliest ranchos in the Salinas Valley.

As the Spanish era ended, Alta California was essentially self-sufficient. Outside needs were largely met by American traders anchored in Monterey.

The first decade of Mexican rule brought little change to the Central Coast.

Major modification of land-use was delayed until secularization of the missions (1834-1836). This action followed years of rising demands for land by the expanding Mexican population.

Secularization precipitated a small-scale "land grab" along the Central Coast.

Scores of grants were awarded between 1834 and 1846. The choicest land had been mission properties; stocking of these new estates was facilitated through acquisition of mission herds. Properties remained unfenced and the cattle roamed widely.

Urban growth was inconsequential in the Mexican era.

Still, withering of the missions resulted in evolution of nearby villages without pueblo "status": Carmel, San Luis Obispo and San Juan Bautista.

The Central Coast was not altered much during the decades following American control.

The Gold Rush did create a market for rancho beef even as in Southern California.

Changes in land utilization along the Central Coast began in the mid-1850's.

As the Gold Rush slackened, many miners elected to become farmers. Their numbers were augmented by new arrivals moving westward, unaware that much of California's good land was not "free" as had been true farther east. Without too much regard for the rights of Mexican rancheros, many Americans squatted on land that impressed them. Their actions were eased because of unsettled rancho titles following passage of the congressional act of 1851 that required Mexicans to prove ownership.

Circumstances that contributed to rancho deterioration in Southern California likewise operated along the Central Coast.

In any event, the breakup of most ranchos had been completed before 1870. Much land became property of Anglo-Americans, a number of whom had been at the gold camps.

Sheep ranching, first encouraged by wool demands during the Civil War, became widespread in the 1870's.

It remained important for a generation. During this time many Basque herders came to the Central Coast. In the 1880's Monterey County was the state's third-ranking producer of livestock.

Grain farming was the next major development.

By the 1880's fields of winter wheat stretched for miles across coastal valleys. This was large-scale farming, employing eight-horse gangs of plows, harrows and seeders. Monterey and Moss Landing were major ports; inland, accessibility to railheads was important. The Central Coast, whose El Camino Real had been the principal roadway before statehood , lapsed into a backwash after the Southern Pacific completed its Valley Line between Los Angeles and San Francisco through the San Joaquin Valley in 1876. Construction of the Coast Line southward from San Jose into Soledad took place between 1868-1873. Finally, in 1901, the Coast Route was open entirely between San Francisco and Los Angeles.

Major agricultural changes along the Central Coast took place after the turn of the century.

The through rail line improved marketing from many districts while irrigation agriculture was developed with steam-powered pumps in early use. Many immigrants, including Scotch, Swiss, Danes, Italians and Portuguese, began settling in the valleys and commenced farming on a share-crop basis. Sugar beets and alfalfa were earlier crops. In the twentieth century the Central Coast has become an important producer of dairy products, fruits, nuts, and vegetables for both in-state and national markets.

## A LATE CENTURY OVERVIEW

What of the Central Coast today? It has become an urban land residentially, with population concentrated in near-coastal agricultural lowlands (Map E–1) and along the strand.

In lowlands subject to ameliorating maritime influence fruit and vegetable farming is big business and land values are high, with returns per acre among the best in the nation.

Besides climate, permissive factors include fertile alluvium, moderately good water supplies, and access to market.

Cities, still somewhat small, serve as local agricultural centers.

They provide residence for farm owners and full-time personnel and facilities for processing and shipment. They are also travel stops and a few are county seats. Non-agricultural manufacturing is limited.

Inner lowlands, water deficient and with less climatic appeal than the coast, remain sparsely populated.

Extensive properties have livestock while dry-farmed grains are produced. In general these basins have not experienced that rapid change that has affected some portions of the sub-region.

The coastal strand, once isolated, has appeal for recreation and residence (especially for monied senior citizens).

Recreation has become a dominant function of many coastal places. Military bases also helped localize population in Monterey and Santa Barbara counties.

There is some continuance of military installations.

Major development began with World War II and persisted through the Korean emergency into the missile age since Vietnam. The Coast has obvious advantages: mild climate, proximity to harbors, good surface transportation, and an abundance of land without highly competitive alternative uses.

Reciprocal relations between the Central Coast and its three vicinal subregions have been strengthened with improved transportation and population growth.

The Bay Area and Southern California provide many manufactured goods and wholesale services for the Central Coast and afford urban recreation and shopping facilities. In turn, residents of these more populous subregions support Central Coast resorts and provide a significant market for agricultural commodities. Many of their young adults study at Santa Cruz and San Luis Obispo.

Relations with the San Joaquin Valley (Central Valley) are more one-way: the Coast provides milder vacation and retirement spots.

As detailed discussion of the Central Coast as a single entity is difficult, four subdivisions will be reviewed: (1) the **Western Lowlands**, distinguished by specialized agriculture; (2) the **Interior Basins**, used for cattle ranching and grain farming; (3) the **Shore**, used particularly for recreation and residence; (4) the **Ranges**, economically restricted by slope.

### THE WESTERN LOWLANDS

Favored by modifying influences of Pacific air and good transportation facilities, the Western Lowlands is one of nation's chief summer producers of cool-season vegetables and deciduous fruits, valued at scores of millions of dollars annually.

These structural depressions with their fertile alluvium have more physical appeal for the way-farer than the Great Central Valley or most agricultural areas: (1) they are relatively narrow—hence their mountainous backgrounds are more conspicuous; and (2) in summer they are more likely to be relatively cool.

The following lowlands will be included in this section: **Lompoc-Santa Ynez, Santa Maria, Arroyo Grande, San Luis, Salinas, Pajaro,** and **Northern San Benito** valleys (see maps 7-1, 7-2, and 7-4).

### THE LOMPOC-SANTA YNEZ VALLEYS

The southernmost Central Coast lowland consists of the contiguous east-west trending Lompoc-Santa Ynez valleys (map 7-2).

The Santa Ynez River drains the south slopes of

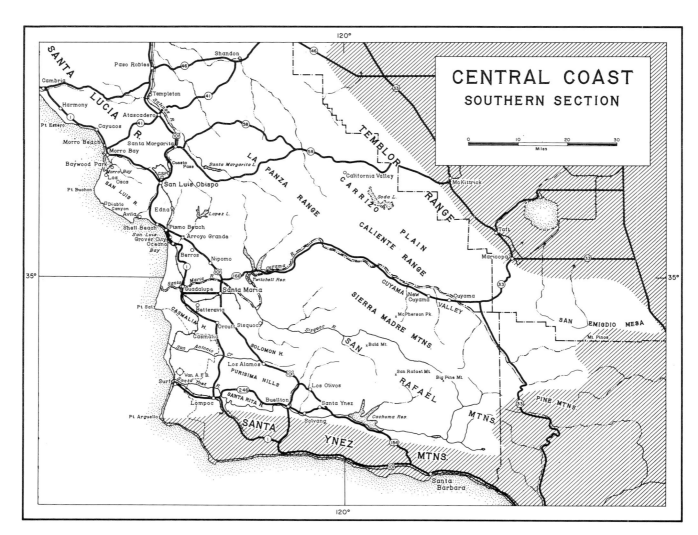

**Map 7-2.** Much of the interior portions of the Central Coast, east of U.S. 101, is nearly empty.

the San Rafael Mountains, whose 6000-foot summits are sufficiently high and extensive to provide adequate water for the lowland as well as some for export to the Santa Barbara Coast. Normally the water table in the Santa Ynez Valley remains within 20 to 30 feet of the surface.

From a narrow upriver canyon, the Santa Ynez widens into a circular basin centered on the hamlet of Santa Ynez. Farther west the canyon narrows again where the river cuts through Miocene volcanics and dissected marine terraces (the *Santa Rita Hills)*. About 12 miles before the river enters the Pacific the lowland plain widens into the Lompoc Valley. The cultivated fields of the valley floor contrast with the coast sage, oak woodland and chaparral (inland) cover on the slopes to provide pleasant vistas.

Through the nineteenth century utilization of the two valleys remained comparable.

Chumash Indian rancherias, missions (La Purisima Concepcion and Santa Ynez), Mexican ranchos, cattle, sheep, general livestock, and grain farming (until after the Southern Pacific Coast Line was completed in 1901) formed the sequence.

Irrigation agriculture has developed since 1900 yet Lompoc farming previously included establishment of one of California's earliest agricultural colonies (in 1874).

Since the 1920's the small Lompoc farms have generally flourished. Land is leveled to grade, fields are fenceless, land values high; Santa Barbara County has effected careful zoning, thus protecting farmland against wanton urban encroachment. Cropping patterns have gradually changed; walnut groves, once widespread, have

**Figure 7–4.** The plant geneticist has played an important role development of new varieties. Only two major seed producers remain in the Lompoc Valley. (dwl)

disappeared, as have cherries. In the 1920s the entire valley sometimes suggested a carpet of yellow until competition from the Great Plains curtailed mustard-seed acreage.

The Lompoc has long been the nation's leading source of flower seeds.

In early summer its floor becomes a patchwork of all possible floral hues (Fig. 7-4). Earlier southern France provided flower seeds for the United States. As appreciation of coastal California materialized seed flowers were grown from the Salinas Valley to El Monte (Los Angeles Lowlands). Production has been focused on the Lompoc, with about 1500 acres under cultivation. With considerable public shift from planting of seeds to purchase of young plants at nurseries, acreage has lessened. Flower growers usually lease their lands. Cultivation also occurs in the Santa Maria, Arroyo Grande, and San Benito valleys. Seed-flower production is highly specialized. A key figure is the plant geneticist, responsible for new varieties.

Flowers have also been shipped fresh to California's metropolitan markets. Other crops include beans and a variety of vegetables. But in the late twentieth century the *new* things have been vineyards and wineries.

The hilly surfaces between the Lompoc and Santa Ynez valleys around Buellton are devoted to livestock ranching. There are a few somewhat secluded poultry farms.

Two plants near Lompoc produce diatomaceous earth.

**Figure 7-3.** "Exurban" housing, west edge of Santa Ynez. There is appreciable commutation to Santa Barbara. (dwl)

The large diatomite deposits here, residues of billions of single celled Miocene sea plants, are among the purest in the world.

Diatomite has been mined since 1893; it is estimated that a 75-year reserve remains. Diatomite has scores of uses, particularly for filters.

There has been less twentieth-century land use change in the Santa Ynez Valley than in the Lompoc, especially east of Santa Ynez (village) where livestock ranching remains dominant.

Cattle ranching is truly a way of life; farmhouses are well-appointed and sleek herds of Aberdeen Angus or Herefords graze behind painted fenceposts. Partially because of its proximity to Santa Barbara, which retains a tradition of the Hispanic colonial eras, the upper Santa Ynez is widely known for the raising of fine Palomino horses.

The western Santa Ynez is devoted to irrigation agriculture; despite alluvial bottomlands that valley is less favored climatically than the Lompoc.

A Danish colony was established at Solvang ("sunny meadow") in 1911. Although settlers had difficulty adjusting to irrigation agriculture, lands around Solvang proved productive— a few windmills lend an exotic note to the landscape. Besides winter grains and hillside grazing, the valley floor produces such crops as alfalfa, legumes, and sugar beets. Increased output of vegetables has prompted expanded pump irrigation.

Nearness to Santa Barbara has enhanced recreational use of the Santa Ynez Valley.

Cachuma Lake provides a much-used aquatic playground; it is trout-stocked (Ch. 6). The Santa Ynez is a major California center for dude ranches.

**Lompoc** (31,000) is a farm town that has become a bedroom community for Vandenberg Air Force Base.

After quadrupling in a decade (1957-1966) Lompoc quieted down. A fourth of its work force commutes to Vandenberg. Median education levels exceed state averages (many college graduates in engineering, mathematics and physics). It has become less conservative, has blocks of tract housing (but no leapfrogging into farm lands!) and a shopping center. Basically middle income, it still has a significant number of lower income (Hispanic) farm workers.

Santa Ynez Valley towns have different functions—there is limited commutation to Vandenberg.

**Solvang** (2200), intentionally made picturesque with half timbers and tile (or synthetic thatch) roofs in business blocks (but *not* in the residences!)

caters to an expanding tourist trade with its restaurants and gift shops.

*Mission Santa Ynez* probably has the finest paintings of any California mission. *Mission La Purisima Concepcion* near Lompoc has been restored as a state historical monument intended to depict a mission as it was in colonial days. **Buellton** (700), long known for its split-pea soup, has grown as a crossroads stop (at the junction of U.S. 101 and Ca. 246). In function it suggests Baker (Ch.4). In the past decade **Santa Ynez** (circa 1000) has become an affluent retiree and commuter (to Santa Barbara) place—a few well-to-do even fly to work in the Los Angeles area!

### Vandenberg Air Force Base

This Air Force base, on the periphery of Lompoc Valley, makes a signal contribution to the nation's "defenses."

Involved for many years in military space launches, it is slated for use with the Space Shuttle. In 1941 the Army established Camp Cooke on marine terraces to the north; after the Korean emergency it was deactivated; in 1956 it became the site of an Air Force Intercontinental Ballistic Missile (ICBM) facility, redesignated Vandenberg Air Force Base in 1958 and encompassing nearly 100,000 acres.

Facilities include a SAC strategic division for operational testing of ICBM's, an aerospace test wing for launching of satellite systems. and the Western Test Range, which provides instrumentation and operational control for ICBM and space launches.

**Figure 7-5.** The *visitors* Solvang. Apart from the commercial areas Solvang ressembles other California communities. (dwl)

**Figure 7-6.** Santa Maria, viewed toward west with U.S. 101 freeway "bypass" in foreground. Santa Barbara County zoning has been stricter than much of the state hence haphazard urbanization into surrounding farmlands has been averted. (Caltrans).

Factors germane to establishment of Vandenberg included curvature of the coast around Point Arguello, spacious ocean areas to the west and southwest, prior government land title and accessibility to California space industries. Hundreds of millions of dollars have been expended on the base; personnel includes military, civilian employees and contractors' crews—more than 60,000, including dependents. Impact of these numbers and their payrolls has been influential in communities as distant as Santa Barbara and San Luis Obispo.

## THE SANTA MARIA VALLEY

This deltaic plain is surrounded by sand dunes and marine terraces (Map 7-2). Despite a mere 20,000 acres under cultivation it has an impressive agricultural output.

The lowland, approximately 20 miles long and six miles wide (north-south), did not have a Spanish mission but late in the Mexican era it was divided among three ranchos. The Valley experienced California's usual nineteenth century transitions. Access to harbor facilities at Port Harford (Port San Luis) was fortunate.

Agricultural patterns have developed since 1900. Today there is diversity of product; vegetables have particular importance.

Sugar beets became important early in this century after construction of a refinery; subsequently acreage has declined. Pump wells, power lines, and standpipes suggest irrigation practices. Shabby appearance of many farmhouses reflects land consolidation and owner residence in Santa Maria while weathered barns dramatize the one-time importance of draft horses. Since 1940 output of vegetables has expanded; fluctuations in acreage of different varieties is in response to market conditions. Artichokes are conspicuous only near the coast and alfalfa on the inner edge of the lowland. Important vegetables include lettuce, broccoli (spring and fall crops), celery (mostly a fall crop), cauliflower (year-round) and potatoes. Winter mildness permits leaving the Netted Gem (Russet Burbank) potatoes in the ground until shipment; hence potato cellars are unnecessary. Strawberry production has expanded markedly since introduction of fresh freezing; sandy soils afford good berry land and the climate allows a longer harvest season than anywhere else in California. A typical scene during most of the year is provided by groups of Hispanics who perform the

---

*The Santa Maria Valley shares a coastal lowland with the Lompoc Valley and the Arroyo Grande Valley . Dissected marine terraces, locally called mesas serve as dividing uplands.

field labor. Farm operators include a considerable number of Japanese.

The Santa Maria has had a fair water supply.

But with more intensive truck farming pump wells steadily depleted the water table until Twitchell Reservoir was constructed on the Cuyama River in the late 1950's. Water stored in the reservoir during the rainy season percolates underground during the summer.

The Santa Maria and mesas to the south have long yielded petroleum. In the 1980's the first offshore platform was placed in the Santa Maria Basin north of Point Arguello; others are anticipated.

Together with inland Cuyama Valley they make Santa Barbara County the leading producer of the Central Coast. There are a coking plant and a refinery north of Guadalupe as well as two small refineries near Santa Maria.

**Santa Maria** (52,000), the center of "north (Santa Barbara) County", clamors to become "bigger and better." It is buoyed by oil, agriculture (including much processing), military, commuter residence and highway (G.E.M.) functions.*

Founded in 1874, Santa Maria, known for its wide streets, is the trade center for its Valley and residence place for many farm workers (and owners) and Vandenberg commuters. Much of its growth has come in the past quarter century. Boosters cite land, labor, water, transportation and low taxes as incentives to attract industry. Produce sheds and processing plants are prominent along railroad spurs. There is also an industrial park at the airport (and feeder air service to Los Angeles, San Francisco and Stockton).

Santa Maria is already the largest city of the southern Central Coast and has received the major impact from Vandenberg. Motels and restaurants along its main street (and the freeway) reflect its importance as a highway stop on U.S. 101. Hancock College has an eastside campus.

Since construction of Vandenberg there has been much residential growth and some leapfrogging especially around Orcutt.

A southside shopping center has developed. Subsequently there has been in-filling. With federal renewal funds an east-edge central district complex was built. Two higher income residential parks have materialized on rolling mesa land in county territory to the south.

Santa Maria is distinctly a northside-southside town.

About a third of its residents are Hispanics (with a

**Figure 7-7.** Guadalupe, a farm labor town on Santa Fe Southern's Coast Line, is miniscule relative to Santa Maria on U.S. 101 to the east. (dwl)

barrio to the northwest) and there is Hispanic antagonism to Anglo dominance of city affairs.

**Guadalupe** (3500), on Ca,. l and the Coast Line of the Southern Pacific, is the Valley's principal vegetable packing and shipping point. It is significant as a farm workers' residence town with much evidence of Asians and "Texas" Mexicans (regarded as aliens by local Hispanics).

**Nipomo Mesa**, an undulating marine terrace separating the Santa Maria from the Arroyo Grande Valley to the north, produces chickens, lemons and avocados.

It was long used for grazing and winter grains. Then came an expansion of poultry farms, many owned by senior citizens on modest properties; high operating costs produced a demise in the late 1950's but the western breeding ranch of Arbor Acres (now property of Egg City), one of the world's largest breeders of meat chickens, was established. Farther east on hillsides near Twitchell Reservoir, groves of lemons and avocados have been planted; enthusiasts insist the climate is as mild as the Oxnard Plain (Ch. 6). Many residents of the little "eucalyptus homesteads" are retirees or commuters.

## THE ARROYO GRANDE VALLEY

The diminutive Arroyo Grande Valley (map 7-2) produces a variety of truck crops.

---

* In both Santa Barbara and San Luis Obispo counties there is a growth schism. "South County" (Santa Barbara and San Luis Obispo) favors "holding the line" while "North County" (Santa Maria and Paso Robles) desires growth.

**Figure 7-8.** Garden peas in the San Luis Valley. Dairying had more importance in the past. (dwl)

Allied "valleys" include the Oso and Flaco. This was part of Mission San Luis Obispo's grazing lands before formation of an irrigation district in 1882 encouraged agricultural development. The several thousand acres are double or even triple-cropped. Urban growth (see section on The Shore) has almost eliminated globe artichokes. Recent efforts have been made to reduce recurrent problems of floods and drifting sand dunes.

## THE SAN LUIS AREA

Emphasis upon pastoralism in the San Luis Area (focusing on the diminutive San Luis Valley) contrasts with the vegetable growing in the lowlands previously discussed.

An adequate irrigation source is absent and level land is restricted; hilly uplands separate the Area from adjacent lowlands to north and south but produce considerable forage.

Good grass and cattle herds made San Luis Obispo one of the more prosperous missions; but by the late 1830's its land had been divided into ranchos.

Contemporary land use patterns were established early. Wealthy dairyman E.W.Steele and his brothers purchased four ranchos in 1866, brought in hundreds of dairy cows and began selling cheese in San Francisco. Other dairy operators followed and several cheese factories were operating in the 1870's. Since the 1880's Swiss, Italian and Portuguese immigrants and their descendants have conducted the dairy farms.

Nearby Army installations permitted the dairymen to shift from manufactured products (cheese,

butter and condensed milk) during World War II. Then, for a generation, fluid milk was shipped to Los Angeles and San Francisco areas. Subsequently much land has been used for beef cattle. The fewer remaining dairies, with more cows per farm, market Grade A milk locally.

Of late there has been some cultivation of garden peas and some planting of deciduous orchards and vineyards southeast of San Luis Obispo.

**San Luis Obispo** (40,000), university town and county seat, is one of the important cities of the Central Coast—and truly one of its preferred residence places.

Before the recent growth of Santa Maria, it had been the principal city between Santa Barbara and Salinas for decades . It is in the San Luis Valley, inland from the coast.

Surrounding hills, which shut out sufficient Pacific air that summer afternoons can be warm, provide a distinctive setting; newer residential districts on slopes include many view lots. The city retains some of its Hispanic colonial heritage in street names. The number of downtown specialty shops reflects the city's longtime importance as the retail center for an extensive, though sparsely populated, portion of the Central Coast.

As a "half-way point" between San Francisco and Los Angeles, San Luis Obispo obtains considerable travelers' trade.

It is also a gateway to coastal recreation areas along Rt. 1 and its mission enhances its tourist appeal.

Public payrolls loom large; it is the site of **California State Polytechnic University**, on a spacious

**Figure 7-9.** Downtown sign, San Luis Obispo. Note the pleasing effect as contrasted with the blatant billboards signs in some California communities. (dwl)

campus. The institution, which appeals to many metropolitan students, emphasizes engineering and agriculture. Also here are *Cuesta College,* Camp San Luis Obispo (now home of the California National Guard, and California Men's Colony, a state correctional institution (on a portion of Camp San Luis Obispo lands). The city, led by the planning faculty at the university, strongly favors architectural review, sign control and modest growth. Still, outlying mobile home parks and expanded shopping facilities are conspicuous.

## THE SALINAS VALLEY

Self-acclaimed "Salad Bowl of the World," the Salinas Valley is the ranking agricultural section of the Central Coast.

Its prodigious output places Monterey County among the nation's ranking farm counties.

The Salinas, vividly described by Steinbeck in *East of Eden*, is the largest lowland of the Central Coast. Steinbeck's description, excerpted, is:

> The Salinas Valley...is a long narrow swale between ranges of mountains...I remember that the Gabilan Mountains to the east of the valley were light gay mountains full of sun and loveliness and a kind of invitation...The Santa Lucias stood up against the sky to the west and kept the valley from the open sea, and they were dark and brooding...I always found myself in a dread of the west and a love of east...
> On the wide level acres of the valley the topsoil lay deep and fertile...I have spoken of the rich years when the rainfall was plentiful. But there were dry years too and they put a terror in the valley...
> First there were the Indians...then the hard, dry Spaniards came exploring through...they collected souls as they collected jewels...
> Then the Americans came—more greedy because there were more of them. They took the lands, remaking the laws to make their titles good.... *

This attenuated syncline extends southeastward for more than 120 miles from Moss Landing to Santa Margarita (Map 7-4).

Its width exceeds 12 miles along Monterey Bay but inland it becomes quite constricted.

The Salinas *looks* prosperous; there is an air of rural substance exemplified by well-maintained farmhouses and carefully tilled earth.

**Figure 7-10.** Artichokes at Castroville. Production of this vegetable is limited largely to the coastal "fog belt" along the littoral of the northern Central Coast (dwl).

From the air the Valley rolls out like an elongated hall runner woven in many shades of green. Yet the more discerning highway traveler notes the many field hands, their buses and barracks, and the decrepit residential blocks so conspicuous in Chualar, Gonzales and most other Valley towns.

Fields are leveled to grade, although irrigation methods have changed—instead of field ditches, one notes sprinklers and long aluminum tubes. There is a noticeable absence of fences in the lower Valley especially but windbreaks ( generally eucalyptus) are conspicuous.

### Artichokes and Lettuce, Strawberries and Grapes

The agricultural prospects of the Salinas were recognized early.

Two missions, Soledad and and San Miguel Arcangel, were established by the Franciscans. Next, during the Mexican era, 32 land grants were assigned. The Valley, with Monterey as port, became a leading California source of tallow and hides.

Then the Salinas underwent the usual Central Valley sequence.

Cattle expanded during the Gold Rush but herds were decimated during the drought of 1862-64. An influx of Americans followed.

Most estates were divided but some large ranchos remained into the twentieth century. Grain farming expanded in the lower Valley after establishment of shipping facilities at Moss Landing in

---

* From *East of Eden* by John Steinbeck. Copyright 1952 by John Steinbeck. Reprinted by permission of The Viking Press, Inc.

1866. Transition from sheep to wheat and barley proceeded with construction southward of the Southern Pacific's Coast Line; by the late 1880's barley was replacing wheat.

Some evidences of contemporary agricultural diversity appeared relatively early.

After the drought of 1862-1864 dairying started in the lower Valley. Danish, Portuguese and Swiss dairymen moved into the Salinas, sometimes leasing from large landholders.

Several evaporated milk plants were operating by the early twentieth century; after 1920 shipment of fresh milk to San Francisco increasingly replaced local manufacturing. Dry-farmed beans were grown early; during World War I acreage expanded, then again in the mid-1920's after a short decline. The Tariff Acts of 1894 and 1897 favored sugar beets in western United States. Following construction of the state's largest beet factory at Spreckels in 1897, a rapid shift from grains to sugar beets occurred; beets achieved their maximum acreage within three years. Meanwhile irrigation replaced dry farming. After 1920 vegetable growing became significant. Presently the Salinas has multifarious varieties who annual output returns scores of millions of dollars.

Irrigation has been an important factor in agricultural development in the Salinas.

The mission fathers attempted stream diversion but irrigation was not practiced between 1830 and 1877. It seems ironic that the drought of 1862 decimated herds in a basin with a relatively high water table; the deep alluvial fill affords an excellent underground supply. In summer the river does not have much surface flow; much of the runoff from its 4330 square mile watershed flows underground. Pump irrigation, which initially used steam engines, was developed in conjunction with sugar beets.

A serious depletion of the underground basin was created as early as 1930.

In years of heavier runoff, the basin recharges itself during the winter. In drier years water-table decline has allowed salt intrusion three miles inland from Moss Landing. Like most California lowlands, the Valley has also experienced floods; damage has been serious about one year in seven. Hence a countywide flood-control and conservation district was established; it completed *Nacimiento Dam* in the eastern Santa Lucia Range in 1957.* An additional 500,000 acre-foot reservoir was completed on San Antonio River in 1965.

Tripartite land-use division into lower valley, middle valley and upper valley describes contemporary crop patterns in the Salinas.

Physical variations such as topography, fog cover, summer heat, length of growing season and frost threat have contributed to evolution of present-day distribution.

From Moss Landing to Soledad the lower Salinas is favored with a long growing season, deep alluvium and cool summers (nocturnal inflow of fog reduces morning temperatures until it "burns off").

Brussels sprouts and globe artichokes have been major crops on "heavy" peaty soils around Castroville since the 1920's (Fig. 7-10). Introduced from Mediterranean Europe by Italians, the artichoke cannot tolerate either frost or summer heat, which restricts its habitat even in California. The artichoke, which took years to "popularize", found its earlier markets with people of southern European extraction. A perennial, it is planted every four years; the harvest season can be regulated through irrigation and pruning—winter marketing has been preferred because of less compe-

---

* There are virtually no irrigation districts in the Central Coast and this fact makes a distinct difference between this subregion and the Great Central Valley.

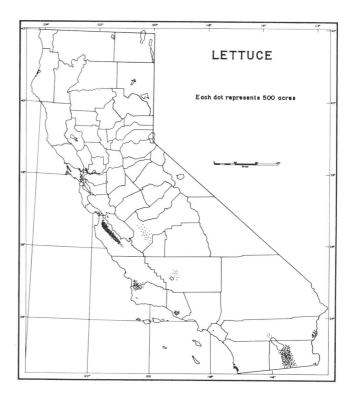

**Map 7-3.** Map of lettuce production in California.

tition. Canned marinated artichokes have gained a market for salads and acreage has expanded (at expense of lettuce). Aided by easier irrigation (with aluminum piping and sprinklers), there is more year-round harvesting than in earlier years.

Some 55,000 acres of lettuce are grown farther inland around Salinas (Map 7-3); the Valley has been the nation's ranking warm-season producer for over half a century.

Since the 1920's the Salinas has produced between a third and a half of nation's crop between April and November. Declining sugar yields occurred about the time that urbanization was encroaching upon lettuce fields in Los Angeles County and American people were changing their diets to include salads. Originally smaller, Salinas fields have become larger.

Cool summers and the long season gave the Salinas an advantage over most eastern districts as long as the crisp Boston and New York varieties were grown. But American housewives preferred firmer heads, which suggested a better buy. The firmer *Great Lakes* variety is climatically less demanding than older varieties; hence the Salinas has had increasing competition from more northerly parts of eastern United States—it remains a near-monopoly for California. Introduction of new varieties that can tolerate more summer heat has extended the production area inland.

A single field will yield only one crop of lettuce annually.

But double-and triple-cropping is practiced, rotating lettuce with other vegetables; acreage has been stabilized for many years. Lettuce is shipped almost continuously from May through November (in winter Imperial Valley lettuce is commercially dominant).

Production is highly specialized and mechanized although there is still much hand labor.

Lettuce has been cut by "assembly-line" methods for almost half a century. The practice of field packing in cardboard developed fairly early; boxes were rushed to packing houses and the vegetable shipped in dry ice to avoid spoilage that had occurred with the earlier wet pack (in ice) method. Still more recently, use of the "flat-pack" has lessened damage from shipment. Bulk shipment is also used for lettuce for shredding commercially by restaurants. The long season permits employees to reside in Salinas, moving to the Imperial Valley briefly in winter while children remain at home in school.

Such crops as onions, strawberries, carrots, broccoli, tomatoes, cauliflower and sugar beets are also grown in the lower Valley "fog belt"—truly this is a salad bowl!

### Leading Monterey County Farm Products
### (ranked by economic value)

| | | | |
|---|---|---|---|
| lettuce | 1 | nursery stock | 13 |
| cattle | 2 | peppers | 14 |
| strawberries | 3 | market milk | 15 |
| celery | 4 | barley | 16 |
| tomatoes | 5 | grapes | 17 |
| broccoli | 6 | potatoes | 18 |
| sugar beets | 7 | dry pasture | 19 |
| cauliflower | 8 | onion (proc.) | 20 |
| artichokes | 9 | garlic | 21 |
| cut flowers | 10 | asparagus | 22 |
| carrots | 11 | onions (green) | 23 |
| beans (white) | 12 | cabbage | 24 |

Figures do not include upper Salinas Valley within San Luis Obispo County—data from Monterey County Agricultural Commissioner.

Sugar beets regained significance for half a century (after 1935) with government acreage controls, rotation, better tilth, mechanical thinning and elimination of Cuban imports (in the 1960's). Although acreage doubled it has declined again with a worldwide sugar glut.

On westside terraces between Salinas and Gonzales, where whitewashed barns and large Holstein herds are evident, dairying has importance.

Feed lots reflect value of floodplain land for truck. Many dairy operators with bottomland sold their acreage long ago to vegetable growers. However much of the vegetable land is owned by "old-timers" and leased to the major growers.

Cropping patterns are complex (and the list of important crops lengthy!)

Acreage of *strawberries*, which replaced grains northeast of Salinas, has lessened although yields are higher. The Valley has met keen competition, with labor supply critical. Tolerance of Mexican "green card" holders seems to be higher than is true near the Mexican border (Ch.5). *Carrots*, originally grown as livestock feed, have been a million-dollar crop, although the Salinas has had competition from the lower Rio Grande Valley of Texas where fields are as large as 1000 acres. Carrot production in the Salinas expanded when carrots in plastic bags gained popularity in supermarkets.

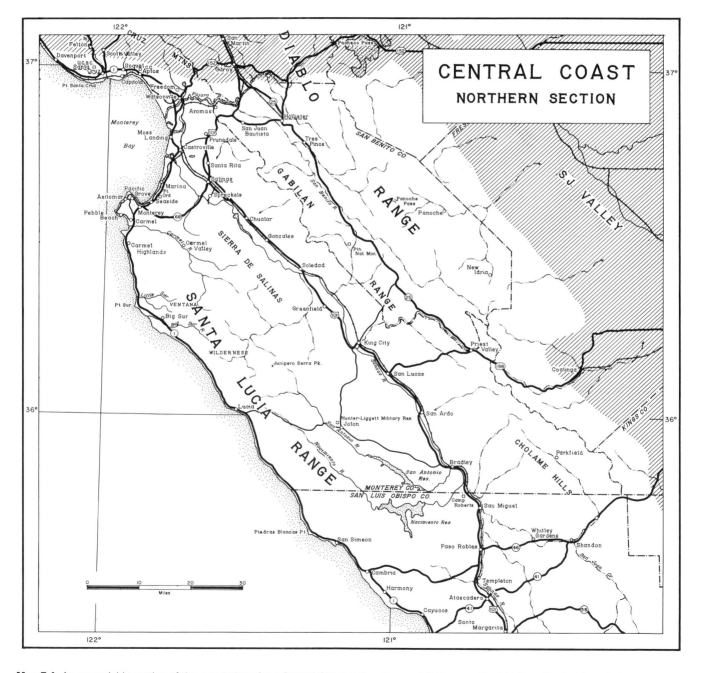

**Map 7-4.** An appreciable portion of the population of the Central Coast is found around Salinas, on the Monterey Peninsula and along the Santa Cruz Coast.

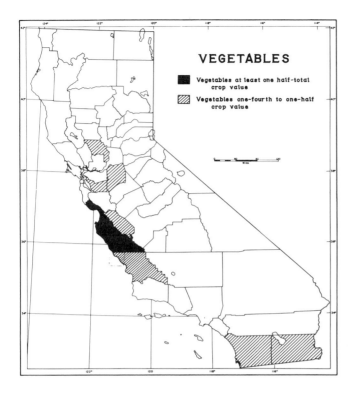

**Map 7-5.** Map of vegetable-dominant counties.

*Celery* is a relatively recent introduction into the Salinas; discovery that superior quality crops could be grown there over a longer harvest season (late June until January) led to acreage reduction in The Delta Lands, previously the leading producer (Ch. 9). Dietary habits have also increased consumption of this low-calorie vegetable. *Onions*, a late-season crop, are usually shipped to eastern Asia. *Broccoli*, which can be grown throughout the year, is planted in fields previously in lettuce, thus averting seasonal idleness. Expanded output of *cauliflower* reflects a decline in the Santa Clara Valley. Nursery growers from the Santa Mateo and Santa Clara counties have raised *cut market flowers* for over a quarter of a century (reflecting urban pressures in the Bay Area). Acreage increased nine-fold in a decade.

Throughout the Valley labor-saving devices continue to develop.

Mechanical harvesting has been applied to more and more crops. New techniques with vegetables also include seed taping, precision planting and application of herbicides (to reduce weeding). There is concern in the towns especially relative to future employment for farm workers and as to health hazards from the many toxic sprays used in farming.

The *middle* Salinas, between Soledad and San Ardo, forms a transition zone between the coastal fog belt and interior conditions (see Interior Basins).

Summers tend to be appreciably warmer than around Castroville but the growing season is shorter. South of King City the Valley narrows appreciably. Lower terraces are cropped and sprinkler-irrigated whereas higher terraces produce *winter grains* and adjoining hillsides are grazed. Fields of *alfalfa*, *sugar beets*, and *beans* (small white, large lima, pink and garbanzo) are conspicuous.

The supplemental feeding of livestock pastured seasonally on adjacent uplands forms the chief use of alfalfa. Also, several large feed lots are present. Sugar beets replaced some beans for a while after elimination of imported Cuban sugar. Early spring and fall crops of lettuce are grown now even south of King City, a reflection of lessened competition from other areas at these seasons.

Acreage of *tomatoes* has also expanded around King City at the expense of bean fields; if prices are favorable,the crop is shipped fresh; otherwise, it goes to canneries. Beans, which acquired more acreage during World War II, prefer the hotter summers of the mid-valley; as legumes they make good rotation crops.

The middle Salinas has become California's "varietal wine grape capital" (Fig. 7-12) Acreage (circa 30,000) exceeds that of the Napa Valley and Sonoma County combined.

Vintners tend to represent established firms relocated from the Santa Clara (Paul Masson) or Livermore (Wente) valleys, seeking new acreages. Holdings tend to be much larger than farther north and often are found on terraces where they have replaced grains. A McFarland firm (Salinas Valley

**Figure 7-11.** Moss Landing, once an important wheat-shipping port, is on the coastal edge of the Salinas Valley. (dwl)

**Figure 7-12.** The Salinas Valley, around King City and east of Atascadero, has become an important area for varietal grapes. (Winegrowers Council).

Vineyards) has 10,000 acres; Southdown Land also made a major investment. More than a dozen varieties have been planted, including Cabernet Sauvignon, Chardonnay, Pinot Noir and Zinfandel. There is concern for overproduction of wine in California; some predict that Cabernet Sauvignon could become California's *vin ordinaire*.

Vineyards have become important too farther south between Paso Robles and Nipomo Mesa.

One of the northernmost in California, the San Ardo oil field (opened in 1947) has been a major producer (see "Leading Oil Fields of California," Ch. 9).

The reserve was long known but because of its low gravity its recovery awaited new cracking processes and expanded California consumption.

The character of the Salinas changes south of San Ardo—the Valley narrows and is undulating rather than flat.

Fog is uncommon hence some summer afternoons feel "oven-hot." If sea breezes penetrate this far inland, they tend to be desiccating winds that stir up dust. The Army maintained one of its largest western training stations at **Camp Roberts**—many ex-servicemen remember the Salinas without enthusiasm—the base has been used for reserve and National Guard training.

The deep alluvial layer of the lower Valley is absent and irrigation agriculture limited. Yet at its southern extreme, where the Santa Lucia Range is lower, more maritime effect is reflected by lush oak woodland. Winter grains, livestock pastures, plus almond orchards around Paso Robles and poultry around Atascadero, are representative.

California produces nearly all of the nation's *almonds* (see Ch. 9). There are over 6000 acres around Paso Robles. Initially planted as a land-promotion scheme, some trees have been replanted. Some orchards are on steep slopes. Earlier, almonds were uneconomic and needed tariff protection. Foreign markets became a concern again in the 1980's. Too, much hilly land in and around the upper Valley has been seriously eroded by over grazing.

**Market Places, Large and Small**

Many Salinas communities function as local farm towns, providing residence for farm personnel and ofttimes produce-shipping facilities. Agricultural processing and supply has some consequence in most towns.

**Salinas** (100,000), largest and most important city in the Valley, is seat of Monterey County and the site of Hartnell College.

It began as an early American cattle town; memories of its formative years are renewed annually by the Salinas Rodeo. Its consequence as the Valley service center increased after the arrival of the Southern Pacific in 1872.

Salinas is a prosperous trade center, shipping point and residential community. Along the railroad tracks its industrial zone is characterized by packing houses, machine shops and industrial plants. Sometimes the air is "sweet" with the smell of chocolate! Expanding industry produces such items as foods (candy, jams, milk products and frozen foods) and shipping containers (paper and plastic) and occupies the site of former slums which housed farm workers.

Salinas is a city of three "faces." The Southside has the C.B.D. and "Main Street extension," the homes of the affluent (business and professional and landowners) plus a marginal low-income area adjacent to the industrial zone on the east.

**Figure 7-13.** Merchant-supported "free parking" garage in downtown Salinas. A number of smaller cities also allow "free" parking on downtown streets. (dwl)

The central district has been revitalized due to merchant determination: facade renewal, free off-street parking, civic center and auditorium, new county center and rehabilitated "wino" district. An expanded Hartnell College campus is on the southwest fringe.

The *Northside* has Northridge (regional shopping center),newer middle-income housing younger (Anglo-Filipino-Hispanic) families. *Eastside*, formerly Alisal, with Dust Bowl shanties (i.e., "Hooverville"), merged into Salinas in 1964; it is chiefly Hispanic. Salinas offered a reduced tax rate and services (such as sewers).

There is *strong* community support for a "better" rather than "bigger" Salinas. The Master Plan proposes a near-circular shape with controlled growth and in-filling. Meanwhile Salinas shares the cultural advantages of Monterey Peninsula and is gaining cultural activities.

Lesser lower Valley communities include Moss Landing, Castroville and Soledad (7000), with a large state penal institution.

**Moss Landing** (unincorp.), erstwhile grain port, whaling station and sardine packer, is a picturesque assemblage of weathered canneries, fishing boats and shanties. Kaiser has a plant to extract magnesium from seawater; there are also a large Pacific Gas and Electric steam plant and the marine station operated by a consortium of State University campuses.

**Castroville** (3000), with artichoke shipping sheds conspicuous, is a residential town.

Middle Valley towns are likewise of limited size.

**King City** (7500), the principal town since its founding, is a shipping point and residential place with attractive homes of ranchers. It caters to highway travelers and has acquired three wineries and food processing plants (chili peppers and corn nuts).

Two upper Valley towns (Paso Robles and Atascadero) are larger than most Salinas communities.

**El Paso de Robles** (15,000) is one of California's "for real" cattle country towns, a highway stop and "coming" retirement community.

Attractively sited among oak groves (and surrounded by almond orchards) Paso Robles has acquired added importance as a crossroads since improvement of Ca. 46 across the Santa Lucia Mountains. Many Southern Californians, bound for the Big Sur Coast and San Simeon, now drive north on I-5 then west on Ca. 46. There are suggestions that a number of Angelenos will retire to this

**Figure 7-14.** Paso Robles and environs. The course of the Salinas River, paralleled by U.S. 101, is conspicuous. (dwl)

area (based on land sales).

"Western" in atmosphere and outlook, Paso Robles serves as the node for the sparsely populated ranching country to the east, tributary to Ca. 46. It has recovered from years of economic slowdown which followed closure of the Army's Camp Roberts—this is reflected by new facades in the central district. Earlier Paso Robles was known for its hot sulphur springs, used by Native Americans even before the colonial period.

**Atascadero** (23,000) is better considered a fragmented retiree "district" than a city.

Suggestive of Clearlake (Ch.12), Paradise (Ch.10) or Yucaipa (Ch.6), it is basically a retirement place without a well-defined core. Retail stores are strung along U.S 101. The town is popular with San Joaquin Valley retirees and has many garden patches. Many commute to work in San Luis Obispo— housing there is more expensive. A state hospital adds a payroll.

## PAJARO VALLEY

The diminutive Pajaro (120 square miles) presents one of the Golden State's most esthetically-pleasing agricultural-residential landscapes.

It is bounded by Monterey Bay, by spurs of the Santa Cruz Mountains and marine terraces (Map 7-4).

Although this deltaic lowland experienced successive periods of grazing and grain farming, present-day land-use was anticipated with successful planting of an apple orchard in 1853. Arrival of the Southern Pacific in 1870 facilitated marketing in San Francisco. With establishment of a sugar refinery (later moved to Spreckels) sugar beets

were grown on rich muck soils. Lettuce and vineyards (in the 1920's) eventually replaced the beets.

The Pajaro has long been known for its apples. However vegetables yield larger total incomes (Map 7-5).

Orchard expansion occurred in the 1890's with strawberries (for central California markets) as a cover crop. In the early twentieth century, briefly, before large-scale production in Washington state, the Pajaro was the leading apple producer west of the Rockies.

Orchards on the Valley floor were pulled out to provide for lettuce land in the 1920's. Now the Pajaro vies with Sebastopol (Ch. 8) as California's leading apple producer. It has about 8000 acres, returning $10-12 million annually. With 20 inches of precipitation, irrigation is generally unnecessary. The apples are grown on well-drained fringes of the Valley and orchards range in size from 10 to 100 acres.

The climate does not favor good "market" color hence yellow varieties were long favored, especially the Newtown and Bellflower, picked in September. Drying and canning were once important but as the demand for fresh fruit has increased in California, small-size Delicious, marketed in small Cello-packs, has tended to replace the Bellflower.

Despite its limited size the Pajaro has varied agricultural output. Products include strawberries and apricots, milk, poultry, alfalfa and vegetables (tomatoes, Brussels sprouts, and broccoli) in addition to the apples, sugar beets and lettuce already noted.

Acreage of artichokes is expanding. And flowers

**Figure 7-15.** Picking strawberries, Pajaro Valley. Sometimes the *entire family* of the Japanese farmers assist with the crop. (dwl)

(grown by "refugee" firms from the Santa Clara Valley and with orchid greenhouses from South San Francisco) have much increased.

Strawberries are often grown by Japanese, whose entire families may work in the fields. A patch will yield well for three or four years. It is then plowed under, the land fumigated and new plants set out. Little land is sold. It is costly when available on the Valley floor. A dramatic Valley development has been raising of string beans for freezing since the invention of hydraulic pole-setting and string machines.

**Watsonville** (30,000), longtime trade and shipping point, is experiencing urbanization "spillover" pressure.

It was laid out in 1852; attempts to develop a port (in 1902) were short-lived and premature development of a sea resort also failed. Recently *Pajaro Shores*, with condominiums, has succeeded. Newer homes have also been erected on the north side and in nearby **Freedom** (6400), with many Bay Area retirees in modest cottages (Fig.7-16). Retirees plus commuters (to the Monterey area) suggest Watsonville must either go "up" (high rise) or expand horizontally. Packing sheds, cold storage plants and processing plants are along the railroad tracks in south Watsonville.

The central district, with older business blocks, is threatened by fringe-area shopping developments. Meanwhile, an east-side satellite, *Pajaro* (in Monterey County) has older industrial plants plus residence for farm workers. About a third of the population is Hispanic and there is a serious socioeconomic "gap" in the area.

## THE NORTHERN SAN BENITO VALLEY

There is an apparent dual land-use personality in the San Benito Valley.

The northern portion, focusing on Hollister, is a continuation of the Santa Clara Valley and merges into the better-known lowland to the north so that any geographical division must be arbitrary.

The narrow southern portion ("upper valley") is dry and rolling; it is used for livestock, grains, and increasingly, grapes.

Land-use evolution tended to follow the usual Central Coast pattern.

The Spanish located Mission San Juan Bautista in 1797. In the early American period two groups, W. W. Hollister and Flint, Bixby and Company, maintained large flocks of sheep in the San Benito. The

**Figure 7-16.** Retiree-migrants from the Bay Area find Watsonville an attractive place.(dwl)

Bixby firm acquired much grazing land elsewhere in California, eventually including the present site of Long Beach. Development of irrigation agriculture has been significant in the present century.

There is appreciably less agricultural production in the northern Valley than that of some Central Coast lowlands.

The San Benito contains only 40,000 acres of irrigated land which is rather intensively farmed.

Rainfall averages around 13 inches and is supplemented by pump wells. The Hollister Irrigation District stores a limited amount of water in Paicines reservoir. The California Water Project anticipates additional reservoirs and spreading grounds to maintain the water table; the water situation is not extremely critical yet.

The northern Valley has considerable agricultural diversity; fruit orchards are prominent around Hollister.

The soils are loamy and air drainage favorable. The northern Valley ranks third statewide in apricots and is an important producer of prunes.

Several hundred acres of winter pears are found on heavier soils near San Juan Bautista; walnut groves are also significant and acreage has increased. Grapes are conspicuous yet production is inconsequential in comparison with leading San Joaquin Valley district.

The warm sunny summers favor seed maturation; the Valley is an important producer of such vegetable seeds as lettuce, radishes and onions—Ferry-Morse Seed Company maintains a large ranch east of San Juan Bautista. Besides crops for seeds, a variety of vegetables is grown, including fall potatoes, lettuce, tomatoes and garlic (the lower Valley and the adjacent Santa Clara is the

Figure 7-17. Five p.m. "rush" in downtown Hollister. For a few minutes, at least, such traffic suggests large metropolitan centers. (dwl)

nation's leading producer).

**Hollister** (18,000), trading center, county seat and shipping point, is the single community of consequence.

It suggests a miniature, less affluent San Jose (pre-1950). The town has had steady growth since its founding in 1868. Both commuters and retirees are increasing in numbers. Packing houses are conspicuous along railroad spurs.

**San Juan Bautista** (1400) seems the epitome of the mid-nineteenth mission village. The old earthen plaza with its mission, Castro House and picturesque Plaza Hotel is a state monument.

## THE INTERIOR BASINS

The Interior Basins are *terrae incognitae* for most Californians.

They form a land apart from the more favored Western lowlands just discussed; there is neither a through rail line nor a good north-south highway through this portion of the Golden State.

Physically the Interior Basins are hampered by rain-shadow location east of two rows of southern Coast Ranges. They suffer from aridity and experience slight influence from maritime air and coastal fog, hence they are hotter in summer and colder in winter.

There are no sizable towns. Hamlets are little-known crossroads, perhaps with a schoolhouse, a service station and possibly a general store.

This sparsely populated portion of the Central Coast has three principal depressions—upper **San**

**Benito Valley, Cuyama Valley** and **Carrizo Plain**—as well as lesser basins (map, Fig. 7-2).

## THE UPPER SAN BENITO VALLEY

The San Andreas Fault extends along the upper San Benito Valley southward from Tres Pinos for a distance of 40 miles.

The trough is frequently less than a mile wide, with marginal fault facets and stream terraces, some severely eroded. As gateway to Pinnacles National Monument (see Ranges) and traversed by Ca. 25, the upper San Benito is more frequented and better known than other Interior Basins.

Ranching, with winter grains and beef cattle, remains the characteristic land use.

Properties tend to be large and ranch headquarters are often well-appointed; barbed wire and windmills, like grasslands and oak groves, are characteristic features of the landscape. Undulating terrain, as well as dryness, hampers more intensive land use.

Thousands of acres of varietal grapes are raised around Paicines.

Almaden Wineries, a prominent ex-Santa Clara Valley vintner was "driven out" of South Bay by urbanization. The firm has successfully relocated its operations in the north end of the upper San Benito.

## CUYAMA VALLEY

The Cuyama, mountain-girt with an area of 300 square miles, is a synclinal basin between the Sierra Madre (southwest) and Caliente ranges (northeast) (Map 7-2).

Canyon cutting and gullying have frayed the surrounding slopes; there is an impressive badlands north of Pine Mountain Summit. The upper valley is narrow but the middle valley, underlain by thick alluvium, widens into an aggraded surface with a broad floodplain.

Until the end of the Mexican era, when two land grants were awarded, the Cuyama was ignored.

Around 1900 a few Anglos settled in the Valley, homesteading and constructing roads along peripheral canyons with small streams. Utilization was dependent upon grazing and dry-farming. Homesteaders eked out a precarious livelihood—the distance to railhead (Maricopa) was far for many ranchers.

**Figure 7-18.** New Cuyama, a "company" oil town in the desert, Cuyama Valley. In distance contrast irrigated fields with the barren slopes beyond. (Atlantic Richfield Corporation).

The Cuyama is the driest portion of the Central Coast and grain farming is risky. Rainfall averages about five inches on the valley floor. The Valley produces a good yield of hay and grain once in three to five years. However it normally affords fair grazing land with its surface cover of annual grasses (fescue and Brome), rabbit brush and sagebrush.

About 10,000 acres have been placed under cultivation since successful drilling of pump wells nearly half a century ago.

Presently the already-deep water table is declining and there are too few landholders to justify importation of water. Peas, potatoes, onions and tomatoes have been grown, as well as sugar beets. Feed (alfalfa) and irrigated pasture have been dominant, enhancing livestock production in the Valley. Experimental pear orchards and vineyards have been planted.

After Richfield (Arco) discovered petroleum (in 1948) another transition commenced. Isolation and disbelief in oil prospects had hampered earlier drilling.

The Cuyama became the fourth-ranking producer in California (see "Leading Oilfields, Ch. 9). Crude oil moves by pipeline to a refinery near Long Beach.

There are no towns of much significance in the Valley.

**New Cuyama** (1100), a "model" ex-company town has developed with community hall, shopping center and high school (Fig. 7-18).

As in other arid lands, one wonders what will happen after the oil is depleted.

Meanwhile, queried about attitudes of residents, one person said, "They like this open country. Most of them dread the thought of having to live in Los Angeles or the Bay Area."

**THE CARRIZO PLAIN**

More suggestive of the Great Plains east of the Rocky Mountains than of California's Central Coast, is the Carrizo Plain.

Located in eastern San Luis Obispo Country (Fig. 7-19), it is half a mile above sea level. This remote basin along the San Andreas Fault has internal drainage and a playa in its center. Considered worthless by the Spanish, it is one of the drier portions (precipitation averages about eight inches) of the Central Coast. Climatically it is suggestive of the southwest San Joaquin Valley but slightly cooler (see Overview A). Dozens of "dry holes" have been drilled in hopes of repeating the success of Cuyama petroleum.

Utilization is based upon winter grains and the grazing of sheep and cattle.

Today much of the Plain belongs to large corporations (such as Tenneco, successor to Kern County Land Company).

Strip farming is practiced; with fallowing, there is

**Figure 7-19.** Carrizo Plain; sheep browsing on grain stubble. To some this isolated basin suggests the western Great Plains. Extensive holdings are devoted to winter grains or seasonal pasturage. (dwl)

almost always enough moisture for a satisfactory harvest of Baart wheat, which brings a good price for flour making (Map 7-6).

The Carrizo is sparsely populated but the future may eventually bring change.

In anticipation of receiving water under the California Water Project, plans were announced for *California Valley* and many lots were sold. Allegedly several Hollywood entertainment figures anticipate another Palm Springs! One enthusiastic retired wheat farmer from Montana noted, "It looks just like the Great Plains but without those miserable winters." Meanwhile there is a three-room elementary school, but high school students "board out" in Atascadero, 60 miles to the west.

## THE SHORE

The littoral of the Central Coast long remained far less accessible than the Southern California coast.

In recent decades that isolation has disappeared and a momentous change has transpired.

Recreation and residence constitute the principal use, even as that of the Outer Lowlands is irrigation agriculture and travel trade and that of the Interior Basins is ranching.

There is slight evidence that the littoral will become a heavily-traveled corridor for rapid surface travel between Los Angeles and San Francisco. Public opposition would be strong and there are physical impediments—terrain, fog, and winter storms. Yet vehicular traffic has much increased, especially in summer. The problem of terrain has lessened somewhat but fog and storms pose continuing hazards along this Coast. The Santa Lucia Range, rising steeply from the Pacific over considerable distance, forms the chief topographic obstacle.

Several factors have recommended localization of human activity along The Shore.

The highlands that tend to ascend from the Pacific strand have helped restrict human activity to locales with more benign terrain. Localization to specific portions of the littoral is partially a matter of human barriers as well. Large landholdings have reached to the shore since colonial days. Persistence of some large parcels to the present is

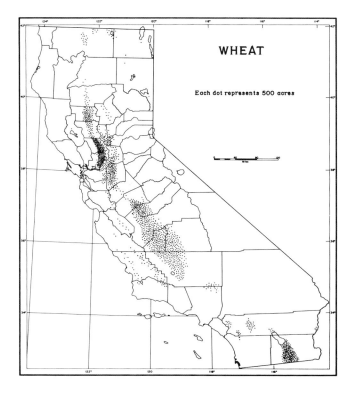

**Map 7-6.** Map of California wheat acreage. San Luis Obispo County, with the upper Salinas Valley, the Carrizo Plain and a portion of the Cuyama Valley, is a ranking producer.

due partially to the limited value of much of the land for intensive use. Governmental ownership has been another reason: national forest, military reservation and state parks.

### The Coastline Plan

Measures considered necessary to contain growth the length of California's thousand miles of coast and to provide public coastal "open space" have engendered much controversy.

The electorate approved legislation (in 1972) establishing a State Coastal Commission and six regional commissions, which submitted a plan to the Legislature in 1975. In the interim the regional commissions acted upon thousands of requests for local shoreline use. Within a thousand yards of the seashore high rise structures, large condominiums and other obstacles to ocean views were denied.

The Plan proposes purchases of nearly all of the 386 miles of undeveloped shore from Mendocino County to Big Sur ( already most of the strand in Marin and San Francisco counties is publicly held). California appears to have the world's most comprehensive program of coastal protection albeit many years too late. In the 1980's developers and their supporters began to weaken the program effectively, as did the federal government with its expanding program of offshore oil leases.

The following foci of activity will be discussed: **San Luis Obispo Bay, Morro Bay,** the **Big Sur Country,** the **Monterey Peninsula** and the **Santa Cruz Coast** (Map 7-4).

### SAN LUIS OBISPO BAY

San Luis Obispo Bay does not provide the best anchorage on the Pacific Coast but the San Luis Range (to the northwest) offers some shelter from prevailing (northwest) winds (Map 7-4).

The Bay, discovered by Cabrillo (in 1542) provided a point of shipment for tallow and hides from Mission San Luis Obispo and later from local Mexican ranchos. The Pacific Coast Railroad, a narrow-gauge line, was extended from Port San Luis (Port Harford) into the Santa Ynez Valley. Crude oil from the Santa Maria and San Joaquin valleys has been shipped from Avila for over half a century.

For over a century the shore of San Luis Bay has had recreational attraction.

**Pismo Beach**, with summer coolness, began beckoning southern San Joaquin Valley residents in the 1880's.

In 1935 **Pismo Beach State Park** was established; it extends along the ocean for six miles. Popularity of the delicate Pismo clam has long necessitated severe 'clamming' limitations.

**Figure 7-20.** A segment of Pismo Beach and the Coast Highway (U.S.101). The towns along the strand of San Luis Obispo Bay have increasing importance. Between San Francisco Bay and the Santa Barbara Coast this is the single area where highway travelers actually see the Pacific without taking byways. (Caltrans)

Patronage of resort communities along San Luis Bay has long been favored by accessibility. This is the single section between the Golden Gate and the Santa Barbara Coast where U.S. 101 reaches the Pacific. Improvement of east-west highways has made the area more accessible to residents of the southern San Joaquin Valley.

### Five Cities

Known locally as the "Five Cities", a mini-metropolis is emerging along San Luis Obispo Bay.

These once-detached farm and beach villages are coalescing into a semi-continuous mass. Population approaches 40,000, spurred by shoreline recreation, retirement and commutation to Vandenberg Air Force Base, Santa Maria and San Luis Obispo. Predominantly native Anglo residents have middle to low incomes. Political separation and proximity to Santa Maria and San Luis Obispo for shopping limits retail trade.

Only three of the five "cities" are actually incorporated.

While they might benefit from the example of Fremont or Pacifica (Ch. 8) merger seems unlikely; there are three separate city governments.

**Arroyo Grande** (13,500), an old Swiss-Portuguese farm village, has the single high school and hospital as well as much of the retail trade.

Initially a shanty town for World War I veterans, **Grover City** (11,000) was incorporated in 1959 to prevent its absorption into Arroyo Grande. It is essentially a lower socioeconomic community with many ex-Dust Bowl retirees from the San Joaquin Valley. Home gardens are much in evidence.

**Pismo Beach** (8000) is a sea resort with two attractive residential areas (seaside *Shell Beach* and hillside *Pismo Heights).*

**Oceano** (unincorp., 1300) principally houses Hispanic farm workers while **Avila** (unincorp.) serves as a beach town for San Luis Obispo. On any weekend thousands of "duners" congregate at Oceano's *Nipomo Dunes.*

### MORRO BAY

Although unimportant as a commercial harbor, Morro Bay has recreational appeal and increasing significance as a residential area.

*Morro Rock* (a 576-foot high volcanic mass) shelters this segment of Estero Bay but it suffers from absence of a productive hinterland. As a recrea-

**Figure 7-21.** Route 1 and the San Simeon shoreline provides a picturesque appeal for the vacationist. (Caltrans)

tional area, the Bay is favored by position near U.S. 101, halfway between Los Angeles and San Francisco.

**Morro Bay** (9900) is now the most urbane resort between Santa Barbara and the Monterey Peninsula.

Once it was a reluctant seaside hamlet with few facilities. Now there is a solid strand of dwellings (more expensive upslope, of course) housing at least 12,000. A growing number of elderly Angelenos are joining retirees from the San Joaquin Valley. Water shortage is pending (prior to still-uncertain extension of the California Water Project).

The Bay (sports fishing and sailing), the Rock, eucalyptus groves, the state park (with golf course and museum) and several state beach parks lend appeal to the environs, only 12 "freeway" miles from U.S. 101.

Morro Bay now has dozens of motels, a growing cluster of Bayside seafood restaurants, numerous gift and craft shops. Residents, old and young alike, desire a "quiet" village lifestyle. There has been strong (and united) opposition to a offshore supertanker anchorage and to large-scale housing developments. However, much growth has occurred inland around *Baywood* and *Los Osos,* to-

**Figure 7-22.** Hearst-San Simeon Historical State Park. Formerly the baronial retreat of a newspaper magnate, this estate in the western slopes of the Santa Lucia Mountains, opened to the public in 1958, soon became a prime tourist attraction and prompted accelerated traffic along Ca. 1.(Caltrans)

gether containing about 15,000 inhabitants (many are commuters to San Luis Obispo).

**Cayucos** (unincorp.) attracts many ex-Dust Bowl retirees from Kern County. Merger with Morro Bay is unlikely—both towns oppose it (taxes in Morro Bay would go up).

Electricity is generated at two points in this area. In the 1950's Pacific Gas and Electric erected a steam plant (utilizing seawater for coolant). In 1985 the same firm began generating nuclear power from a long-controversial and expensive facility farther south at *Diablo Canyon* (Fig. H-6).

## BIG SUR COUNTRY

Much appreciated by vacationists, artists, writers and travelers who are willing to sojourn longer than is required to traverse U.S. 101, is the coastal fringe of the Santa Lucia Range, from Morro Bay to Carmel.

Sometimes called "Big Sur Country" (after the promontory of that name, Map 7-4), this wild land has long empty stretches resulting from rugged terrain, government ownership, and large private holdings.

The Big Sur Country long remained one of the most isolated portions of the Central Coast.

It was only in 1852 that the first settler of European descent established Rancho El Sur. In the 1870's George Hearst began to acquire the barony that eventually totaled tens of thousands of acres. Before 1900, a horse-and-wagon physician , Dr. John Roberts, envisaged a true coastal highway along the nebulous Coast Trail. Eventually surveys were made and in 1937 the road was opened after years of arduous work by convict as well as free labor.

This spectacular scenic highway has gained much (many feel too much) popularity.

Known as the "Carmel-San Simeon Road". or merely Route 1 it was compared by Aubrey Drury (in *California, an Intimate Guide*) with famed Grande Corniche of the French Riviera east of Nice (Fig. 7-21). Since establishment of Hearst Memorial State Park (Fig. 7-22) traffic volume has much expanded. Vehicular congestion has materialized despite new bridges and road widening. Choice vantage spots have been selected for private residences (Fig. 7-23)

Winter rains often bring slides that block the road, sometimes for weeks. Two state highway maintenance stations have crews continuously on call. Between San Simeon and the Sur River, all supplies had to be brought in by pack animals until road opening in 1937.

For over a century there has been scattered live-stock ranching along the Big Sur Coast.

River valleys and marine terraces provide flattish grazing land but animals are also pastured "on top" (on the ridge tops).

In the days when only a "durable" product could stand the trip to market Monterey (Jack) cheese originated on the Molera Ranch (in 1892). Until World War I, when European grating cheeses became unavailable, this cheese was little known elsewhere; now it is commonplace in California.

Often fog-bound, this coast, which novelist John Hersey compared with his *Shangri-La,* is both wild and enchanting. It consists of surf and breakers, sheer slopes, magnificent vistas and rugged head-lands.

Despite lighthouses at Point Piedras Blancas and Point Sur, which can be seen from many miles at sea on clear nights, many a vessel has gone ashore in bad weather. But in spring ceanothus and lu-pine blooms appear at the most improbable places. Later, coast sage festoons whole hillsides with yellow coverlets. Since completion of the highway a series of inns, lodges and restaurants have opened; some have acquired wide repute.

There are many delightful spots to please the visitor along Route 1.

*Pt. Lobos State Park,* at the south end of Carmel Bay, has proved an inspiration to many an artist (Fig. 7-24). Here are intimate little China Cove, sea lions (atop offshore rocks), walking paths (and wildflowers in spring) and the wind-contorted Monterey cypress. Carmel Highlands, a short dis-tance away, is an exclusive residential develop-ment overlooking Carmel Bay; its inn has at-tracted noted guests. Elsewhere there are se-cluded summer cottages in several narrow valleys lined with redwoods.

More than half a million annually visit *Big Sur Valley,* one of the most popular areas. *Pfeiffer-Big Sur State Park,* an ideal family vacation spot, has camping, fresh-water swimming and wading, horseback riding and miles of hiking trails—if one can obtain a campsite. Along this valley are a number of rustic lodges.

*Hearst-San Simeon State Historical Monument* overlooks San Simeon; the $30 million castle was the fabled estate of the wealthy publisher (Fig. 7-22). Within two years after its opening to the public (in 1958) there had been 700,000 visitors. The park

**Figure 7-23.** Built by a San Francisco architect this home site has been acclaimed the "world's most beautiful." Certainly it is one of the most spectacular sites in California.(dwl)

has much affected tourism along the Big Sur; around nearby **Cambria** (2000) motels and many additional retail businesses have been estab-lished. Still, the village retains some of its rustic charm and attracts artists and retirees.

## THE MONTEREY PENINSULA

The Peninsula has a colorful history, scenic appeal and attractive residential habitat that few places in California can approach (Fig.7-24).*

Northwestern tip of the Santa Lucia Range, the hilly Peninsula juts thumb-like into the Pacific, separating Carmel Bay to the south from larger Monterey Bay (Map 7-7).

**Monterey** (29,000), colonial capital of California, has been revived by military activity, tourism and retirement residence.

Previously the city had experienced several "ups and downs." The capital of Alta California from 1775, for nearly three-quarters of a century, it was the political and social center of the province, though Los Angeles surpassed it in population at times. Monterey was modest by nineteenth cen-tury United States standards yet Dana wrote more favorably of it than of other California villages.

With American statehood and the Gold Rush, Monterey lost its capitol and its importance; it

---

*Human pressure threatens this lovely land. A local planner com-mented resignedly, "There is no way that five per cent or even .1 per cent of the American people can live here without utter devastation of this environment."

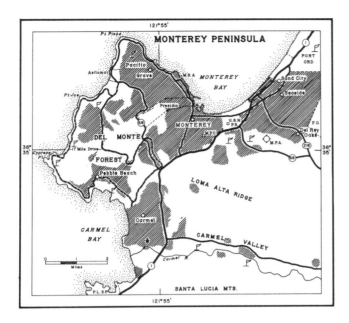

**Map 7-7.** With population growth around Monterey and Carmel, this area is now listed as a S.M.A..

languished for thirty years. There was a little trade from surrounding ranches and local whaling but the population stagnated. Lack of growth helped preserve the colonial heritage for the present. With a favorable corridor eastward into the San Joaquin and the Mother Lode beyond, Monterey might have become one of California's largest cities. Instead, even agricultural development of the Salinas Valley had limited effect on the town. It was bypassed by the main line of the railroad and later by the highway. Even the county seat was transferred to Salinas in 1872.

The Southern Pacific magnates awakened Monterey; in 1878, after a branch rail line was built, the "Big Four" built Del Monte Hotel and hastened Monterey's evolution into a vacation spot of continental renown.

Then came commercial fishing and a salmon cannery (in 1902). However it was the rise of sardine fishing (in 1916) that created "Cannery Row", setting for the Steinbeck novel. For a few years Monterey had 30 canneries and employed several thousand workers seasonally. In the late 1940's the sardine mysteriously disappeared; the canneries have been converted into warehouses or entertainment spots.

Military installations have contributed significantly to the economy of Monterey and environs.

The local Army headquarters is the *Presidio,* a 360-acre preserve which has occupied its present site since 1902. The Army maintains a language school here. Not far away, the famed Del Monte Hotel has been a postgraduate school for Naval officers since World War II. To the northeast *Fort Ord*, long one of the Army's principal indoctrination centers, is now the home of the 7th Infantry.

In recent decades Monterey's central core has been much altered.

Traffic flow has been improved and parking facilities much expanded. Considerable retail trade is now conducted in fringe-area Del Monte Center, attractively sited amidst large oaks.

There is much tourist appeal.

Besides the Presidio historic abodes (better maintained than most colonial structures in California) there are the famed two-story "Monterey-style" dwellings that originated with the Larkin House in 1835. Monterey shares with its Peninsula significance as an art colony. Then there is a Fisherman's Wharf, a good spot for a seafood dinner. Cannery Row has been "revived" with tourist facilities (theatre, gift shops, and restaurants). The *Aquarium*, opened in 1985, is a major tourist attraction. Not surprisingly, Monterey has a sizable number of motels. There is also a convention center downtown.

Monterey spreads back from the arc of its blue bay, sprawling over terraces and rising against the pine-sloped Santa Lucia Range.

The colonial origin is reflected in the crudely rectangular street pattern. The community is a cultural hodgepodge with its *paisanos* (descendants of Spanish-speaking settlers), Chinese, Italians, and Hispanics as well as many others.

The area and population of Monterey may double in the near future. Annexation of a 6000-acre ranch into the city is anticipated.

**Seaside** (38,000) "just grew" as an "off-base" community between Route 1 and Ft. Ord.

It has "stolen" some of Monterey's lower-priced retail stores as well as the "auto row" of The Peninsula. Definitely a lower-income town, it has off-base housing for married military personnel and the modest dwellings of thousands of retired Army "non-coms." Many of the area's black and Filipino groups reside here.

**Marina** (29,000) to the north is a newer "suburb", chiefly residential, with high taxes, costlier rentals and extreme housing pressures.

**Pacific Grove** (16,500), which merges with Monterey on the west, is a middle-income residential community with many retirees.

**Figure 7-24.** The Monterey Peninsula forms the northern end of the Santa Cruz Range. Monterey is in the foreground with the Presidio(lower right) and the Naval Postgraduate School(lower left). Carmel and the Carmel Valley are in the distance.(Aero Photographers, Sausalito)

It was founded in 1869 as a Methodist encampment and was long a strict, righteous community with a strong chautauqua. Its "made in the Middle West" atmosphere contrasts vividly with Monterey, despite many ethnic groups, including Portuguese . The waterfront is suggestive of New England. Here are Stanford University's Hopkins Marine Laboratory, a bathing beach, and even glass-bottomed boats. The retiree group is large but less affluent than residents of Carmel. *Asilomar Conference Grounds,* on its western edge, is an unique state park.

**Carmel-by-the-Sea** (5000) is one of California's most inviting residence places.

South of The Peninsula on its own bay (Fig. 7-24), this rustic Greenwich Village, in its pine-scented woodland, seems to have more esthetic appeal than any other California coastal community, with its quaint cottages, its white-sand beach and its rocky headlands.

The town focuses upon a small central district, The Village. Devoid of flamboyant advertisements and with varied architectural styles, its little "shoppes" seem almost English. Despite mission proximity, Carmel is not of colonial origin. The merit of its site was recognized by academician David Starr Jordan in 1870. Artists and writers began building cabins in the pines; their numbers increased after the fire of 1906 destroyed part of San Francisco's "inspiration."

Without curbs, sidewalks, house numbers (there is no residential mail delivery) or street lamps, Carmel contrasts strikingly with most California communities. Townsfolk have striven as hard to preserve the charming environment as most cities have struggled to become "bigger and better." Indeed Carmel is a dream for tourists, writers and monied retirees.

*Mission San Carlos Borromeo,* originally at Monterey, was moved to its present site on a terrace overlooking the lower Carmel Valley in 1771—a better agricultural site and removed from the demoralizing influences of Monterey's military. San Carlos, built of local sandstone, is distinctive among the missions; it is now picturesque with its Sacarcenic-domed tower and floral setting. After secularization the mission fell into ruins, but has been much restored since 1884 and remains a Church property.

**Del Monte Preserve** (5100) is one of coastal California's loveliest spots, used for golf, residence and even mining.

Its development was commenced on The Peninsula by Pacific Improvement Company (in 1879) which, a few years later created the *Seventeen-Mile Drive* and *Pebble Beach.* Along the shore are much photographed and much painted spots, especially *Midway Point* with its famed *Lone Cypress.* Blue ocean, rocky promontories, white sands, the hilly terrain clad with a dark-hued pine

**Figure 7-25.** Pacific Avenue, Santa Cruz, seemed to be one of California's more successful downtown malls. But youthful visitors, who made few purchases, tended to discourage older shoppers. (dwl)

forest, and Monterey cypress form its appeal. And in spring fields of wildflowers burst into bloom.

Pebble Beach and Cypress Point golf courses have been listed by *Time* magazine among the nation's ten finest. Private lands intersect the Seventeen-Mile Drive, flanked by luxurious homes in varied architectural styles, often screened by vegetation. Affluent senior citizens, wealthy San Franciscans and top-rank military personnel reside here. On the north side of Carmel Bay is *Pebble Beach*, famed watering spot with Del Monte Lodge. Here sports cars assemble each spring during the *Laguna Seca* races at Ft. Ord. South of Pacific Beach the Del Monte Properties Company has mined white plaster sand since 1890. Its uses have increased through the years: plaster, stucco and glass are important.

## THE SANTA CRUZ COAST

Along the north shore of Monterey Bay the Santa Cruz Coast has a setting suggestive of California's other south-facing littoral, the Santa Barbara Coast (Ch. 6).

Both areas had missions, are noted aquatic playgrounds with universities, have agricultural moment and are preferred residential areas. However along the wooded south slopes of the Santa Cruz Range redwoods press near the shore, as if in partial compensation for Santa Barbara's balmier climate.

The appeal of the Santa Cruz Coast has been recognized since the days of the colonial Spanish.

Mission Santa Cruz was established in 1791. Then, as expected, during the Mexican period there was cattle ranching. Americans began moving into the area in the early 1850's; production of vegetables and lumbering in nearby redwood forests gained consequence early. By 1900 general farming had been replaced by specialized agriculture.

Present-day farming is quite specialized, with a variety of higher-value products.

Strawberries and other berries, bulbs, cut flowers, and nursery stock are important east of Santa Cruz and Brussels sprouts to the west. Mushrooms are grown underground in caves and in concrete cellars. Capitola is the center for production of begonia, dahlia, and tulip bulbs.

Avocational gardening of barrister John H. Logan (in 1890) accidentally produced the blackberry-raspberry cross known as the loganberry. Also, east of Santa Cruz, dissected slopes long considered of little value now command high prices as residential sites with views of Monterey Bay.

A conspicuous change to vegetables occurs immediately west of west of Santa Cruz. Lower terraces, exposed to the force of wintry storms yet long farmed, produce grains, beans and especially Brussels sprouts.

This belt continues almost to the western limits of San Francisco. Cattle graze on lower slopes of the Santa Cruz Range. Santa Cruz County and the western side of San Mateo County to the north provide more than 90 per cent of the nation's sprouts. This biennial produces small "heads" (sprouts) on stems. Although perishable, they have been shipped throughout the United States. Recently about 70 per cent of the crop has been

**Figure 7-26.** Natural Bridges Beach State Park, Santa Cruz.(dwl)

fresh-frozen. Much of California is either too warm in early fall or too cold in winter— hence the localization.

## A Quite-Livable Coast

**Santa Cruz** (41,000) has long been the largest sea resort along the Central Coast (Fig.7-27). It is also a county seat, university town, residential center (with many retirees and commuters to the Bay Area), serves as a central place and has some manufacturing. The city is growing "reluctantly."*

This is California's Atlantic City, with differences— although the Miss California contest has been held here. Santa Cruz enjoys year-round popularity, but is especially frequented in summer. Conversion of Route 17 into an expressway coupled with population growth in the Santa Clara Valley , much increased its use. Santa Cruz has a good beach of soft white sand, which is cleaned daily. Its breakers are "just right" for children and for surfers. Along the shore are the Casino and boardwalk. The municipal pier is the point of departure for deep-sea fishing; albacore, salmon, mackerel, ling cod and red snapper are taken.

Santa Cruz evolved on the west bank of the San Lorenzo River.

It was founded (in 1849) opposite the Mexican pueblo (now part of Santa Cruz) around the plaza of the ruined Mission Santa Cruz. In 1861 Brewer *(Up and Down California)* found Santa Cruz already an attractive American village. By the 1870's the milder weather (sunnier than the Bayside city) and the beach were already attracting San Franciscans. Arrival of the Southern Pacific (in 1880) enhanced its recreational use, which expanded following construction of a waterfront casino (in 1906) and decline of Alameda as a resort town.

Small wonder this charming city, with its climatic mildness, is one of the favored retirement spots in California.

With many Victorian frame houses, its roses and De Laveage Park (forested, with some redwoods) it suggests an English town. The discerning visitor will note many small cottages— between students and retirees, there are many here with limited incomes.

There are suggestions of industry.

There is leather tanning, lumber processing, frozen foods and even chewing gum.

The **University of California** occupies a spacious wooded ( redwood) campus.

---

* A prominent local businessman, queried as regards the prospects for a large-scale housing development, said, "Why? But naturally I would favor 'clean' industry that hires local people." Santa Cruz is a self-content community.

**Figure 7-27.** Monterey Bay and Santa Cruz. The city has an effective "green belt" ordinance. This renowned beach resort and residence town is at the mouth of the San Lorenzo River (extending vertically through middle of picture). The spacious University of California campus occupies a marine terrace (far right) at the northwest edge of Santa Cruz. The principal artery to the Bay Area, Ca. 17, parallels the San Lorenzo River and merges with Ca. 1 near the middle of the picture. Dark areas in the foreground are redwood groves. (Greater Santa Cruz Chamber of Commerce, photo by Air Photo Co. of Palo Alto)

Its 2000 acres is located on marine terraces and lower slopes of the Santa Cruz Mountains. Opened in 1965 it consists of a series of Oxonian cluster colleges. "Town and gown" schism has lessened—students have made an effort to cooperate with the community.

East of Santa Cruz the much-wooded north shore of Monterey Bay is increasingly urban—its collective population approaches that of Santa Cruz.

There are several small communities with much commuter and retiree residence. In addition there are eight state seashore parks along the coast. Those with overnight facilities become much crowded.

**Soquel** (5800) is a center for bulbs, orchards and vineyards— in its early days it was a redwood camp.

**Capitola** (11,000) with a small beachfront central district, has a shopping center as well. Initially (founded in 1876) a beach resort, it is the center for begonia gardens. It focuses on its Cove, with fishing pier, bathing beach and waterfront condominiums.

**Aptos** (unincorp., 8700) is the site of Cabrillo College a county community college with a campus which overlooks Monterey Bay.

## THE RANGES

The southern Coast Ranges collectively are used extensively for winter grains and vernal grazing (Fig. 7-28), as watersheds, and in several instance as play-grounds. In the past lumbering was important in the northwest (Ch. 8) and locally there has been mining.

Ranching is more widespread here than elsewhere in major California uplands (map 7-4). The wayfarer along Coast Highway hardly appreciates these highlands, especially in midsummer slopes are browned and apparently of little value. More southerly ranges (the Sierra Madre and San Rafael) have limited use.

## THE SANTA LUCIA RANGE

Largest of the southern Coast Ranges, the Santa Lucia faces the Pacific from Estero Bay to Monterey Bay, a crowflight distance of 125 miles.

This complex faultfold block presents a 3000-foot scarp wall to the sea through much of its length. It affords a picturesque portion of the Golden State with varied landscapes to please the visitor: the scenic Big Sur Country (previously discussed), Carmel Valley, San Antonio Valley and Ventana Wilderness. Back-country portions of the range are suggestive of the southern Appalachians, including a "Li'l Abner Dogpatch" atmosphere in some remote dwellings.

The valleys within the Range were especially appreciated by the colonial Hispanics.

Missions were established at Carmel and northwest of Jolon. Then the Mexicans awarded a series of grants along the coast and in the Carmel and San Antonio valleys. But rougher portions of the Range remained unused in colonial times.

**Figure 7-28.** No other California uplands seem so suitable for dry-farmed winter grains and livestock ranching as southern Coast Ranges. This scene is about 15 miles south of Maricopa. (dwl)

Much of the Santa Lucia is still isolated. A limited number of roads wind from the Salinas Valley into the drier east side.

A few roads cross the Range between Carmel and Morro Bay. Most important are Ca. 68 in the extreme north and improved Ca. 46 between Paso Robles and Cambria. Between Greenfield (Salinas Valley) and Carmel, G-16 takes a northwesterly course and follows Carmel Valley. The Nacimiento (G-18) winds from the Salinas Valley to the coast south of Lucia, descending the western scarp to Route 1 via a dramatic series of switchbacks.

Higher summits rise a mile above sea level; their apex is *Junipero Serra Peak* (5862 ft.).

Densely wooded, they receive some of the heaviest rainfall along the Central Coast. Here western (lace) lichen, mistakenly called "Spanish moss," dangles from trees and the damp forest floor has ferns.

One of the most accessible forest wildernesses in the Golden State is Ventana Wilderness Area.

It was established (in 1931) inland from Big Sur Valley and is not too distant from urban areas. Its best seasons are spring and early summer, when stream fishing is permitted and wildflowers bloom (in April). Hikers must obtain a permit after July 1 (because of late summer dryness and fire hazard). Favorites with hikers are the two-day Pine Ridge Trail from Big Sur Park to Carmel Valley and Blue Ridge Trail from Carmel Valley to Ventana Peak (4734 ft.).

There is varied livestock ranching within the Santa Lucia.

Some dairying is still conducted in the southwest (near Morro Bay and San Luis Obispo). Swine are allowed to run wild in some parts of the back country, feeding upon acorns. Seasonally in the drier and more open eastern portion of the range beef cattle are grazed.

**Carmel Valley** is an accessible, charming and long-used portion of the Range, extending inland about 20 miles.

Varied appeals include proximity to Monterey and Carmel, chaparral and oak woodland slopes, spring wildflowers, the autumn gold of cottonwoods and sycamores, the purplish haze that softens slopes and the shelter from chilling coastal fog. Near its mouth have been fields of artichokes.

The lower Valley has gained considerable recognition for residence and for recreational use. Only two hours from San Francisco by automobile, it is popular with Bay Area residents, retired military

**Figure 7-29.** Swine feeding on acorns in Santa Lucia Mountains. (dwl)

personnel and others. A number of "picture-window" homes across numerous dead-end roads have vistas across remaining beef ranches, truck patches and horse-set country homes to the lush "opposite" slopes. **Carmel Valley** (5500) is an unincorporated spread-out village with varied retail services including guest ranches and lodges, usually complete with swimming pool. Down valley *Hacienda Carmel*, a retirement community, reflects the popularity of the Valley with senior citizens.

A contrast from the lower Carmel Valley, **San Antonio Valley** displays open, summer-parched oak and grass settings.

The Spanish established *Mission San Antonio* (in 1771); after secularization, until its restoration, it lay in ruins. The attenuated San Antonio, followed by a major tributary of the Salinas River, is scenic—once it provided a link along *El Camino Real* but it was long ago bypassed. Old rancho lands along the floodplain have water but homesteaders on rolling uplands were less successful. Lakes Nacimiento and San Antonio, man-made, provide vacation spots for boating enthusiasts.

On the fringe of this remote eastern portion of the range is *Hunter-Liggett Military Reservation*. Purchased from the Hearst Corporation at the start of World War II, its land is still used for maneuvers in connection with Ft. Ord and Camp Roberts.

## THE GABILAN RANGE

Forming the eastern wall for the Salinas Valley, the Range (Map 7-4) is used chiefly for pasturage with

**Figure 7-30.** Golf course clubhouse, Carmel Valley. (dwl)

local recreation.

A continuation of the Santa Cruz Range southward from Pajaro water gap, this anticlinal mass has rolling uplands clothed in chaparral or grass and oaks. Although the Range is less rugged than the Santa Lucia, there are few transverse highways. One can best see contemporary utilization by flying along the range.

The Gabilan has provided pasturage since colonial times; its northern segments were contained within Mexican ranchos. Vast areas are still used for ranching and there is a maze of back roads; numerous check dams have been built along water courses to provide water for livestock.

Recreational use is centered at *Fremont State Park* (atop a 3169-ft. summit) and *Pinnacles National Monument.*

Pinnacles, with its eroded spires and crags, contrasts with the gentler slopes typical of the Gabilan. The relatively small (12,818 acres) monument was the site of Tertiary volcanism; the "pinnacles" are erosional remnants. Spring is the ideal season to visit the monument which becomes dry and dusty later in the year. It is best appreciated afoot; a series of trails enables exploration of its jagged topography.

## THE DIABLO RANGE

The attenuated and sinuous mass best named the Diablo Range (despite such local aliases as Call and Temblor) is the innermost of the southern Coast Ranges. It is structurally complex, with intermontane basins and such prongs as the Oakland-Berkeley Hills.

The Range extends from The Knot in the southeast to Suisun Bay in the north. The northern basins are part of the Bay Area, hence are discussed later (see Ch. 8).

Utilization is modest. It includes residence as well as ranching and grain farming.

Residence is concentrated in the north (see Ch. 8). Throughout the Diablo Range, despite the fact that it is among the driest of the southern Coast Ranges, cattle ranching and production of winter grains form typical use.

Within the folds and rifts of the Diablo Range are a number of small intermont lowlands.

Many little *sagponds* in these depressions have water intermittently. Because of the combination of dryness and isolation, livestock ranching prevails.

The Golden State has had two principal centers of quick-silver (mercury) production, *New Idria* and *New Almaden.*

Quicksilver has had strategic value in times of international tension; in more normal times California producers have been marginal because mining costs are lower in Spain and Italy. The New Idria group extends for miles in San Benito County within the Diablo Range. Operations ceased in 1973.

## SOUTHERN RANGES

The wildest, most rugged and most remote ridges in the Central Coast are found in the southern ranges, *Sierra Madre* and *San Rafael.*

**Figure 7-31.** The dryness of the southeastern corner of the Central Coast is reflected in the Temblor Range (the *local* name for the southern Diablo-Mt. Hamilton Range). (dwl)

Highest elevations in the entire subregion are found here. Only a few winding dirt roads penetrate into this part of the Central Coast; much of it is brush-covered and empty.

**San Rafael Wilderness,** established in 1968 within the Los Padres National Forest, is northeast of the Santa Ynez Valley. Core of the Area is a 35,000-acre refuge set aside in 1951 to protect, without evident success, the California condor.

The condor, the world's largest flying "land bird," is a vulture. Unfortunately this wilderness contains little carrion for the condor, whose numbers have possibly been obliterated.

This wilderness is strictly for the husky backpacker—there are few trails and the terrain is rugged, with dense chaparral and steep cliffs. The northern portion is known as the *Hurricane Deck* because of its interesting ventiform rocks.

## LOOKING AHEAD

The Central Coast has close economic affinities with the San Francisco Bay Area and with Southern California.

Thus it seems less cohesive as a subregion than it may have been in the past. Its respective fringes are being drawn toward Los Angeles and San Francisco.

The Monterey Bay cities, despite their claims of independence, and leadership, are spiritual outliers of the Bay Area.The Santa Maria and Santa Ynez areas have a similar relationship with Southern California. San Luis Obispo County, an increasingly populous and coalescing nucleus, is the most independent portion of the subregion.

It is centrally located between the state's two metropolitan centers. Its university affords a potential industrial and intellectual seedplot—it is not yet apparent whether San Luis Obispo can rise from its agrarian and retirement-oriented environment. For some years a professor-turned-mayor fostered community betterment.

The Central Coast provides important services for the remainder of California: recreation and retirement sites, travel services, military bases, penal facilities, nuclear and fossil fuel generated electricity, higher education, and of course farm, mineral and manufactural products.

Much of the rural Central Coast seems likely to remain agricultural (or ranch) oriented.

Yet urbanization has already affected some quality farmlands (as around Santa Maria and Salinas). For many irrigated districts, the California Water Project (Ch. 9) and possibly sea water conversion maybe the ultimate solution to the problem of water table decline. Agricultural intensification is a likely response to the expanding populations of the Bay Area and Southern California. By contrast large expanses of nonirrigable grain and range land may experience slight change.

The Central Coast reveals some pronounced conservationist tendencies, sometimes despite local economic advantage.

These should hearten devotees of the outdoors. Several industrial and electric power plants have been kept from utilization of prime shoreline locations. This ban-industry concept may, in some locales, be too pervasive and thus help perpetuate the dependent, subordinate status of rural segments of the Central Coast.

Yet there is a threat to the "quality of life" in the Central Coast.

Already there are hints of crowding and congestion in Monterey and Santa Cruz. And if the "exurban flight" from the Bay Area and Southern California continues, the subregion will sacrifice some of its openness and charm.

What is to be the future of the "101 corridor?"

Will surface travels shift increasingly to Interstate 5? Will future travelers make fewer stops enroute? Or is the future to bring increased traffic flow on the highway? And what of a high-speed rail corridor (which presumably would use the Coast Route of the Santa Fe Southern)? Is California to have metroliners—if so, will energy problems bring them sooner than we one thought? How will the Central Coast be affected?

**Figure 8-I.** Morning rush on Interstate 680 south of Ca. 24 interchange. Worsening highway traffic is one of the more serious problems of the Bay Area. (dwl)

Chapter Eight

# THE SAN FRANCISCO BAY AREA*

# THE SAN FRANCISCO BAY AREA

The San Francisco Bay Area, centrum of northern California, provides literally thousands of vignettes.

A Vietnamese family thrilled with their new home in Hercules, throngs at noon around the Student Union at "Cal", two young lovers walking slowly along the Carquinez Scenic Drive, a group of Japanese tourists lunching at Fisherman's Wharf, two children standing behind the motorman on a B.A.R.T. train and excitingly reporting acceleration and deceleration between stations to their parents, a black mother and her daughter buying fish at the Housewives' Market in downtown Oakland, the closing moments of a Stanford-San Jose State football game, an older couple glancing out from their picture window in the Berkeley Hills and watching fog ooze through the Golden Gate...one could find so many, many more.

The natural setting of the Bay Area has a superlative endowment.

Framed by scores of hillocks and a few conspicuous promontories, the aquatic-centered lowland provides one of the earth's more felicitous blendings of water and land. Bejeweled and sybaritic, it is a charming landscape that titillates the senses.

Only infrequently has a conurbation evolved so completely around a hollow centrum—over five million people reside in this expanding conurbation, whose complexity is compounded additionally by the presence of nine counties.

The fringes of the Bay shore have filled rapidly and the Bay Area is now ingressing into the lowlands of the Napa Valley and the Santa Rosa Plain, as well as farther south in the Santa Clara Valley and increasingly into the intermontane basins within the Diablo Range.

Like other great Occidental metropolises, the Bay Area has much urban complexity. Its functions become most involved in its three-dimensional heart, the city of San Francisco. The unifunctional suburban bedroom on the periphery is much less complex.

The Bay Area gained its physical form upon the edge of the Great Ice Age.

With the melting of the continental ice sheets, the level of the ocean rose and seaward penetrated through the Golden Gate to flood the structural depression to the east to create San Francisco Bay. Engulfment detached segments of the southern Coast Ranges to form islands such as Yerba Buena

and Angel. The scalloped shoreline of the Bay has peninsulas and headlands.

The southern Coast Ranges are not as high here as elsewhere but their complex old rocks have been folded and faulted and dissected into steep-sloped hills.

Generally elevations do not exceed 2000 feet; prominent landmarks include *Twin Peaks* and *San Bruno Mountain,* both less than a thousand feet high, *Mt. Diablo* (3749 feet) and *Mt. Tamalpais* (2604 feet). The Bay Area, like much of California, is riven by faults: the *Hayward, San Andreas* and *Sunol* are the best-known.

Since the mid-nineteenth century the Bay Area complex has evolved from a succession of villages scattered along the Bay strand. Ideally situated for ocean traffic in the pre-railroad era, San Francisco achieved urban dominance so rapidly that potential rivals never successfully challenged it.

Similar to the Los Angeles Basin (Lowlands), coalescence of individual cities into a continuous metropolis along the east shores of the Bay has been a product of the automobile age.

Physical linkage of separate political units, sizable housing tracts and suburban shopping centers have been especially marked in the second half of the twentieth century. Yet despite construction of seven automobile bridges, the Bay still imposes a barrier in movement between sundry parts of the Bay Area.

The necessity of effective regional planning within the Bay Area has had long recognition.

---

*This section was reviewed initially by James Parsons, University of California, Berkeley.

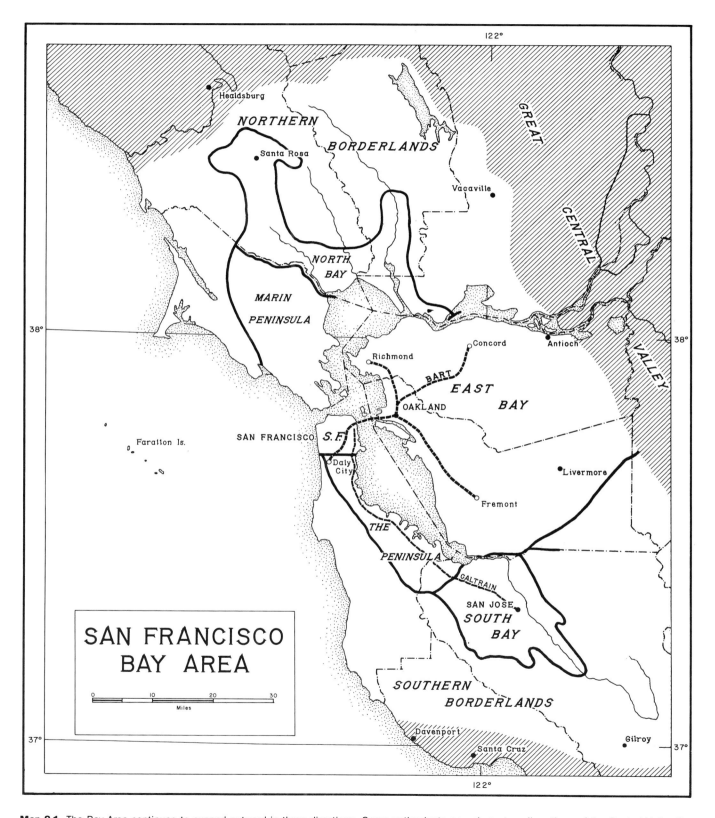

**Map 8-1.** The Bay Area continues to expand outward in three directions. Some enthusiasts now chose to call portions of the Central Valley the Bay Area. Ties with the Pacific Basin are understandable from this map.

Proposed plans in the 1920's and 1930's went awry because of local county and city partisanship. Pressures for regional planning have increased with rising population (at times at the rate of 4000 to 5000 monthly). *

Such concerns as Bay pollution, atmospheric pollution, filling of shallower Bay margins, water supply, rapid transit, parks, airports and highways are matters of concern in all nine counties.

Organization of this book and complexity of the Bay Area conurbation justify discussion successively of these subdivisions: **The Bay, The East Bay, The Peninsula, South Bay** (northern Santa Clara Valley), **San Francisco, Marin Peninsula, The North Bay, Northern Borderlands** and **Southern Borderlands.**

**Figure 8-2.** The San Francisco Bay Area with Daly City, Colma, South San Francisco at bottom of photo. San Francisco in center of picture. San Bruno Mountain clearly delimits "the City" on the southeast. Marin County (upper left), North Bay (middle rear) and East Bay (upper right). (San Francisco Examiner).

## SAN FRANCISCO BAY **

With its western (Golden Gate) and eastern (Carquinez Strait) water gaps, San Francisco Bay affords a sea level route into the interior of central California. The Bay Area, without this aquatic heart, would be more suggestive of other American conurbations despite its hills. The Bay gained its present dimensions after the Pleistocene Era. However, the ancestral embayment was created around 150,000 years ago, when ocean waters flooded a portion of the depression that contains much of the Area. As a consequence of Anglo-American interference, especially bayfill, the size of this water body has been reduced since 1850 by about a third (to approximately 400 square miles).

The Bay, overall, is relatively shallow—at low tide much of it is less than 20 feet deep. However the entrance (below the center of the Golden Gate Bridge) is more than 300 feet deep where the Sacramento River cut its path to the sea eons ago. The deepest portions of the Bay are channels eroded by the Sacramento River and its tributaries—these form the passageways to the several ports. Additionally there are approximately 50 yacht basins and anchorages along the Bay shore.

Through tidal scour and the outflow of the Sacramento River through Carquinez Strait, the Bay is continuously flushed. Still, silting of the Bay has been increased as result of 19th century hydraulicking in the Sierra Nevada gold country (see Chap. 10).

Despite concern that the Bay could "die", hopes exist that efforts of citizens may yet save it. After decades of accelerated pollution, treatment plants

have been constructed. However 40,000 acres of the southern Bay and lesser areas elsewhere are claimed by corporations or individuals. These areas still may become locales for such uses as airports, factories and residences. Future decisions of the Bay Conservation and Development Commission (BCDC) and decisions of the state legislature to provide the necessary solutions will be critical. The courts have been trying for many years to reach a decision relative to Westbay, a corporate entity which claims 21 miles of frontage in San Mateo County (Westbay has been challenged by environment-protection groups).

There are a multitude of uses for the Bay. Besides its scenic values, it is one of the world's important harbors for seagoing vessels. Recreational uses are multiple too; boating is especially conspicuous on weekends. Leslie Salt, with production centered at Newark, has the nation's largest solar evaporation plant for salt production (sodium)— relocation elsewhere in the Pacific is anticipated. An intrinsic value of the Bay is the effect it has on weather modification in the entire Bay Area (and, to a lesser extent, in the Central Valley, especially The Delta).

*The "Balkanization" of local government in the Area has been deplored by many. The Association of Bay Area Governments has been working on a regional plan. The San Francisco Bay Conservation and Development Commission was established in the mid-1950's to control promiscuous filling of the Bay. This agency was made permanent by the state Legislature in 1969. Other agencies in the Area include the Rapid Transit District (B.A.R.T.) and the Bay Area Air Pollution Control District.
**This section been reviewed by the Army Corps of Engineers staff in Sausalito.

## THE EAST BAY *

The East Bay continues to be eclipsed, news-wise, by the prestigious city "across the bay."

Yet The East Bay is ten times larger than San Francisco. Most assuredly, in terms of habitation, The East Bay has more consequence. Nearly three times as many people reside there as in San Francisco. This *contra costa* (opposite coast) has considerably more flattish terrain.

Since the opening of the *Bay Bridge* over half a century ago the population of The East Bay has grown impressively. Now five of the seven largest cities in the Bay Area are in The East Bay and their collective population exceeds that of San Francisco.

The East Bay is nearly synonymous in extent with Contra Costa and Alameda counties (Map 8-2).

It extends from Antioch on the western edge of the Delta Lands (Ch.9) southwesterly to Milpitas (Coyote Creek estuary).

*This section has been reviewed by Donald Holtgrieve and Thomas Pagenhart of California State University, Hayward.

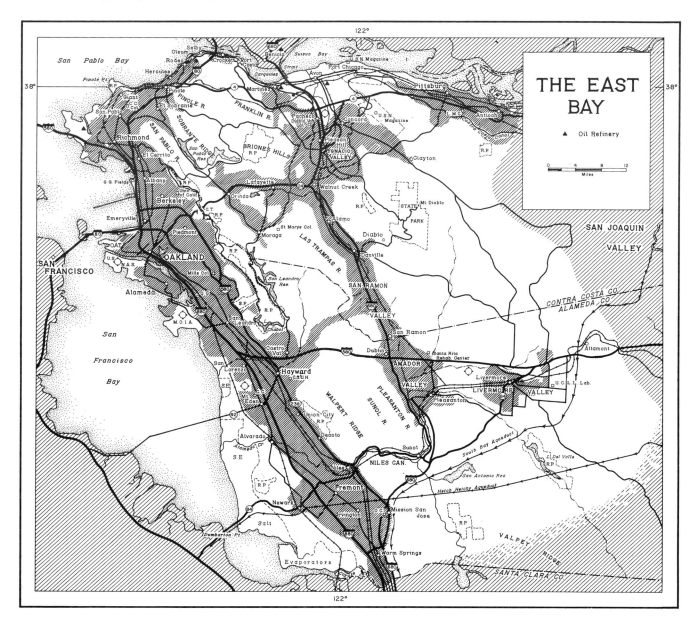

**Map 8-2.** The East Bay should continue to have much open space. The slope and bedrock of much of hill land (ridges) is unsuitable for housing. Fortunately much of it is set aside as state parks (designated RP). or regional parks (designated RP).

The East Bay, like San Francisco, has Coast Range topography. At its northern end the *Diablo Range* splits into the *Berkeley-Oakland Hills* (known farther south as Sunol Ridge) as its western prong and with *Mt. Diablo* as the high point of its eastern arm. Between these prongs and their spurs are *The 680 Corridor* and allied partially-separate intermontane basins. In the second half of the twentieth century these "backlands" have been much urbanized.

Even apart from San Francisco, the East Bay would form an impressive conurbation—it has nearly two million residents.

Much open space remains, either set aside for parks or used for livestock grazing. Yet once-separate towns have coalesced. Too, economic functions have become more elaborate; they include industry, commerce, residence, warehousing, retail and wholesale trade, higher education, recreation, agriculture. and even mining. Long-important, agriculture has declined with urban growth—the situation is suggestive of the fringes of metropolitan Los Angeles.

## AN ATTRACTIVE HABITAT

The East Bay, in some respects, is more attractive physically than is San Francisco.

Its climate experiences wider extremes, with cooler nights than San Francisco and slightly warmer afternoons—skies are frequently clear in the East Bay when San Francisco is shrouded in fog.

The East Bay has more extensive flattish terrain than San Francisco, despite the Berkeley-Oakland Hills.

Possibly one reason for original settlement of San Francisco was the unattractive mudflats along the east side of the Bay (as well as shallow near-shore Bay waters).

While the margins of Bay were covered with tule marshes, much of the plain was grass-covered, with some groves of live oaks and floodplain forests of oak, sycamore and willows along water courses. Vestiges remain in the Berkeley-Oakland Hills of once-extensive redwood groves.

### From Missions to Metropolis

The Mission fathers found the East Bay attractive. Nevertheless the Spanish ignored it for a generation after the founding of Mission San Francisco.

*Mission San Jose,* established in 1797, prospered. San Jose was successful ecclesiastically too—more baptisms were recorded there than at any other mission.

Under Mexican rule almost the entire East Bay was contained within land grants—more than twenty ranchos were created prior to 1847.

By contrast, during the Spanish period, only a single grant was made. But it was the vast Rancho San Antonio, given to Luis Peralta in 1820. It encompassed the land upon which the cities of Berkeley, Oakland and Alameda have evolved.

At the end of the Mexican era Rancho San Antonio was one of the showplaces of Alta California. The East Bay contained some of the choicest grazing lands of the province. A single property, Rancho San Ramon, maintained as many as 14,000 cattle, 4000 sheep and 400 horses.

Much of the East Bay acreage passed moderately soon from Mexican to Anglo-American ownership.

Some choice properties, including Rancho Santa Antonio, were occupied by squatters. Court litigation over this property continued into the 1880's but the Peralta family retained almost nothing of its holding.

The owners of *Rancho San Leandro* eventually took their case to the United States Supreme Court and succeeded in ordering the squatters to pay for their land.

Because of proximity to San Francisco markets, agriculture in the East Bay went through cycles of cattle, grain and sheep into specialized agriculture more quickly than most of Mexican California.

### VILLAGES BECOME MULTI-CITIES

Towns were established in the East Bay early in the American period.

Antioch, Hayward, Martinez, Niles, Oakland, Pacheco and San Leandro were founded in the first decade of statehood. These tended to be farming communities; many early-day settlers were disappointed gold seekers. While Oakland was established in 1850 by squatters on Rancho San Antonio, Livermore and Pleasanton were platted later along the Central Pacific right-of-way.

Oakland has always been the nucleus for population expansion in the East Bay.

Growth was not rapid, however, prior to the opening of the Central Pacific Railroad in 1869. In fact, for many years thereafter it lacked deep-water

**Figure 8-3.** Oakland has become one of two leading container cargo ports of western United States. (The Port of Oakland).

harbor facilities. Throughout the nineteenth century the "stranglehold" that early settler Horace Carpentier, allied with the "Big Four" maintained on the waterfront retarded growth. Thus the city remained primarily residential.

As late as 1900 Oakland was scarcely a seventh as large as San Francisco. Since the East Bay was not ravaged by fire after the earthquake of 1906, thousands from San Francisco relocated across the Bay. Even before 1906 Alameda, Oakland and Berkeley were gaining importance as commuter centers. It was less expensive to commute across the Bay by ferry than to ride north up the Peninsula by train.

Growth was prompted too by other factors. Oakland acquired a deeper dredged port in 1898 while the entry of the Santa Fe Railroad into the Bay Area in 1900 destroyed the rail monopoly of the Southern Pacific. Industrial development also was an important growth factor. A forerunner of Pacific Gas and Electric began delivering electricity from hydroelectric plants in the Sierra Nevada and Standard Oil Company (now *Chevron)* commenced construction of its refinery in the new town of Richmond in 1902. Soon the population of Oakland trebled.

Industrial relocation in the East Bay has been considerable, especially along rail lines and the *Nimitz Freeway* (Interstate 880) south of San Leandro. Additional expansion took place in Contra Costa County, along the strand of San Francisco Bay and eastward along Suisun Bay.

Some plants have vanished from the older centers

(Oakland, Berkeley, Emeryville and Richmond) but much relocation has occurred in the East Bay. Hayward, for example, has more than a dozen industrial parks.

## BY LAND, SEA AND AIR

Transportation services, including rail, highway, maritime and air, have contributed much to the economic growth of the East Bay (Map 8-2).

The area initially tended to be isolated somewhat physically because of water, sometimes shallow on the west and north, and the Coast Ranges to the east. These handicaps have been overcome quite successfully.

Trunk railroads provide good facilities. These include Santa Fe Southern and Union Pacific (formerly Western Pacific). Lines follow two principal corridors from the Central Valley.

Southern Pacific and Santa Fe tracks follow the shores of San Pablo and Suisun bays. The Union Pacific and the Southern Pacific also follow a southern course through *Altamont Pass,* Livermore Valley, and Niles Canyon.

A cross-lacing of trackage covers the Bayshore lowland that forms the urban complex of the East Bay. Moles and piers project prominently into the bay at Alameda, Oakland and Richmond to facilitate freight transfer between the East Bay and San Francisco. The Dumbarton and Benicia rail bridges cross the "ends" of the Bay.

The speed and ease of automotive travel across the Oakland Bay Bridge precipitated abandonment of the Key System commuter trains but the function of the East Bay as an important residence for San Francisco workers continues, abetted by the B.A.R.T. system.

Extensive waterfront developments in Oakland and along the Contra Costa shore northward from Richmond provide the major centers for sea-borne commerce.

Tidal flats along much of the shallow shore were long used for disposal of sewage and industrial wastes.

More recently, a series of marinas and yacht harbors have been established in San Leandro, Alameda, Oakland, Berkeley, Richmond, and Pittsburg.

The East Bay provides the warehousing and trucking hub for the total Bay Area.

**Figure 8-4.** Bay Area Rapid Transit train, Concord line, with San Francisco in rear. (Bay Area Rapid Transit).

This is doubtless explained by available space, location east of the Bay and diversity of associated transport media.

Another means of passenger conveyance in the Bay Area is provided by *Bay Area Rapid Transit* (B.A.R.T.). Its ultimate value as a public carrier remains problematic.

Service was established in the East Bay in 1972 and extended to San Francisco and Daly City in 1974. The three-line system, which serves three counties with 71 miles of track, continues to have problems. In its earlier years it failed to operate at night and on weekends. Its elaborate "state-of-the art" controls still fail at times. It seems to offer service to higher-income suburban residents rather than lower-income inner-city people. With imperfect service and higher fares, it has carried fewer passengers than anticipated. There is inadequate vehicular parking at stations.

The "X-shaped" system has as terminals Daly City, Fremont, Concord and Richmond, with the focal point and headquarters in Oakland.

The principal seaports of the East Bay are Oakland and Richmond.

Oakland ranks as one of the three leading container seaports of western United States (Fig. 8-5). Through the years its total tonnage cargoes have increased; thus it has replaced San Francisco as the ranking port of the Bay Area, with employment of 23,000.

As a seaport Oakland benefits from good highway (used by numerous truck lines), rail and air facilities. The port is served by more than a score of steamship lines (active chiefly in the Pacific Basin and especially with Japan).

Oakland, unlike many U.S. ports, long had greater export than import cargo. Exports include Central Valley agricultural products (fruits, nuts, vegetables and cotton) and steel products while imports include tropical foodstuffs (bananas, coffee and nuts), beverages, steel products and clothing.

The 19 miles of waterfront, two-thirds of which is city owned, consist of three principal segments (Inner, Middle and Outer harbors).

*Inner Harbor* (or Oakland Estuary), between Alameda and the mainland with Grove Street and

Ninth Avenue terminals, handles steel import and break bulk cargo. *Middle Harbor* with bordering moles (Union Pacific to south and Southern Pacific to north) has the Seventh Street Terminal (chiefly container cargo) and the piers and warehouses of Oakland Naval Supply Center. *Outer Harbor*, immediately south of the Oakland Bay Bridge, has the Oakland Army Depot and the Sea-Land container terminal.

Litigation and politics long hampered Oakland's waterfront activity. Finally, court action (in 1907) gave the city control and allowed other railroads (than the Southern Pacific) to use the waterfront. Poor coordination between the railroads was resolved long ago.

Oakland's dominance as a central California port began with the Pacific Theatre during World War II. Afterward came the expansion of trade with Japan and Asia and the development of container cargo.

Despite its industrial activity, Berkeley has lacked sea commerce.

Chiefly this resulted from shallow offshore waters. Nevertheless a yacht harbor was developed in the 1930's.

Richmond, with a 7.5 mile waterfront, has both inner and outer harbors, and is known for handling of petroleum.

Less than half the waterfront is city or state owned; the remainder is non-publicly controlled. Private facilities include the Parr-Richmond Terminal and Chevron facilities.

Sundry dockside facilities continue northward along the "Oil Coast," such as the California and Hawaiian sugar mill at Crockett.

*Oakland International Airport,* south of Alameda, long was the single major commercial airfield ("in-state" flights began at Concord in 1986).

Despite its attractive passenger terminal and 3500-meter runway, it is in the "air shadow" of San Francisco International Airport—the multitude of flight schedules of Los Angeles and San Francisco is absent. Airport expansion would necessitate additional Bay fill. Prestige and "early start" prompt many East Bay residents to use the San Francisco field. There has been helicopter service between Oakland, the Ferry Building and San Francisco International Airport.

The East Bay's well-developed highway network has been improved by bridges, tunnels, tubes and freeways.

Six trans-Bay bridges—*Carquinez* (1927, *San Ra-*

*fael* (1956), *Oakland Bay* (1936), *San Mateo* (1919 and 1967), *Dumbarton* (1926) and *Benicia* (1962)—connect East Bay communities with other parts of the Bay Area. Opening of the San Rafael Bridge led to the end of passenger ferries on the Bay for some years.

There has been recognition of need for another bridge or tunnel to reduce congestion on the heavily-traveled Oakland Bay Bridge. B.A.R.T. has not proved to be a satisfactory substitute.

Tunnels and tubes likewise have eased and quickened traffic movement. *Posey Tube* between Oakland and Alameda was opened in 1928; during rush hours traffic jams have been commonplace even though a second tube was added in 1963. The *Broadway Tunnel* (Ca. 24) completed in 1937, facilitated suburban growth into intermontane basins of eastern Contra Costa County following World War II.

## "GREATER" OAKLAND

There is a continuous conurbation between Niles and Richmond that *might* be identified as metropolitan Oakland.

Urbanization has expanded in recent decades on the northern (Oil Coast), southern (near South Bay or the northern Santa Clara Valley) and eastern (Intermontane Basins) fringes.

Separate political cities (more than three dozen!) vary considerably—they range from exclusively residential to largely industrial to complex multifunctional.

Generally there is a tendency for railroads, docks and industrial plants to be situated near the Bay shore, then older housing areas and "downtown" retail centers, and finally, increasingly newer (sometimes more spacious) housing upslope into the Berkeley-Oakland Hills and beyond into the intermontane basins.

Thus this urban subdivision of The East Bay seems logical: **Northern Bayshore, Central Core, South Alameda Bayshore, Oil Coast** and **The Interior**. It recognizes the urban complexity which has evolved.

### The Northern Bayshore

While Richmond and its neighbors are all near the northern fringe of "elder" East Bay urbanization, cities are distinctly different.

**Richmond** (81,000), the ranking seaport (in tonnage) of the Bay Area, is an industrial-residential-warehousing community. The city has continuing socioeconomic problems that began with overgrowth during World War II.

It is at the north end of the East Bay's "black belt." The black population declined in the 1950's but subsequently has more than doubled. Possibly Richmond may become a black majority city. Besides the conspicuous westside ghetto, contiguous *North Richmond* (unincorporated) is largely black. Because of considerable black underemployment and low incomes, per capita incomes are among the lowest among East Bay cities.

Nevertheless Richmond has a diversified industrial base.

In addition to its Chevron refinery, one of the largest in California, there are more than 100 other industries. Besides distribution facilities (*especially* Safeway Stores), Richmond also has the Post Office's northern California bulk mail distribution center and a regional Social Security office.

The city evolved after 1900, adjacent to the western terminus of the Santa Fe Railroad.

Establishment of the Chevron (*then* Standard Oil) oil refinery (1902), then harbor dredging (from 1912) assured growth. But as late as 1940 Richmond was a rather inviting "little town" despite industrial activity (including a Ford assembly plant and the oil refinery). The city was known for its gardens and its commercial greenhouses.

Probably no Golden State community was affected more by World War II; Richmond became "California's war baby." Population quintupled (to over 100,000) after Kaiser created great shipyards with workers operating 24 hours a day—for a time schools conducted triple sessions. New residents included many from the rural South (including many blacks) and from the Great Plains.

After the shipyards closed many remained in temporary wartime houses. Then, in the early 1950's, 17,000 housing units were removed and thousands left Richmond.

Subsequently Richmond stabilized economically. Tax rates remained high for 30 years (until propositions 13 and 4), allowing such improvements as street beautification and a Civic Center. In the 1980's Richmond again became "pro-growth" city.

Richmond has more amenities than visitors traveling Interstate 80 appreciate.

These include a country club, two yacht basins, two regional shorelines (one, Point Pinole, once was intended to become the site of a steel mill), a downtown park and spacious Wildcat Regional Park (in the Berkeley Hills).

Richmond is definitely a "blue-collar" town.

Affluent Richmond employees tend to live in El Sobrante, El Cerrito, Marin County or the Interior Basins of the East Bay. Yet Richmond has in *The Point* a Bay-facing neighborhood suggestive of Sausalito.

"On the flats" to the north **San Pablo** (22,000) became a socially-depressed "white enclave" surrounded by Richmond—but the town is changing.

Many Anglo ex-shipyard workers in wartime housing relocated here. The town is devoid of manufacturing but much space was designated for manufacturing. Educational attainment has been low and unemployment and crime rates were high— understandably youth left the city. Now many working couples, including Asians and Hispanics, able to afford more costly housing , have moved to condominiums and single-family houses in San Pablo. The handsome mission-style civic center reflects community spirit.

Also surrounded by Richmond, **El Cerrito** (24,000) is the real misfit of the triumvirate—it is one of California's higher-income communities.

A mass of white (hillside dwellings) within verdant slopes of the Berkeley Hills, it is popular with professional peoples and business executives.

Founded late (1909), it has always had residential appeal; most of its confines have views of the Bay, San Francisco and the Golden Gate. There is a country club. Only a small strip is on the "flats" near I-80 with retail shops and an expanding ethnic population.

### The Middle Core

Principally residential, **Albany** (16,000) provides a transition from Berkeley to Richmond.

Founded in this century, Albany continues to grow slowly. Yet on the seaward side (along I-80) only a few of the planned high-rise condominiums were built because of environmentalists' opposition. But long-planned shoreline development, with recreational facilities, housing and retail shops, is occurring.

The city is the site of the *Western Regional Research Laboratory* (U.S. Dept. of Agriculture) as well as the better-known *Golden Gate Fields* (horse racing). Predominantly Anglo, including many personnel associated with U.C., Berkeley, Albany has an Asian minority (especially Thai and Vietnamese) as well as middle-income blacks. Rising costs of housing is tending to create an

**Figure 8-5.** Berkeley, looking eastward into the Berkeley Hills. University Avenue leads from Eastshore freeway to the University of California campus. (dwl)

upper-middle income community.

A city of multiple faces, **Berkeley** (107,000) is one of the more complex cities in California. Primarily, of course, it is the site of the long-prestigious *University of California.*

There is also the Berkeley of the affluent hillside dwellers, as well as the black community on the flats. Additionally there is the Berkeley of the commuters (university staff, students and others)—may come "in" to work but many work elsewhere. Then there is the Berkeley of the street people, the mostly young who come in search of the excitement the city offers. Finally, often overlooked, is industrial Berkeley, old and deteriorating.

This is a community of achievement—two fifths of its work force is managerial/professional.

Not surprisingly, Berkeley is a city of "gracious living" albeit not for everyone. The city has a high ranking in California and the nation for median value of residences although many dwellings are old. In years of formal education it ranks third in California. Its governmental activities are outstanding, although too liberal for many conservatives.

Truly this is one of the Golden State's most lively cities, *especially* around the U.C. campus. And its high tax rates have reflected a city which cares about people.

Despite a traffic plan that closed some streets (to "through" traffic) and emphasized walking, bicycling and public conveyances, congestion around the University especially suggests San Francisco. Narrow streets (unlike those of Davis—Ch. 9) have made establishment of bicycle paths difficult.*

Berkeley is endeavoring to maintain and upgrade residential quality. Yet considerable dilapidated housing remains in the western portions of the community. Like Santa Monica (Ch.6) there has been a strong rent-control policy.

Its hillside "community" is a distinctive portion of Berkeley.

Here, amidst winding streets, are some of California's inviting older homes—architectural gems that helped establish a "style." Yet there are newer houses also—and many residences afford views of the Bay. Residents include affluent business people and industrialists and senior (and retired) professors. Berkeley considers *Tilden Regional Park,* along its eastern border, as "its" park.

*Another* Berkeley centers on the University (widely identified as merely U.C. or Cal), world renowned for its academic achievements and its faculty.

The initial unit in the University of California system, and impressively landscaped, it occupies 720 acres and ascends into the Berkeley Hills; buildings are of light granite or concrete. Sather Tower *(The Campanile)* rises upward 100 meters. The *Lawrence Radiation Laboratory,* on slopes above the campus, has been one of the nation's principal centers of nuclear research.**

---

*Berkeley is essentially a rectangular city with a grid pattern except in the Hills. There are three major east-west and eight main north-south streets. A drive across the city soon reveals its socioeconomic variations.

**Dormitories, nearby, on the hillsides, reflect the increasing shortage of space. Among many prominent structures are the main library (Doe), containing the Bancroft Library, the Stadium (astraddle the *Hayward Fault),* the Life Sciences Building, and the Student Union.

**Figure 8-6.** Berkeley passed a bond issue to place its segment of B.A.R.T. (the Oakland-Richmond line) underground. The transit plaza seen here is on Shattuck Avenue. (dwl)

Thousands of students and younger faculty live in neighborhoods near the campus. University-oriented retail activity focuses on *Telegraph Avenue*—which is also a hub for the "street people." Bookstores, pubs, coffee shops and record stores are much evident. Increasingly apartment units are replacing single-family dwelllings.

Berkeley has been the locale of lesser known academic institutions as well: Armstrong College (business), several divinity schools and state institutions for physically-handicapped students.

West of the University the central city is an important Berkeley "face" even though the C.B.D. is small for the size of the city.

It focuses on University (leading west to I-80), where motels are much evident, and Shattuck (north-south). In recent decades Berkeley has declined relatively as an East Bay shopping center. There are no department stores and the number of specialty restaurants is disproportionately large. There are many older, modest residences and a sizable number of senior citizens, but there is good public transport (busses and *underground* B.A.R.T.).

Southwest Berkeley is *black* Berkeley.

Approximately a fourth of the city's residents are black and many are second or third generation in Berkeley. Better educated and more sophisticated than newer ethnic arrivals in the Bay Area, many are university employees or civil servants. Recently both the mayor and the local congressmen were black lawyers (and U.C. graduates).

Along the railroad tracks and east of Interstate 80 (Eastshore Freeway) is *western* Berkeley, including the industrial area.

Although there are several hundred plants the number is decreasing; a number of buildings are old and shabby. Some industries have moved elsewhere where there are lower taxes and lesser congestion. Types have included soap, foods and pharmaceuticals. The waterfront, recreation-oriented, generates few taxes.

**Emeryville** (5000), long almost-wholly industrial and suggestive of Vernon (see Ch. 6), has become a better-balanced city. Now it is less-compressed along Bayshore railroad tracks and extends into the Bay.

Controversial Bayfill led to "a second" Emeryville, suggestive of a small Foster City, on "The Peninsula" west of Interstate 80. Here are the city hall, corporate offices, G.E.M. facilities and costlier multi-story apartments (near San Francisco but apart from its problems), and a marina.

**Figure 8-7.** The core of *old* Emeryville, along San Pablo Avenue. (dwl)

The old town (east of I-80) has changed too. Some of its remaining time-worn buildings are vacant. New structures house "think factory" research and development firms who find the town's central location favorable. Despite a paucity of trees and no cemeteries or churches, there *is* a high school. Working blacks and senior citizens have appreciated the low tax rates. Scores of factories remain.

The community was established around 1900 when meat packers and San Francisco race track operators sought a new site. Later the racetrack was replaced by industrial structures. In 1928 the district attorney (Earl Warren) claimed it was the most corrupt town in United States. Permitted by local option, draw poker is still played.

### Oakland

After decades as "San Francisco's Newark" there are hints that **Oakland** (354,000) is *finally* becoming truly *the* city of East Bay. Strongly non-Anglo it is indeed an international melange. Its people seem resolved to give their city new vibrancy and cohesion. Although slightly larger (in area) than San Francisco, Oakland houses only half as many people but it is the core of the East Bay.

Similarities between these two "rival" communities exceed the contrasts.

Major differences may be the tourism, banking and number of corporate headquarters. Oakland outranks San Francisco in number of "big league" sports teams, with the A's, Seals, and Warriors. San Francisco is more consequential in music, museums and the arts although both have symphony orchestras.

While San Francisco has more federal and state offices, both are county seats. San Francisco is more important as a center of higher education.

**Figure 8-8.** Oakland. Lake Merritt and Peralta Park (foreground) with downtown Oakland in the middle of the picture and west Oakland beyond. Northwest end of Alameda is in upper left, then Inner Harbor, Naval Supply Depot and Middle Harbor and Outer Harbor (to left of Bay Bridge). Note path of the Nimitz Freeway (I-880). (Oakland Chamber of Commerce, photo by R.L. Copeland).

Per capita incomes are comparable. Both have sizable ethnic populations (with more Asians in San Francisco and more blacks in Oakland).

The percent of the professional-managerial work force is somewhat higher in San Francisco (an appreciable number of this group reside in the Oakland Hills). Median years of formal schooling is comparable (Oakland has a higher per cent of middle income residents) and serious crime rates are comparable.*

As a transportation center Oakland has more overall importance. Yet the probability of Oakland's airport eventually conducting more flights than San Francisco's (which is in San Mateo County, not San Francisco) seems unlikely. Oakland has gained as a seaport at the expense of San Francisco (and other ports as well). Oakland, as a truck and rail center, is much more consequential.

Oakland ranks second to San Francisco in the Bay Area as an industrial center. Still, both cities have shown relative decline.

The site for Oakland was selected well.

Squatters founded the town beside San Antonio Slough (directly east of San Francisco) in 1850. The tidal flat became the site of Oakland harbor which now has 19 miles of waterfront.

Like San Francisco Oakland is a city of hills and plains ("the flats") (Fig. 8-9). The level land, understandably, contains the downtown area as well as the port, industrial districts and sizable areas of lower-income housing.

---

*Senior author Lantis queried a dozen or so young women office workers in downtown Oakland: "Do you feel safe on the streets of downtown Oakland at night with an escort?" Every one answered in the affirmative but most indicated they would feel unsafe in some parts of the city. Obviously, Oakland suffers from "bad press."

Oakland continues to suffer an image problem. Whereas everyone has heard of San Francisco, to much of the world Oakland remains a "nowhere" city. And if the city is known, too often it is associated with limited culture, crime, and drugs.

### The Flats

Most of the commercial and industrial activity of Oakland, like that of San Francisco, focuses on the Bayshore plain.

In contrast to San Francisco the extent of flattish terrain is broader and more continuous. Thus the downtown area, west Oakland, intermediate neighborhoods and east Oakland are found here.

### The Central City

A dramatic renaissance, nigh completed, has been been taking place for many years.

It now appears that despite surrounding ethnic neighborhoods with lower incomes and high unemployment, downtown Oakland is becoming "someplace." Jobs have materialized for some inner city residents. Transport access by freeway linkages (to Interstates 80, 580 and 880) and B.A.R.T. has improved and parking facilities increased. There is more entertainment but adequate retail trade outlets are still indefinite.

Focus of downtown economic revival has been the $200 million *Central City Project,* as well as other developments.

It has involved a series of high-rise office buildings, two parking garages (with spaces for 4300 automobiles), a 500-room hotel (the first since the 1920's!), many smaller retail shops and pedestrian malls (with good access to the B.A.R.T. interchange). More recent have been construction of a convention center and anticipation of a large federal structure (for General Services Administration), and a headquarters for the entire University of California administration (still problematic).

At the north end of Downtown, focusing on 20th Street, attempts are underway to attract a second department store. Buildings in this area include apartments as well as corporate headquarters.

Praised for its architectural design, the Oakland Museum occupies at seven-acre site and stresses California (art, history and wildlife). Other cultural features are nearby.

Another addition has been the Performing Arts Center, in a renovated cinema palace (built in the 1920's), which has provided a place for the Symphony Orchestra and other events.

**Figure 8-9.** Urban renewal in west Oakland: the Oak Center project. (dwl)

The site for Laney College was created by urban renewal (removal of slum housing). Oakland is rather unusual among California cities in having a downtown community college.

Rehabilitation of *Old Oakland* is underway. South of the present downtown center, this was the heart of nineteenth century Oakland.

Restoration of an area of ancient commercial structures, now known as Victorian Square has been completed and houses a variety of shops.

Major renovation is scheduled for *Chinatown.* Only a fraction of Oakland's Chinese reside here (the majority reside in east Oakland) and the district, relatively little known, has lacked the cohesion of its San Francisco counterpart. It has provided a haven for single males (Filipinos, blacks and Anglos) but recently has acquired a sizable Vietnamese populace. Boosters predict that eventually it will rival San Francisco's Chinese district as a tourist attraction.

Waterfront resurrection adjacent to the port, at the foot of Broadway (the principal Oakland street) has created in *Jack London Square* a rival to San Francisco's Fisherman's Wharf.

The Square provides the headquarters for the Port of Oakland as well as motels, seafood restaurants and specialty shops. Continuing development is anticipated.

Also on the downtown fringe (but on the northeast edge) is *Lake Merritt* and contiguous Lakeside Park, providing attractive open space.

An affluent Anglo-majority residential isle, contrasting with surrounding black neighborhoods, adjoins the Lake. There is a vague suggestion of Chicago's Northside lake front or New York's

**Figure 8-10.** Downtown Oakland, Broadway and 14th—many of the faces are American black, Hispanic or Asian. (dwl)

Central Park. The number of high-rise apartments (popular with retirees) has increased. Urban renewal has occurred on the northwestern fringe in the Waverly district where multi-story apartments have replaced a mixture of older houses and commercial structures.

### The West End

Two similar districts, *west Oakland* and *north Oakland,* comprise the west end. Older residences and sizable ethnic populations are found in both areas.

Residentially, this was nineteenth century Oakland; many dwellings remain from the century past. For several generations this has been the core of black Oakland (some census tracts are more than 90 per cent black).

Considerable change has occurred in the past several decades. Population declined by 40 per cent in the 1960's (due to rights-of-way for B.A.R.T. and freeways). Many dilapidated houses were destroyed and vacant lots are still conspicuous. Urban renewal has centered on two projects. One, Oak Center (Fig. 8-9) produced renovation of sturdy (and often large) houses while the other, Acorn resulted in new multi-story low-rent housing.

A more rapid transition in north Oakland (towards Piedmont and Berkeley) from poverty to middle incomes is found. Yet unemployment has been high in both districts and there has been considerable social frustration.

### East Oakland

Oakland's flatlands, southeasterly from the downtown area, are served by transport facilities which include B.A.R.T.'s Fremont line, rail lines and several freeways. Many dwellings here, built to house middle-income workers during World War II, have more recently been occupied by some of the city's least affluent residents. Ethnic composition, both Hispanic and black, is sizable.

From northwest to southeast, districts here include *San Antonio, Fruitvale, Seminary* and *Elmhurst.* The first two, closer to downtown Oakland, have provided longtime residence for many of the city's Hispanics. In recent decades an influx of blacks has occurred. Many dwellings here date from earlier decades of the century.

Seminary and Elmhurst, farther east, contained much open farmland in 1940. Numerous small houses were hastily built during World War II. With elimination of many houses in west Oakland, these relatively-inexpensive dwellings were seemingly the only ones many black residents could afford. Subsequently many Anglos left this area and a number of retail firms moved elsewhere or closed. Presently some census tracts are 95 per cent black. During periods of unemployment many residents could not make house payments and merely left. So the city gained another sizable blighted area—here one finds much drug traffic as well as considerable theft.

An attempt to revitalize a segment of east Oakland materialized with the *Elmhurst project.* Infusion of federal and state monies, plus efforts of residents and others, seems to have arrested the deterioration.

An important facility in east Oakland is the *Oakland-Alameda County Coliseum Complex.*

This development, surrounded by sizable parking lots (and with easy access to B.A.R.T.), houses three major league athletic teams (A's, Seals and Warriors). There is no similar concentration of professional "big league" teams at a single California site. Opened in 1956, the Complex cost $25 million.

### The Oakland Hills

Higher-income Oakland tends to reside in the western flanks of the Oakland-Berkeley Hills, from San Leandro northward to Berkeley. Many houses are aged and lots are often small but there is good maintenance and landscaping is attractive. There is a maze of winding streets but two freeways (I-580 to the west, Ca. 13 to the east) help ease ingress and egress. The area is a focal point for higher education in Oakland.

**Figure 8-11.** The well-maintained older homes of Alameda. (dwl)

There is some variance in neighborhoods relative to quality of housing as well as prestige. The "more desirable" neighborhoods, in the *Claremont Hills* and *Montclair* districts, are vicinal to Piedmont and Berkeley.

Four regional parks plus a city park reach along the eastern fringe of Oakland. Thirty regional parks are scattered through Alameda and Contra Costa counties; they contain 30,000 acres. The largest of the four within Oakland is *Anthony Chabot* (4750 acres); next in size is *Redwood* (207 acres).

The *East Bay Regional Park System* was established in 1934 around watersheds (and storage reservoirs) of East Bay Municipal Utilities District (East Bay MUD) and has subsequently been expanded and now includes some Bayshore Parks.* The parks afford a diversity of recreational facilities, including camping, fishing, golf, picnicking and swimming.

*Joaquin Miller Park,* contiguous to Redwood Regional Park, is a city park, somewhat comparable to Los Angeles' Griffith Park. Farther south is Knowland State Arboretum and Park, site of the Oakland Zoo.

Within the Hills, in close proximity, are three college campuses. *Mills College,* perhaps the best-known women's institution in the West, has a spacious campus. Another women's college, *College of Holy Names,* is nearby. A newer institution is *Merritt College,* one of the two-year Peralta Colleges.

The East Bay's equivalent of Beverly Hills or San Marino, is **Piedmont** (10,500). This independent residential enclave, surrounded by Oakland, is an exclusive hillside town which developed at the beginning of the twentieth century around a resort spa.

Suggestive of a "little San Diego", **Alameda** (82,000) serves as a naval base, beach resort and

residence place. One of the older communities in the East Bay it has been unique in the Core Area because it still has had space for growth in latter half of the twentieth century (due to Bayfill).

Time-wise, Alameda has experienced different functions. Alameda was a garden and orchard town in its early years. From 1870 to 1939 it provided an "Atlantic City" for the Bay Area with its Neptune Beach.

For a considerable period the warehouses of Alaska Packers' Association and the California Packing Company (*later* Del Monte) stored millions of cans of Alaskan salmon and canned vegetables and fruits (from central California).

During the years of the two World Wars Bethlehem built ships along Oakland Inner Harbor. In the early 1940's housing was almost as scarce as in Richmond.

World War II saw the conversion of the north end of the island into *Alameda Air Station.* The 2000-acre facility has provided a home base for aircraft carriers of the Pacific Fleet. Thousands of Naval personnel and civilians have been employed there.

Alameda, largely residential, has many older homes. Maintenance and town pride suggest Oak Park (a Chicago suburb)—many families have resided there for three generations.

Bayfill permitted Alameda to expand westward after 1950. Now the South Shore has apartments and townhouses, a man-made lagoon, two yacht harbors and a shopping center. The city has two miles of sandy Bayside beaches and a beach park (part of the East Bay Regional Parks) has replaced Old Neptune Beach.

Bayfill also allowed southward expansion on *Bay Farm Island* which Alameda shares with the Oakland airport. Houses were still constructed in the 1980's in a setting suggestive of Foster City.

## SOUTH ALAMEDA BAYSHORE

Urbanization south of the East Bay core has occurred principally in the second half of the twentieth century.

As expansion has continued southward from Oakland toward San Jose, once-small farm towns, surrounded by truck gardens, orchards and dairies, have fused into the Bay Area conurbation.

---

*Like San Francisco and Los Angeles, East Bay cities bring water for urban use from the Sierra Nevada. The key storage unit is Pardee Reservoir on the Mokelumne.

The alteration, suggestive of that of The Peninsula and South Bay discussed subsequently) has been favored by open flatland and proximity to central cities as well as transportation facilities (railroads and the Nimitz Freeway, now Interstate 880, especially). *

Near the East Bay core, **San Leandro** (66,000) underwent transformation before some communities to the south. Expansion took place into surrounding territory (unincorporated) as industry was aggressively and successfully sought.

Even before World War II there were assembly plants (Chevrolet and Caterpillar). Scores of industrial plants whose products included data processing, communications, paper and chemicals) appeared. More recently San Leandro has lost some of its "rust belt" industries; some land has been used for warehouses, wholesale facilities and multi-family housing.

Strong civic pride is obvious in this Mediterranean (Portuguese and Italian)-Asian city. During the 1940's rows of tract houses appeared as the population doubled. As farther north in East Bay the west slopes of the *San Leandro Hills* (a continuation of the Oakland-Berkeley Hills) have been covered with residents of the more affluent. Despite limited land for parks, there are Bayshore golf courses and a marina. In the central district much renovation has occurred.

The contrast between the poverty of east Oakland and the tidy affluence of San Leandro is readily seen by driving southward (along such streets as E. 14th St.). For many years, through strong neighborhood associations San Leandro "erected a wall" against the "unwanted" (i.e., lower-income non-whites). Subsequently the total population has become more mixed).

## The Hayward Complex

With its major crossroads position (west by bridge to San Mateo and The Peninsula and east over Altamont Pass into interior East Bay and the Central Valley) near the midpoint (north-south) of Alameda County the population of the Hayward Complex (Castro Valley, Hayward and San Lorenzo) exceeds 200,000. It ranks high as an East Bay economic hub and its metropolitan node is still evolving.

Like some other California metropolitan hubs, **Hayward** (102,000) is still adjusting to its role. Its diverse economic supports include higher education, services, manufacturing and transportation.

Hayward's population has increased fifteen-fold

since 1930 and the city has changed considerably.

Prior to 1940 Hayward was a sedate farm town with a Portuguese "power base" along the edge of Walpert Ridge (western segment of Diablo-Mount Hamilton Range). Population expanded belatedly, in contrast to San Leandro. By the 1950's Hayward was growing rapidly as Bay flatlands became industrial parks and housing tracts.

Expanded commerce and industrial output has contrasted with quasi stagnation in the core area of the East Bay to the north.

Manufacturing, with many products, includes numerous smaller firms. Presently about two-thirds of the area zoned for manufacturing is occupied.

There are a dozen industrial parks and growth has been rapid. Although there are several large plants small operations predominate. Warehousing and distribution facilities have also expanded; the national headquarters for Mervyn's Stores is in Hayward.

The character of Hayward's central district has been modified.

For example, a pedestrian area has been established around the city hall. Retail trade has been affected by competition from Southland, one of the largest Bay Area malls, adjacent to I-880, and other shopping centers. It has gained importance as an area for residence (especially senior citizens), banking and professional services.

Higher education is consequential in the city.

In addition to the only California State University campus in The East Bay, on a spectacular hillside site overlooking the Bay Area, there is also Chabot, an Alameda County community college.

Hayward forms an important East Bay transportation center.

It is crossed by several freeways, has truck terminals and is served by two railroads as well as B.A.R.T.. Its airport is the leading general aircraft port in the East Bay.

Hayward has matured socially after overcoming some of its earlier cultural schism.

Without the large percentages of lower and higher incomes found in Oakland and San Francisco, the city tends to be a middle-income community. The sizable blue-collar populace includes many commuters but a lesser per cent since industrial and commercial growth in Hayward. While the Portu-

---

* *Throughout* urban California, freeways and automobiles have allowed hasty outward expansion of metropolitan areas in the second half of the twentieth century.

**Figure 8-12.** Fremont's artificial Central Park lake—belated fusion of farm villages allowed space for a distinctive downtown area. (dwl)

guese element remains important the populace has become more heterogeneous, with many Filipinos and Hispanics as well as blacks.

Several politically-separate cities, San Lorenzo, Castro Valley and Union City, are essentially satellites of Hayward. In function they are primarily residential.

**Castro Valley** (44,000, unincorp.) is faintly suggestive of El Cerrito. Its hillside setting (and views of the Bay) and tranquility have given it popularity with upper middle-income business and professional people.

**San Lorenzo** (22,000), on Bayside flats, has become more of an upper-middle income residence. In bygone years it was basically a Hispanic farm labor hamlet.

**Union City** (51,000) too has changed. Formerly a blue-collar town industrial town, it has become a more typical Bay Area suburb. Its steel mill is gone but other industries remain. In the past half of its residents had Spanish surnames.

### The South Bay Connection

Where does East Bay end and South Bay begin? Terminology is vague but assumedly Fremont is in the contact zone.

***Fremont*** (165,000), despite some early-day antecedents, is inherently a *new town*. *

---

* This section has been reviewed by Carol Kurtz, C.S.U., Chico and Butte College.

**Figure 8-13.** Fremont. Although it has one of the largest areas among California cities, much of its space is unsafe for construction (Fremont Chamber of Commerce, photo by Air-Photo of Palo Alto).

Located here is Mission San Jose, one of the more prosperous of the Spanish colonial establishments. Its building was restored late in the twentieth century. Prior to amalgamation in 1956 of five farm hamlets *(Niles, Centerville, Irvington, Mission San Jose* and *Warm Springs),* much of present-day Fremont was non-urbanized farm land. By the 1960's growth was rapid and within a decade of incorporation a strong civic spirit had developed.

Although it ranks fourth in population in the Bay Area, Fremont differs considerably from other larger cities in the subregion.

While it has nearly twice the areal extent of either San Francisco or Oakland, its skyline is low— buildings taller than two stories are uncommon.

Fremont lacks the extremes of wealth and poverty found in other larger Bay Area cities. Its residents, principally Anglo, lack the ethnic diversity which typifies a number of Bay Area communities. They include many commuters to the Peninsula and Silicon Valley.

Population density is low; with wide streets, the congestion of San Francisco is absent. There is abundant off-street parking. Some feel that despite Central Park and two nearby regional parks insufficient space has been set aside for public preserves.

The downtown area differs from the core of older American cities. It consists of a large regional shopping center (there are others as well) and a city park with a civic center and a lake (Fig. 8-12). Some residents feel that dominance by a single corporation has reduced the attractiveness of the city core.

Fremont has gained a good industrial base—and has space for future growth. Current establishments include one of two auto assembly plants (now jointly operated by Toyota and General Motors) in California.

For several decades it appeared that Fremont might become one of California's largest cities.

The most attractive areas for urbanization have been occupied. It has been realized that environment restrictions (especially earthquake hazard) will discourage utilization of Bayside tidal flats (currently used for salt evaporation) as well as eastside hill slopes.

Politically surrounded by Fremont, **Newark** (39,000) differs from its larger neighbor. There is industrial diversity, many winding streets, and a variety of ethnic backgrounds.

**Figure 8-14.** This is Port Costa in the late twentieth century. Hints of of revival as a recreational-residential place continue. (dwl)

Industrial products have included salt, trucks, and chemicals.

Newark is an *older* westside (lower incomes)-eastside (middle income residents around a man-made lake) city predominantly with single-family, owner-occupied homes.

Despite limited area, fill-in is expected to double the population soon after 2000. The populace includes Hispanics, East Asians (an increasing number of Japanese, Chinese and Filipino professional people), and Anglo. As in Fremont, there are many trans-Bay commuters.

## THE OIL COAST

Along the shores of Contra Costa County (San Pablo and Suisun bays) the northward extension of the East Bay has long been identified as the *Oil Coast* (Fig. 8-2). As one motored north of Richmond on U.S. 40 (or more recently on I-80) there was a feeling of having departed from the Bay Area conurbation. But in the late twentieth century here, as in southern East Bay, much population growth has occurred—villages have become cities—places of residence and commutation.

The Bayshore lowland to the south is absent—spurs of the Diablo Range sometimes rise immediately from the Bay's edge. Inland, slopes unsuitable for habitation (shale is widespread and slippage conspicuous) are used for grains and beef, for urban water storage and for recreation.

Aquatic fringes have had varied use—increasingly it has become residential.

In the past there was a scattering of industrial villages, paralleling the shore and rail lines. Port-type manufacturing has been prominent.

The *Contra Costa Canal* (see Central Valley Project, Ch.9) has added industrial water supply to other advantages for manufacturing plants.

Outer slopes have provided space for "tank farms" of petroleum refineries. Additional products have included sugar, steel, chemicals and containers.

The Oil Coast forms one of the Golden State's two major petroleum-refining centers.

Chevron (at Richmond), Union (at Oleum), Shell (at Martinez), Phillips (at Avon) and Exxon (at Benicia) operate refineries here (Fig. 8-15).

Past isolation from urban concentration favored "smelly" activities, as did deep-water facilities, availability of sizable markets in the Bay Area and central California, and ease of extending pipelines from the southern San Joaquin Valley.

Explosives and smelting represented the earliest major industries to locate here.

Two major producers of powder and explosives operated plants at once-isolated spots for three quarters of a century. Both firms had decentralized underground magazines; facilities covered hundreds of acres. Production earlier in San Francisco had been related first to Sierran mine camps and then to railroads.

In 1884 Selby Smelter abandoned San Francisco because its operations caused air pollution. There was longtime cooperation between its cartridge factory and the Benicia Arsenal. Its successor, American Smelting and Refining, processed such metals as antimony, gold, lead and silver; company docks allowed unloading of ore ships.

Now drowsy, *Port Costa* ranked among the world's great wheat exporting places of the late 1800's.

It was central California's ranking grain port. Supported by rail facilities, deep water (averaging 30 feet at dockside at low tide),access to the Golden Gate, the Port Costa Strip extended for four miles along Carquinez Strait. In the mid-1880's half of all wheat ships departing from the Bay loaded at its warehouses—some on pilings over water.

Once too canning of fruits, fish and vegetables was consequential along the Oil Coast. Still, this locale never ranked with Oakland or San Francisco.

But a persistent landmark has been the C and H. (California and Hawaii) sugar refinery at Crockett, in operation since 1897 in an erstwhile flour mill on Carquinez Strait. It was established by Hawaiian growers to provide access to continental markets. It has been the world's largest cane-sugar refineries (and one of two on the U.S. Pacific Coast). Raw sugar comes from Hawaii in bulk (unbagged) to lessen shipping costs.

**Figure 8-15.** Richmond, the south end of the Oil Coast. View westward includes Chevron refinery, the San Rafael Bridge and the Marin Peninsula across San Pablo Bay. (Chevron Corporation)

**Commuters (and others) live here**

Oil Coast communities tend to be elder Bay Area towns.

Some were supply points enroute to the gold fields while others were farm villages. Several began as company towns. Now they are enwebbed within the Bay Area metropolis.

Fusion into a continuous agglomeration, as farther south in the East Bay, remains incomplete.

Terrain and interposition of large industrial plants has made conurbation difficult.

At the southwest end of the Oil Coast a quartet of former hamlets, once inhabited by local workers, now house many commuters.

**Rodeo** (5300; unincorp.) reveals its past and remains a lower socioeconomic blue-collar town.

**Pinole** (18,000) is more suggestive of a new town, housing thousands of commuter-families.

**El Sobrante** (unincorp.), a newer hillside town (east of I-80) is similar in function.

**Hercules** (17,000), once a tiny powder-company village, is essentially a "new town" of the 1980's. With an Anglo minority, it has become an "international" community with many commuters.

**Martinez** (27,000), seat of Contra Costa County, originated as a Gold era (in 1849) seaport. Its functions include oil refining, other manufacturing, services and commuter residence.

Its consequence as a seaport was nearly destroyed by silting (the result of hydraulic mining in the Sierra). There is now a breakwater, an aquatic park and a marina. For decades Martinez has been a railroad (Southern Pacific) bifurcation point (for the *Shasta* and *Valley* lines).

Much recent activity along the *I-680 Corridor* has taken place farther south. Martinez has not competed too successful against better-located, less-conservative cities. Since the 1960's more concern has been shown belatedly for planning and in-filling of vacant land. Older neighborhoods have the charm of yesteryear. Much residential and industrial activity has taken place in the southeast quadrant (near I-680 and Ca.4).

East of the I-680 Corridor (in Martinez) the east end of the Oil Coast provides a transition from the Bay Area to Delta Lands. Exclusive of Federal preserves, population traditionally was concentrated near the shore in Pittsburg and Antioch. Since reconstruction of Ca, 4 as a multi-lane route and with continued population growth in East Bay, sizable housing tracts have been built south of the freeway "wall."

**Pittsburg** (42,000) which experienced several transitions in the past, has become a "dual personality" residence town. For decades there was much reliance on an adjacent steel mill in county territory.

Columbia Steel (U.S.X.), with the largest mill in central California, imported cold pig iron from Utah and fabricated it into tin plate and structural steel. After experiencing the decline of the U.S. steel industry, it has been rebuilt as a joint Korean-U.S.X. operation. Other products nearby have included chemicals.

Initially *New York of the Pacific* (in 1849) Pittsburg was intended to become California's leading seaport. Later, as the center for low-grade coal mined on the north side of Mt. Diablo it became *Black Diamond*, and finally, Pittsburg. It was also a center for salmon fishing. It survived in the twentieth century as a residence place for steel workers.

**Figure 8-16.** The Oil Coast (right) and North Bay (left) on opposite sides of Carquinez Strait and Suisun Bay. (dwl)

**Figure 8-17.** Pittsburg seems to be on the "way back." These town houses are between Suisun Bay and the downtown area. (dwl)

The original townsite, north of Ca. 4, has changed considerably in recent decades. In the 1960's it appeared that Pittsburg was becoming a largely-black community. Downtown retail activity declined after opening of retail shopping centers in Antioch and Concord. By the 1980's there was a marina and adjacent townhouses. Downtown revival is being attempted by an Oakland firm.

South of Ca.4 an Anglo commuter community with new retail shops continues to expand towards Mt.Diablo. Many residents, who can no longer afford housing costs in Concord, commute to the B.A.R.T. terminal (in Concord). A community college (Los Medanos) is also here.

**West Pittsburg** (unincorp.) is expanding with less-expensive tract housing.

At the western edge of The Delta (Ch.9), **Antioch** (55,000) has been essentially an Anglo town and is regarded as the socially-preferred residence place of the eastern Oil Coast. There is diversified industry as well as generation of electric power.

Once a Gold Rush landing, Antioch lacks consequence as a seaport. In recent decades it has been favored as an industrial site due to abundant flat land, access to fuel, tidewater location and available water. Manufacturing has included paper, chemicals, furniture and machinery.

Downtown Antioch has declined since construction of a regional shopping mall (East County Center) south of Ca. 4.

Through annexation Antioch's area has more than doubled in the past several decades and continued growth is anticipated.

## INTERIOR EAST BAY*

Much of the East Bay lies within the northernmost Diablo Range. And between the Diablo Prong (east) and the Berkeley-Oakland Hills (west) are clustered a series of small intermontane basins. These form a Bay Area equivalent to the San Diego Back Country and suggest the southern San Fernando Valley and Hollywood Hills of the Los Angeles Basin in their utilization. But they are more moist and hence more verdant. Despite warmer summers (and colder winters) the summer fog of the Bay strand is lacking.

Like North Bay and the Santa Clara Valley these areas form some of the expanding urban complex of the Bay Area, especially since improvement of such routes as Interstates 580 and 680 and the opening of Caldecott Tunnel (on Ca. 24).

Previously, from the days of Mexican ranchos, farming (including orchards) constituted the principal land use.

Several foci seem apparent within Interior East Bay: the **Tri-Valleys** (Amador, Livermore and San Ramon), the **Walnut Creek Complex** and **Central County**. Much of the area of course is within the uplands of the Diablo Range.

### The Tri-Valleys

Improved access to the Bay strand (via I-580 and I-680) coupled with "fill-in" and costlier comparable housing "closer in" has encouraged urban growth, disappearance of peaceful pastoral land and the unwanted title of "smog capital of central California" to these valleys, actually a single lowland with an imperceptible divide. Complete urbanization appears probable.

### The Amador Valley

In the mid-twentieth century the Amador Valley was a rural land, known (if at all) for vineyards, cattle and grains and the Hearst Ranch. Dublin and Pleasanton were small villages.

In the 1960's **Pleasanton** (50,000) nearly quintupled in population. For some years it was two towns, the original community and the new town along the interstates. Functions have become more diversified.

The old downtown now features "boutiques"; in northwestern Pleasanton is a sizable shopping center (Stonegate), considerable housing for commuters, and a large industrial park (Diablo) with four multi-star hotels (near the junction of I-680 and 580). An earlier "growth acquisition" was a research institute (Kaiser).

In this once-quiet village, many residents abhor the changes. A long-established institution is the Alameda County Fair.

**Dublin** (20,000) in recent decades has been a "boom town". It has gained distributional facilities, corporate headquarters, a large central shopping center and many commuter residents.

Not incorporated until the 1980's, outside interests were enthusiastic about open land, good transport and lower taxes.

The original hamlet (1950 population 200) has vanished. Earlier tract housing tended to be inexpensive. Now costlier homes, especially on

---

*This section has been reviewed by Martin Mitchell, geographer/planner, Danville.

**Figure 8-18.** First Street, Livermore—a viable central district. (dwl)

**Figure 8-19.** Smoggy East Bay at sunset from Mt. Diablo. East of the Oakland-Berkeley Hills most residents of interior East Bay reside in the basins. The I-680 Corridor is obscured by smog across the middle of the photo. (dwl)

westside slopes, are occupied by upper-middle income residents.

*The Livermore Valley*

Farther east, the Livermore Valley retains more of its rural atmosphere than the Amador. Despite growth of Livermore, sprawl has been contained.

Viticulture has been important in the Valley for over a century.

Quality white (including Sauvignon and Semillon) and red (including Carignane and Zinfandel) varieties are grown. Wente, best known of the wineries, considered leaving the Valley in the 1960's because of worsening smog, then decided to stay.

Considerable growth in Livermore occurred after the establishment of two research laboratories at the start of the "atomic age."

Thousands are employed at vicinal *Lawrence Livermore Laboratory* (LLL), a branch of the University of California, and *Sandia Labs* (an affiliate of Western Electric). Both have conducted research for the Atomic Energy Commission and other agencies. Possibly this has been the world's largest center for atomic bomb research. LLL alone has a 640-acre secret preserve.

**Livermore** (56,000), because of the laboratories, grew earlier than other Tri-Valleys towns (its population doubled in the 1960's). Without the competition of a regional shopping center, its downtown area remained viable.

The influx of scientists essentially created a "new" liberal city, peopled by employees of the two laboratories. The former image of a northside (lower income Hispanic)-southside town was blurred; now many flights are conducted from the Livermore airport (general aircraft).

*The San Ramon Valley*

At the western base of Mt. Diablo, the San Ramon Valley, despite recent urban engulfment and location along The 680 Corridor, is regarded as a choice rustic lowland of interior East Bay. Population growth and automotive traffic have lessened somewhat its appeal. Size and cost of dwellings reflect the fact that this is an *upper-middle income* portion of the Bay Area.

Earlier this expanse of oak grove-grasslands and walnut groves *(relicts* remain) gained popularity for the "ranchettes" of the country club and riding horse "set."

**Danville** (30,000) which is essentially residential, retains a pleasant "downtown". On its eastern edge is little-known *Diablo* with its country club. To some of its long-established wealthy residents, occupants of nearby Blackhawk, widely advertised and possessing security gates, are regarded as "new rich showoffs."

**Alamo** (2,000), a residential outlier of Walnut Creek, is regarded as slightly more prestigious (housing is costlier) than Danville.

In recent years the most dramatic change in this Valley has occurred in **San Ramon** (30,000). It has become the major workplace of this attenuated depression. Population increased multi-fold in the 1980's as vacant space for new housing disappeared to the north and south, areas somewhat more accessible to employment west of the Oakland-Berkeley Hills.

Some years ago Western Electric planned a major industrial operation in the village and considerable area was zoned for commercial-industrial use, especially the Bishop Ranch. Open space has at-

**Figure 8-20.** Chevron office facility, I-680 Corridor, San Ramon. Thousands of white and pink-collar workers, formerly employed in downtown San Francisco, cannot afford to live in the Tri-Valleys and may commute from Manteca, Modesto or even the Foothills of the Sierra Nevada. (dwl)

tracted sizable office facilities of Chevron, Pacific Telesis and other corporations. Unfortunately many employees cannot afford the housing costs and much commuting takes place. It is estimated that eventually 50,000 will work in San Ramon but few workers will reside there.

### The Walnut Creek Complex *

The quasi-rural, affluent suburban lifestyles found in the Walnut Creek Complex are not too common in California.

The secluded valleys, hilly terrain and wooded slopes provide an inviting area. This setting has attracted well-to-do Bay Area executives and professional people, including growing numbers of affluent retirees despite some summer afternoon heat. Growth has lessened some of its appeal.

**Walnut Creek** (63,000), the retail and service center of the Complex, has an economically-favored location.

On the edge of Diablo Valley, it is located at the crossroads of I-680 and Ca. 24, with B.A.R.T.'s Concord line. Residentially it is somewhat less elite than neighboring communities to the west.

From the freeway the third dimension of its central district (there is no regional shopping center in the Complex) bespeaks a larger city. Suggestive of San Mateo or Beverly Hills, it appears to be a reversal of the trend away from downtown areas. Here one finds specialty shops, department stores, financial and professional offices and some corporate headquarters.

*Shell Ridge*, a spur of the Diablo Range, largely

zoned for open space, divides "newer" Walnut Creek (east) from the original townsite. There, older and smaller dwellings tend to sell for more than the larger, expensive development-homes east of the Ridge.

*Rossmoor* has been a successful "prototype" for an increasing number of California and (national) refuges for well-to-do "senior" citizens (i.e., over 45). Devoid of schools, it surrounds a golf course.

**Orinda** (22,000), considered to be one of East Bay's most socially-prestigious addresses, is nearly surrounded by three regional parks. It is the locale of John F. Kennedy University.

By choice unincorporated, there is "little" organized civic activity. Large lots with expensive (but not "showy") dwellings, lush vegetation and winding streets, provide a pleasant environment appealing to executives and their families.

**Lafayette** (23,000) has affluent-to-wealthy residents supportive of maintaining the "good life". There is a "village" retail core as well as minimum lot sizes.

Socially, some find a suggestion of Burlingame or perhaps Marin County here.

In a sunnier, less-wooded valley, **Moraga** (16,500) is another higher-income town. The site of a college, it still had "growing" room in the 1980's.

When St. Mary's College relocated here (from Oakland in 1928) the Moraga Valley was a land of orchards. Once a small men's college nationally-known for its football teams, St. Mary's is now co-educational (with more women than men).

---

* The term *Walnut Creek Complex* lacks local meaning. It is used here to identify Walnut Creek, Orinda, Lafayette and the Moraga Valley.

**Figure 8-21.** Downtown Walnut Creek. The Shuttle Bus connects central area with B.A.R.T.'s Concord line. (dwl)

## Central County (Diablo Valley)

Until the mid century Diablo Valley was a productive agricultural area with several serene hamlets. A generation later it had been overwhelmed by population expansion from Bayshore cities.

Suggestive of Fremont, **Concord** (110,000), largest city of interior East Bay, did not make the transition from farm town to major Bay Area city (now the largest in Contra Costa County) smoothly. It is conspicuously residential, despite some light industry and much retail trade. It is still gaining cohesion.

A visitor in the 1960's probably recognized the amorphous mass of less-expensive housing tracts with considerable leap-frogging. By the 1980's shrubs and trees had matured and much in-filling had taken place. Lately there has been a reduced rate of population growth.

An unique facility has been *Sun Valley*, acclaimed "the world's largest shopping center" at the time of its construction.* It now forms the west end of an attenuated central strip that includes a smaller shopping center and the *Plaza* (the renovated core of the former village), locale of an attractive civic center. Several high-rise structures (including a Bank of America records center) give a false center of an established downtown from a distance.

Now Concord spreads eastward (from Sun Valley, I-680 and the B.A.R.T. terminal, where adjacent parking is *impossible*.

Toward the east (in Clayton Valley) housing tends to be less expensive. Recently, in the 1980's, urbanization expanded into the politically-separate farm village of **Clayton** (4000).

*Ignacio Valley*, to the south and blending into Walnut Creek, is the locale of the costliest Concord housing. Residents include many Bayside commuters; there are many junior executives who now find cost of residence in the Walnut Creek Complex prohibitive.

To the northeast there are many modest dwellings (and much commutation to the Oil Coast). But a retail development adjacent to the airport has brought many changes. Unfortunately Concord now abuts against the Naval Weapons Depot whose frontage along Suisun Bay provides the chief West Coast shipping point for military ammunition.

With maturation, Concord has gained several amenities. There is a community park system with a pavillion (7000 seats) where the Summer Festival is held, and an east-side "green belt" at the base of Mt. Diablo.

**Figure 8-22.** The new and the old, downtown Walnut Creek. High-rise structures, viewed from I-680, may convince the stranger that Walnut Creek is a much larger city. (dwl)

**Pleasant Hill** (31,000) may be the "most representative" suburban town in interior East Bay. Despite some light manufacturing and Diablo Valley College it is principally residential.

Civic spirit is cohesive; a Youth Commission appears to have lessened the "generation gap". Recreational facilities include a contiguous regional park with golf courses.

Dramatic growth in the 1960's eliminated most of the vacant space. Subsequently there has been slight growth.

### THE SOUTH BAY **
### (Northern Santa Clara Valley) ***

Once called "the Valley of the Heart's Delight" and acclaimed the "fruit bowl of America", South Bay (northern Santa Clara Valley or Silicon Valley) has become the Golden State's fourth (and the nation's 30th) ranking *metropolitan statistical area* (M.S.A.) (Map 8-3). Its population exceeds 1.5 million; for many years annual growth exceeded 20,000. This is "middle-income America", with some variance—some view it as "Los Angeles devoid of the glitter."

---

* Although people from all parts of Contra Costa County shop here, there seems to be a reticence on the part of some residents of the Walnut Creek Complex to shop at Sun Valley. The social psychology of shopping habits can be interesting!

**This section has been reviewed by Richard Ellefson, San Jose State University.

*** Unfortunately terminology has blurred. Before 1960, the Santa Clara Valley was considered an *outlier*, not an integral part of the Bay Area. The terms *South Bay* and *northern Santa Clara Valley* are not exact synonyms. South Bay *probably* should include Palo Alto and Fremont.

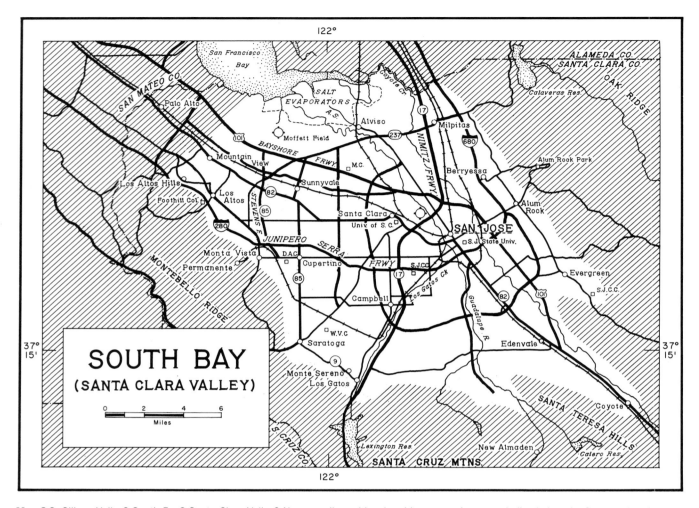

**Map 8-3.** Silicon Valley? South Bay? Santa Clara Valley? News media and local residents use the terms indiscriminately. One wonders how well the newsperson who refers to South San Francisco as "in South Bay" knows his local geography!

Santa Clara County now has 15 incorporated cities. A dozen exceed 25,000 while three are larger than 100,000 population.

About half a century ago the northern Santa Clara Valley contained two small cities, San Jose and Santa Clara, scattered farm villages, tranquil residence places at the base of the Santa Cruz Range and miles of orchards. Urbanization subsequently spread outward from San Jose as well as from once-outlying towns to create a coalescing conurbation.

While urbanization of the Santa Clara Valley was probably inevitable, the rapidity and disorderliness of growth was unfortunate.

Advance planning for orderly growth would have been desirable.

Some have criticized those scientists (and administrators) at Stanford University who created an electronics industry with federal support but with-out allowance near the plants to house thousands of lower-salaried employees.

Others have reproved the greed of those Valley developers who consistently opposed attempts to fashion some orderly growth.

Several factors have contributed to recent growth in the Santa Clara.

Included of course are the availability of jobs. The County has ranked third among California counties in median income. Also, for some years, relatively-inexpensive housing was available. South Bay is certainly accessible to many attractive portions of the Golden State. And the climate is a strong plus.

A myriad of problems has attended rapidity of population gain.

One for many years was the effect of "leapfrogging" tract construction. Despite a good street grid (now including freeways) there is much rush-hour congestion. Public transportation is inadequate (rapid transit has been considered). The Santa Clara Valley has acquired some of the worst smog conditions in central California. Schools have sometimes been crowded. The local water supply became inadequate. And both storm and sewage drains have been problems.

Some concern for the local economy developed in the 1980's.

For several decades the electronics industry had appeared to be "on top of the world." Competition from other parts of the United States (especially Texas and Massachusetts) and from other continents (especially eastern Asia) became serious. In some instances this represents an ability to undersell Silicon Valley. Hence widespread layoffs occurred and some firms ceased operation entirely. A sizable surplus of industrial space occurred. Now employment in service activities exceeds that in industry.

Ethnic diversity has increased; some of the same groups found elsewhere in the Bay Area are here.

This includes the largest Hispanic community—in part a legacy of the agricultural past. Asian groups have increased; the Valley now has the largest Vietnamese populace in central California. Italians are numerous and Irish, Portuguese and Scandinavians are well represented.

In contrast to Marin County and the northern Peninsula, but similar to the East Bay and North Bay, South Bay functions more or less independently of San Francisco, thus its separate designation as a M.S.A.

For example, less than a tenth of employed residents commute to employment outside the county while daily inflow of workers exceeds outflow.

Relative to its occupance, the Santa Clara Valley, income-wise (and in part ethnically), has four principal areas. These are: (1)the floor of the Santa Clara Valley (2)the East Side (3)the West Side and (4)the base of the Santa Cruz Mountains.

The Valley floor tends to consist of an endless number of less-costly tract houses, with three or four bedrooms, two baths, double garages, small lots and six-foot fences around backyards.

The East Side, especially the "close-in" southeast, contains many modest older houses.

West of the *older* Southern Pacific "commuter's line", the West Side also has many tract houses but properties tend to be larger and dwellings more costly. Large suburban shopping centers are found here.

In a "thermal belt" the Western Foothill Belt tends to have more luxuriant vegetation and afternoon shade. It has long appealed to newcomers from "the East." For decades it provided a delightful rustic center amidst orchards. Lots tend to be larger, houses custom-built and landscaping more imaginative.

Historic evolution accounts for partition into 15 politically-separate cities. Higher-income areas were unwilling to be identified as parts of San Jose.

This is a nationwide dilemma. More extreme "segregation" exists around many American central places. San Jose proper is more affluent (higher family incomes) than California overall.

## IN THE MIDDLE

The central portion of the Valley has always been the most populous part. The four largest cities, including San Jose and Santa Clara, are found here.

Dating from the founding of Mission Santa Clara and the original Spanish pueblo (San Jose) in 1777, Santa Clara and San Jose are among California's oldest European settlements. Initially separate, they were linked by The Alameda, a broad tree-lined segment of El Camino Real. The two communities coalesced long ago.

### San Jose and Environs

**San Jose** (760,000) ranks with Sacramento and Anaheim-Santa Ana as a newcomer among the principal metropolitan centers of the Golden State. It is still adjusting painfully, like the others, to such status.

When compared with San Diego, San Jose has less consequence in retail and wholesale trade, in multi-star hotels, in "four-star" restaurants, as a cultural center generally, in major league professional sports and in research.* San Jose does have a well-regarded state university.

With a population of less than 100,000 in 1950 San Jose was still a big "farm town."

Once, briefly, it was the capital of California and for decades has been a county seat. It experienced a short-lived land boom, like Los Angeles, but did not boom again for over 60 years. It developed

---

* The ownership of the San Francisco Giants, with foresight, might well have located in San Jose. It is ironic that in the final decades of the 20th century San Jose competes in professional baseball with Lodi and Visalia, and has no major league basketball and football teams although it is nation's 13th largest political city.

**Figure 8-23.** Downtown San Jose. This ancient picture does not reveal the third dimension of renovated central San Jose. (San Jose Chamber of Commerce).

gradually as a farm market town, processing center and local shipping point. Its functions suggested those of Fresno (Ch. 9); industrial activity was oriented toward agricultural productivity.

Over three decades of accelerated urbanization have seen the San Jose municipal limits spread the entire width of its Valley and southward from the Bay for more than 20 miles.

*Downtown* San Jose, despite the presence of San Jose State University, experienced rapid deterioration (1960's and 1970's) followed by impressive redevelopment.

City government was relocated in a civic center, a mile to the north. Many "housekeeping" activities have been moved to other places. A new library has been built (the old structure became The Art Museum). A convention center and several multistar hotels (including the 500-room Fairmount) have been erected. Within a few years central San Jose has changed markedly.

Downtown lost much of its retail function to such fringe developments such as Eastridge (with four department stores). Remaining shops tend to be supported by occupants of an old residential district with much blight—there are many senior citizens with modest means. A noticeable number of shops have Vietnamese-language signs. A residue of old (and small in size) Chinatown is now

inhabited by Japanese and other ethnic groups.

Conspicuous in the new downtown are high-rise structures containing banks, other financial institutions, professional and corporate offices. Construction of I-280 has increased vehicular flow along the south edge of the central district.

It is hoped that the light-rail route (southward) will encourage many downtown employees to ride to and from work.

*North* of the central area considerable industrial activity has developed.

Yet patches of truck gardens lingered into the 1980's. Triple-cropping was practiced but still could not "pay" the rent on corporate-owned land leased at "tax loss" prices until urbanization occurred.

*International Airport*, close-in, is the second-busiest commercial port in the Bay Area and is served by major airlines. It provides a focus for industry. In-state traffic is especially important. Much travel is related to Silicon Valley industrial activity.

The initial industrial belt, paralleling the Coast Line of the Southern Pacific, has remained the principal manufacturing district. For decades nationally-known "brand" foods (such as Del Monte, Pictsweet, Sunsweet and Libby McNeill) were processed here. Such items justified evolution of FMC (Food Machinery and Chemical), whose products long ago became much more diversified. There are many small plants, including subcontractors for the large aerospace and electronic firms of the Valley.

Long-stagnant Alviso was the early-day port for Mission Santa Clara. This Hispanic village was incorporated (reluctantly) into San Jose but re-establishment of a port seem improbable.

Beyond Coyote Creek the *East Side* includes files of modest tract houses (some deterioration has occurred) and suburban shopping centers.

Continued urbanization has filled in ephemeral farmlands.

With elevation upslope into the Mt. Hamilton Range, one finds more expensive custom-made dwellings. The small *San Jose Country Club* district is suggestive of the Western Foothills in lot size, residential value and landscaping. Its appeal is lessened by exposure to afternoon sun.

**Figure 8-24.** The old and the new, downtown San Jose. Much retail activity has been relocated in the shopping centers and "neighborhood" plazas. (dwl)

Much of the East Side has modest housing—this is not the preferred residential sector of the city. It reflects past flood problems, proximity to industry and paucity of orchards or wooded foothills. There are sizable Hispanic and Vietnamese populations.

The *Mt. Hamilton Range,* a segment of the Diablo-Mt. Hamilton Range that extends from Suisun Bay to The Knot (Ch. 7) generally lacks the residence found in interior East Bay.

East of the Santa Clara Valley the Mt. Hamilton Range is used for farming (apricot orchards), livestock ranching and the raising of grains.

*Lick Observatory* is found atop the summit of Mt. Hamilton (4261 feet), 13 miles east of San Jose. It constitutes one of the smallest campuses of the University of California. The observatory was the gift of a San Francisco philanthropist. The 3113-acre campus was selected because of atmospheric clarity (before the urbanization of Santa Clara Valley!). Its 36-inch equatorial refractor telescope is among the largest of its type, whereas the new 120-inch reflector telescope is second to Mt. Palomar's (Ch.6) in size.

*Alum Rock Park*, at the western base of the range, is a San Jose city park and with its chaparral setting is suggestive of Los Angeles' Griffith Park. Facilities include a mineral spring, a bathhouse and picnic spots.

*South and West* of central San Jose much expansion has taken place in the second half of this century. This is a socially-preferred portion of San Jose.

*Rose Garden*, close in, along with the mansions of *The Alameda* (now replaced by office buildings), has been considered a choice residential area, surrounding the city's renowned municipal rose garden. Here is found the campus of San Jose City College.

In-limits San Jose has no district of extreme wealth. But newer upper middle-income development has taken place southward ward, especially in *Willow Glen* and *Almaden Valley*, most recently against the Santa Cruz Range. Surrounding a country club, the latter area has provided the first destination for many nearly-arrived managerial personnel (who aspire to locate in the Western Foothills).

### The Neighbors

**Santa Clara** (90,000), with diverse functions, is an important industrial city.

Half a century ago, it was a small (6000) satellite of San Jose with seasonally-active packing houses

**Figure 8-25.** Eastridge Mall, east San Jose. This is one of a number of regional shopping centers in South Bay. (dwl)

and a small college —except politically, it remains a part of "greater" San Jose.

Significant changes have occurred in *Old Quad* (the core area, now "eastside" toward San Jose). In addition to a civic center and expansion of the University of Santa Clara (more professional schools and women students), multi-family housing (nearly a half of Santa Clarans reside in such structures) has been built. There is concern too for maintenance of "elder" neighborhoods.

Near the railroad tracks and the San Jose airport the northern half of Santa Clara is largely indus-

trial. The four largest employers are electronics firms and there are many smaller jobbers and subcontractors as well. It should be emphasized that Silicon Valley activity includes both *hardware* and *software*. More prestigious firms in Silicon Valley include IBM, Apple and Intel.

The rise of the 500-acre *Great America* amusement park and hotel and convention complex, now city-owned, has been a significant development. The city now has another convention center (6000 banquet capacity).

**Mountain View** (63,000), now an industrial, commuter bedroom (many apartments!) and retail trade community, has always differed in some ways from other South Bay cities.

Initially it was an early-day stage stop between San Francisco and San Jose. Then it was a canning and shipping point for truck gardens and orchards—population was expanded seasonally by migratory workers.

As a legacy of its farming past the city has the second largest number (after San Jose) of Hispanics in Silicon Valley; Asians are also increasing although Mountain View is still an Anglo majority city. About two-thirds of the residents are renters and many dwellings are absentee-owned. Concern exists about upkeep of inexpensive tract houses built in the 1950's. The modest central district

**Figure 8-26.** Sunnyvale missile plant. This 645-acre facility (center) has been one of the leading payroll-generators in central California. Moffett Field (left rear) and the south end of San Francisco Bay are visible. (Lockheed Corporation)

**Figure 8-27.** Almaden Valley country club. Exclusive of the western foothills (i.e., the Santa Cruz Mountains) the environs of the club has formed one of the "prestige" residential areas of the Santa Clara Valley. (dwl)

includes a sizable regional shopping center, adjacent to Palo Alto, built when there was vacant land—it also serves some residents of the northern West Side.

Growth in the latter half of the twentieth century has been as an industrial town; major electronics firms have included Fairchild and Raytheon.

In terms of value-added, **Sunnyvale** (118,000) is the ranking industrial center (aerospace) in Silicon Valley. There are also several federal activities.

Sunnyvale was a small truck farm and orchard community before the electronics boom. Its changing land use began when the Navy established Moffett Field as a dirigible installation; its activity presently relates to anti-submarine warfare. Other functions have been moved to Lemoore (Ch.9).

During the 1960's, after Lockheed established its missile facility at Sunnyvale (in 1957) the population of the the city doubled. Nearness to Menlo Park and Stanford, plus availability of "cheap" land, were considerations. The Lockheed plant, which has been Silicon Valley's single largest industrial employer, has had much impact.

Sunnyvale's economic base was expanded with establishment of N.A.S.A.'s *Ames Research Center* (concerned with interplanetary space probes, a *super wind tunnel*, major computers and high altitude aircraft). It is understandable that Sunnyvale has the highest median incomes of the five Valley-floor cities.

In the 1980's considerable former agricultural land was zoned for industrial and commercial use northeast of U.S.101 and west of N.A.S.A.. Thus

room for expansion exists.

In the contact zone between the Santa Clara Valley and East Bay **Milpitas** (46,000) is suggestive of a small Fremont.

Milpitas was a small Portuguese truck garden place before a Ford Motor assembly plant (now closed) was erected. Growth was so rapid a generation ago that it was necessary to declare a moratorium until educational and sewage facilities could be constructed.

Like Fremont Milpitas suggests a "new town". Empty space in its core has become a civic center and the Town Center (i.e., with regional shopping facilities). Although much space has been zoned for industry, there is considerable commutation to Silicon Valley electronic plants. Residentially, Milpitas tends to be an upper middle-income town.

## THE WEST SIDE

The West Side formed the heart of the Santa Clara Valley's renowned fruit orchards (apples, apricots, pears and prunes) in the "days of old."

There was no town larger than 2000 inhabitants in 1930. It was an area of small rural acreages, and in springtime many Bay Area urban residents drove out to enjoy the vernal beauty.

The contemporary urbanized landscape is largely residential. Dwellings tend to be somewhat more expensive than those of the Valley floor.

This is "white-collar country." Custom houses are more common (tract houses less so), properties somewhat larger and landscaping more imaginative. Sufficient fruit trees have been kept to provide a wooded appearance.

Economically **Cupertino** (40,000) is the least typical community. Its economy is more diversified, with considerable retail trade and industrial plants.

In pre-electronics days Cupertino was a farm hamlet in the orchards. Construction of the world's largest cement plant in the Santa Cruz Mountains on its western edge (initially to provide cement for construction of Shasta Dam (Ch. 11) in 1940 initiated its transition.

More recently it has acquired *Valco* industrial park, (with a large Hewlett-Packard plant), the headquarters for Apple and a regional shopping center and De Anza College.

Separated from Cupertino by the western outskirts of San Jose, **Campbell** (35,000) was another canning town. It was almost "lost" in the maelstrom of

**Figure 8-28.** De Anza College in Cupertino. This is a portion of the wooded west side of the Santa Clara Valley. (dwl).

its larger neighbor before it acquired a distinctive new center.

With a population of 1800, Campbell described itself in the 1930's as the "Orchard City"and bragged of its fruit drying plants and its three canneries. With urbanization Campbell changed from farm satellite to suburb to "neighborhood" of San Jose in the late 1950's. A decade later it acquired a downtown central office-tower-shopping complex mall, *The Prune Yard.*

An upper middle-income residential town of long standing, **Los Altos** (28,000) is much wooded. It successfully imparts a feeling of genteel rustic tranquility.

In the past it housed a managerial group which once commuted to San Francisco on the Southern Pacific. Now it is the residence of many scientists, engineers and others who commute by auto to nearby offices and plants.

## THE WESTERN SLOPES

South Bay's counterpart of more prestigious portions of Marin County and The Peninsula, snuggled into the sometimes-steep eastern slopes of the Santa Cruz Mountains, this area is known locally as the "Western Foothills."

From the picture windows of many rambling homes the oft-smoggy daytime skies and nocturnal lights of San Jose and environs are visible. Many dwellings are secluded within lush oak woodlands. Socially, this is *the* area of South Bay.

**Los Gatos** (29,000) has been a popular residence

place for several generations. Hence it is known more for pleasant living than for its social status.

It also provides a travelers' waystop on Ca. 17 (the semi-freeway between Santa Cruz and the Bay Area).

A portion of downtown Los Gatos has been revived as "Old Town." The "nostalgia kick" makes this area, with its antique shops, popular with weekend shoppers. It also has had a well-known winery (Novitiate of Los Gatos).

While it too had fruit packing houses, the sylvan setting of Los Gatos attracted literary figures. Thus older neighborhoods around the downtown area never deteriorated although there are many older cottages.

**Monte Sereno** (circa 5000) has been one of California's lesser-known refuges of the affluent.

Thousands pass through the town enroute to and from Big Basin Park, oblivious of this wealthy place. The homes of many long-rich Bay Area residents are secluded among the oak woodlands. Of late, however, it has become a bit less sheltered.

Widely regarded as the most socially-prestigious community in the Santa Clara Valley, **Saratoga** (30,000) has long been known for its winery and as an attractive wooded, large-lot city.*

Founded in 1850 Saratoga in early days had prominence both for its mineral springs and as a gateway to Big Basin redwoods. J.D. Phelan, a San Francisco politician, built his mansion *Villa Mon-*

---

* Local planners and others appear to rate the Western Slopes towns, in terms of socioeconomic status, thusly: Monte Sereno, Saratoga, Los Altos Hills, Los Gatos, Los Altos and Cupertino.

**Figure 8-29.** Long-secluded Monte Sereno has been discovered! A number of new houses have been built. (dwl)

*talvo* (now owned by San Francisco Art Association) here.

Many prominent Bay Area business and professional men have homes here. It is a haven for affluent retirees and for the newly-wealthy with social aspirations. In its picturesque central district, *The Village*, are interesting shops. It is the site of West Valley College and Paul Masson Winery.

**Los Altos Hills** (8000), upslope from Los Altos, was incorporated to prevent its inclusion into its less-wealthy sister city.

The western portion should probably be considered exurban. Located here, despite strong local objections, is Foothill College, esteemed for its attractive campus and the quality of its two-year programs.

---

## THE PENINSULA *

Question: "When is a peninsula not a peninsula?" Answer: "Obviously when it is *The Peninsula*." **

Most residents of the Bay Area do not regard San Francisco as part of The Peninsula, nor do they really include most of the Santa Cruz Mountains and the Pacific shore.

The Peninsula, as identified here, tends to have its western edge along I-280. It extends along the entire east side of the peninsula, from Palo Alto to South San Francisco.

For more than a century The Peninsula has had several meanings.

It has been associated with millionaires' estates and with San Francisco executives commuting to comfortable suburban homes. The Peninsula has provided a West Coast counterpart of New York's Westchester County. To these long-time images one now needs to add miles of housing tracts, diversified industry and traffic whir along *Bayshore Freeway* (U.S 101),successor to *El Camino Real* (now Ca. 82) as the ranking north-south artery.

In the second half of the twentieth century its most important physical attribute, in terms of population growth, has been location contiguous to San Francisco, affording space for urban expansion.

The appeal of The Peninsula includes climatic mildness, the backdrop of the Santa Cruz Mountains and the bluish waters of the Bay. The area approaches the mildness of San Francisco without much summer fog.

## RANCHEROS, LOGGERS AND COMMUTERS

Peninsula occupance has not duplicated the typical pattern of either the Bay Area or the Central Coast.

While there were no missions between Dolores and Santa Clara Bayshore grasslands provided pasturage for mission cattle. As elsewhere along the Central Coast the land was apportioned into ranchos, beginning with Rancho de las Pulgas, awarded to Jose Arguello in 1795.

In the eastern Santa Cruz Mountains redwood forests were cut during San Francisco's early years.

Mills were built at Searsville (now covered by a lake) and Woodside in 1850 and hauled by oxen or mule to The Embarcadero de las Pulgas, afterward renamed Redwood City.

Commuting to the City was established after the San Francisco and San Jose Railroad (now the Santa Fe Southern's Coast Line) inaugurated service through this area in 1864.

Accordingly much of The Peninsula never experienced the farming sequence that characterized evolution of many portions of the Golden State in post-colonial days.

Most Peninsular communities began after arrival of the railroad, as Menlo Park and San Mateo, or were founded previously, as Redwood City and Menlo Park. San Bruno and Belmont had their start with early inns dating from stagecoach days.

Establishment of estates of San Francisco tycoons began as early as the 1860's.

Among the first was banker William C. Ralston; his Belmont estate was a showplace of central California in the early 1860's. Other prominent business executives located here as well. Leland Stanford established his country estate on the present site of Stanford University in 1876 while most of the others settled there shortly after railroad service began.

Burlingame had gained a reputation as one of the early centers of country-club life in western America by the 1890's. Hillsborough, southwest of Burl-

---

*This section has been reviewed by Richard Ellefson, San Jose State University.
** The *accepted* name is merely "The Peninsula" although some term it "The San Francisco Peninsula" while others refer to it as "The San Mateo Peninsula" or "The Santa Cruz Peninsula."

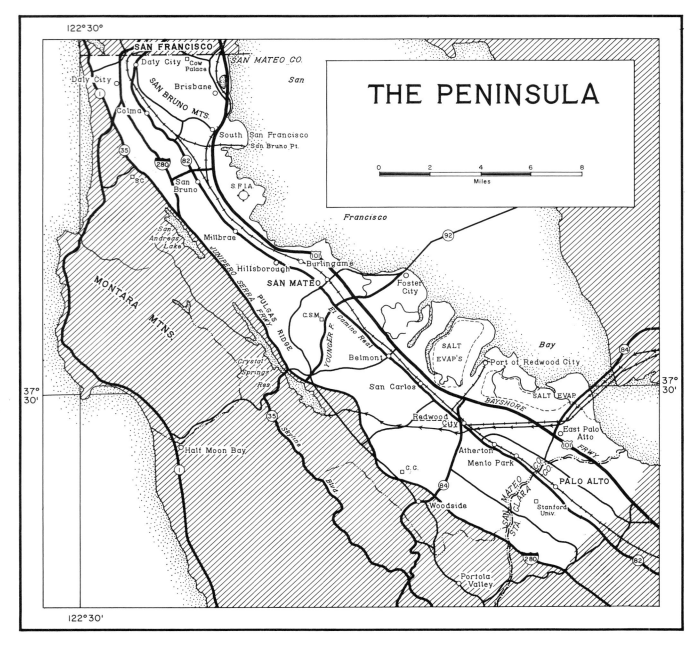

**Map 8-4.** The Peninsula is not a Peninsula! As commonly identified, it excludes San Francisco and the Montara Mountains, a segment of the Santa Cruz Mountains whose western side has a fogbelt cli mate. And it includes Palo Alto, which is within the Santa Clara Valley.

ingame, became the "exclusive" place on The Peninsula after 1912.

Prior to 1980 few counties in the Golden State rivaled the growth rate of San Mateo County in the twentieth century.

It started with the earthquake of 1906, which precipitated a mass migration of middle-income San Franciscans to The Peninsula. Now little space remains for additional growth.

Tract developments replaced fields of vegetables

and flowers between 1950 and 1970. On small acreages cut flowers and nursery stock persisted longer.

There are approximately 800 industrial establishments in the County, employing about 33,000 persons.

The Peninsula remains an area typified by incomes well above the state average. Many residents have had advanced academic training and definite cultural interests.

Through motorists, even in the days before the Bayshore Freeway , between Los Angeles and San Francisco were so likely to be frustrated by a succession of stoplights that they would miss much of the beauty of Peninsula towns. Today's motorist, speeding along multiple lanes, gains still less of an impression.

But here are some of the Golden State's lovely garden suburbs, now mostly molded into a mosaic of urban continuity.

More expensive homes are found at elevations into the Santa Cruz Mountains.

Residents of these communities long tended to look askance at industry. But population spiral and resulting governmental costs have recommended compromise.

Zoning has permitted construction of dozens of light industrial plants, such as publishing houses and electronics plants—organizations that employ well-educated, skilled personnel. Much of the manufacturing is east of U.S 101 near the Bay.

## THE PALO ALTO COMPLEX

Almost a synonym for Stanford University, **Palo Alto** (57,000) has constituted one of America's most attractive cities since its inception. Its solid economic bases include cultural activities, finance, retail trade, residence and industry.

This wealthy center of education is The Peninsula's focal point in art, drama and music. Like its neighbors to the north, Palo Alto is a place of well-maintained homes and gardens —obviously this is not "middle" America.*

Stanford University is not within the city limits (but in county territory) (Fig. 8-30). It was established on Leland Stanford's Farm (livestock ranch) in 1887. Despite its prestige (it is often called the "Harvard of the West") its enrollment (circa 12,500) is lower than many California colleges. It is recognized in such fields as business, engineering and medicine and renowned for its quality undergraduate and graduate programs.

Palo Alto, due to Stanford research and land (Stanford Industrial Park) plus military requests that began with World War II), has become the leading industrial city of The Peninsula. The University has been able to select its tenants and require attractively-landscaped facilities.

Thus this portion of The Peninsula has become one of the nation's primary centers of scientific research. Products include electronics (such as Hewlett-Packard and Varian), plastics , communications equipment and processed film. Much of the Silicon Valley high-tech complex southward from Palo Alto reflects activity at Stanford.

Palo Alto is the ranking financial and retail center of the southern Peninsula. There is a regional shopping center (on Stanford land) as well as a

---

*Politically, Palo Alto is in Santa Clara County, *not* San Mateo County.

**Figure 8-30.** This is "The Farm", Stanford University's 6000 acres. Landmark in the center is the University's Hoover Library tower, with the Inner Quadrangle to the left. The Farm includes a regional shopping center as well as land leased for industrial use. (Stanford University photo by Lloyd Provan).

**Figure 8-31.** Factory on The Farm ressembles a college building. Such structures, handsomely landscaped, blend with Stanford University campus.(dwl)

revitalized central district. There is a multi-story financial center (also on Stanford land).

Citizenry of Palo Alto top the Golden State in years of formal education (i.e., the median). There is understandable concern in such a city for trees, libraries, children's activities and parks (including open space in the Santa Cruz Mountains and along the Bayshore). The setting, cultural and physical, attracts increasing numbers of professional retirees.

With extensive city "open space" in the foothills population density is low. Also Stanford University retains 5000 undeveloped acres.

Essentially residential, **East Palo Alto** (19,000) would be a moderately-attractive community in many parts of America. But amidst the affluence of nearby cities, it is depressed. It has The Peninsula's largest black populace (and an increasing number of Hispanics).

Older than its sibling, East Palo Alto gained many of its blacks after 1940. Initially many were employed at two nearby Veterans Administration hospitals. Its residents are striving to upgrade their town; yet there are socioeconomic problems and incomes tend to be low.

**Menlo Park** (29,000) is one of the Golden State's most felicitous blendings of residence, employment and retail trade. This reflects its proximity to the Stanford campus (Fig. 8-32 and 8-33). Two-fifths of its employed residents are classified as "professional-managerial". The city has long been a leader among California communities in effective urban planning.

The central district, with quality specialty shops, remains viable despite proximity to a Palo Alto shopping center. Given the total circumstances it is understandable that Menlo Park has quality schools, an attractively landscaped civic center and some of California's higher median-price dwellings.

Its "industrial" establishments represent the types that most cities yearn for. Located in industrial parks are such "clean" industries as SRI (Stanford Research Institute), Lane Publishing,

**Figure 8-32.** Menlo Park and south San Francisco Bay. Segment of Stanford University campus and downtown Palo Alto (middle right). (San Mateo County Development Association, photo by Air-Photo Service of Palo Alto)

Shell Oil (data processing), Winthrop Laboratories (missile components), U.S. Geological Survey, pharmaceutical firms and others, as well as regional corporate offices.

Despite absence of Bay views, **Atherton** (8000) is a high-income community suggestive of Hillsborough.

Like Hillsborough it lacks a retail district and industrial installations. Atherton is known for its attractive mansions and well-appointed estates. It was incorporated in the 1920's to avert annexation into Menlo Park. Set in an oak woodland it has "fenced out" its neighbors with ivy, oleander and wood. There is a private college.

**Figure 8-34.** "Representative" street scene in Atherton. Note absence of curbs and sidewalks. (dwl)

## AN ODD COUPLE

Different from most other Peninsula cities, and certainly from each other, are neighboring Redwood City and San Carlos.

Disparities include functions, area, population and ethnic composition.

Both the oldest and least-typical larger city of The Peninsula, **Redwood City** (60,000) is the seat of county government. Other functions include industry, retail trade, sea commerce, recreation and residence.

Relative to Peninsular averages, incomes have tended to be lower, former education slightly briefer, commutation less frequent and social status inferior. Yet Bayshore frontage is more extensive.

An early-day site of redwood mills at the Bay-mouth of a creek, Redwood City failed to attract

**Figure 8-33.** Civic center in Menlo Park, one of the best- planned cities in the Golden State. (dwl)

San Francisco "elite." Although its port has a 30-foot channel, sea commerce is modest (although imports from the Pacific Basin have increased). There is an industrial park (and space for expansion). Redwood City's industrial output has included paper, packaging machines, foods and tape recorders.

An ongoing attempt has been made to revitalize the central district. Surrounded by modest dwellings of lower-income Anglos and Hispanics, it has been shunned by affluent residents of surrounding communities (with an apparent preference for San Mateo and Palo Alto). As in other Peninsula cities, dwellings become more expensive upslope.

Bay frontage east of San Carlos and Belmont was acquired by expansion-driven Redwood City, in part because Leslie Salt did not want its property divided between two cities. The former location of Marine World has become Centrum, a business-professional high-rise complex. On its eastern edge Leslie Salt was forced to scale down (from 60,000 to 15,000 residents) *Redwood Shores* and construct stronger earthquake-prone structures.*

**San Carlos** (27,000) is an upper middle-income Anglo community with electronics firms and a busy Peninsular general aircraft port. Many residential lots are small yet values are high.

The city tends to be "self-contained"—there is considerable community pride. Even older cottages are attractively landscaped and well-maintained. Loyalty to local shops in the trim C.B.D. is apparent. Around a third of the residents are

---

*Some geographers, geologists and others are not convinced that Bayfill developments like Bay Farm (Alameda ), Redwood Shores and Foster City will fare too well with the *next* "1906" earthquake.

**Figure 8-35.** The former locale of Marine World (re-opened in Vallejo in 1986). Considered too valuable for an amusement park, this land is now a partially- completed office complex. (dwl)

"local" retirees, many of whom formerly commuted to work in San Francisco.

San Carlos has had long-established commuter ties with The City. In the 1920's San Franciscans bought small "cheap" lots only to learn the "free-lot racket" included sizable sums for "improvement."

With evolution of the electronics industry San Carlos benefitted from proximity to S.R.I. Thus wage earner residents include many engineers and other well-paid industrial employees.

## THE SAN MATEO COMPLEX

Despite much growth (prior to 1980) in the second half of the twentieth century the San Mateo Complex remains a particularly-attractive portion of the Golden State.

While many residents have higher incomes, there are still lower income people and a considerable range of housing costs.

**Belmont** (25,000) is more of a hillside residential place than other cities on The Peninsula.

No other community has such a small percentage of buildable land. It was named after the estate of San Francisco banker W.C. Ralston—a remnant of his holding (including his mansion) has become the College of Notre Dame campus. Late incorporation was effected in order to prevent absorption by San Carlos. The citizenry elected not to include flat Bayshore agricultural land thus negating space for industry.

Besides its diminutive central district Belmont houses offices of several textbook firms. Since

construction of I-280 an increased number of residents commute to work in San Francisco.

A one-time garden suburb of San Francisco, **San Mateo** (84,000) has become a *mini-metropolis*, the multi-functional hub of a complex of almost 200,000 people. Yet industrial activity tends to be limited.

The county's retail leader, San Mateo is located at the west end of a trans-Bay crossing (Ca.92) which leads to the coast.

The central district has expanded with increasing numbers of fringe high-rise apartments (housing a growing number of wealthy local retirees). It has gained importance as a medical center (with a high-rise physicians' office condominium) and for other professions. It has gained as a focal point in finance, for regional offices and corporate headquarters. South of the core *Hillsdale* is one of the more prestigious Bay Area regional shopping centers. The city has attracted an increased number of state and regional conventions.

For its size San Mateo has socioeconomic complexity.

Local planners identify about 30 neighborhoods. Central and northeastern districts tend to be occupied by blacks ( traditionally many were employed as servants of the wealthy or at the local race track) and Asians.

Modest eastside tracts, constructed on then-inexpensive former marshlands, contrast with the high-rise apartments in the central district and the hillside mansions of East Bay and San Francisco executives in the west. While its population density ranks second to Daly City in San Mateo

**Figure 8-36.** Senior citizens' center, San Carlos. Many San Franciscans retire to this pleasant city. This lady commented, "How lucky we seniors *and* young people too are to live here." (dwl)

County, it is still an attractive community with many trees and well-maintained gardens.

San Mateo is proud of its various attractions, which include a yacht harbor and Bayshore golf course, a small-craft airport, College of San Mateo, with a spectacular hilltop campus and its Japanese gardens.

More residential (and less commercial than San Mateo), socially-prestigious **Burlingame** (28,000) nevertheless has a central district with quality shops.

The community evolved around the first country club in western United States. Polo was played there in its early years. Seemingly "out-of-character," Burlingame garnered in all available contiguous acreage.

While median house values are high, incomes in Burglingame do not average as high as some on The Peninsula. This reflects the considerable retiree populace residing around the central district. Among Burlingame's employed, two-thirds commute to San Francisco. Many are higher echelon governmental employees or executives.

The Bay Area's first preplanned "new town", **Foster City** (30,000) has about "reached" its "fill-out" capacity within 20 years. Primarily residential, it is a community of upper middle-income commuters.

One gains the impression that every house in this Bayfill city has aquatic access, creating a Peninsular Naples (Ch. 6). In contrast with San Mateo, functions are limited although there are retail shops and several hotels.

Set in a lush oak woodland, **Hillsborough** (11,000) is the wealthiest (per capita) incorporated municipality in California. With its superlative views

Figure 8-37. A marina-oriented "new town", Foster City, on Bayfill adjacent to San Mateo, is now about "built out." (dwl)

Figure 8-38. Despite growth, San Mateo remains an attractive place to live and work. (dwl)

of San Francisco Bay, this is strictly a residential place.

A bit similar to Bel Air (Ch.6), but less ostentatious, Hillsborough began with estates of the wealthy. It was incorporated in 1910 to prevent annexation by Burlingame or San Mateo. A third of its area remains open space and the rural setting is maintained with care.

Organized social activity focuses on its country club. Retail stores, factories, even churches, sidewalks and streetlights are absent. There is not even a high school!

A proud, pleasant residential town, **Millbrae** (21,000), houses many "middle" executives and professional people.

"Boxed in" by its neighbors and limited in size (3.2 square miles), Millbrae is destined to remain a small city. The town developed on the estate (source of its name) of financier D.O. Mills.

Climatic mildness (the "first city south of the fog") and proximity to The City attracted a few Italians who formed the nucleus of a colony. Near the San Francisco airport and known for the quality of its schools, its housing prices are inflated. A considerable portion of Millbrae forms a "hillside town."

## NORTHERN PERIPHERY

Geographically San Francisco could make a strong case for inclusion of the northern periphery. Most certainly it is an atypical portion of San Mateo County.

Increasingly, **South San Francisco** (52,000) is a balanced residential-industrial city. It ranks second

**Figure 8-39.** College of San Mateo occupies a hill-top campus which provides attractive vistas of The Peninsula and the Bay. But its site gets a bit wet and windy during wintry storms. (dwl)

to Palo Alto on The Peninsula in value of manufactural output—nearly half of its total area is zoned for industrial use.

Nineteenth century drawing rooms, antecedent for most Peninsula cities, were lacking in "South City." This was the locale of part of the original "home ranch" of Miller and Lux (see Ch. 9) and was planned as an industrial city by a meat packer around 1900. A number of its present-day residents are descendants of Italian and Portuguese "slaughterhouse slaves." During World War II it was an important place for shipbuilding.

The city has changed considerably in recent decades. The shipyards, steel fabricating plants and meat packing plants are gone—in their places are attractive industrial parks with hundreds of factories and a produce terminal for San Francisco. Among the transitions have been *Westborough*, a planned westside housing development. There is now a waterfront marina, a yacht club and a golf course, as well as hotels.

South City provides a good location for warehousing and manufacturing; it has access to rail, freeway and air facilities. Meat, from the Central Valley or even the Corn Belt of the Middle West is packaged here. Other products have included chemicals, machinery, paints, candy, clothing, plastics and fabricated steel. Recently, pharmaceuticals and biotech (Genentech is here) have been added.

South City is unique in several respects. Its tax rate is one of the lowest in the Bay Area and there is limited municipal debt. While the large trees typical in Peninsula cities are lacking (even though many streets are named for trees!), homes tend to be trim and residents work in San Francisco. This is *middle* America—higher and lower incomes tend to be limited.

**San Bruno** (35,000) is essentially a bedroom community for thousands employed at the San Francisco airport or in South City. Retail trade has local importance.

The city differs from most cities in San Mateo County in that its residents work near their homes—there is little distant commuting. San Bruno is a community of modest, well-maintained dwellings on small lots. Its downtown has been hurt by a "typically" middle-income regional shopping center on the site of a former racetrack (Tanforan). The number of "local" retirees has increased while industrial output is modest.

California's second (and the world's eighth) ranking commercial field, *San Francisco International Airport* is in county territory adjacent to San Bruno and South San Francisco. Its existence on Bayfill in San Mateo County continues to be controversial.

Even in 1927, when it was established as a municipal port, there was not sufficient space within San Francisco. It has been repeatedly expanded; a second terminal was added in 1953 and runways realigned. The parking garage is often filled. Considerable expansion was necessary with the doubling of traffic during the 1980's. Already the port handles hundreds of thousands flights annually.

Many county residents have opposed expansion despite the payrolls (the work force at the airport or adjacent industrial plants, hotels, motels and restaurants exceeds the entire population of adja-

**Figure 8-40.** Serramonte Center, Daly City, is on the trace of the San Andreas fault. (dwl)

cent Millbrae!) and tax revenues. Objections include noise, air pollution, problems of sewage and solid waste. Expansion of B.A.R.T. to the airport (from Daly City) has been much debated.

**Brisbane** (3000), a tranquil hillside residential place, is adjacent to U.S. 101, San Francisco, South City and Daly City.

It is exclusively a bedroom community but there is a regional shopping center in adjacent county territory.

**Colma** (800) could long fittingly have been called the "city of the dead." It has 13 cemeteries for space-short San Francisco. Costs of its city government are provided by sales taxes on monuments, floral arrangements and from a small shopping center (the town *has changed).* There are still fresh-market flower farms.

*San Bruno Mountain,* which effectively "separates" much of San Francisco from The Peninsula, was the basis of argument over housing versus open space.

The issue was finally resolved in the 1980's after years of dispute. Much of it will remain an "open-space" state park while the fringes will become residential.

A residential continuation of San Francisco within San Mateo County, **Daly City** (83,000) is a "double" city—it has considerable retail trade as well as commuter residence.

"D.C." is unique within its county, for like San Francisco, it extends from the Pacific across the *entire* peninsula.

The city began when scores fled there from San Francisco in 1906—its location is ironic, since it is bisected by the San Andreas fault!* In its earlier decades it was known as a "sporting town" with casinos and bars, greyhound races and championship boxing matches

East of El Camino Real (Ca. 82) *Old* (central) "D.C." represents an extension of the Mission District (of San Francisco). It has town houses, narrow lots and a sizable number of blacks, Hispanics, and Italians.

*Westlake,* "newer" westside Daly City, evolved at mid-century when several thousand middle-income homes were constructed as an extension of *southwestern* San Francisco. Westlake subsequently was acclaimed one of the nation's best suburbs by a national magazine which cited its attractive homes, its state beach park and its commuter access to nearby B.A.R.T.    Farther south is *Serramonte,* a more recent development

with a regional shopping center.

The state-owned *Cow Palace,* in eastern D.C., is the site of large conventions, sporting events (including livestock) and shows.

---

## SAN FRANCISCO **

Few cities in the world can match the superlative setting of **San Francisco** (750,000). It has been acclaimed *Baghdad-by-the-Bay.*

In the past fortunate visitors would sail out of an offshore fogbank through the Golden Gate on a sunny day. Today's newcomer is thrilled to drive across one of the Bay bridges or descend by aircraft under clear skies.

The visitor (and resident alike) delight in the beauty of the Bay, the light hues of this "layered city", Yerba Buena and Treasure Island, Alcatraz, the downtown skyscrapers, the Ferry Building, Coit Tower, the Marina, the Presidio, and the oak, redwood and grass-covered "far hills" of The East Bay, The Peninsula and Marin County.

Near the midpoint of the west coast of conterminous United States, San Francisco has a location that favors the Pacific Rim connection.

But the immediate setting of the city itself creates transportation problems; it lies at the northern tip of a narrow, hilly peninsula (the "end" of the Santa Cruz Range), surrounded by water on three sides.

### "The City"

San Francisco continues to be the cultural and economic capital of central and northern California.

It shares status with Los Angeles as a financial core of western America—and with a considerable portion of the Pacific Basin as well.

San Francisco never really had a childhood—it was almost born a city.

The Gold Rush forced that role upon it within months so that San Francisco missed the normal evolution of most cities. From Atascadero to Yreka and eastward into Nevada, when one states "I am going to The City," San Francisco is still implied.

This is truly a municipality in the classic Occidental *(and* Oriental) tradition.

---

* Older dwellings especially may not be able to withstand the "next 1906."

** Jean Vance and Max Kirkeberg, both San Francsico State University, reviewed this section for an earlier edition. Prof. Kirkeberg has reviewed it again.

It is complex, mature, densely populated, a bit decrepit in places, "extreme" in its human accomplishments and its vices —and there is a definite downtown orientation. For its small area, San Francisco is indeed a paradox.

In contrast with San Diego or Los Angeles, population density is much higher per square mile.

San Francisco is a vertical city inhabited by apartment and flat dwellers. Probably no other American city so connotes Boston culturally. Yet the waterfront and the Bay bridges are suggestive of Manhattan. Twin Peaks or Coit Tower provide a bit of the spirit of the observation tower atop the Empire State Building.

The vehicular traffic of San Francisco resembles Manhattan too.

The *CalTrain*-operated commuter trains "down" the Peninsula on the Santa Fe Southern's Coast Line can be compared with the Long Island Railroad. The Bay Area Rapid Transit system suggests the subways and the tunnels that link Manhattan to its satellites.

### The Hills, the Bay, the Pacific

San Francisco rises upon the northern tip of the Santa Cruz Range on the northern tip of the wooded peninsula that separates the Pacific Ocean from the Bay—half of its terrain is undulating rather than hilly.

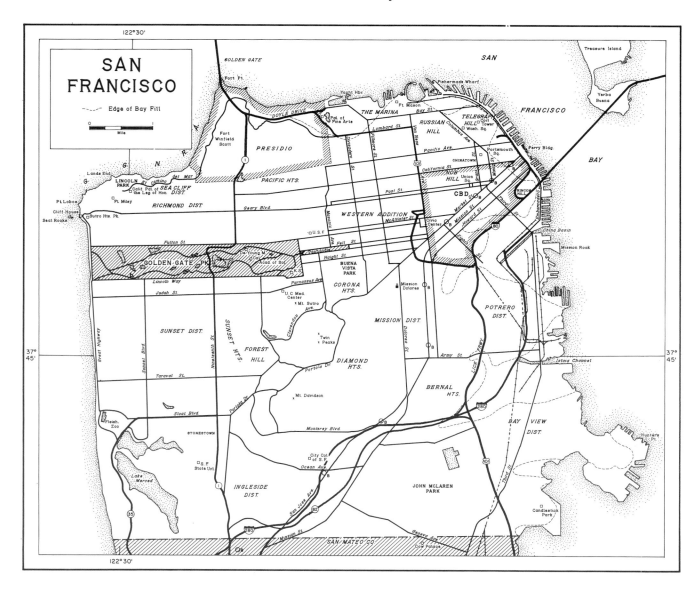

**Map 8-5.** San Francisco occupies the extreme northern fringe of the Santa Cruz Mountains. Within its 50 square miles are more than 40 hills.

**Figure 8-41.** The skyline of San Francisco. (dwl)

The hills consist of red cherts, sandstones and shales of the *Franciscan* series (Jurassic) while the flat lands are underlain by Quaternary deposits. *Mt. Davidson* forms the high point, at 929 feet.

The Bay strand, naturally-indented, has been straightened by fill projects for over a century. The Pacific shore is almost ruler-straight.

San Francisco's maritime surroundings provide the city with an equable climate (July average 58 degree F., seasonal range 12 degrees F.).

Winds become more northerly when the Hawaiian High shifts northward in summer but low pressure inland pulls in moist ocean air. Flowing across the California Current and areas of upwelling of colder water from ocean depths, this air produces the characteristic fog for which San Francisco is renowned.

The warmest (and least foggy) month is September rather than July or August. Some consider the foggy coolness invigorating but many prefer the milder weather of the Mission District (east central San Francisco), The Peninsula or The East Bay. San Francisco is one American city where a down jacket (or even a fur coat) may not be uncomfortable on an August evening.

## Sea Captains and Financiers

It is geographically understandable that the Spanish and English sea captains who visited coastal California in the sixteenth century failed to discover San Francisco Bay.

The offshore fog and the Angel Island "screen" effectively hide the Golden Gate.

Members of the Portola expedition who "discovered" the Bay in 1769 did so from the land. In the following years lackadaisical explorations around the Bay failed to reveal any stellar settlement sites.

Nevertheless, at the insistence of Father Serra, a mission site was chosen and in 1776 the Presidio

**Figure 8-42.** San Francisco occupies a peninsular fingertip between the Pacific Ocean and one of the world's great natural harbors. The city is linked to central California by the Golden Gate Bridge, upper left, and the Bay Bridge, lower right. Marin County's Richardson Bay is visible beyond Alcatraz and Angel Islands, upper right. (San Francisco Convention and Visitors Bureau)

was established at Fort Point and Mission San Francisco de Asis (Dolores) was placed on the east side of the peninsula, then near the Bay shore.

The Spanish colony on San Francisco Bay never became large.

The water supply was undependable, there were few Indians and the environment somewhat unsatisfactory for agriculture. The garrison at the Presidio was always modest; regular troops were no longer stationed there after 1835.

Present-day San Francisco originated elsewhere, with the Mexicans in 1835 at the tiny port village of Yerba Buena, on a cove of that name, following secularization of Mission Dolores.

The Bay can be tricky, with its winds, currents and tidal flow. Hence early seafarers desired a landfall near the Golden Gate.

The earliest buildings were erected at the approximate site of contemporary *Portsmouth Square*. As late as 1846 it was a *mere* village of 500 inhabitants. Although a pueblo was never officially established the U.S. Circuit Court nevertheless awarded the city the traditional four square leagues in 1865.

Yerba Buena was renamed San Francisco in 1847; the first dock was constructed later in the same year. After the discovery of gold in 1848 San Francisco was almost abandoned within a few weeks as its citizens left for the mines. But within months, as the word of gold spread, the Mexican village had become an American tent city with a "floating population" in the thousands.

At times in the early 1850's a number of crew-abandoned ships could be found in the Bay. And within three years six conflagrations swept the shanty town.

As San Francisco grew it was first extended eastward into the Bay—between "fill" piles and redwood rafts were employed. It expanded westward too, beyond *Telegraph Hill*. *Rincon Hill,* somewhat less foggy became the choice residential district.

San Francisco, despite economic fluctuations, was the only "big" city of the American West in the 19th century.

Decline of the Sierran mines occasioned much unemployment and bankruptcy by the late 1850's. But soon the wealth from the silver mines of Nevada's Comstock Lode restored prosperity. In time commerce and industry replaced precious metals in the city's economy.

Industrial establishments appeared southward to China Basin; they included the initial refinery to process Hawaiian sugar. The city was linked by rail (with Oakland and trans-Bay ferries) in 1869. Meanwhile immigrants from China and Italy developed a fishing industry, first north of Telegraph Hill and then at *Fisherman's Wharf.*

For more than a generation after the railroad was built no rival challenged the city seriously as the "colossus of the Pacific."

Identified by Frank Norris as "The Octopus", the Southern Pacific was more commonly merely called *the railroad.* It monopolized trade within the Golden State. Anticipating arrival of the Central Pacific, the Pacific Mail Line, which had transported many gold seekers, opened its trans-Pacific trade.

Many developments took place in San Francisco in the 1870's.

Mining kings and railroad magnates built their mansions on *Nob Hill.* Meanwhile, a partial solution to transportation problems posed by steep terrain occurred when cable cars began to operate in 1873.

Partly because its social leaders imported French chefs, the city gained a reputation for fine food. Meanwhile the landscaping of *Golden Gate Park* commenced.

Outgoing commerce was expanded with shipment of grain from the Central Valley to Liverpool and other world ports. Lumber schooners began operating from the Northwest (Ch.12) with depletion of redwood groves near the Bay.

Growth of the city continued during the 1880's.

The Spreckels expanded Hawaiian sugar production while shipping across the Pacific was ex-

**Figure 8-43.** The "Muni Metro" operates beneath Market Street. (dwl)

panded. About three-fourths of all of California's industrial productivity occurred in San Francisco. Robert Dollar, a shipper of Mendocino redwood, moved into the trans-Pacific trade and created a major steamship company.

With population density increasing blocks of multiple residences (flats) appeared. Then, at the end of the century, San Francisco's commercial development was promoted further by Alaskan salmon and gold.

With a populace of 342,000 in 1900, San Francisco was the tenth largest city in the United States.

*Montgomery Street,* while no longer on the waterfront, had become the financial center of western America. *Market Street* had become a famed thoroughfare and the Palace Hotel internationally known.

The city experienced its greatest disaster in 1906.

At dawn on April 18 movement along the San Andreas Fault resulted in the earthquake that crumbled brick walls, shattered houses and broke dishes and windows. Gas hissed from broken mains and water lines ruptured. In the fiery three-day holocaust that followed, damaged approached $350 million in a four square-mile area, an estimated 2000 lives were lost and 28,000 buildings were destroyed. Only after the dynamiting of buildings did the fires burn out at Van Ness Avenue on the west. A redwood metropolis, San Francisco had fed the fire well.

Within five years San Francisco had been rebuilt.

A more beautiful city replaced the somewhat ugly, if picturesque Victorian metropolis even though little of the *Burnham Plan* of 1904 was adopted.* Meanwhile San Francisco's growth was being hastened by other events.

Opening of the Panama Canal in 1914 was followed by a major fair, the *Panama-Pacific International Exposition,* in 1915. The canal opening created a market for San Joaquin Valley oil along the Atlantic seaboard.

Expanding irrigation agriculture in central California, especially in the Central Valley, made San Francisco and its satellites around the Bay the center for a large food-processing industry.** War in Europe stimulated some industrial growth, especially shipbuilding.

After World War I San Francisco gained additional importance as a port.

Coastwise trade expanded as refrigerated fruit was shipped increasingly to western Europe, bananas and coffee came from South America and

pleasure and trade cruises developed with Australia and the South Seas.

By 1930, San Francisco, while a city of 634,000, gave a feeling of being larger, but it was no longer the ranking metropolis of the Golden State.

During the decade that followed it lost its dominance as a West Coast port. Waterfront strife coincided with expanding Oakland commerce at a time when Los Angeles commerce was enlarged by petroleum shipments.

Water was brought as a supplemental source (*also* an added supply for San Mateo County) from Yosemite's Hetch Hetchy Valley—this controversial achievement is noted in Ch. 10.

Meanwhile Trans-Pacific air flights were established in 1936. And the Bay barrier was lessened with opening of the Golden Gate and Oakland Bay bridges. While the population increase during the 1930's was slight, San Francisco was affected less by the Great Depression than many American cities.

War in the Pacific (1941-1945) had a momentous impact on San Francisco *and* the Bay Area.

Many military facilities were located in the Area and large numbers of service personnel moved in and out of San Francisco A tremendous volume of supplies moved westward from the Bay. Shipbuilding and ship repair became major industrial activities and other types of industry were much expanded. Residential facilities were seriously taxed.

While San Francisco has experienced much change in the past 40 years or so, much of the population growth and increased activity has taken place on the periphery of the Bay Area.

There is almost no space within San Francisco (whose city and county limits are identical) for industrial or residential expansion. *Stonestown,* in the southwestern corner of the city, was one of the nation's outstanding suburban developments of the early 1950's (extensive renovation took place in the 1980's). For its size, San Francisco's popula-

---

* A group of civic-minded San Franciscans employed Daniel H. Burnham, Chicago architect and city planner, to plan a "new" San Francisco. His proposal included a civic center, traffic circles, diagonal boulevards, one-way streets, parks, subways and a 30-mile Outer Boulevard. Journalistic opposition, political bickering, public apathy and haste to rebuild prevented extensive use of the plan.

**Much of the benefit of economic growth in central and northern California to San Francisco has been indirect. San Francisco has had the brokerage houses, the banks and other corporate headquarters, and the insurance companies rather than the flour mills and sugar factories.

tion density is exceeded in the United States only on Manhattan Island. Consequently except for housing in Diamond Heights most changes have been vertical.

Such longtime economic supports as retail shopping, industrial plants and transportation facilities have been dispersed widely about the Bay Area.

The most dramatic change in the physical appearance of San Francisco in the second half of the twentieth century has been in its downtown skyline. Many deplore the new skyscrapers and elevated freeways yet others argue that with the small area, "vertical growth" has been essential.

### A Bit of "Everything"

The functions of San Francisco are diversified but they have become increasingly skewed in recent decades. Corporate activity, finance and tourism have increased but oceanic transport and manufacturing have declined markedly.

### Wall Street West

A concentration of statewide banking chains, insurance firms and corporate offices are found in San Francisco. Activity has extended outward from the *Financial District*, principally to the east.

Considerations have included district offices of the Federal Reserve, central location relative to the American West ( including Hawaii) and the momentum of an early start.

Relative to Los Angeles, San Francisco has shown some recent decline as a corporate center.

Until recently the two cities were comparable. However, some San Francisco corporations have been merged with firms having headquarters elsewhere while some firms have moved out of the "central city". Office space tends to be expensive. Into the early 1980's new high-rises had been added and there was a continuing demand for space. Subsequently there was concern about the loss of corporate offices.

### Tourists and Conventioneers

Almost from its beginnings, San Francisco has lured occasional visitors and tourists. For some years visitor-entertainment has been a billion-dollar affair annually.

The city is well qualified to entertain visitors. Besides famed restaurants and multi-star down-

town hotels it provides night life, quality specialty shops, ethnic neighborhoods (*especially Chinatown*), the waterfront (including long-established *Fisherman's Wharf* and now Pier 39), parks, opera, symphony, museums and theatre (although less than New York or Los Angeles), major league sports and scenic vistas. Its compactness favors walking. Also, of course, there are the *cable cars*.

With its facilities (including the *Moscone Convention Center*, San Francisco is one of the nation's major convention centers. Organizations of every believable type meet here.

### Ivory Towers

San Francisco is more important as a center for higher education than is sometimes appreciated. It is the locale of the University of California's Medical College (the *original* one, associated with U.C., Berkeley) and Hastings Law School. San Francisco State University, fourth largest of the 19 California State Universities, has a handsomely-landscaped campus in southwest San Francisco; amidst a diversity of programs it is known locally in the arts. Other institutions include the University of San Francisco, the University of the Pacific's dental and medical schools, Golden Gate University, San Francisco City College and Heald College (technical).

### The Navy and the Army

Military activities make an important contribution to the economy of the city. The *Presidio* predates the civilian community by half a century.

While it no longer has strategic importance it provides the the command headquarters for the U.S.Sixth Army. This installation, offering one of the most attractive settings of any Army post in the nation, covers 1540 acres and has annual operating expenses expenses of scores of millions, with many thousands of military personnel and hundreds of civilian employees. Letterman General Hospital is on its eastern edge and in the southwest, long-closed Marine Hospital may reopen as an *AIDS* facility. Nearby a large Veterans Administration hospital is at Fort Miley which overlooks Seal Rocks and the Pacific.

The headquarters of the *Twelfth Naval District*, which has a number of facilities scattered around the Bay Area, is also in San Francisco.

In the city the Naval Station on Treasure and Yerba Buena islands is particularly important.

## Spices and Evening Attire

San Francisco has lost much of its importance as an industrial city—less than a tenth of its work force is engaged in manufacturing.

The city was California's ranking industrial center for three fourths of a century after the Gold Rush. As late as 1900 half of the Golden State's industrial output was fabricated in San Francisco. Since the middle 1920's Los Angeles has been the leader. Now, of course, both San Diego and Silicon Valley have greater output.

Yet remaining manufacturing still has diversity although San Francisco does not compare with Los Angeles and Chicago. Activity tends to be oriented towards local markets (furniture, foods, clothing, finished metal products and printing).

In recent decades sizable operations have been relocated elsewhere. Larger plants now tend to be occupied by a myriad of smaller firms.

Traditionally foodstuffs have been processed from California produce, especially from the Central Valley, and including items like beer, dairy products, beef, fruits, vegetables and soft drinks or from imported raw materials (such as cacao, copra, coffee and sugar).

San Francisco proper lacks the significance of Los Angeles in electronics and missiles and automobile assembly—land was unavailable within the city.

There are dozens of clothing firms, although output ranks well below Los Angeles. Ladies' suits and coats and men's attire have importance. In recent decades the city has gained recognition as a style center for winter clothing, as contrasted with the sports apparel of Los Angeles.

Much of the manufacturing is found in the southeastern Bayfill areas with freeway and rail facilities and the more recent segments of waterfront development.

High land values, congestion, small areas of level terrain and limited railroad frontage have hampered industrial expansion for many decades. Thus most of the industrial development in the second half of the twentieth century has occurred elsewhere in the Bay Area.

Relatively early, meat packers, steel fabricators, powder-makers and smelters had left the city. San Francisco companies have tended to maintain offices and warehouses in the city but establish new plants elsewhere.

Port-type manufacturing was more important in the past.

The first machine shop was opened in 1849 and working of iron and steel has been conducted since the Gold Rush. But in space-short San Francisco there has not been sufficient inexpensive land for such activities as oil and sugar refining.

## By Land and Sea

Transportation has always been important to San Francisco. After all, it is a major California hub. But its semi-insularity and congestion create problems, sometimes vexatious.

### Freeways and Lesser Ways

Because of its size and location San Francisco tends to be a terminal point for highway travel.

While approximately 100 truck lines operate into San Francisco shortage of space has prompted location of terminals in the East Bay.

As in many cities there is a central inter-city bus terminal.

Since San Franciscans successfully halted an integrated cross-city freeway system (to the delight of many residents but the frustration of many visitors), the small size of the city is fortunate (map, 8-5).

Two freeways (U.S.101 and I–280) enter San Francisco from the south ,then merge into *The Skyway* which is designated I–80 to lead towards the Bay Bridge and Oakland. From the north (Marin County) U.S.101 *loses* its freeway designation at the Golden Gate Bridge (it continues south through the city as Ca.1).

The *Central Freeway*, which was to link U.S. 101 with the Golden Gate Bridge, was never completed.

Highway traffic through San Francisco was eased with opening of *The San Francisco-Oakland Bay* (in 1936) and *Golden Gate* (in 1937) bridges. Since their construction hundreds of millions in tolls have been received. The Bay Bridge has two levels; alterations effected in 1962 permit oneway traffic on each level. Some feel that absence of a lane-movable center divider on the Golden Gate Bridge is unfortunate (others like the flexibility of adding lanes during rush hour).

### Trams and Trains

San Francisco's rail facilities suggest those of Manhattan while Oakland's position is suggestive to that of Jersey City.

The original *Central Pacific* line eastward over Donner Pass had its terminus in Oakland. Bay

**Figure 8-44.** San Francisco, east of Bayshore (U.S. 101) has been the traditional industrial portion of the city. New functions are evolving. (Caltrans)

Area terminals of the Santa Fe and the Union Pacific *(formerly* the Western Pacific) are also in the East Bay. The Santa Fe Southern maintained ferry service between San Francisco and Oakland from 1861; its freight cars also can cross the Bay via Dumbarton rail bridge.

San Francisco gained its single "main line" railroad initially with construction of the *San Francisco and San Jose* (now the part of the Santa Fe Southern)—service commenced in 1864. The route was completed to Los Angeles as the Coast Route in 1901. A mini-terminal replaced (in 1976) the venerable relic of the Panama-Pacific Exposition. Service is limited solely to Caltrans-subsidized Peninsula commuters. Amtrak trains continue to terminate in Oakland.

Yard and terminal space poses a problem in congested San Francisco; even the Santa Fe Southern has its facilities in Bayshore (northeastern San Mateo County) while the Santa Fe is in Richmond. The former state-owned *Belt Line Railroad* route, which provided service along the San Francisco waterfront, may be revived as a tourist trolley.

With its city-owned *Muni* and *Central City Circulation Plan* San Francisco is better served than many American centers.

The *Municipal Railway* (Muni) is a combination of buses and lightweight rail (or street) cars. Part of its system utilizes the *Muni Metro* beneath Market Street.

The *Bay Area Rapid Transit* complex links San Francisco with East Bay (Fig.8-4).

The trackage extends from Daly City through downtown San Francisco and beneath the Bay to Oakland and East Bay points. It is still plagued by mechanical problems and disappointing patronage—it is yet to attain expectations.

### A Waterfront in Decline

Maritime commerce has been important to San Francisco since its founding. Naturally tide-scoured, San Francisco Bay also affords an entry into the Central Valley.

Even before there was the village of Yerba Buena Native Americans navigated the Bay. It was then used by the Yankees in the hide and tallow days.

The *Port of San Francisco* long extended from Hunter's Point (south) to Fort Mason (northwest).

The *Port Authority* regulates the piers and intervening slips, concrete terminals and warehouses and the Belt Line Railroad.

Dissatisfaction with waterfront speculators prompted the electorate to yield port control to the state in 1863. Prior to its return to city control in 1969 San Francisco had the nation's single state-controlled waterfront.

The waterfront has declined since mid-century.

Although specialized facilities exist general cargo is emphasized. Most recent development has occurred along the southeastern shore rather than the crowded *Embarcadero.*

*Mission Rock Terminal* opened in 1950 and *Army Street Terminal* in 1967. Unneeded piers and environs northwest of the Bay Bridge have been converted to other uses including a yacht basin, waterfront park and residential development. The *Ferry Building* remains a landmark. Traditionally, foreign steamship lines utilized odd-numbered piers north of the Ferry Building.

Two areas have been used for fishing vessels.

Small boats that bring fresh fish (from grounds off the Golden Gate) tie up at *Fisherman's Wharf.* Large purse seiners which have operated in Alaskan waters (summer) and southern hemisphere waters (winters) have used China Basin off-season.

San Francisco is no longer a leading West Coast seaport.

Factors included waterfront labor strife (after World War I), port competition (especially Oakland and Los Angeles), the handicap of state port control and especially the rise of container cargo (which made San Francisco's finger piers obsolete). Air travel precipitated the decline of passenger traffic.

The sea commerce strongly resembles that of

Oakland. Through the years leading exports have included machinery and vehicles, cotton fiber, chemicals animal products, metals and grains. Major imports have included tropical vegetable products, metals, wood and paper and *costlier* foreign autos. Commerce with Hawaii and inter-coastal trade (via Panama Canal) has been important. The Pacific Basin has been an important source of imports while the Pacific Basin and northwestern Europe have been important export destinations.

After the Bay bridges opened, the once-important (as many as 50 million fares annually) ferry service to the Ferry Building declined markedly (and was terminated in 1958). Service to Marin Peninsula, resumed in 1962, continues. Rail freight by barge continues to be important between East Bay and San Francisco.

**Seemingly-Simple Patterns**

Over much of its surface San Francisco has a rectangular street pattern despite its two score-plus "heights."

Layout of early-day streets and peninsular shape (map 8-5 and Fig. 8-74) has complicated the design.

Early in the American period Market Street was laid out near the trail where *carretas* laden with hides and tallow rolled to Yerba Buena Cove. Thus the compass orientation of the early sites of San Francisco and Los Angeles is almost identical.

In the cases of Rincon, Telegraph, Russian and Nob hills terrain was disregarded hence the motorist sometimes experiences a roller coaster effect. But around Buena Vista Park, the Presidio and Seacliff district and other elevations, streets conform more logically to the terrain, or have been curved for "effect."

Attenuated Golden Gate Park breaks the north-south street continuity of western San Francisco without serious results.

While residents of the city consider driving around San Francisco "no big deal" visitors are sometimes "freaked out" by traffic flow, grid patterns and steep grades on such hills as Buena Vista, Nob, Russian and Pacific Heights. Knowing the fastest and easiest routes, the San Franciscan can cross the city in about half an hour. After all, it contains only 49 square miles.

There are relatively few principal thoroughfares.

**Figure 8-45.** Japanese tea garden, Golden Gate Park. (dwl)

Internationally-known *Market Street* is the principal downtown boulevard. But use has been complicated by "no left turns" and limited crossings (due to an adjacent non-conforming grid).

*Geary*, extending from the central district to the Pacific, is a principal east-west boulevard.

The broad waterfront street, *The Embarcadero* (200 feet wide), extends from *Fisherman's Wharf* to China Basin. Then Third Street continues south to Bayview.

Several other streets have particular importance. Much traffic uses Nineteenth Avenue (south of Golden Gate Park) and Presidio Boulevard (north of the park) which function as Ca. 1. *Portola Drive* links Market St. with Route 1. Marking the western limit of the original city, Van Ness Avenue and then Lombard Street westward serve as U.S. 101 between the Golden Gate Bridge and U.S. 101.

Existing freeways facilitate trans-city traffic movement.

*Bayshore* (or James Lick) Freeway, U.S. 101, leads toward both the Oakland Bay and Golden Gate bridges.

Several decades ago San Franciscans successfully opposed completion of the Embarcadero and Cen-

**Figure 8-46.** The Mission District: Mission St. north of 17th St. (dwl)

**Figure 8-47.** Seacliff District, southwest of the Golden Gate Bridge. (dwl)

**Figure 8-49.** Young residents and multi-resident housing, Hunters Point. (dwl)

**Figure 8-48.** Russian Orthodox Church on Geary Avenue, Richmond District. (dwl)

tral freeways (a victory for San Franciscans, *not* commuters and visitors). *

## Pacific Rim People

San Francisco *could* eventually become an Asian-majority city. Chinese, still primarily from south China, have increased in number with changes in immigration policy. Moreover, in recent decades, the assemblage of Vietnamese, Cambodians, and Koreans has grown while Arabs, and others have migrated to San Francisco also. Filipinos form a huge group.

Already San Francisco, like Oakland and Los Angeles, has become an Anglo-minority city. And the composition of its populace continues to change.

In 1942 an enforced exodus of Japanese took place; after World War II some (but not all) returned. Blacks, recruited initially to work in defense plants, increased in numbers for several decades. After mid-century some middle-income Anglos with children could not find sufficiently-large affordable housing; many relocated in "suburbs" elsewhere in the Bay Area. Still more recently more affluent Hispanics and blacks with families have abandoned San Francisco for the same reason.

San Francisco, from its inception, has had a reputation as a tolerant place. For the United States, its residents have always been a "special mix"—from Chinese to Bohemians to Beats to Hippies to Gays.

Some gays are affluent professional folk with mobility. They appear to be attracted by the "openness" as well as the lifestyles and the physical beauty. Others are recently-arrived, young and with low incomes. Most are Anglos—but the influx has lessened.

Anglos in San Francisco are not a representative cross-section of Americans.

They include mature (and elderly) affluent couples on "preferred slopes", younger couples (both working) and employed singles (who sometimes "afford" costs by sharing housing).

## The Central District

Downtown San Francisco, compact in size, lies within a crude square (approximately two square miles) in the northeastern part of the city.

It is bounded by the Bay (northeast), Van Ness (west), Broadway (north) and the freeways (south and east).

Important functions include tourism, retail trade, finance, and corporate headquarters.

With its many skyscrapers central San Francisco long contrasted with the low skyline of urban California—this is decreasingly true.**

Since it was virtually rebuilt after the earthquake of 1906, nineteenth century structures, still characteristic of some American cities, are absent.

San Francisco has much importance as the site of corporate headquarters.

Firms tend to be involved with such activities as agriculture, mining, lumbering, construction, and utilities.

For three decades after 1950 continuing construction of skyscrapers more than 400 feet tall led to much loss of the "natural" skyline. New buildings reflected the importance of the central district as an executive and services center. San Francisco ranks fourth, nationally, after Los Angeles in square footage of office space.***

By the 1980's it appeared that the demand for office space in San Francisco as elsewhere in the country may have been met (at least for a while). Causes included mergers, buyouts, office relocation elsewhere (as the East Bay) and high rents. Belatedly the electorate in 1985 approved a *Downtown Plan* that slowed new construction and insisted upon upper-story setbacks.

Downtown San Francisco remains the ranking retail center in California *north* of Los Angeles. It has a stagnant volume of constant-dollar sales which contrasts with the *absolute* decline in most C.B.D.s of American cities.

Among major cities in United States San Francisco is almost alone in retaining such a sizable number of affluent residents "close-in." These, along with visitors (including many from other parts of the Bay Area) and newcomers, sustain the retailing, entertainment and cultural facilities of the central city.

---

* Arguments included: (1) freeways remove land form a space-short city (2) they desecrate the landscape (3) travelers are less likely to stop and patronize city merchants (4) the through traveler can *avoid* San Francisco by using I-880 and I-680 in the East Bay (5) they fragment and destroy neighborhoods (6) they serve commuter *not* city residents (7) they encourage evermore traffic creating more noise, pollution and parking problems.

** High-rise structures are appearing in a number of California cities. Besides Los Angeles, San Diego, San Jose, Long Beach and Sacramento, this is true of such smaller cities as Glendale, Concord, and San Mateo.

*** Occupance of the Crocker Plaza Building is indicative of variety. It includes executive suites of Wyatt Corp-oration, Aetna Life Insurance, E.S. Merriman and Co., Arthur Young and Co., Foremost-McKesson Corp., as well as accountants, credit card services, engineering firms, tax consultants, construction companies, pension consultants and retirement consultants.

*Union Square*, with its underground parking garage, forms a core for Downtown.

Surrounding blocks contain the major cluster of hotels, clubs, fine import shops, prestigious department stores (such as Macy's, Nordstroms, Saks Fifth Avenue and Neiman-Marcus). specialty shops (art, books, furniture, jewelry, lingerie, music and perfumes), tourist bureaus, restaurants and night spots. A distinctive feature is the sidewalk flower stalls.

Banks, insurance companies and foreign consulates tend to be concentrated on Montgomery and California streets.

The district has expanded northward with additional skyscrapers; major developments have included Embarcadero Center and the *Golden Gateway*. The Golden Gateway, with town houses, apartments, and offices in high-rise structures, has been a major urban renewal. More costly has been the adjacent *Embarcadero Center*, a junior-size Rockefeller Center with shops, offices, a hotel, restaurants and stores.

While automated activities have relocated elsewhere, those employing considerable numbers of office workers and/or requiring much face-to-face contact remain. Thus Geary Street is the focus of the legitimate theatre. Also found in the district are broadcasting studios and petroleum company offices.

*Market Street,* used for parades and pageants, bisects the central district. Considerable renovation accompanied the B.A.R.T. and Muni "underground" construction.

Lower (northeastern) Market Street has provided a pivotal area for nautical supplies, transportation offices and hotels. Within a single high-rise structure the offices of four of the five firms that dominated the Hawaiian economy were previously located. Southward, beyond the Sheraton-Palace Hotel, is the city's *Great White Way*. Prior to recent renewal, it had gotten somewhat shabby. It has been flanked by restaurants, bars, theatres and retail shops.

*South of Market,* focusing on 3rd and 4th streets, has also experienced change.

The *Yerba Buena Redevelopment Area* with the *Moscone Convention Center* has replaced some of the inexpensive hotels, bus terminals, wholesale offices, newspaper offices and parking facilities.

This area has provided a buffer between the downtown area and the warehouse district (east); the small commuter railroad depot is on its eastern edge. *Rincon Hill*, on the northern edge, was the *original* elite residential area (before Nob Hill). More recently it has provided a warehouse area but an alteration in use is anticipated.

A monumental change in South of Market will take place with the construction of the multi-billion dollar *Mission Bay Project*. This major Santa Fe Southern program, covering 210 acres, has been delayed some years because of doubts about its composition. Apparently multi-story buildings will be less lofty than originally planned, while more space will be given to residential and park use.

To the northwest, *The Tenderloin* is another worn area whose use is much debated.

This area, between Powell (east) and Hyde (west) and south of O'Farrell, became more sleazy in the 1960's. It has been known for its higher crimes rates, cheaper hotels, cafes and bars. It has remained a focal point for prostitution.

For many years residents included elderly single poor plus single downtown employees (such as doormen, bartenders and waiters) whose salaries have restricted their housing options. In the 1980's Vietnamese and other Asians were added. Their presence seems to be producing significant "upgrading" of the area.

There have been several attempts to tear down the old hotels and replace them with new multi-star ones. But there has been strong pressure to keep this area as a viable neighborhood for residents and not for tourists.

West of Market Street on the southwest edge of the central district is the *Civic Center*, with a concentration of governmental activity.

Generally buildings follow the French Renaissance style. Older granite and newer concrete structures house the city hall, public library, state offices (San Francisco and Los Angeles function as sub-state capitals), civic auditorium, Opera House, (where the *United Nations* was founded) and Veterans Building (which houses the Museum of Art). More recent additions have been the *Davies Center for the Performing Arts* and a State Office Building.

Downtown San Francisco is *the place* for one of the nation's favorite urban tourist centers.

There are multiple explanations for its appeal. They include its distinctive *character*—an aspect found in New Orleans and New York but uncommon in most American cities. This image is created in part by the resemblance to a many-tiered white wedding cake rising dramatically above the Bay. There is also the legacy of the exotic seaport, which San Francisco long shared with Marseilles and Shanghai.

The C.B.D. has the facilities to house and feed the visitor well—few American cities have a comparable reputation for varied cuisine. The many hotels, including recent additions, are much famed.

Another aspect is the multiplicity of vistas, such as from Twin Peaks or Telegraph Hill or the upper stories of several hotels. The Bay bridges provide another element, and the Bay itself with Alcatraz Island is a definite attraction. And where else is there a Fisherman's Wharf so convenient to so many people? Few American cities can provide the exotic flavor of a Chinatown or North Beach. Finally there is the cosmopolitan population of the city. It is no surprise that a Gallup poll has indicated that Americans regard San Francisco as their favorite city.

## The Many Neighborhoods

San Francisco is among the nation's costliest cities in which to "live comfortably." Yet there is much variance within its many well-identified residential districts.

While median incomes are comparable to state-wide averages, they are highly deceiving. There are extensive areas that house working people on modest incomes but San Francisco is also a "moneyed" city occupied by middle-aged couples and wealthy widows. It also has a "poverty row" of unemployed and poorly paid.

Property values in attractive neighborhoods tend to be prohibitive for younger couples with children. Recently-married couples often reside in a small

apartment until the arrival of the first child, then the loss of an income and need for larger quarters prompts retreat to a suburban housing tract. Official concern has publicized The City's clear drift towards "childlessness."

### A Tilted City

San Francisco has been described as a "tilted city"—its vertical dimensions permit much of its populace to live on view lots overlooking the Bay, the Pacific or city lights.

In this frost-free setting, the declivities provide charm but the slopes can frustrate the visiting motorist or pedestrian.*

This is a city also of gardens, squares and parks.

Some squares are small—perhaps occupying a single block (as do Union Square and Portsmouth Square). Population density and narrow lots (25-foot) make it easy to overlook the many *little* parks. Because so many townhouses extend the width of lots and rise from sidewalks, visitors are generally unaware of the backyard gardens in many parts of the city, obscured from street views.

San Francisco's largest park is *Golden Gate*—with its "panhandle" extension eastward it stretches half the width of the peninsula.

This is an impressive preserve, seemingly more so than Paris' Bois de Boulogne, Los Angeles' Griffith Park or Central Park in New York. While it was established in 1868 its conversion from barren dunes and wasteland into magnificent landscaping is credited to John McLaren, who became superintendent in 1887. ** There is concern that inadequate maintenance funds are causing deterioration of the Park's shrubs and trees.

There are miles of driveways and bridle paths, flower beds, lakes, wide expanses of lawn—and the Japanese Tea Garden. Besides Deer Park there are buffalo and elk. The reserve includes two stadia, Kezar (now used for high school football) and Golden Gate (for track and soccer).

Cultural activity is centered in *The California Academy of Sciences* and *De Young Museum*. Two old windmills (one has been renovated) rise above

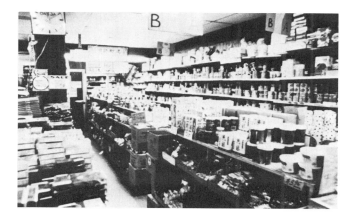

**Figure 8-50.** Chinese grocery store, Richmond District. (dwl)

---

\* Eventually, the reshaping of *Diamond Heights*, whose steep slopes long had negated residential use, in the 1960's was achieved by much cut-and-fill, followed by a construction of a street pattern appropriate for the terrain.

\*\* *John McLaren*, a newer park and still only partially developed, was established in his honor in southeastern San Francisco. *Candlestick Park*, where major league football and baseball is played, is berated by players and fans for its winds and foggy summer nights—it is on the far southeastern edge of the city.

the western fringe of the park. Not far north is *Cliff House*, with Seal Rocks offshore and *Sutro Heights Park* above.

*Lincoln Park*, farther north, provides views of the Golden Gate. It contains *California Palace of the Legion of Honor*, with the largest art museum in San Francisco.

On the city's northwestern fringe is the *Golden Gate National Recreation Area*.

Much of this spectacular reserve is north of the Golden Gate in Marin County. It has become the most-visited facility in the National Park system.

## Inner Districts

Much of "vintage" San Francisco was destroyed by the fire of 1906.

But vestiges of the late nineteen-century city exist around the fringes of the burned area. These include the Western Addition and the Mission District.

Now an ethnic melange, the *Western Addition* has changed through several generations.

When the Addition was subdivided in the 1870's it became new San Francisco. It survived *The Fire* (1906) then experienced rapid growth. At mid-century there was much Victorian " gingerbread" with exuberant trim and scrolls. Row on row, block after block, were two-story duplexes with no space between houses and with no greenery along the streets. Gothic arches, Byzantine domes and bay windows were in abundance.

Then came *Western Addition I and II*. This urban renewal led to destruction of many of the best Victorian structures. An exodus of Jews and many of the Russians took place, now the Jews and many of the Russians are gone. Subsequently gentrification has occurred.

*Japan Town* remains, adjacent to Post Street. It is smaller than the Japanese community in Los Angeles. Around mid-century a big increase in black population occurred. Then extensive renovation of remaining Victorians was undertaken; conflict took place between traditional redevelopers and those who chose to retain the "best of the old."

Located here also are the University of San Francisco and the University of California's Extension Division.

Transformation is taking place in various parts of the Western Addition. On the southern periphery change is noticeable on Buena Vista Hill. Other areas reflecting modification are around Alamo Square and the southern edge of Pacific Heights. Gays have moved north from The Castro into the *Duboce Triangle*.

Blacks have been one of San Francisco's most-active ethnic groups.

They have concentrated in three areas, *Western Addition, Bay View* and *Ocean View*. Conditions remain difficult for many although significant "upward mobility" has taken place. There is much underemployment with attendant social problems.

Victorian restoration and rising property prices have driven some blacks out of the Western Addition. Many blacks, unable to afford San Francisco rents, reside in the East Bay. Thus blacks form a significant portion of the ride-to-work trans-Bay commuters.

South of the Western Addition an extensive area consists of the adjacent Potrero and Mission districts.

A sizable blue-collar populace has resided here since the *Great Fire*. As has been noted, much of the Potrero has been industrial.

Focal point of San Francisco's Spanish-language peoples, is *The Mission District*.

There has been considerable recent immigration including many Filipinos. Many residents of the District are foreign born. There are other ethnic groups, especially from Latin America. For San Francisco much housing is noticeably depressed. By contrast, *Outer Mission* to the southwest includes more affluent *Excelsior*.

*The Castro*, on the northwest fringe of The Mission, has become one of the most visible gay centers on earth. It has appeared to reflect the city's tolerance of atypical American cultures.

Besides the Western Addition and the Mission, several other districts help impart an international seasoning to San Francisco.

North of the central district and surrounding the three summits, *Nob Hill, Telegraph Hill* and *Russian Hill*, now identified by expensive apartments, are Chinatown and North Beach. The latter is reflective of changing ethnic make-up of the city.

*Chinatown* has achieved wider renown than most of the nation's "foreign" districts.

It reflects considerable alteration of the area that acquired such a reputation for it mystique and its opium dens—that vanished in 1906.

Chinatown today is a tightly-packed district centered on narrow Grant Avenue and *Portsmouth Square*, the *visitors'* Chinatown, adjacent to downtown San Francisco on the northeastern slopes of

Nob Hill. With its Chinese and American neon signs and "Chinese" architecture Grant presents an interesting scene. Parallel Stockton Street, north of Clay, gives a better impression of real workday Chinatown.

The Chinese initially were miners and builders of the Central Pacific Railroad; later they became domestic servants, produce sellers, gardeners. Now their activities represent the entire gamut of American life. This district contains the largest concentration of Canton Chinese in America. *

It has developed importance as a garment-making center but has been cited for 12-to 14-hour work days and pathetic wages.

Many recent immigrants (via Hong Kong) are *north* Chinese— apparently there has been cultural schism between long-time residents and the newcomers, reflected in political and social differences and violence that has occurred between younger Chinese.

*North Beach*, bisected by diagonal Columbus Avenue (between Russian Hill and Telegraph Hill) has changed also.

In bygone times this area was ethnically diverse (Italians, Irish, Mexicans, Germans and others). By the beginning of the twentieth century the Italians had become dominant. Now the Mexicans' traditional national church, *Our Lady of Guadalupe*, is non-ethnic. In the 1950's the *Beatniks* came to Upper Grant. The Italians have dispersed throughout San Francisco (and the Bay Area). The old *Bohemian* haunts on Telegraph Hill were replaced by additional apartments.Today, except on the wealthy east and north fringes, North Beach is predominantly Chinese.

## Outer Districts

Incomes of many San Franciscans are among the highest in the nation. In some instances these reflect generations of corporate wealth and of accumulation.

But like other groups, many Anglo "old family" wealthy have retreated to other parts of the Bay Area. Remaining affluent tend to occupy the hills, especially in northern San Francisco. Thus a near-continuous higher-income belt extends westward from Russian Hill through Pacific Heights and the Marina to Seacliff. It tends to be coincident with good views of the Bay and the Golden Gate.

Here, and in southwestern districts beyond Golden Gate Park many Anglos, plus a growing number of Asians, occupy many of San Francisco's single-family residences. Dwellings in all parts of the city tend to be well-maintained for their age, even though over two-thirds are rented.

*The Marina*, a "newer" (1920's) district west of North Beach and north of the Western Addition, extends to the Presidio. The rebuilt *Palace of Fine Arts*, is a legacy of the Panama-Pacific Exposition (1915). On its northern edge, The *Yacht Harbor*, has a "fashionable" location—and sailing in the Bay is popular.

Between Golden Gate Park (south) and the Presidio (northwest), *Richmond* is a populous area with modest dwellings. It has a polyglot population (including Russians) which is most notably Asian—many affluent Chinese have relocated here. **

To the east *Pacific Heights* has some quality dwellings—it is regarded as one of San Francisco's "best" addresses. *Seacliff* west of the Presidio also has spacious, well-landscaped residences.

On the southeast edge of Golden Gate Park *Haight-Ashbury* has "recovered" from the trauma of the 1960's when it was known as the "hippie" utopia. The district is again considered "respectable"—it has evolved from *hippie* to *yuppie*.

South of Golden Gate Park and west of Twin Peaks and Forest Hill, the *Sunset* "build-out" occurred in the mid-twentieth century. As late as 1940 much of its southern portion was unoccupied sand hills. Dwellings consist primarily of single-family houses in an interesting combination of "older" and contemporary architectural styles. It has the largest Anglo middle-income group in San Francisco but is becoming one of the fastest-growing Asian neighborhoods.

To the southeast are found the costly homes of *Forest Hill* and *St. Francis Woods*. Ascending the slopes of Mt. Davidson, they provide views to the Pacific.

Besides Diamond Heights, the newest districts in San Francisco, developed around mid-century, are *Stonestown*, adjacent to Lake Merced on the San Mateo County line, and *Ingleside* to the southeast. The zoo and San Francisco's only country club are here.

---

* Burton H. Wolfe years ago gave a scathing presentation of this ghetto of 80,000. As such the district received widespread publicity. The viewpoint of a native Chinese who came to America as a young adult is given by C.Y. Lee in his novel *The Flower Drum Song* (New York: Farrar, Straus and Cadahy, Inc.).

** This is more obvious in the residents than in the cultural landscape. While there are few signs in Chinese on Geary, Chinese shopping is better reflected on Sixth Avenue. A locational factor in Richmond has been the direct bus connection along Geary to Chinatown.

Stonestown has the single auto-dependent suburban type of shopping center within San Francisco and the high-rise apartments of *Park Merced* were were erected by the same firm that developed Park La Brea in Los Angeles (Ch.6). The campus of San Francisco State University is here, with City College of San Francisco farther east.

### Whither San Francisco?

As the end of the twentieth century approaches, San Francisco seems to reflect the problems and amenities of post-industrial Pacific Basin California and the nation.

As in other larger American (and Californian) cities, the problems are vexatious and worsening. They result from such social circumstances as poverty, congestion, drugs, inadequate supervision of children (by working couples), insufficient public funds and shifting population mix within the city.

Half a century ago San Francisco had about a third of the population of the Bay Area. It was a place where people worked and lived. Now San Francisco is more of a "dual personality" city to a degree absent elsewhere in California.

During weekday business hours the "population" doubles— thousands commute in from the Peninsula, Marin County, East Bay and more distant points by private automobile, trains and B.A.R.T., ferries and buses. But at night and on weekends San Francisco becomes the place of its full-time residents *plus* tourists and such service personnel as policemen and firefighters, maintenance staffs, computer technicians, hotel and restaurant employees.

In San Francisco, as elsewhere in the urban world, use of private automobiles becomes increasingly difficult.

The city is fortunate to have good public transportation. Finding a streetside parking space *almost anywhere* in San Francisco has become a continuing game of musical chair (the number of local vehicles exceeds the number of parking spaces). The problem is aggravated by narrow lots (hence more driveways) and too few garage facilities for multi-unit housing. Hence in San Francisco, as on Manhattan, the cost of owning a private vehicle becomes increasingly prohibitive.

For commuters, travel time becomes lengthier as highways become more congested.

In the second half of this century, as in many "mature" cities of northeastern United States there has been a dramatic "flight" out of San Fransisco.

About the same time, it involved relocation of industrial firms elsewhere in the Bay and movement of middle-income families with children "to the suburbs." Beginning about 1980, as the availability of office space lessened and rents increased, a number of corporations began moving all or part of their operations, either to other parts of the Bay Area, or to metropolitan Los Angeles.

A contrary movement has been in the in-migration of people from other lands.

This has entailed primarily Asians and Hispanics. Hence the city's population increased by some thousands during the 1980's.

A modest "revival" of the Port of San Francisco has occurred.

An increasing number of cruise ships are visiting the city. Oakland seems to be reaching physical capacity for freight. With computerized cargo the 40-foot channel of San Francisco is proving advantageous. But rail linkage south of the Bay Bridge is a problem.

One of the serious problems, potentially, may be inadequate preparation for the next "1906-size" earthquake.

Geologists know this will happen, eventually. A central emergency facility has been established and test drills conducted. Conceivably the high-rise structures will survive, but a "rain of glass" seems probable. Thousands of older masonry structures have not been reinforced. Numerous frame buildings are closely spaced. Too-many overhanging cornices *(why,* after 1906?) remain. Should a Richter *plus-8* earthquake occur during

**Figure 8-51.** Marin Peninsula, a land of crumpled terrain. Sausalito is in foreground to the left of Richardson Bay. Belvedere is to the lower right. (Aero-Photographers, Sausalito)

working hours, thousands of casualties and general pandemonium seem probable. City officials are finally aware of the problem and annual "1906" tests are conducted.

### MARIN PENINSULA

Marin—the name seems to connote "gracious" living. Among the counties of the Bay Area this one has the least people. And it is about the wealthiest county, per capita, in western United States (and 11th in the entire nation). Apart from the vicinity of

its public institutions there are virtually no lower-income locales. An influx of "new rich" in the latter twentieth century alienated some long-time residents as property prices went "sky high".

This is a realm of the affluent, not the super-rich—there are few estates. It is liberal, politically, understandable in a county that leads the Golden State in years of median formal education.

Marin Peninsula, much indented but crudely triangular in shape, offers a felicitous combination of ocean and Bay, grassy vales and wooded hills, sunshine and fog. Truly this is a special land. Some biased

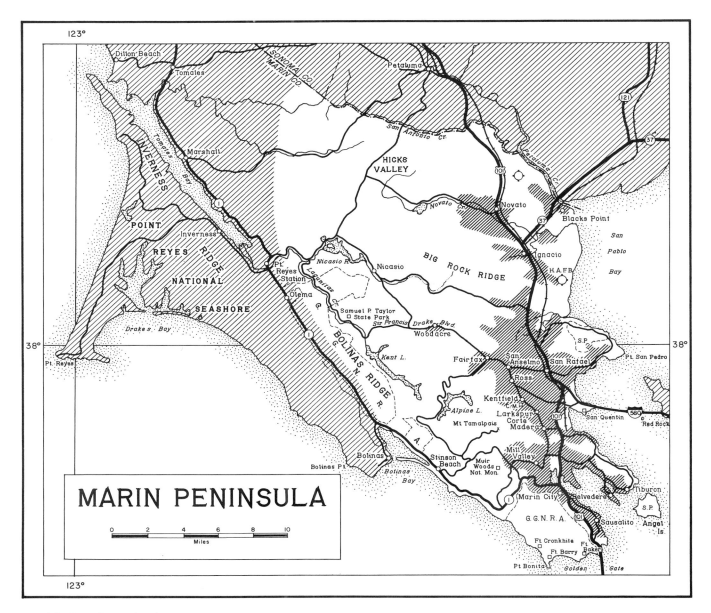

**Map 8-6.** Most of Marin County is contained within the near- empty Marin Hills. Most residents live around Richardson Bay (Sausalito to Belvedere) or near U.S. 101.

**Figure 8-52.** Marin City—black Marin County. (dwl)

residents would like to believe that it has perpetual spring.

In its utilization, Marin has differed in degree from other parts of the Bay Area, from which it long tended to be set apart.

Until the opening of the Golden Gate Bridge (1937) the Marin Peninsula was isolated from the remainder of the Bay Area by water except on the north. The transportation barrier was reduced further with construction of the San Rafael Bridge. Early in the Anglo period, briefly, logging and milling of redwood was important. Subsequently the Peninsula has been a milkshed, a suburban bedroom and a playground.

In contrast with San Francisco, Marin's populace is largely Anglo although there is considerable diversity.

Other important components include Italians, Scandinavians, Jews, Irish, Portuguese and French. And a tenth of the residents were born in the United Kingdom and the number of Asians has increased.

## THIS BLESSED LAND

It is easy to develop a love affair with Marin—its scenic appeal comes from its combination of natural vegetation, terrain, water and climate.

The peninsula presents a maze of hilly terrain, rising to *Mount Tamalpais* (west peak, 2604 feet). (Fig. 8-51)

From steep canyons streams descend to form small fans or enter some of the numerous embayments. Though the bewildering array of slopes may seem to lack pattern, there is a definite northwest-southeast orientation. On opposite sides of Tomales Bay the parallel ridges are particularly prominent.

Impressive sea cliffs as high as 250 feet and terraces are along the relatively-straight Pacific shore. The triangular *Point Reyes Peninsula* is almost separated from the remainder of the county by the rift of the San Andreas. This isolated section remains the most sparsely populated portion of the area.

Before San Francisco growth demanded lumber, Marin had more extensive forest cover, with redwoods in canyons. In a few years the forest had been cut; today the peninsula is mostly grassland, alternately green and lush or seared.

Variation between the foggy, windswept Pacific shores and the sunnier Bayshore results from the height and width of the Marin Hills. These circumstances have furthered the appeal of eastern Marin as a residential area. While suggestive of the Peninsula, Marin is more scenic because of Bayside slope and indentation.

## MILK COWS AND COMMUTERS

Prehistoric man found the Marin Peninsula livable—so several hundred shell mounds suggest.

Ostensibly too this is the locale of Sir Francis Drake's visit in the *Golden Hind* in 1579. He appropriately called it *Nova Albion*.

Colonial Spanish use of the Peninsula was meager; *San Rafael Mission*, 20th in the chain, was not established until 1817.

Its position near the northerly end of Alta California and the difficulty of transBay navigation probably discouraged greater utilization.

The mission was established because the padres felt that the climate of Mission Dolores was contributing to a high mortality rate among its neophytes. Secularization came within 17 years. Physical evidence for the original San Rafael structure has vanished.

A series of land grants were awarded during the Mexican period and more use was made of the peninsula.

A British visitor, Sir George Simpson, was impressed in 1841 with the ability of Marin's slopes to feed cattle through the winter. Dairying and grazing remain the chief forms of rural land use; generally terrain makes this area unsuitable for tillage.

Before construction of the Golden Gate Bridge the peninsula had a limited population.

Its total habitance in 1890 was only 13,000. But between 1940 and 1990 the populace has increased from 53,000 to more than 225,000. Temporarily during World War II the population swelled with shipbuilding at Sausalito. More significant in recent decades has been Marin's importance as a suburban home for East Bay and San Francisco commuters.

**Figure 8-53.** College of Marin, Kentfield.(dwl)

**Figure 8-54.** Lytton Place, downtown Mill Valley. A visitor might almost feel oneself in England. (dwl)

## HOUSES AND BEACHES

Despite emphasis upon suburban residence and recreation, the economy of Marin County is varied.

Other functions include agriculture, commerce, and government. Growth industries, particularly defense, have been absent (except during World War II); with costly housing and limited space, Marin has been growing less rapidly than some parts of the Bay Area—and many residents actively oppose additional growth.

### Boating and Hiking, Swimming and Fishing

Coupled with proximity to urban masses, Marin's diverse setting makes it one of the Golden State's popular local vacation lands.

A 504-acre national monument, *Muir Woods*, dedicated to the renowned naturalist, is California's most accessible "larger" redwood grove. It nestles at the base of Mt. Tamalpais. On pleasant holidays and weekends it becomes so congested that parking is difficult and there is concern for the well-being of its vegetation. There are also redwoods in *Samuel Taylor State Park*.

Actually three summits *Mount Tamalpais* allows excellent view of the Bay Area. It has been popular with sightseers, hikers and picnickers since "early days." A highway winds to the summit. *Mt. Tamalpais State Park* has camping and picnic grounds and a small amphitheatre.

The most-frequented locale for salt-water bathing in the Bay Area are the beaches along Marin's western shore. Most of it is a portion of the *Golden Gate National Recreation Area*. There is also *Stinson Beach*, which has a state park with picnic sites;

it has long been utilized and becomes crowded. Other state beach parks are located along Tomales Bay. In late summer the waters of this shallow bay may reach 78 degrees F. Fog is a handicap, especially in earlier summer.

Along the eastern shore, in Richardson Bay and smaller coves, boating and sports fishing are popular. This is also true of Bolinas Bay and Tomales Bay along the western shore. Popular seafoods include oysters, salmon, perch, eel and clams.

As a state park, *Angel Island* has become another Bay Area playground.

Formerly, it was used as a military installation and also an an immigrant station. Its recreational facilities are limited although ferry service is available from Tiburon. Hiking is popular.

### Dairying and Grazing

With hilly terrain suitable for utilization, it was logical that Marin County, accessible to urban areas, should become the leading source of San Francisco's milk for half a century. But prospects for dairying have become problematic.

In the future it seems probable that Marin open lands will be used as watersheds or as parklands.

The Novato district reached its maximum milk production in 1950. Subsequently dairies east of U.S.101 have disappeared. Throughout the county, water quality control has been added to other problems due to waste drainage into lowlying areas. Now small dams are frequently needed to contain the effluent.

In northwestern Marin County dairying will probably continue for some time. But the number of cows has declined markedly and alfalfa is brought from the Central Valley or western Nevada. Farms have become larger and the number of dairies has declined. Some dairy farmers have relocated in Sonoma or Stanislaus counties. And some former dairy pasture is now used for grazing of beef cattle.

### Forts and a Prison

The principal governmental functions (other than civil) have been principally of a penal or military nature.

The state prison at *San Quentin*, established in the 1850's near San Rafael, is one of the nation's largest and most widely-known. Crowding and obsolescence have prompted consideration of its relocation.

Former Army bases facing the Golden Gate lost their importance (and were merged into the *Golden Gate National Recreation Area* in 1972) which has 38 miles of shoreline in San Francisco and Marin counties.

The Coast Guard still maintains docks on Point Reyes, but *Hamilton Air Force Base* has been deactivated. Assumedly it will become a combination of land for housing and industry. Radar facilities have been maintained for Bay Area defense atop Mt. Tamalpais.

Still operative, and of much interest to visitors, is the Corps of Engineers' *Bay Model* in Sausalito.

### Along the Way

Marin Peninsula is a gateway to San Francisco and conversely to northwestern California.

This function has gained increased usefulness since the opening of the Golden Gate (U.S. 101 and Ca. 1) and the San Rafael (Ca.17) bridges. Thus there are attendant traveler services.

### "Nice" Places To Live

The dozen little cities of eastern Marin are among California's wealthiest and most picturesque communities. Only four are larger than 10,000 and rapid growth is unlikely. Since 1960 the population of the county has grown less than 25,000.* A quartet of these "nice places", Belvedere, Tiburon, Ross and Kentfield, have been listed among America's most-expensive "suburbs."

A Sausalito realtor, queried about the cost of a house, said "It *might* be possible to get you something for several hundred thousand but the average price is much higher." The *rule of thumb* in Marin County is, "The closer a property is to the Golden Gate Bridge, the more expensive it is."

Conversion of U.S. 101 into a freeway has encouraged some growth in the northern end of the county. But despite newer housing, water and slope contribute to a continuing appeal. The peninsula, with its many expensive hillside dwellings, has long lured affluent business and professional people.

Hillside **Sausalito** (7500), with its sublime setting, manages to "cram" four faces (residence, industry, yachting and tourism) into two-plus square miles.

In the nineteenth century Sausalito was a "wild" seaport known for its gambling. It has long been a

---

* Determined to "hold the line" on growth, Marin residents have several times voted down measures to import water from the Russian River.

choice residential town for affluent San Francisco commuters and known for its quality schools. Every house on the slopes that rise steeply from Richardson Bay appears to have a view.

Visitors crowd waterfront *Bridgeway* on weekends. Along this this winding street are quality restaurants and quick-service joints, antique and gift shops, art galleries and bars. The The influence of the artist is evident.

To the north where there is more flat land, *Marinship*, site of World War II shipbuilding, has a number of small factories (including several computer firms). Then there is the community of houseboats (about a thousand in county territory) which the County would like to "sanitize."

Two of California's most expensive communities, *Tiburon* (6500) and *Belvedere* (2400) share Tiburon Peninsula, across Richardson Bay from Sausalito.

On hillside lots facing San Francisco are multi-million dollar homes. More than half of the hilly peninsula has been set aside for open space.

Haughty wealthy Belvedere occupies a hilly isle attached to the mainland by two causeways. Wholly residential, it is the site of *San Francisco Yacht Club*.

Unlike Belvedere, Tiburon attracts many tourists. Its prettied-up downtown, largely owned by one individual, has charm.

*Marin City* (2500), on the fringe of Sausalito, is a lower-income residence town.

Established as a "temporary" World War II public housing project for shipyard workers, it became an all-black community. Though attractively sited, it

**Figure 8-56.** Larkspur's skyline gives a hint of a third dimension. (dwl)

has been plagued by low incomes and high unemployment.

"Tightly" self-contained *Mill Valley* (13.000), with an older and wealthier (than county average) population, has approached "near build-out."

Much of its area remains unoccupied though wooded. Additional hillside residence is improbable due to slope and fire hazard.

Its esthetic "village" core occupies the site of the redwood mill that gave the town its name. Many business and professional commuters find the town, at the base of Mt. Tamalpais, to be idyllic.

With its older residences and quietude, it is a bit suggestive of Victoria (B.C.) in a redwood (rather than oak) setting. Situated in the basin of Widow Reed Creek it has a bewildering "dendritic" street pattern.

The twin towns of *Corte Madera* (8600) and *Larkspur* (7400) actually differ significantly. Corte Madera has appreciable retail activity while Larkspur is largely residential.

They share the basin of Corte Madera Creek and have a single school system.

Larkspur, nestled against the northeast slopes of Mt. Tamalpais , is much wooded. Some of its residents contend it has the choice setting in Marin County with redwoods in Baltimore Park Grove. Hillside condominiums have risen on view lots.

Corte Madera, centrally located in "east" county, has several shopping centers as well as a sizable ecological preserve. It has had flood problems near U.S. 101 during winter storms and high tides— hopefully they have been alleviated as result of much landfill.

Four small communities (and a clutch of hamlets farther west) snuggle along Cascade Creek (a tribu-

**Figure 8-55.** Some of California's costliest housing is in Marin County. A little dwelling in Belvedere, with a "match-box size" lot, can cost upwards of a million dollars. This house is built on pilings over Richardson Bay—with a marvelous view of "The City." (dwl)

**Figure 8-57.** Fourth Street, downtown San Rafael. (dwl)

tary of Corte Madera). There are distinct variations in social status, as well as area and population.

**Ross** (2800), exclusively aloof with many descendents of "early" Anglo families, is culturally active (flower festival, amateur theatre, concerts). There are many senior residents in highly-priced single-family bungalows, shingle-sided.

**Kentfield** (unincorp., circa 2200) has many expensive homes, College of Marin and a quality "regional" hospital.

San Anselmo (12,200) has considerable retail trade but somewhat less-expensive residences. It is the site of San Francisco Theological Seminary.

**Fairfax** (7400) is also a "closer to middle income" town. This one-time lumber camp has a sizable Italian populace (evidenced in its restaurants).

*Sir Francis Drake Highway,* understandably congested at times, provides a main street for the above towns and provides linkage with Samuel Taylor State Park (redwoods), Tomales Bay and Pt. Reyes National Seashore to the west. A series of small hamlets enroute is occupied by city workers who enjoy the rustic setting.

**San Rafael** (47,000), Marin's county seat, is the principal service center and ranking industrial city.

Once a mission site, San Rafael has changed markedly through the decades. It has had advantages of early start, central eastside and cross-roads location.

Less opposed to growth earlier than some of its neighbors, San Rafael has "paid a price." Limits were extended northward in the 1960's to include Los Golinas Basin, now the suburban site of its distinctive county center (with much free parking) designed by Frank Lloyd Wright.

San Rafael, with east-west elongation (much of its northern half is hilly open space), has in-filled with a number of multi-family units (especially condominiums). Planners identify several neighborhoods, located within two basins separated by wooded uplands.

This *is* a city and it almost overwhelms the economy, politics and finances of its county. The central district, with a number of quality specialty shops, serves also the communities noted above. Despite high land prices and circulation and parking problems it remains viable despite North Gate (one of the county's few regional shopping centers) along U.S. 101 on the city's northern edge.

Through travelers on U.S. 101 tend to get a biased view of San Rafael. Winding (and elevated), the freeway is flanked by industrial plants (generating half of the value-added within the county). A large insurance company relocated here from San Francisco.

**Novato** (49,000), Marin's leading commuter town, has achieved its ambition—it is now the largest city in the county.

Sprawling across the hills and dales of Novato Creek basin, this former dairy village was receptive to growth for several decades. As in many other cities, a belated feeling for "controlled" growth has occurred. But the population has expanded more than ten-fold in the past 40 years.

For Marin, Novato is less socially-prestigious than towns to the south—and the commute to The City is longer! The central district remains small and ill-defined (there are several shopping centers). Essentially an Anglo white-collar town still, the ethnic population remains small. Novato has

**Figure 8-58.** Typical rural landscape near San Pablo Bay. Sheep are cropping grain stubble west of Vallejo. (dwl)

fewer professional-executive residents than is typical of the county. Some industrial-commercial activity has occurred. This includes a book distribution center (McGraw-Hill), small software firms and other organizations.

After years of debate it appears that the former site of Hamilton Air Force Base will be developed for housing and industrial use.

While it is *up the road apiece* from Marin County, **Petaluma** (42,000), the service center of southern Sonoma County, is fittingly considered an *outlier* of Marin County, with much growth as a commuter bedroom. It has attracted national attention with its *Petaluma Plan* for controlled growth.

Founded in 1851, Petaluma evolved westward upslope from Petaluma Creek, developing a fan-shaped pattern. While costlier houses were on the slope there was no "wrong side of the tracks." Definitely waspish, Petaluma has had a considerable Italian and Portuguese population, hence Catholicism has been important.

For decades the hundred of surrounding family poultry farms aided its prosperity. Demise of the small poultry people led to a period of stagnation.

Conversion of U.S. 101 to an expressway in the 1960's, coupled with spiraling housing costs in Marin County, prompted evolution of a new "twin" tract town, east Petaluma. Concerned city officials formulated an *annual growth limitation plan*. Challenged by developers, the concept was sustained in 1976 by the refusal of the U.S. Supreme Court to review the case. *

Petaluma has tended to become two towns. "Old" Petaluma supports its renovated central district while eastside tract-town tends to shop in local neighborhood centers. The long-neglected waterfront has been revitalized. A population of over 50,000 seems probable, despite growth limits, by 2000, with over half of the total in east Petaluma.

---

## THE NORTH BAY **

Between the Delta Lands of the Central Valley (to the east) and Marin Peninsula (to the west) the North Bay was long "just beyond" the northern margin of the Bay Area. Now urbanization has expanded well beyond the tidal flats around the north shores of San Pablo and Suisun bays to penetrate into the valleys on the southern fringe of the Northwest (Ch.12).

Assuredly utilization of North Bay will intensify as population pressures increase.

However much of the area remains sloughs, tule marshes and grasslands along the lower courses of Napa River, Sonoma Creek and Petaluma Creek. Agricultural land here is used principally for grains or livestock ranching (Fig. 8-58). While better-drained lands to north and southwest were included within colonial land grants, portions of these "inferior" lands were not. Current returns from hay are sufficient to pay taxes and permit landowners to retain their property in anticipation of eventual urban use. Recently some larger hay producers have refused "free" treated wastewater, arguing that the market cannot support additional hay producer and that the hay cannot be "exported" and compete with the product grown on cheaper land.

Apart from urban growth, a significant change has been the construction of 12 crystallizing ponds covering 12,000 acres, where Leslie Salt recovers sodium chloride from the Bay for industrial use.

## SIX AND A HALF CENTRAL PLACES ***

Urbanizing North Bay, especially Benicia, Napa and Vallejo, began to evolve during World War II. In recent decades urbanization has been most dramatic adjacent to the *Redwood Highway* (U.S.101) around Petaluma and Santa Rosa and along the *I-80 corridor* around Benicia, Fairfield and Vacaville.

**Vallejo** (95,000) long existed as one of California's larger cities dependent upon a single employer—in this instance the federal government.

The community was established in 1850, to be the capital of California. It served this function for two years (1850-1852). Opening of a Navy yard in 1852 provided an economic boost. Then construction of a rail line from Sacramento made it a wheat-shipping port. But the Central (Southern) Pacific acquired the line, thus ending Vallejo's dreams of becoming a major rail terminus. Meanwhile it had become a flour-milling center. The city's many

---

* Economists, geographers, planners, environmentalists, developers, Chambers of Commerce officials and others nationwide followed the case, which appears to be having considerable impact on suburban and urban America.
** The late Alfred Butz, of Santa Rosa Junior College, reviewed the manuscript for the previous work, *California, Land of Contrast*. Margaret Trussell, CSU, Chico and Gary Anderson, Santa Rosa Junior College, have reviewed this section.
*** Although larger cities in North Bay are identified with the Bay Area conurbation, the reader will note that nearby rural areas are discussed subsequently as *Borderlands*.

314 The Heartland

older business blocks and houses reflect its age and intermittent growth.

During World War II, expansion at Mare Island (with construction of submarines and other smaller vessels) created much temporary housing. Subsequently for several decades growth was stagnant. Now there is appreciable commutation and also retiree residence. Relocation of *Marine World* from Redwood City in 1986 has promoted additional growth.

The central district has been renovated, with attractive retiree (many ex-Navy) residences. Commercial and waterfront industrial development is anticipated. Residential expansion is taking place east of I-80. Dependent as it has been on the Navy, Vallejo has gained an appreciable ethnic (black, Hispanic and Filipino) populace. Also, reliance on a narrow payroll source has prompted many youth to depart, leaving an aging population.

*Mare Island Navy Yard* (Fig. 8-59) occupies a hilly

island at the mouth of the Napa River overlooking San Pablo Bay. The 3000-acre base began as a Navy dock (1851) and became a Navy yard the following year. Employment, which reached 40,000 during World War II, appears to have stabilized. The yard has absorbed the functions of the now-closed San Francisco Navy Yard (i.e., Hunter's Point). In recent years atomic submarines have been built at Mare Island. Nearby is the campus of the *California Maritime Academy*.

**Benicia** (23,000), attractively situated (albeit windy) on hilly terrain overlooking Carquinez Strait, has had diverse economic supports. Recent growth has been prompted by commuter residence and port activity.

Benicia, founded in 1847, aspired to become the major port of the Bay Area. In 1853 it was temporarily the capital of California. Its capitol building is now a state historical monument. It also had a seminary (now Mills College in Oakland. For many

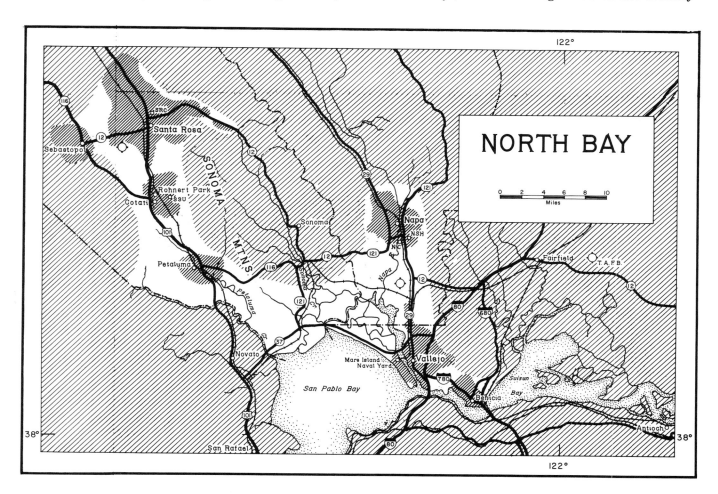

**Map 8-7.** Not too many decades ago North Bay was considered a portion of Northwestern California. As the population of cities like Napa and Santa Rosa grows, they are enmeshed more into the Bay Area.

**Figure 8-59.** Vallejo and Mare Island, separated by Vallejo Channel (lower course of Napa River). (dwl)

decades Benicia was the site of an Army Arsenal (now in Herlong—Ch. 2). Formerly there were also food canneries.

In the late 1960's an industrial park was established. Facilities include an oil refinery (Exxon) and unloading docks for foreign cars. Upslope, residential construction has increased since opening of the Martinez-Benicia bridge at the junction of I-680 and I-780.

**Fairfield** (74,000)), seat of Solano County, has experienced much growth as result of expansion of the Bay Area conurbation as well as its military installation.

*Travis Air Force Base*, site of the largest Air Transport wing, has contributed significantly to growth. Use of Travis as a staging point during the Korean

conflict prompted tripling of population in the 1950.s. The Vietnamese war led to further growth. Then, opening of a large brewery in the 1970's prompted industrial expansion as well. Solano College is located here also.

In the 1980's adjacent *Cordelia* and *Suisun City* were experiencing the effects of Fairfield's considerable growth.

**Vacaville** (62,000) is supported by government, highway services, industrial activity and commuter residence.

Traditionally surrounded by orchards, it was a farm community with agricultural processing.

At mid-century growth began to quicken with commuters to Travis A.F. Base, and more recently to other parts of the Bay Area. Vacaville has a prominent Department of Corrections institution. Many motorists remember Vacaville as a convenient stopping point (especially for food) on I-80 between the central Bay Area, Sacramento and other interior places. A number of firms have been attracted to *Vaca Valley Industrial Park*, on marginal land (agriculturally) west of I-505.

**Napa** (57,000), service center for the Napa Valley and seat of its county, has experienced considerable opposition to growth.

A *"bigger and better Napa"* trend was slowed by voter plebescite in 1973. Subsequently the county reduced the city's *sphere of influence* by two-thirds. Founded in 1848, Napa was long concerned with cattle ranching and grape growing. It has had varied but modest industrial output (including foods, sports apparel, leather goods, steel products and electronics). Employment at county offices,

**Figure 8-60.** During World War II Vallejo's Georgia Street suggested downtown Reno. In the late twentieth century, with considerable retirees residing nearby, it is more peaceful—"the action" is at Marine World. Photo taken at 8:40 p.m. (dwl)

**Figure 8-61.** The Grape Yard, Napa. Increasingly one finds tree-shaded commercial parking lots in California cities. (dwl)

**Figure 8-62.** Downtown Santa Rosa Mall. This accessible regional shopping center attracts shoppers from Lake County and points farther north in Northwestern California. (dwl)

the state hospital and the community college provide stable payrolls. While it is not a wealthy town its charm has appealed to retirees and commuters. While Napa has been predominantly Anglo it has had sizable Hispanic and Italian groups.

Among changes in recent decades have been downtown restoration (with a *semi-mall)*, shopping centers with tree-shaded parking lots, channel straightening and flood control of the Napa River (accompanied by linear parkways, bike and equestrian paths.

**Cotati** ( 5,000), once a sleepy farm hamlet, has become a commuter place.

Considerable growth in California's only hexagonal pattern town resulted from invasion by students at the nearby university who have rejected the middle-income suburbia of Rohnert Park and have enjoyed Cotati's rural air. The percentage of absentee landlords and rentals has been high and the number of liquor establishments conspicuous.

Basically a college and commuter residential place, **Rohnert Park** (33,000) has evolved as a *new town*. It is the site of Sonoma State University, one the newer institutions in the California State University system.

Conceived by three Santa Rosa developers, the city originated in 1962 on Rohnert Nursery land and has been strongly growth-oriented. Land has been set aside for a regional shopping center. For a time, its industrial park was unsuccessful in attracting plants. Subsequently small-scale industries, warehouses, and truck terminals have appeared. Hewlett-Packard has constructed a sizable plant in the southern part of the city.

**Santa Rosa** (105,000 and SMA circa 360,000), the metropolis of western North Bay, is the service center for the Santa Rosa Valley and the southern Northwest (Ch. 12). Diverse economic supports include county government.

An older North Bay town, Santa Rosa is no longer an outlier of the Bay Area although it has acquired commuters less rapidly than some anticipated—only a small fraction of workers are employed outside Sonoma County.

Considered one of California's more appealing residential locales, Santa Rosa has drawn many affluent retirees. The "over 65" group is twice the state average. Residents include scores of millionaires (many retired). There are some pleasing neighborhoods, especially on low slopes of the Sonoma Mountains with large oaks.

While continued growth seems inevitable, there is strong determination to keep Santa Rosa desirable—there is much support for sign control and architectural design review.

Santa Rosa provides many services (such as retail, financial, medical and realty). Its county government complex is placed in a park-like setting as is well-regarded *Santa Rosa Junior College*. It is the leading industrial city of North Bay; several score of plants fabricate local products and also produce apparel and electronics.

Downtown Santa Rosa has changed with the competition of a regional shopping center. There is now a downtown mall near a renovated civic center.* Many *local* merchants have not been able to

---

* Santa Rosa is one of a number of California cities that have constructed downtown malls. Others include Santa Maria, Santa Monica, Glendale, Bakersfield and Pasadena. While many have done well, those in Sacramento, Fresno, Riverside and Pomona have proved less successful.

**Figure 8-63.** Dairy farm, Point Reyes. Such private holdings vanish in the National Seashore as farmers retire. (dwl)

The San Francisco Bay Area 317

Long associated with the its apple-growing environs as a portion of the Northern Borderlands, **Sebastopol** (7500) is becoming an outlier of metropolitan Santa Rosa.

It serves western Sonoma County and houses an increasing number of commuters to Santa Rosa.

## THE NORTHERN BORDERLANDS

Outward from the Bay Area toward the Sacramento Valley and the Northwest, the Northern Borderlands forms a transition zone of on-going change. As urbanization continues around larger North Bay cities the Borderlands extends outward. Elsewhere hilly terrain, weather (coastal fog), distance from central places (especially San Francisco, Oakland and Sacramento) and possibly political limitations, have discouraged urbanization.

The Northern Borderlands forms a pleasing part of pastoral California.

Despite the lengthy summer drought with seared countrysides, there is a suggestion of rural England during winter storms and spring drizzles when the lush greens of the grasses and the park-like groves of oaks are memorable.

## POINT REYES PENINSULA

Bleak windswept Point Reyes Peninsula, pointing westward like a great arrow is a mere 35 miles northwest of San Francisco. Congress created *Point Reyes National Seashore* in 1962 to maintain open space on the outskirts of the Bay Area, scarcely ahead of the subdivider.

Within a few years after its establishment, hundreds of thousands of visitors were utilizing it annually. Eventually the parkland will contain 53,000 acres; about half of that has been acquired. Much of the other acreage will remain in dairy farms for some years ahead.

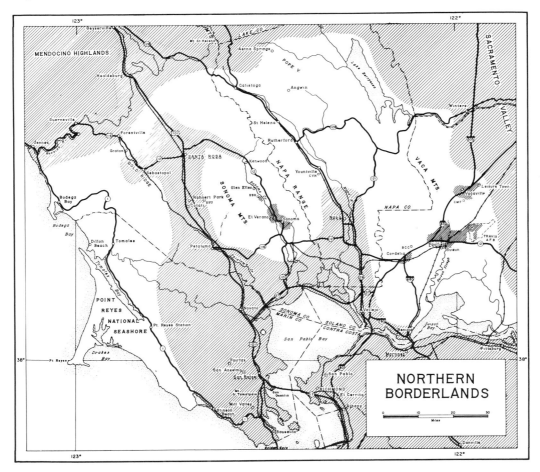

**Map 8-8.** The Bay Area continues to reach outward into the lowlands of the Northern Borderlands. So far there is no community as large as 15,000.

**Figure 8-64.** Some see in the Sonora Coast, seen here near Jenner, a ressemblance to eastern Canad'a Gaspe Peninsula of Maritime Canada. (dwl)

The Seashore provides a place to hike and to picnic; more than 40 miles of trails have been established. There are 45 miles of beach, but the water is too chilly and the sky too foggy for most water enthusiasts.

## THE SONOMA COAST

The coast of southwestern Sonoma County and adjacent Marin County. between Tomales Bay and the mouth of the Russian River, presents a low rolling surface.

Ocean-facing slopes are grass covered. This area contrasts with the rugged Big Sur Coast (Ch.7) farther south and the Mendocino Coast (Ch. 12) to the north. Inland, on steeper lands redwood and Douglas fir persist although much of the countryside was logged in the past.

People of European descent were attracted early to this Coast. Four land grants were established in the Mexican colonial era. Early in the American period its appeal included its accessibility (both overland for individuals and from Bodega Bay for shipping goods to market), adequate precipitation for dryland farming, tillable soils and adjacent redwood forests.

Yet appreciation of the Coast for recreational use developed late.

Present-day activity is centered on *Bodega Bay* (400), a small resort and fishing hamlet upon a south-facing water body suggestive of Morro Bay (Ch. 7).

Inland from the shore the southern part of the Sonoma Coast forms the northwestern fringe of the Marin-Sonoma dairy belt. Farther north the Coast grades into a lesser logging area and a resort development near the Russian River.

## SANTA ROSA VALLEY

With spreading urbanization around Petaluma and Santa Rosa, the Santa Rosa Valley, the heartland of Sonoma County, is losing its Borderlands status.

With its northern extension (into the Upper Russian Valley) it has been somewhat a counterpart to the Santa Clara Valley south of San Francisco Bay. It is appreciably cooler in summer than the Great Central Valley; in winter it is cool, damp and luxuriantly green.

While the Santa Rosa is known for its fruits (especially apples, grapes and prunes), livestock and poultry have greater value. Surrounding Petaluma, on meadows extending northward from San Pablo Bay, is a dairyscape of rolling terrain.

Herds of Holstein and Brown Swiss, 100 to 400 cows per farm, together with white fences and buildings, often weatherbeaten , and files of eucalyptus windbreaks are commonplace. In few places in California is permanent grass pasture so conspicuous.

Since decline in the Santa Clara Valley and Marin County, Sonoma County has been more important as a milkshed for the Bay Area. Dairy herds have become larger and milk output per cow has increased. As in Marin County and elsewhere, waste disposal is a problem.

Sonoma County is also the leading source of riding

**Figure 8-65.** The pleasant apple and grape producing Gold Ridge, west of Sebastopol, is "threatened" by urbanization— it is too close to Santa Rosa. (dwl)

horses for the Bay Area—thus today there are more horses than in pre-tractor days! Much hay is also raised for Bay Area "horse farms."

Still an important supplier for the Bay Area, the Petaluma district was once the self-acclaimed "egg basket of the world."

Decades ago the landscape was dotted with 2000 small mom-and-pop poultry farms (decaying chicken houses are *still* visible). Present output comes largely from less than ten major firms whose "egg factories" are isolated from main highways.

The Sebastopol district *(formerly* known as *The Gold Ridge)* is one of California's two leading apple-producing areas. It is known especially for the *Gravenstein* variety.

This hilly western fringe of the Santa Rosa Valley has cooler summers than much of California while winters are cool enough to permit dormancy. Redwoods on hilltops are reminders that this is an outlier of the Northwest.

The district has contributed significantly to California's ranking (second to Washington) among Western apple-growing areas. The Gravenstein is a golden summer apple much used for pies and sauce. There has been local processing but some is shipped as fresh fruit. Acreage has declined; some sons have been reluctant to follow their fathers. Orchards tend to be small and there has been little interest in replanting.

A major farming shift on the northern Plain and nearby lowlands has been the dramatic expansion of grape acreage and the decline of prunes.

It was in Sonoma County that the legendary

**Figure 8-66.** The tranquility of the Sonoma Valley is lessening with continuing growth. Jack London's "Valley of the Moon" is popular with retirees and commuters. (dwl)

Augustin Haraszthy introduced quality European grapes in the 1850's. For some years Sonoma was the leading California producer of varietal grapes. Although Sonoma grape acreage did not rebound from Prohibition era decline as soon as the Napa Valley. It was only with the increased wine consumption after 1960 that Sonoma production expanded.

Sonoma County, although less renowned than Napa Valley, has been a long-time source of such better-quality dry table wines as Burgundy, Sauterne and Zinfandel. Sonora County champagne and sparkling Burgundy are considered some of the nation's best.

In the second half of the twentieth century a marked increase in viticulture occurred in the northern part of the Santa Rosa Valley (between Santa Rosa and Healdsburg) and northward into *Alexander Valley.* Traditionally grapes were grown on small family-owned properties but a marked expansion of corporate-owned operations materialized. Large acreages of such varieties as Cabernet Sauvignon and Pinot Noir were added to the "traditional" ones.

**Healdsburg** (10,000), established early (1852), has long had importance as a center for viticulture and lumbering.

It is being affected by the outward reach of Bay Area urbanization as well as geothermal developments at *The Geysers* to the northeast. Tourism related by Wine Country attractions is likewise important.

## SONOMA VALLEY

The open-ended Sonoma Valley, which Jack London called *The Valley of the Moon,* dangles appendix-like southeastward from the Santa Rosa Valley. It is considered by many to be one of the choice residential areas in the Golden State.

Thus it is not surprising that an increasing number of affluent senior citizens have moved here. Despite lack of a speedy link (such as U.S. 101) into San Francisco, continued urbanization seems inevitable.

Like many productive California lowlands, the Sonoma is undulating. It has "small landscapes" that suggest the Appalachian Highlands or rural New England with a different clime and vegetation. Lower slopes, as well as the Valley floor, are dotted with small residential ranches.

**Figure 8-67.** Grape harvest in the Napa Valley. (Wine Institute).

Narrow winding roads and long lanes leading to sheltered dwellings crisscross the Sonoma in a crude rectangle. Large oaks, seasonally-flowing creeks and hedges of flowers add beauty.

Vineyards (increasing even on "marginal" low spots towards San Francisco Bay) and fruit orchards (declining) and grazing land (sheep and beef cattle) intermingle into a complex land-use mosaic. There is also a major turkey producer (allegedly the world's largest, with additional output in Egypt and Europe).

The old mission town of **Sonoma** (8000) is becoming less sleepy. It is the largest of several communities. Annexation has occurred but the city hopes to plan anticipated growth.

## NAPA VALLEY

A near-synonym for quality dry wines, the Napa Valley may provide the ultimate answer in the next quarter-century: "Will California be able to preserve its quality agricultural lands on the fringes of metropolitan areas?

Many residents of the Napa have the determination. The value of their open landscape has been thoroughly recognized—long before its loss to urbanization. Throughout the Valley rural areas are now zoned with 40-acre minimums.

Even though the county population has expanded from 28.000 (1940) to over 100,000 (1990), a "target" population of 110,000 has been set for the year 2000. And if the rural environment can be maintained there is the problem of the vineyards as an lure for commuter residence.* Moreover the vine-

yards are attracting more visitors, hence more traffic and more smog.

Nearly two score miles long, Napa Valley extends southward from *Mt. St. Helena* (a 4344-foot landmark) to the edge of San Pablo Bay.

To some the Napa Valley seems more European than Californian. The many spacious two-story dwellings contrast with the usual California farmhouse. And the stone bridges suggest Europe, or perhaps New England.

This settled landscape reflects the early establishment of Anglo agriculture in California—American inhabitants began locating here even before the Mexican War.

The lower Valley, south of Napa, merges into the North Bay portion of the Bay Area. On treeless meadows grazing of beef cattle is characteristic. Between Napa and Yountville the traveler sees orchards of deciduous fruit. Increasingly where there is more summer heat and sandy soils, the land produces grapes. The upper Valley, centering on St. Helena, is devoted almost exclusively to vineyards.

### Famed for Viticulture

Valleys of the Northern Borderlands, particularly the Napa around St. Helena, have wide renown for the quality rather than quantity of wine produced. A much larger portion of the nation's less expensive wines come from the San Joaquin Valley.**

---

\* A recent census reveals that one of each five commuters was driving 60 to 80 miles daily in order to reside in the Valley. But then more and more commuters to the Bay Area live as far away as the Foothills of the Sierra Nevada.

\*\* Many of the grapes made into quality wines in the Napa Valley are actually grown in the San Joaquin Valley and trucked to the Napa Valley for processing.

**Figure 8-68.** Vintage 1870 Yountville. This old winery is a tourist attraction. Tourism continues to grow in popularity in the "Wine Country." (dwl)

Like those prepared elsewhere in these Border-lands, many of Napa wines are the result of family operations that date back several generations.

Now, however, many of the wineries are corporate-owned.

Through lengthy trial and error varieties have been developed that respond best to slight differences in soils and climate. * Rainfall, for example, increases from 31 inches annually at Napa to 38 inches at Calistoga. Grape varieties, although all are members of the Old World family *vinifera*, have been modified and are considered *California* varieties.

Napa Valley grape acreage has more than doubled in the decades since 1960. Now within a small area are grown the equivalent of a number of Europe white, red and rose types approaching in quality the wines of France, Germany and Italy.

The Cabernet Sauvignon of the Napa has been rated the world's best red Bordeaux and Pinot Chardonnay the world's best white while Pinot Noir, Grenache and Johannesberg Riesling have been rated *excellent*.

"Vintage year" is less meaningful in the Napa Valley than it is in Europe, since so many wines are produced within a small area. But a good year for one variety can still be a less-successful year for another variety. Yet there appears to be less year-to-year variation than in Europe.

## Country Places

Other than Napa, discussed previously, Valley towns tend to remain small agricultural centers, retirement spots and tourist stops.

Proximity to the urban Bay Area, climatic mild-

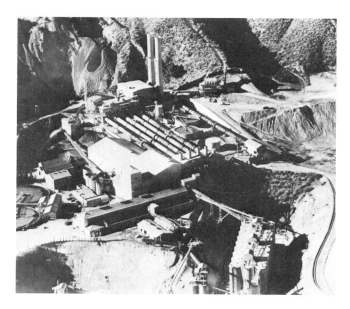

**Figure 8-70.** Permanente Cement, west of San Jose in the Santa Cruz Mountains. (Permanente Cement Corporation)

ness, scenery and an air of quietude may explain why these "village greens" have much popularity as homes for senior citizens, many from metropolitan backgrounds.

**Yountville** (3100) is popular with retirees (many in mobile homes) and tourists (*especially* its restored winery, Vintage 1870). The village "padded" its population upon incorporation (in 1966) by including residents of the *State Veterans' Hospital*.

**St. Helena** (4800) is the leading shipping point for quality wines. Its business blocks and well-maintained older homes add appeal. As a retirement center, it has a large sanitarium.

In the hills east of the Valley, *Angwin* is the locale of Pacific Union College, a small sectarian institution.

**Calistoga** (4200), at the north end of the Valley has had a longtime reputation as a health resort and has attracted many retirees. It is a crossroads town with agricultural concerns. Like the Lake County spas farther north, its hot springs are the result of volcanic activity.

## Secluded Valleys

There are several smaller lowlands east and north of Napa Valley. Some are isolated and all display climatic transition between the Northern Border-lands (i.e., the Bay Area) and the Sacramento Valley, colder in winter and hotter in summer.

**Figure 8-69.** Monticello Dam and Lake Berryessa. This federal facility, part of the Central Valley Project, provides water for Solano County. The lake is popular with Bay Area residents for aquatic recreation. (Bureau of Reclamation, photo by A.G. D'Alessandro)

---

* Important climatic factors include total seasonal heat, length of growing season, growing-season humidity, winter temperature and air temperature.

Until recently the Vaca Valley would have been included; because of its continued urbanization it was listed earlier with North Bay.

*Berryessa Valley*, once devoted to livestock and grains, is now beneath the waters of Lake Berryessa (Fig. 8-69). Isolated *Pope Valley* to the north continues to be used for livestock ranching.

## THE SOUTHERN BORDERLANDS

Even as the Bay Area blends into Northwestern California (Ch.12) with the Northern Borderlands, on its southern periphery it phases into the Central Coast (Map 8-9). Conditions that have resulted in a thinning of population are comparable (hilly terrain, foggy weather and distance from central places.

These subdivisions of the Southern Borderlands are identified: **Santa Cruz Range**, **Half Moon Littoral (Coastside)**, **southern Santa Clara Valley**, and **Mt. Hamilton Range**.

## SANTA CRUZ RANGE

This is the stellar southern Coast Range. The distinctiveness of the Santa Cruz is due to its physical features and its proximity to millions of residents of the Bay Area. The central California equivalent of the San Bernardino and San Gabriel mountains of Southern California, it affords urban dwellers easy access to a forested upland.

Physical aspects magnify the attractiveness of the Santa Cruz.

Instead of the chaparral and grasslands typical of more southerly and easterly ranges, the Santa Cruz has had extensive redwood and live oak forests. Some redwood preserves have become public reserves but others are privately-owned. Esthetic values are too high to permit extensive cutting. But this was the first area to experience large-scale redwood logging, soon after the Gold Rush.

The Santa Cruz forms a complex fault structure with two principal blocks.

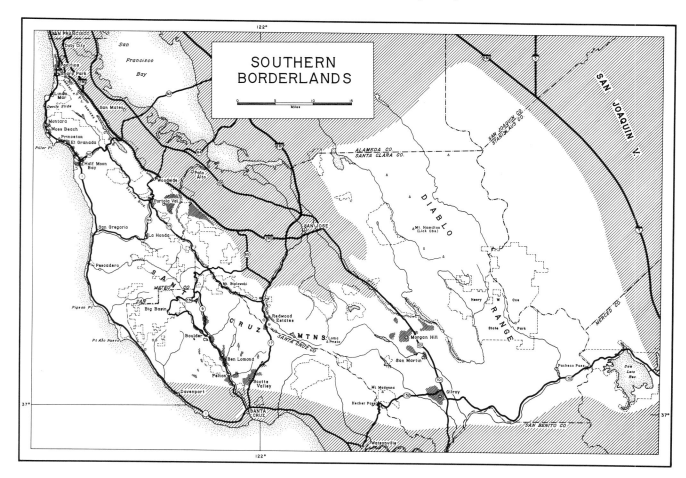

**Map 8-9.** The Bay Area continues its outward "push" southward.

The blocks are separated by the San Andreas rift which contains *sag ponds*, now known as San Andreas and Crystal Springs lakes. San Bruno Mountain and the city of San Francisco occupy portions of the northern block.

Few, if any, California highlands are so extensively laced with faults as the Santa Cruz. Yet upland areas are surprisingly flat. Although summits rise to merely 2,000 to 3,000 feet, the range receives more rainfall than most of the southern Coast Ranges. Moisture, plus cool maritime air and redwood and live oak forests with fir, pine, and madrone, have given it a special charm.

Still extensively wooded, the mild Santa Cruz forms an excellent playground for nearby urban dwellers. It also contains numerous residences of senior citizens and commuters to peripheral cities as well as small ranches.

In summer this range is one of California's most visited rural uplands. Skyline Boulevard (Ca. 35) and I-280 provide good access from San Francisco, Santa Cruz and environs.

The *San Lorenzo Valley* in the heart of the range, is suggestive of both the Appalachian Highlands and English hill country. Flanking Ca. 9 are woods, wineries, delightful little inns and restaurants. There is a cool greenness that is unusual in the surrounding areas in summer. The names too are charming and inviting: *Brookdale*, *Quail Hollow*, *Ben Lomond* and *Ice Cream Grade* are a few.

In summer this is one of California's most-visited uplands. I-280 and Skyline Boulevard (Ca. 35) continue northward into San Francisco.

**Scotts Valley** (8000), along Ca. 17 farther east, and finally incorporated, suggests a Southern California mountain town.

Despite its varied amusements and its sprawl (and seemingly limited concern about growth), it is an inviting residential community.

Several state parks were established because of their redwood groves.

One of the earliest groves set aside (in 1902) for public enjoyment, **Big Basin Redwoods State Park**, is one of the most frequented preserves in the system in summer. In winter there is virtual solitude. The park has streams, hiking trails, picnic grounds and campsites in addition to the tall trees.

Adjacent to the U.C., Santa Cruz campus is *Henry Cowell Redwoods State Park*; its *Big Trees Grove* (43 acres) has been frequented for a century. Still

**Figure 8-71.** Urban spillover from the northern Santa Clara Valley is taking place in the southern Santa Clara Valley around Morgan Hill and Gilroy(seen here). (dwl)

farther east is *Forest of Nisene Marks State Park* (undeveloped).

The Santa Cruz is the single southern Coast Range to have towns of significance.

Although its communities tend to be residential in nature with resort facilities, Boulder Creek has a Lockheed missile installation.

Other than Scotts Valley, most of the larger towns are found in the San Lorenzo Valley: **Ben Lomond** (2300), **Boulder Creek** (3000) and **Felton** (3500). While associated with the Santa Clara Valley, places in the Santa Cruz Mountains west of I-280 popular with the "Society horsey set" are probably better considered *exurban* rather than suburban. *Woodside*, definitely exudes a rustic air while **Portola Valley** (4000) is both costlier and more isolated.

**Los Altos Hills** (7000), despite its location, is probably better considered suburban. Located here, despite objections of many residents, is *Foothill College*, esteemed for the quality of its two-year program.

Mining has contributed to utilization of the Santa Cruz Range for many decades.

*New Almaden* has been California's all-time second source of *quicksilver*. Working of these deposits, south of San Jose, lasted for a century. The operation, whose 100 miles of tunnels extend below sea level, is waterfilled. Now it is *New Almaden National Historic Landmark District*. Smaller mines in the vicinity operated intermittently for a while after World War II.

Manufacture of *cement* has been much more consequential in the second half of the twentieth century.

Market proximity is the primary consideration in the location of cement mills; the two in the Santa Cruz are near Bay Area markets.*

Pacific Cement at Davenport, on the edge of the Santa Cruz Coast, is the older producer. The firm also produces considerable sand and gravel. Permanente Cement is a Kaiser affiliate in western Cupertino. It was originally constructed to provide cement for construction of Shasta Dam (Fig. 9-66). With more than three times the capacity of the Davenport mill this plant is one of the largest in the world.

## THE HALFMOON LITTORAL

Sometimes called *Coastside*, to distinguish it from the Peninsula (the Bay side of the Santa Cruz Mountains), the Half Moon Littoral extends for 60 miles from San Francisco's southwestern outliers toward Davenport (Fig. 8-2).

Like the Santa Cruz coast it adjoins, the Littoral consists of marine terraces varying in width from yards to more than a mile.

It is backed by the steep western slopes of the Santa Cruz Range which are generally heavily-wooded.

Isolation persisted for decades.

Before the 1920's (and highway improvement) most commerce was conducted by small coastal freighters. Today Ca. 1 is used for travel. **

Once whaling was of importance. Then Portuguese and other farmers settled on the terraces.

Although there are suggestions of urban encroachment, farming remains the principal use of the Littoral.

This foggy, windy coast has lacked the appeal of the drier Peninsula east of the Santa Cruz Range. Horticulture, dairying, poultry, and fog-belt vegetables constitute the principal agricultural pursuits. Horticulture, a multi-million dollar activity, has become more important in recent decades . Winter grains also retain significance.

Among the vegetables, artichokes have partially replaced Brussels sprouts, especially in San Pedro Valley and along Half Moon Bay. *** Other vegetables include beans, peas, lettuce, carrots, potatoes and cabbage.

Despite sandy beaches, headlands and closeness to metropolitan millions, the tourist potential of the Littoral has lagged.

Bay Area residents sometimes surf or fish, especially along Half Moon Bay. Restaurants and lodges are rather modest, indicating one-day visits. While weather-beaten farmhouses are suggestive of Maine, the white buildings of *Pescadero* appear trim. Some see a resemblance to New England's Cape Cod.

Although some hamlets originated early in the Anglo period, urbanization came belatedly to the Littoral. Town growth has been influenced by availability of flattish terrain, metropolitan access and water.

In places the slopes of the Santa Cruz Mountains rise precipitously from the Pacific.

**Pacifica** (40,000), a white-collar commuter town principally with with single-family tract houses, is a virtual continuation of San Francisco and Daly City.

Like Fremont in East Bay it is essentially a "new town." It was formed in 1957 with the merger of nine villages. Earlier tract dwellings were relatively inexpensive; newer units have been more costly. Density remains low. More than half the working residents are employed in San Francisco.

**Half Moon Bay** (9000), while providing local services (there is a small shopping center) has importance too as a commuter town. Plans for anticipated growth had to reduced drastically because of the California Coast Plan.

Accessible via Ca. 92 with The Peninsula and The East Bay, the town's *general plan* had anticipated a population of 110,000 by 1990! In any event, available water would appear to be a limitation ("Hetch Hetchy" water is purchased from the city of San Francisco).

## SOUTHERN SANTA CLARA VALLEY

A continuation of South Bay (northern Santa Clara Valley) south of *Coyote Narrows*,**** the south-

---

* Understandably California, with the nation's largest population and continued growth, leads in cement production. Besides the Bay Area mills, others are operated north of Redding, in the Sierra Nevada and near the Los Angeles Lowlands in the Mojave Desert. The principal ingredient is limestone, which is widespread; market determines location.

** *The Devil's Slide*, between Pacifica and Point Montara, has repeatedly blocked the highway during winter wetness.

*** Many Americans apparently dislike Brussels sprouts, which appear to rank with liver, brains, and prune juice among foods unpopular with some people.

**** Despite the name Santa Clara Valley (after the mission) the Santa Clara River is in Southern California (Ch. 6). Coyote Creek flows north into San Francisco Bay.

ern Santa Clara Valley is a segment of the graben-like trough occupied by San Francisco Bay (northward) and the San Benito Valley (southward).

Before its northern segment became urbanized, as has been noted, the entire Santa Clara was acclaimed the "Fruit Bowl of America."

Since farming began, the Santa Clara has been favored for agriculture. Location near tidewater and San Francisco afforded marketing advantages. There is a long mild growing season and soils are fertile. In the past it seemed that the Valley had an adequate supply of water.

## A Cornucopia of Produce

It is difficult to capsulize the agricultural residue of the Santa Clara Valley.

Traditionally the Valley yielded considerable quantities of fruits and berries, vegetables, alfalfa, poultry and dairy products. Much of this has either vanished or is sharply curtailed.

Past distribution tended to reflect terrain, water availability (costs and needs), soils and land prices. Usable land has become increasingly critical so that emphasis is upon perishable commodities for local markets.

Between 1947 and 1974 cultivated land decreased from 99,000 to 23,000 acres. Now local Hispanics and illegal entrants do much of the field work once done by Filipinos and migratory American-born "field tramps."

*Cherries*, which prefer well-drained soils, were traditionally grown in the western Santa Clara *and* south of Coyote Narrows. Acreage persists in the latter area. The white-fleshed Royal Annes were grown for canning while the red Bings and Black Tartarians have often been consumed as fresh fruit.

The Santa Clara has been known for its quality wine grapes.

In the past considerable acreage existed along the eastern base of the Santa Cruz Mountains. More recent plannings were made east of Gilroy but viticulturalists tend to relocate in the upper San Benito Valley and in the middle Salinas Valley.

Determination that the southern Valley could remain agricultural has dimmed. After construction of an I.B.M. "think tank" south of Coyote Narrows in the middle 1970's urbanization began to accelerate.

## Two Ex-Farm Towns

At mid-century virtually all the towns of the Santa Clara were farm centers. Within several decades that image had disappeared north of Coyote Narrows. In the past quarter of the century it has shown indications of occurring in the southern Santa Clara as well.

**Morgan Hill** (25,000), forty years ago was little more than a roadside fruit-shipping point. Now it reaches the width of the southern Valley, houses many commuters and has industrial parks.

**Gilroy** (25,000) traditionally has been the leading city of the southern Valley.

It has had agricultural processing industries and shipping. In the 1980's its growth rate was smaller than that of Morgan Hill. As population fill-in continues, added population with more commuters is anticipated.

## MT. HAMILTON RANGE

Use of the portion of the Diablo-Mt. Hamilton Range east of southern Santa Clara is much more limited than farther north.

Despite Ca. 152, an increasingly-traveled east-west link between U.S. 101, I-5 and Ca. 99 over *Pacheco Pass*, there are few roads in this part of the range.

*Henry Coe State Park*, second-largest in its system, is truly unknown even within the Bay Area. Roads enter only the fringes and except for hikers and campers, slight use is made of the preserve.

The contrast in utilization with the Santa Cruz Range is conspicuous. This is truly a Central Coast borderland. The widespread activity, grazing and dry-farming, is much more representative of the Central Coast than of the Bay Area.

## THERE *ARE* PROBLEMS

The San Francisco Bay Area, the nation's fourth most-peopled conurbation, is highly-regarded by residents and visitors alike, and one can be enchanted by its endowments and overlook its problems. *Of course* the view, day or night, from a descending aircraft or from Twin Peaks is spectacular. And one can savor with pleasure the specialty of the house at one of the many quality restaurants. But when looks at the Bay Area in detail...

Problems there are, and some of them are worsening.

Already San Francisco and Oakland are non-Anglo majority cities as the affluent and many

**Figure 8-72.** Prunes drying in the sun east of Gilroy. Sun drying of fruit, the traditional method introduced from Mediterranean Europe, is being replaced by artificial drying. Most of California's prunes come from the Central Valley now. (dwl)

**Figure 8-73.** The "hub" of downtown Woodside, a horse-set area in the Santa Cruz Mountains west of I-280. (dwl)

with middle incomes continue to take residence elsewhere. Thus the "problems" are left behind to be resolved by increasingly Asian and Hispanic residents.

There are troubling social problems. While *AIDS* is constantly newsworthy, there are other medical problems. What about the needed social services? And the elimination of smog, disposal of wastes, maintenance of streets, reduction of crime?

Many dwellings in the Bay Area, as elsewhere in California, are not adequate. And as in metropolitan Southern California, there is the growing problem of homelessness.

The population of the Bay Area continues to increase. *Where* can the newcomers live? One can sympathize with restrictive feelings of those in Marin County, or Petaluma, or Walnut Creek who want growth to stop. But does it make sense for people to commute from the Sierran Foothills, or even from Dixon? *Reasonable* open space *must* be maintained and often terrain dictates it. *Obviously* the solution is not to create more Redwood Shores or Bay Farm on Bayfill. Presently, the cost of owning a home in many parts of the Area is prohibitive for many of its residents.

What about jobs? In the Bay Area as in Southern California, in a post-industrial society, many jobs (often paying well) are related to the vagaries of "defense." It can be argued that this is better than "no jobs at all." One prominent state legislator has advocated "filling the entire Bay"—if that will give the needy work.

There are many other things as well. Is the Bay Area losing its uniqueness? Will San Francisco lose still more prominence to the rest of the metropolis? If so, will this result in less unity? How many, and what types of major satellite cities are emerging? How far outward can the Bay Area be expected to spread?

Transportation is a worrisome problem as the population increases and commuters travel farther. What will be the solution when America (and the world) exhausts its supply of petroleum? Should B.A.R.T. lines be extended? And how can ridership be increased? And what of airports? Obviously San Francisco International's traffic cannot increase forever. And the other airports, San Jose, Oakland and Concord—their locations do not bode well for expansion. Is *any* concern being given to a commercial airport in North Bay?

The future of the Bay Area's rich Central Valley hinterland is of much concern. Some worry about loss of additional prime farmlands to urbanization. But there is the matter of foreign sales, which declined in the 1980's.

**Figure 8-74.** Downtown San Francisco— Geary at Powell. Photo taken on a *rare* June day when temperature approached 100° F. (dwl)

What about that next catastrophic earthquake? Sufficient preparations do not seem to have been made. Why not?

Finally, it seems that other than Southern California possibly, the Bay Area has closer ties with the Pacific Rim than the rest of California. Is the best effort being made to maximize those connections?

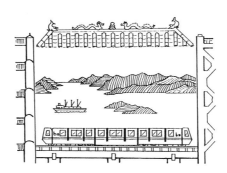

**Figure 9-1 upper left.** Kiwifruit, Butte County, central Sacramento Valley. Consumption of the *Chinese gooseberry* continues to increase. Another recent fruit introduction is fejoa. (Alkop Farms, Inc.)

**Figure 9-3 upper right.** Play of the professional Sacramento *Kings* has made Sacramento *more* aware that it is a metropolis. (Photo by Rocky W. Widner).

**Figure 9-2 lower left.** Ca. 99 near Visalia. This is the "main street" between Central Valley cities. It is (lower not a freeway yet between Red Bluff and metropolitan left) Sacramento. (dwl).

**Figure 9-4 lower right.** Processing of Foster Farms chickens, Livingston. Research indicated that Californians were willing to pay more for a quality product. Foster Farms *exceeds* federal *pure food* standards (San Francisco Chronicle, photo by Jerry Telfer).

Chapter Nine

THE GREAT
CENTRAL VALLEY*

* This chapter has been reviewed by Howard Gregor, U.C., Davis.

# THE GREAT CENTRAL VALLEY

California's banana-shaped midland, the Great Central Valley, yields more agricultural wealth than most of the nation's states. Cotton and rice, oranges and plums, sugar beets and tomatoes—all these and scores of other crops in impressive quantities—'tis little wonder the Valley intrigues the visitor interested in farming. *

It was an English writer on America who said that California's interior is divided into three valleys: the Sacramento, the San Joaquin and the Great Central Valley. England has no monopoly on provincialism; there are people in San Francisco who think "The Valley" means that little vineyard-grown backwater called the Napa; San Joseans refer to the ...Santa Clara as "The Valley"; while down Hollywood way a little corral full of stucco houses and stations wagons known as the San Fernando rates local headlines as "The Valley." And well known is John Steinbeck's impudence in titling a book of his stories "The Long Valley," when everyone but eastern reviewers knew it was the ... Salinas he had in mind.**

The Central Valley, despite its centrality and its economic moment, is scenically California's stepchild—one finds no romantic thrill in such widely-known "local literature" as Carey McWilliams, Frank Norris or John Steinbeck. Probably none of California's other subregions has so little physical attraction— many visitors tend to be charmed more by its deserts.

An elongated structural trough of low elevation, the Valley is California's "food basket," yielding half of the state's farm income. It has become one of the world's major irrigated areas in the twentieth century—currently three of its counties rank among the top five national in total agricultural output. It has superlative endowment as a farming subregion—level terrain, productive soils, groundwater and streams for irrigation, a lengthy season with a dry harvest period, good transportation, and access to expanding domestic, Pacific Basin and other overseas markets.

Slightly smaller than the Mojave Desert or the Sierra Nevada, this attenuated basin approximates 25,000 square miles in area and houses about 14 per cent of California's people. It extends for about 450 miles from the foot of the Grapevine (south of Bak-

ersfield) in the south to Redding in the north—thus it is more than half the length of California.

Mountain-girt, the Valley is readily defined—the single break in its highland rim occurs at *Carquinez Strait* where the Sacramento River debouches into San Francisco Bay after receiving the discharge of the San Joaquin River.

On the east there is a gradual transition from the valley trough into the Sierra Nevada and the Southern Cascade (map 9-1).

The Klamath Mountains and the Southern Cascade merge to produce the northern margin and the linkage of the Tehachapi Range with the southern Coast Ranges provides a southern closure. The southern (i.e., the Central Coast) and northern (i.e., the Northwest) Coast ranges define the western border.

The Valley has marked elongation in a northwest-southeast direction.

Its width averages approximately 50 miles. On clear days the surrounding summits are readily visible—an impressive sight when the peaks are snow-capped after a winter storm.

Traditionally the Central Valley is known as the San Joaquin Valley southward from Lodi and the Sacramento Valley northward from Sacramento. Between these two subdivisions is the Delta Lands, the low-lying terrain at the confluence of the Sacramento and San Joaquin rivers.

---

* The terms *Central Valley, Great Valley, Great Central Valley, Valley of California* and "The Valley" have all been used in the literature. In this chapter they will be used somewhat interchangeably.
** Lawrence Clark Powell, "San Joaquin Valley." Reprinted from the October 1948 *Wilson Library Bulletin* by courtesy of the W.H. Wilson Company, New York, and permission of the author.

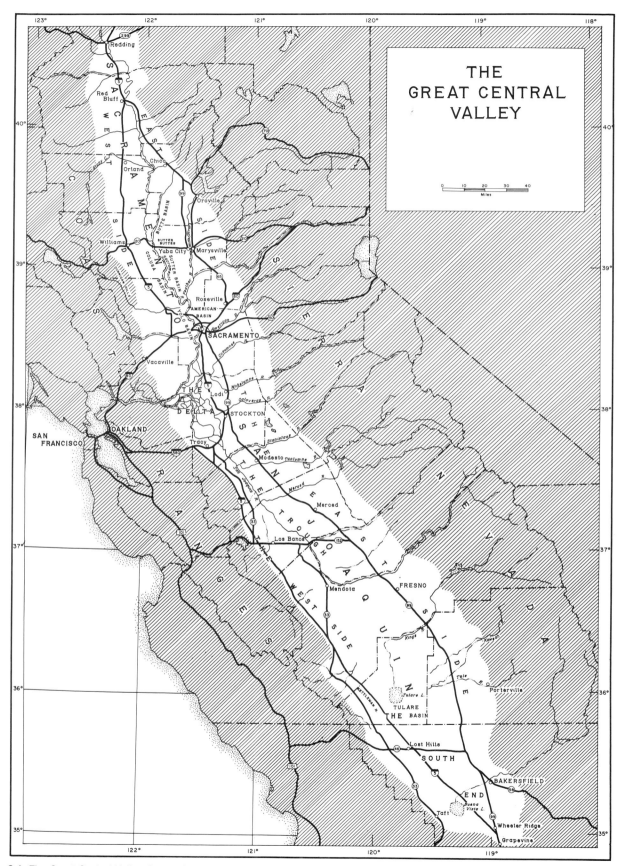

**Map 9-1**. The Great Central Valley, increasingly an urban land. The U.S. Census Bureau now identifies ten SMA's in the Valley. Yet the area remains the premium agricultural realm of the Golden State and the American West.

The southern San Joaquin Valley, without natural drainage to the ocean, is also known as Tulare Basin whereas the northern Sacramento Valley, between Redding and Red Bluff, is the Redding District, unique for its undulating terrain.

## THE PHYSICAL REALM

Despite much human alteration of soils and vegetation, the natural environment of the Central Valley, so important to its agricultural utilization, retains many evidences of its pristine environment.

### Geosyncline

The Great Valley is a fault-fold basin with a lengthy and complex geologic history.

It is the residue of a larger geosyncline whose margins were buckled upward to become the ancestral Sierra Nevada and the Coast Ranges. The Valley has been subjected to longtime alluvial deposition from surrounding highlands, chiefly the Sierra Nevada.

Deposition has tended to be intermittent; at times arms of the ocean penetrated into the basin. Beneath the surface is an unconsolidated alluvial fill that in places exceeds 2000 feet in thickness. Beneath this alluvium are sedimentary rocks several miles in depth that have yielded much natural gas and petroleum.

Despite their occupance of a single depression the Sacramento and San Joaquin valleys have had somewhat dissimilar histories.

The San Joaquin is markedly asymmetrical with its north-south axis displaced westward. The Sacramento Valley is more symmetrical, with the Sacramento River flowing southward near its centerline (or even to the eastern side north of Colusa).

The Sacramento River enters its basin at the northern tip of the Valley and flows southward with sufficient volume to transport its load. By contrast, the San Joaquin and its principal tributaries enter their position of the trough from the east, frequently with too little volume to transport their debris as the gradient decreases and stream flow lessens in summer.

### Alluvial Fans and Red Lands

Subdivisions of the Great Valley includes these physiographic units: alluvial uplands, low alluvial plains, flood basins, floodplains, delta islands and isolated hills.

The dissected *alluvial uplands* (terraces) are discontinuous along both the western and eastern edges of the Valley.

They represent an ancient Valley floor, slightly uplifted and below whose level streams have cut the present floodplain. Included are the gravelly red lands and such low uplifted promontories as the *Montezuma Hills* and the Corning Ridge. In the western San Joaquin the terraces surround such Coast Ranges outliers as the *Kettleman Hills*.

The low *alluvial plains* lie between the contemporary floodplain and the dissected uplands.

They include alluvial fans and have gently sloping surfaces, well drained except during flood stage. In the San Joaquin the fans, much wider on the Valley's eastern (Sierran) side than on the western (Coast Ranges), are of sufficient size and low gradient that their scope is difficult to perceive at ground level.

The *flood basins* of the Sacramento Valley are flat, poorly drained surfaces from Butte County southward.

Between the alluvial plains and the flood plains, they form a system of sloughs or tule marshes, surrounded by natural levees. There are seven such basins, five larger ones *(Butte, Colusa, Sutter, American* and *Yolo)* and two lesser ones *(Marysville and Sacramento).* Although commonly dry, these areas become shallow lakes following periodic floods; silt from standing water has repeatedly settled upon them. Since construction of bypass channels and erection of Shasta and Oroville dams, they have been less frequently inundated. Of comparable nature is the *Valley trough* in the San Joaquin.

The *floodplains* parallel the Sacramento and Feather rivers.

They extend from the river banks (natural levees) to the flood basins.

*Delta islands* have developed south of the Sacramento Valley proper at the confluence of the streams whose waters flow toward San Francisco Bay.

In addition to the Sacramento and San Joaquin, delta rivers include the Cosumnes, Mokelumne and Calaveras. The mean surface of the islands lies at sea level, with natural levees forming the original fringes of individual islands. (Island interiors, sometimes 10 feet below sea level, were tule marshes before drainage and cultivation).

*Tulare Basin,* occupying the south end of the San Joaquin Valley, was long considered the result of "damming" by the alluvial fans of the Kings River from the east and Los Gatos Creek from the west.

It is now felt that the interior drainage has resulted from recent geologic subsidence. The Basin has contained intermittent lakes: *Buena Vista* (southwest of Bakersfield) and *Tulare* (west of Corcoran).

Most of the isolated hills are outliers of the Coast Ranges.

Such anticlinal ridges include the *Kettleman Hills,* Lost Hills and *Wheeler Ridge.* A distinctive landmark of the Sacramento Valley is the nearly circular *Sutter (Marysville) Buttes,* the erosional relict of an igneous mass that was later penetrated by molten rock in the form of a volcanic cone. An elevation of 2117 feet is attained in South Butte.

## Clays, Sands, Gravels—and Peat

With their smooth surfaces, considerable depths, near stonelessness and absence of extreme chemical imbalances, soils of the Central Valley are productive generally for plant growth.

Nevertheless there are rather extensive areas east of the Valley trough in the San Joaquin with alkaline conditions.

Soils have formed from stream-transported detritus of volcanic (from the Cascade Range) or granitic (from the Sierra Nevada) bedrock.

Textures vary considerably from fine clays near the major streams along the trough to coarse sands and gravels on upper portions of alluvial fans. There are considerable areas with loam.

Many Sacramento Valley soils, members of the Chernozemic group (i.e., *Mollisol* order, or dark grassland soils), have much agricultural worth.

However, the "redland" soils around the margins of the Sacramento Valley often contain hardpan and tend to be coarse. They are used chiefly for seasonal pasturage. Conversely, the flood basins are often underlain by poorly-drained clays.

Soils in the San Joaquin Valley likewise tend to be productive.

On fans east of the Valley trough lime-accumulating brown soils are widespread. But there is an alkaline belt east of the San Joaquin River. *Aridisols* of the western San Joaquin Valley also are productive when irrigated.

If drained, the deep peat and muck of the Delta Lands also are highly productive.

The peat is deep but it is susceptible to fire destruction. Motorists encounter signs along highways warning of peat flammability.

## December Fog and a Summer Desert

Basically, the Central Valley has the interior Mediterranean (dry-summer subtropical) climate with summer heat and winter mildness. Additionally, latitudinal length results in more-frequent winter storms and increased precipitation to the north.

Thus Red Bluff averages 24 inches annually whereas Bakersfield, actually classified as a desert, receives less than six.

Four climatic types are associated with the Central Valley (see Overview A) : *subtropical desert, subtropical semiarid* and *mild-summer* and *hot-summer* phases of the dry-summer subtropical or Mediterranean.

Half of the San Joaquin Valley is either desert or semiarid, with summer heat and aridity reaching their extremes in the southwesterly corner.

In summer, stepping out of an air-conditioned building in mid-afternoon can be suggestive of a blast from an oven.

Modified in summer by cooler air flowing inland from the Pacific via San Francisco Bay as result of low interior pressure, the Delta Lands is mild-summer subtropical (Mediterranean).

Diurnal temperatures in summer are tempered as much as 10 degrees below those only a short distance north or south— Stockton has a July average of only 73 degrees.

The Sacramento Valley is considered hot-summer Mediterranean. While many summer afternoons tend to be nearly as hot as those in the San Joaquin (infrequently, during hot spells, maximums exceed 110 degrees), cooler spells of a day or so do occur. *

Winter cyclonic activity in the Sacramento lasts longer and storms bring more precipitation than falls farther south. In the lee of the Coast Ranges, the western Sacramento tends to receive less moisture than the east side.

Despite the apparent stillness of air on a midsummer morning, winds are frequent in the Central Valley.

Dust storms at times have been noxious in the southwestern part of the San Joaquin Valley. Stirring up of dry peat from the surface of the Delta Lands is also bothersome and represents economic loss of rich soil.

The growing season in the Valley is approximately nine to ten months long.

---

* Residents of the Mendocino Coast predict summer temperature in the Sacramento Valley by the onshore "pull" of fogbanks. When the fog is "soupy" in Fort Bragg, a resident may greet a friend with "Guess the Sacramento Valley is sizzling again today."

While the observant traveler is cognizant of earlier "leafing out" around Bakersfield than around Redding, air drainage and local altitude tend almost to be more important than latitude. The Delta, with its maritime effect, has the longest season.

"Northers", polar air masses flowing southwestward across the Cascadian uplands, bring subfreezing winter weather. They can be responsible for unseasonably late spring frosts or early autumnal frosts. Such north winds in summer produce the highest temperatures.

From Thanksgiving through January, another disagreeable feature is "tule fog."

These low-lying radiation fogs, following periods of heavier rainfall and higher humidity, may cover much of the Great Valley. For periods of three to ten days, until passage of a storm, or until the reduced sunlight of this season can "burn off" the overcast, the weather remains clammy and skies may remain overcast day and night.

Traffic accidents increase on highways (especially on I-5 south of Stockton) and communications slow down. Should the fog disappear in mid-afternoon, temperatures during the following night may drop sharply below freezing.

## Floods

The Central Valley experiences the wide annual precipitation deviation characteristic of Mediterranean lands.

Total runoff from the drainage basin of the Valley

**Figure 9-5.** Flooding is *still* a problem in the Central Valley. This scene, between Chico and Orland on Ca. 32 occurred in January during a series of storms when Lake Shasta was full. For three days only commercial vehicles, cravaning behind a Caltrans "guide truck" were allowed to travel here. (dwl)

has fluctuated between 63.3 million acre-feet in 1906-1907 and 9.2 million acre feet in 1923-1924.

Momentous floods have occurred periodically (Figure 9-5).

Flooding sometimes followed mid-winter storms which bring warm rain from the central Pacific to melt the Sierran snowpack prematurely.

Too rapid melting of the snow in spring likewise produces rapid runoff and has converted rivers into destructive ogres. This is more likely in the San Joaquin, west of the true High Sierra.

### Grasslands and Oaks

Distribution of natural vegetation in the Central Valley reflected such factors as precipitation, drainage, soils, topography, soils and water table.

Interspersed with floodplain forests (of valley oaks, California sycamore, cottonwood and willow), xerophytic shrubs and tule marshes, grasslands prevailed prior to plowing the land.

Mixed perennial bunch grasses, dominated by needlegrass, were widespread and denoted adjustment to winter rain, summer drought, and probably fire.

The watercourses (i.e., natural levees) were fringed by groves of trees. Trees also partially covered the well-drained red lands, especially in the Sacramento Valley.

*Broadleaf woodlands,* in addition to the floodplain forests, dominated by the live oak, interior live oak, and deciduous California black oak, have been prominent in the Sacramento Valley north of the Feather River, *especially* in the Redding District (Map 9-3). The trees have reflected the heavier precipitation in the north and have strongly suggested a Middle Western environment that contrasts especially with the sparse vegetation of the arid southwestern San Joaquin Valley.

Even in the early twentieth century, thousands of acres of marshland existed in the Great Central Valley.

Such wetland vegetation was dominated by common tule (California bulrush) reed-like plants growing three to nine feet tall, as well as other coarse, grasslike perennial sedges and water grasses. Along the natural levees of the Delta Lands, in flood basins, and along stream banks upstream, willow thickets were common.

### Watering the Land

Over much of California and particularly in the Great Valley (which contains three-fourths of the

**Figure 9-6.** Tule marsh, southwestern Butte County. Such a landscape was far more extensive before reclamation. (dwl)

state's irrigated crop land—a sixth of the entire national total), irrigation is crucial.

The third of Central Valley farmland which is watered artificially yields most of the farm income and supports much of the population. Dramatically-changing most recently have been those once-barren landscapes of the southwestern San Joaquin Valley. A plentiful supply of canal water has been used here for the first time.

Creation of irrigation districts made possible large-scale irrigation.

Some wheat had been irrigated as early as 1856 in Yolo County but the state's *Wright Act* of 1887 permitted groups of farmers to establish districts to divert water away from the streams. This is contrary to the humid-land English concept of *riparian rights,* which gives landowners along streams full claims to unimpaired stream flow.

Able to tax farm and town alike, irrigation districts have been a major force in providing water for Great Valley fields.

These enterprises were particularly effective in more water-plentiful sectors of the Valley (i.e., north and east). Elsewhere groundwater was tapped (i.e., pumped) even after marked declines in the water table became apparent.

Large scale diversion of water to riverless sectors was proposed in the *Marshall Plan* of 1919 and was finally implemented in 1933 with initiation of the Central Valley Project.

### The Central Valley Project

During the depressed years of the 1930's California voters assigned implementation of the Marshall Plan to the U.S. Bureau of Reclamation.

The electorate narrowly approved of the Central

Valley Project —in Los Angeles County there was two-to-one rejection. A generation later in 1960 the bond issue for the California Water Plan passed only because of an overwhelming "yes" vote in Southern California. Results of these two elections indeed reflect the economic and cultural dichotomy of the Golden State.

California could not finance the Marshall Plan and the Central Valley Project provided palliatives for depression-era unemployment.

The Project, proposed in Washington, D.C. partly as a public works enterprise, was intended to irrigate an additional three million acres, provide hydroelectricity (to stimulate urban and industrial expansion), give flood control, improve navigation on the lower Sacramento River, permit facilities for aquatic recreation and repel salt water from Delta farmlands.*

The Central Valley Project (C.V.P.) essentially consists of a series of dams (and resultant impounding reservoirs) and canals.

---

* Some Californians have felt that allowing a federal agency control of Golden State water has been a serious mistake. For example, there has been much opposition to Auburn Dam (on the American River). The Bureau of Reclamation has contended it is not accountable to the California electorate!

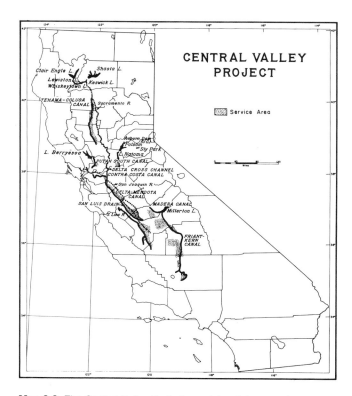

**Map 9-2.** The Central Valley Project consists of dams and attendant storage reservoirs and canals. San Luis reservoir, west of Los Banos, is a joint C.V.P-C.W.P. storage unit.

*Shasta Dam* is the principal storage (and water control) unit of the C.V.P.. It stores runoff from the McCloud, the Pit and the upper Sacramento rivers, thus providing for summer irrigation needs (map. 9-2 and Fig. 11-11). Releases from Shasta, (and regulatory Keswick downriver), produce hydroelectricity (used partly for pumping water southward to the San Joaquin Valley) for general California consumption. Revenues from electricity sales help keep the Project solvent.

Near Tracy (southwest edge of the Sacramento-San Joaquin Delta) water, mostly from the Sacramento basin, is lifted 200 feet into the *Delta-Mendota Canal*. It is then transported 120 miles southward to replenish San Joaquin flow that is diverted at *Friant Dam* from *Lake Millerton* and transferred mostly southward (on the east side of the San Joaquin Valley), as far as Kern County (Figure 10-22) in the *Friant-Kern Canal*.

Additional canals serve the Sacramento Valley, Madera County (from Friant Dam) and parts of the Bay Area. Additional storage and regulation is provided by *Monticello* (Figure 8-69) and *Folsom* dams and lesser structures. Eventually 48 dams and 20 major canals are envisaged. The C.V.P. was expanded in the 1950's to tap the Trinity River (a segment of the west-flowing Klamath River system). Trinity water is now diverted eastward to augment the Sacramento supply; enroute electricity is generated.

### Flood Control and Other Uses

Several dams have been constructed by the Army Corps of Engineers on Sierran rivers that flow into the southern San Joaquin Valley.

These are *Pine Flat* on the Kings River and *Isabella* on the Kern River.

Since the prime mission of the Corps of Engineers in dam construction is flood control, water thus stored is "free" to downstream users. Moreover there is no acreage limitation or the other constraints of the C.V.P..

Like the Central Valley Project units, these dams are multi-purpose structures. Although intended for flood control, they also provide water for irrigation storage, power generation and recreation.

### The California Water Project

The California Water Project (or C.W.P.—see Overview G) commenced the delivery of additional irrigation (and urban) supplies as part of a statewide scheme to move northern waters south (as far as San

**Figure 9-7.** San Luis (rear) and O'Neill(foreground) reservoirs store water from the Sacramento Basin which is flowing southward via the California Aqueduct (right center) and the Delta-Mendota Canal (lower left). (Department of Water Resources)

Diego and the Mojave Desert).

Agriculturally, its chief impact has focused on the west side of the San Joaquin Valley south from *San Luis Reservoir* (Figure 9-7), where it has supplemented depleted underground reserves and also has permitted an additional million acres to be placed under irrigation.

### RANCHERIAS BECOME FARMS

For a lengthy period of time the Central Valley has afforded a human habitat. Before the Europeans arrived the Valley was probably the "heartland of ancient California." It was a marginal area during the Hispanic colonial period but the Valley has gained new importance in the past century to become the "food basket of the American West."

### Penutian Country

Residents of the central third of the Golden State in pre-colonial days, five Penutian linguistic families utilized the Great Central Valley.

Although the Valley tended to be less attractive for primitive folk than the Northwest (Ch. 12), still it afforded a *relatively* easy existence.

Clothing was scanty and the unpretentious dwellings, commonly temporary abodes, were assembled in encampments known as *rancherias*. In the Sacramento and eastern San Joaquin, acorns were plentiful; and nut meat was a basic foodstuff. Grasslands afforded such varied game as deer, elk and rabbit. Many streams were sources of fish.

The five families occupied somewhat different habitats.

The *Wintun* found the Coast Ranges more attractive than the western Sacramento Valley, where their numbers were limited.

The *Maidu* of the eastern Sacramento Valley seldom traveled far—they occupied a choice land with perennial streams and more luxuriant vegetation (woodlands and *California prairie)*.

The *Miwok* of the northern San Joaquin were more ambulatory, migrating between the Sierra Nevada and the Valley floor but spending much time in the foothills.

Principally a coastal people, the *Costanoans* resided mostly around San Francisco Bay.

Possessors of the southern San Joaquin Valley, the *Yokuts* differed from most California Indians in their tribal organization. Most of this people were peaceful although the *Chowchilla* were known as fighters.

Records of these Early Americans are generally limited.

Once the Anglos entered the Central Valley, the Indians tended to vanish. Refuge habitats were usually absent and decimation from European diseases was doubtless critical.

## A Land Without Missions

The colonial Spanish never achieved sufficient need or strength in Alta California to establish permanent settlements in the Central Valley. Nor were the Mexicans or the "mountain men" (the fur trappers) equipped to occupy the land significantly.

Exploration included Gabriel Moraga's trip into the Sacramento Valley in 1808. The Spanish left a legacy of names for some of the larger rivers—for example, *Rio de los Americanos* (now the American River). *El Camino Viejo* (a forerunner of Interstates 5 and 580) was a speedier way between missions in Southern California and San Francisco Bay than better known El Camino Real but scarcely a rival.

Mountain men, both Anglo-Americans and British, visited the Central Valley in the 1820's and 1830's.

Most were not too literate and the fur trappers left few records other than several diaries of their travels. Their permanent effect on the Great Valley was slight.

Permanent European-type settlement of the Great Central Valley was delayed until the Mexican era, although some mission livestock had been pastured on Valley fringes.

More than 50 extensive properties were bestowed between 1836 and 1846, principally in the Sacramento Valley where river access and water supply were better.

Cattle raising became significant. However, marauding Indians posed a threat, as did periodic inundation by flooding rivers during wetter years.

### Entry of the Anglo-Americans

Valley settlement was hastened by the Gold Rush and the early founding of several larger cities as Stockton.

Many of the ranchos, particularly in the Sacramento Valley, had been assigned initially to Anglos, rather than persons of Hispanic ancestry. A number of the early Valley residents, originally lured to the area by mining in the nearby Sierra, turned to farming.

Gold-field supply towns in the central portion of the Great Valley that have retained their importance include Stockton, Sacramento and Marysville.

Generally, early Anglo settlers had come from humid climates. Thus many did not appreciate at first the agricultural potential of a summer-desert land.

Cattle ranching was dominant in the years between 1850 and 1867 since the mine camps afforded an outlet for beef. Among the larger operators near the Valley fringes were John Bidwell, John C. Fremont and Edward F. Beale, who acquired rancho properties.

During the cattle period, most of the Valley remained federal property, unfenced and even unsurveyed. Cattlemen could occupy such land by control of the waterholes. I.E., on the rivers west of the San Joaquin River Miller and Lux acquired vast holdings. Sizable stretches around fringes of the Great Valley are *still* used for livestock ranching.

An epoch of grain farming, 1867-1900, followed the cattle era.

Production of wheat and barley commenced somewhat earlier in the Sacramento (as opposed to the San Joaquin), where heavier winter precipitation encouraged autumnal planting and early summer harvest. An important consideration in pre-railroad days was the navigability of the Sacramento upstream to Red Bluff.

Wheat, especially, was shipped to such distant markets as Europe, China and Australia. Barley was important, principally as feed for draft animals.

Expansion of grain farming in the San Joaquin Valley followed construction of the Southern Pacific's *Valley Line* between San Francisco and Los Angeles.*

The first wheat shipment by rail from the San Joaquin came from Modesto in 1870. Earlier, wheat culture in the San Joaquin had been limited to the northern portion of the valley where it was feasible to haul grain by wagons to docks at Stockton.

For two years in the middle 1870's California actually led the nation in wheat production; most of this output came from the Central Valley.

Acreage in the Sacramento Valley alone increased from 200,000 in 1866 to one million in 1882. Acreage in the entire Great Valley reached its apex in 1884; thereafter acreage declined. Diminution reflected (1) competition within California from other crops; (2) cheaper wheat elsewhere; (3) low gluten content; and (4) declining yields after years of successive production without crop rotation or fertilization.

An appreciable portion of Central Valley settlement after 1880 was related to continued expansion of irrigation agriculture—a concern of several types of agricultural organizations.

The *Wright Act* was of prime importance (especially after several amendments), since it permitted a number of individual ranchers to establish collectively an irrigation district.

Other organizations included the individual and/or the partnership, the stock company, and the commercial group organized specifically to sell water to farmers. Most of the irrigation expansion has taken place in the water-deficit San Joaquin Valley, which has attracted settlers from all parts of the United States, from Europe and from Asia..

Most of the population growth in recent decades has taken place in the larger urban centers.

This reflects higher incomes (as in more elaborate agricultural processing) and increased services, both public and private.

Many of the recent arrivals are former residents of either Southern California or the Bay Area. These would include managers of retail chain branches.

## A LAND WITH MANY PRODUCTS

The agricultural evolution of the Great Central Valley has brought additional crops rather than complete substitution. Thus the first post-Indian land-use stage, livestock ranching, still exists in peripheral areas or in conjunction with other stages.

Grain farming, the second stage, is sometimes practiced simultaneously with the third stage.

Much grain farming is also peripheral, forming small wheat-barley belts around the Valley edges. Today more grain is grown for local flour, beer or livestock feeding than for export.

The third stage, irrigation agriculture, represents more intensive land-use and has developed largely in the twentieth century.

In some districts, complex crop patterns have been created.

With scores of crops produced commercially, representing annual income of billions of dollars, the Valley today is the richest agricultural area of western United States.

Grains remain important—with barley grown more widely than wheat (maps 7-7 and 9-28).

Livestock, including sheep, beef cattle and dairy cows, graze upon natural pasture seasonally and on irrigated pasture or grain stubble.

Many varieties of deciduous fruits, including peaches, grapes, figs, prunes, pears and cherries are raised.

Numerous vegetables, such as tomatoes, squash, and asparagus are grown and are generally canned or frozen for market.

Field crops include cotton, sugar beets, potatoes and alfalfa In addition, nuts (walnuts and almonds), olives and citrus are produced.

### Ranches: Large and Small

Farm units range from corporate cotton ranches and sizable beef and grain ranches to the small family fruit farm.

Some correlation exists between the type of operation and ranch size; greater acreage of grain than cotton is needed to support a family. In turn, the cotton ranch must be larger than the grape farm.

Irrigated properties tend to be largest in the south-

---

* Frank Norris wrote this description of the San Joaquin Valley in *The Octopus* (Garden City,N.Y.: Doubleday and Co., 1901); "The wheat, now close to its maturity, had turned from pale yellow to golden yellow and from that to brown. Like a gigantic carpet, it spread itself across all the land. There was nothing else to be seen but the limitless sea of wheat as far as the eye could reach, dry, rustling, crisp and harsh in the rare breaths of hot wind out of the southeast." (p.202).

339 The Great Central Valley

ern San Joaquin (Tulare Basin); this reflects such factors as recency of land development and the cost of drilling deep pump wells. Large holdings have existed since the days of Mexican land grants and include individual and corporate holdings of thousands of acres.

Agricultural prosperity or poverty is not always revealed by rural farmsteads. Many landowners maintain town residences as do many seasonal farm laborers.

Although one finds exceptions, collectively rural dwellings do not evidence the degree of prosperity suggested in Corn Belt farm houses of the Middle West.

Outbuildings tend to be limited in number although machine sheds are conspicuous. Barns, many in a state of disrepair, tend to be limited to older districts. Larger properties may have barracks-like structures to house field workers, of which many thousands have become derelicts as mechanization has continued.

Since 1980 particularly there have been indications that the "little" independent farm may become extinct. For many farmers economic conditions have suggested the depressed 1930's.

## Field Workers

In the Central Valley labor shortage was not critical during much of the nineteenth century.

Relatively few workers were needed in cattle ranching and grain farming. And when needed, Chinese and later Japanese, who came to California by the thousands, were readily available.

Many Californians of European descent feared the foreign competition. The Asian worked long hours for modest pay. Such labor was discouraged in several ways. Eventually the Immigration Act of 1924 excluded most east Asians.

As irrigation agriculture expanded, additional seasonal labor was needed.

Migratory workers were welcomed; they provided a "cheap" supply. Agricultural schedules that evolved between southern Arizona and the Canadian border provided a long work season.

Many migrants have been destitute and often near starvation in midwinter. Moreover they have lacked social status—their families, particularly the children, were without the benefits accruing to sedentary people with accepted community position.

For some decades much seasonal work was undertaken by compliant foreigners.

These included Mexicans, Hindus and Filipinos, forced to accept lower wages and working conditions unacceptable to native-born Americans.

A period of Great Plains drought plus national depression, the 1930's brought thousands of displaced Anglos to the Valley.

Thus the conditions depicted by Steinbeck's *Grapes of Wrath* and McWilliams' *Ill Fares the Land* materialized. During the decade considerable numbers of aliens, especially Mexicans, were repatriated.

World War II gave many Anglo depression victims an opportunity. to find a more adequate livelihood in West Coast defense plants; some subsequently became successful Central Valley landowners.

Currently many Mexican-born workers are used.

Some are temporary, authorized free-lance employees ("green carders") but many are illegal entrants ("wetbacks").

Organized American labor, in the mid-1960's, demanded more favorable working conditions for native-born workers and elimination of alien competition. Congress was persuaded to terminate the *bracero* (Mexican contract worker).

While some Mexican "green card" holders are used, there are many illegal entrants. Mechanization and possibly unemployment may eventually eliminate migratory work entirely. Already the bulk of the "permanent" farm work is done by local residents, especially of Mexican descent.

A number of Central Valley counties, especially several in the San Joaquin with much farm labor, consistently rank among California's lowest in family and per capita incomes.

Prime reasons are the seasonal work year in agribusiness and relatively low wages.

## Cotton Pickers and Tomato Harvesters

Partially the high degree of mechanization in California agriculture resulted from labor costs.

But the cost of machinery has encouraged larger farm units, cooperatives, and joint hiring arrangements. But as Central Valley farms have become more mechanized, equipment has grown larger, more elaborate and most costly, making it increasingly difficult for the "little" farmer to survive.

Some of the world's most imaginative application of farm machinery has evolved for use in Central Valley fruit and vegetable production.

The first mechanized tomato harvester appeared in 1960. This machine doubtless salvaged tomato production in the state. Refinements have subsequently been made.

Other machinery includes an electronic-sensor asparagus harvester which "picks" only stalks of suitable size and shape.

Still other equipment has been developed to shake trees and catch nuts, or harvest olives, oranges, peaches and even grapes.

It seems likely that in the future soils may be tilled with use of sound waves, computers may be used to determine farm activity and machinery may be directed by remote control and supervised by television monitoring.

An ongoing adjustment to mechanization has taken place.

The shape of processing tomatoes was altered to permit mechanical picking. Possibly some commodities which do not lend themselves to automation may be eliminated from the Great Valley.

### Supermarket Shelves and Asian Rice Bowls

It became necessary, as output expanded, for the Central Valley to rely upon more distant markets, in eastern United States, Europe and eastern Asia. Western United States, with limited population, affords modest outlets.

Various persons have noted that the growing urban centers of California consume increasing quantities of Central Valley products. However, Valley farmers are much concerned with international trade agreements and with world commodity prices and outputs.

Historically the expansion of irrigation agriculture was somewhat dependent on world markets.

One tended to find *Del Monte* brand canned goods "everywhere." Attainment of such markets required cheap labor, improved transportation media and quality control—corporations were able to afford extensive advertising, as could cooperatives.

Since 1980 there have been significant changes and many Central Valley farmers have experienced serious problems.

The cost of machinery and labor, for example, has increased more rapidly than the price of farm products. The "high" American dollar (relative to other currencies) posed difficult problems. Southeast Asia recovered sufficiently from the effects of the Viet Nam war to export again more rice. Mainland China suddenly began exporting cotton. Entry of Portugal and Spain into the European Common Market was disastrous for some

commodities. Now foreign canned fruits and vegetables, from such lands as Australia, Chile and Turkey are being sold in California and the domestic canning industry has declined.

### FREEWAYS AND SHIP CHANNELS

Adequate transportation has been critical in the economy of the Great Central Valley.

Wagons and riverboats were significant in early years, hence the Sacramento Valley (with one-day wagon trips to a navigable river) was favored over the San Joaquin. Now railroads, highways and airlines form the major arteries of commerce.

Though a number of Valley towns, especially in the Sacramento, originated at river ports, relatively little commerce moves along Central Valley streams. However, dredged ship channels have permitted Stockton and Sacramento to again become seaports.

These cities happen to be situated where rail corridors between the Bay Area and eastern United States traverse the Valley axis with its north-south travel routes. But neither seaport fares too well in competition with Oakland.

The level Central Valley contains the chief corridors for north-south and eastward egress from the Bay Area.

Much rail and highway traffic misses most of Sacramento and Stockton.

Two major railroad "giants" serve the Great Valley (Maps 9-3 and 9-15).

The most extensive lines belong to the Santa Fe Southern (an uncompleted merger of the Santa Fe and the Southern Pacific). Its parallel routes cover much of the length of the San Joaquin and Sacramento valleys. In addition, the *original* Central Pacific line extends from the Bay Area through Sacramento and across the Sierra Nevada. The former Santa Fe lines extend from Bakersfield northward across the San Joaquin into the Bay Area.

The Union Pacific line (formerly the Western Pacific) enters the Valley at Oroville, continues south to Sacramento and thence to the Bay Area.

Principal rail points in the Central Valley include Sacramento, Stockton, Fresno, and Bakersfield. Passenger service is provided by *Amtrak,* which connects the Sacramento Valley with the Pacific Northwest, the Bay Area and eastern United States, with "branch" service between Bakersfield and the Bay Area and bus connections between Los Angeles and the Valley.

Principal north-south highway arterials are Interstate 5 (west side) and Ca. 99 (east side).

Between Redding and Sacramento, I-5 carries more *through* and *commercial* traffic (much emanating in the Bay Area) whereas Ca. 99 is used primarily by local residents. Southward from Sacramento, Ca. 99 is an intensively-used freeway with much bus and truck traffic. Along the western side of the San Joaquin, (serving Southern California and the Bay Area), I-5 is beginning to modify local land use.

Several major east-west highways cross the Central Valley. Those especially which originate in the Bay Area carry much traffic.

Most important are segments of two major transcontinental routes through Sacramento, Interstate 80 and U.S. 50. Ca. 70, through the Feather River Canyon, carries far less traffic. Of consequence are such highways as Ca. 299 and Ca. 20 in the Sacramento Valley and Ca. 152 and 58 in the San Joaquin.

A close network of oiled county roads affords some of the world's finest rural highway transit.

Most Great Valley cities are either too small or too close to Southern California or Bay Area international airports to support direct out-of-state flights.

Because of its metropolitan population and its legislative status Sacramento has in-state flights to many parts of California.

There is a modest number of out-of-state flights from Fresno and Sacramento. Other cities are served by feeder lines (including such larger carriers as PSA and Air California). But mostly, smaller cities have "taxi" service to metropolitan airports—with first class fares! Many Valley residents fly their own craft and there is considerable general air traffic.

## THE PEOPLE OF THE VALLEY

As the end of the twentieth century nears, the population of the Central Valley, like that of California's megalopolitan areas, is becoming more representative of the trans-Pacific Basin.

A highly-diversified mix has long existed, especially in the San Joaquin Valley, with Basques in Bakersfield and Fresno, Syrians in Turlock, Swedes in Kingsburg, Azoreans in Gustine, Germans at Lodi and Ripon, Portuguese on the west side and on and on...there are Russians in Sacramento and Sikhs around Yuba City. But the per cent of non-Anglos is less in the Sacramento Valley than it is in the San Joaquin.

While there have long been Filipinos and Chinese and Japanese, now there are Vietnamese, especially in Stockton, and Hmong in Merced and Fresno and even Chico.

A significant push of "old-line" Hispanics from metropolitan Los Angeles into Kern County represents a significant change in the late twentieth century. By contrast, blacks are found largely in Bakersfield, Fresno, Stockton and Sacramento. South Dos Palos is the single rural center.

## "BEWILDERED" METROPOLISES

Although many local residents, and certainly residents of the principal conurbations (Bay Area, Los Angeles, San Diego), regard the Central Valley as a rural area, it is actually an urban land in an *open space* setting. Nearly half of California's metropolitan areas, as identified by the Census Bureau, are in the Valley.

Due to urban increase in its cities during the decades of the 1970's and 1980's, two and a half times the statewide rate, the number of *identified* metropolitan areas (Census Bureau MSAs) in the Valley increased from five to ten! But, in contrast to the Valley's "big four" (Sacramento, Fresno, Stockton and Bakersfield), the other six (Redding, Chico, Yuba City-Marysville, Visalia, Merced and Modesto) were toward the bottom of the nation's 300-plus metropolitan areas in population.

The following hierarchy of Central Valley cities generally corresponds to urban size:

(1) The *true* metropolis, which has at least one major league sports team, two or more colleges and universities, two or more major shopping centers, subregional importance as a transit hub, substantial non-agricultural industries and significant ethnic diversity beyond the "usual" Anglo-Hispanic dichotomy. Lately, Sacramento meets these qualifications and Stockton, Fresno and Bakersfield *approach* them.

(2) the small urbanized center (Modesto, Redding, Visalia and Chico), without all of the above attributes, but with *at least* one college or university, regional shopping center, commercial travelers' motel clientele, substantial agribusiness services,

specialized medical facilities,* and preferred residential (and retirement) status *locally*. The "quad cities" (Olivehurst, Linda, Yuba City and Marysville) *collectively* and *debatably* meet the qualifications.

(3) the small city, which may be as populous as the small urbanized center, but is too proximate to bigger cities to have most of the qualifications (Merced, Tulare, Davis and Woodland are examples).

(4) the local farm center, which has viable commercial and social services, may have a population of only a few thousand (Exeter, Delano and Selma are examples).

(5) the *dying* hamlet, which despite possible residential gain, has lost most of its retailing and commerce (including bank and high school) to larger nearby cities. It may retain a post office, *limited* day-to-day retail services (gasoline, groceries, tavern) and a few railside agricultural services.

Throughout the Great Central Valley urban sprawl, albeit on a smaller scale than in major California metropolitan centers, is taking place.

There is usually pronounced antagonism between city and county government (county officials tend to be more conservative and more rural in viewpoint), indifference to development by outside interests and failure to recognize smaller-scale repetition of "mistakes" previously made in the major metropolitan centers.**

The three principal subdivisions of the Central Valley—(1) **Sacramento Valley**; (2) **Delta Lands**; and (3) **San Joaquin Valley**—have physical distinctions, differing histories and contrasting utilization that justify more detailed discussion of the contemporary landscapes of these sections.

## SACRAMENTO VALLEY (North Valley)

To some the Sacramento Valley suggests a transplanted Middle West. A trip on Ca. 32 from the Sierra Nevada to the Coast Ranges is reminiscent of the transition along Interstate 70 from Missouri into western Kansas.

East of Orland one sees fruit orchards and an occasional cornfield; beyond the Sacramento River west of Orland (and I-5) one finds dry-farmed grains, grazing beef cattle and few trees away from seasonally-dry streams.

The towns too bear greater resemblance to those of the Middle West than do most in California. Time-worn brick buildings in downtown districts and white clapboard dwellings in older residential sections are characteristic.

Groves of deciduous trees along the Sacramento River and its perennial west-flowing tributaries (on the east side of the Valley) likewise suggest the lower Missouri basin.

The Sacramento Valley is only half the size of the San Joaquin Valley but the rainy season is longer and annual precipitation is appreciably higher, *especially* in the north.

Between these two basins and east of the Delta Lands, approximately at Lodi and between the Cosumnes and Calaveras rivers, is an indistinct boundary, separating the San Joaquin and Sacramento valleys.

The Sacramento drainage basin, despite its lesser size, has twice the annual discharge of the San Joaquin basin.

While there is not too much difference in summer temperatures, winters in the Sacramento Valley are definitely wetter than those of the San Joaquin *(especially* in comparison to the *southern* San Joaquin) and the probability of unseasonable frost more likely.

One can easily subdivide the Sacramento Valley into four "land-use portions": (1) the **Redding District**; (2) the **West Side**; the **Flood Basins** (i.e., the Rice Bowl); and (4) the **East Side**. Further subdivision is made in the following sections.

---

* In the mid-1960's a surgical nurse from Los Angeles could snidely say "Chico is a great place for an appendectomy, hysterectomy, appendectomy, period." Now brain, cancer, open-heart and plastic surgery are performed. Also available is psychiatric care and radiation therapy. Helicopter ambulance service reaches as far as Susanville.
** Davis and Chico, more urbane due to sizable university communities, tend to be exceptions.

In one instance, a geographer opposing sprawl, was jeeringly called "an idealistic academic elitist!" by a county supervisor. When a fringe-area development is being discussed before county or city officials, these are some of the viewpoints one is apt to hear: "I came from Los Angeles to get away from congestion and smog" (retiree); "Who says we need this Circle Mart discount store?" (college student); "We're on our way—watch this city grow!" (Chamber of Commerce secretary); "I have been saddened to see our town grow from 7000 to 45,000" (locally-born public librarian); "So what's wrong with a Southern California developer building a housing tract on this 40 acres?" (county supervisor); "You can't stop progress! Are you going to deny loyal red-blooded American workers their source of livelihood?" (labor leader).

## THE REDDING DISTRICT
### (The Upper Sacramento Valley) *

Semicircular in shape, the Redding District occupies the northernmost (or "upper" portion) of the Sacramento Valley. It extends about 30 miles north-south and has an east-west width of 30 to 40 miles (occupying the central portions of Tehama and Shasta counties).

---

* The Redding District was initially reviewed by David Harrow, formerly at California State Polytechnic University, and subsequently by Philip Tincher of Shasta College.

**Map 9-3.** The Sacramento Valley is traditionally divided into the West Side and the East Side.

**Figure 9-8.** Redding (right) with its lately-added twin, Enterprise (left). This is *the* metropolis of the *real* interior northern California. (dwl)

The physical appearance of the upper Sacramento Valley has not changed too much from the way geologist Brewer described it in 1862. The surface is underlain by the cemented formation known as the *"red lands"* which gave Red Bluff its name.

The Sacramento River has cut its *Iron Canyon* along the axis of its Valley. Away from the river, the undulating countryside, generally several hundred feet higher than the Valley floor south of Red Bluff, is covered with an oak woodland, seasonally green or seared a burned gold. This landscape is alien to the Central Valley—an unsuspecting stranger might mistake it for the Edwards Plateau of Texas.

Limited cultivated land lies along the narrow Sacramento floodplain between Redding and Anderson. Elsewhere extensive livestock ranching prevails on the red lands.

While rural incomes accrue primarily from stock ranching, the number of properties and animals, especially sheep but also cattle, has declined. There are a few dairies (serving local markets) and scattered deciduous fruit orchards. Bedding strawberries are raised for shipment to the Central Coast (Ch. 7).

Wood processing has constituted an economic mainstay but operations have declined in the late twentieth century—logs are trucked from adjacent highlands to several mills beside rail lines. Even corporate plants have had difficulties with fluctuations in market conditions and availability of timber.

Prominent names have included U.S. Plywood, Diamond International, Kimberly-Clark and Simpson (Figure 9-9).

Principal communities are Red Bluff and Redding, seats of Tehama and Shasta counties respectively.

There are differences between the two, suggesting Fort Worth (i.e., Red Bluff) and Dallas (i.e., Redding) in their *formative* (pre-metropolitan) days.

The "unofficial" capital of "far northern" California, ***Redding*** (55,000) is the largest city.

Redding, whose west side ascends river terraces into northern Coast Range fringes, is bisected by the Sacramento River, (thus allowing costlier dwellings views of mounts Shasta and Lassen as well as the river). It has the most spectacular setting of any Central Valley city. With its location it would have been the logical capital for the once-proposed state of Shasta.

**Figure 9-9.** Integrated wood products plant, Anderson. This factory has produced lumber, pulp, paper and sundry other forestry products. (Kimberly-Clark Corporation).

The small metropolis provides a service center for the extensive highlands that surround it on three sides.

Yet the downtown area has become a "disaster." Local merchants, with support of a federal grant, converted the central core into an air-conditioned mall with underground and surface parking. Then a Southern California developer constructed another regional shopping mall along Interstate 5 to the northeast.* Much additional retail trade is conducted along this expressway. The service function is evidenced by the scores of practicing M.D.s (including many specialists). Construction, mining and wood products contribute also to the economy.

As a gateway (at the junction of Ca. 299, Ca. 44 and I-5) to major recreational areas and the leading "break" point on I-5 between Sacramento and Eugene, Redding has much importance as tourist stop (there are dozens of motels).

Redding is liberal *only* in comparison with surrounding conservative areas. It is strongly Democratic (southern), a legacy from construction of Shasta Dam. Like most of the northern reaches of California, its urbanized area is dominantly Anglo and Protestant. Yet Redding is less urbane that either Chico or Davis.

Several communities are within the Redding complex. ***Enterprise*** (7500), a growing district with modest dwellings, is now within the city limits, as is ***Central Valley*** (4000), the poorest area, with considerable unemployment. ***Anderson*** (7500), with a large wood products plant, is politically independent. Fringe-area commuters reside westward along Ca. 299 and eastward into the Cascade Range.

"Authorities" have rated Redding differently. *Best Towns in America* lists it as one of two in California but *Great Towns in the West* has ignored it. *Places Rated Almanac* gives it high marks for setting and recreation but low scores for education, health care, and economic opportunities. Shasta College is one of few two-year colleges in extreme northern California; there are no four-year institutions.

***Red Bluff*** (13,000), "trapped" economically between two larger nearby centers (Redding and Chico), is a ranching, governmental and lumbering place.

Except for local services and county government, it might have declined in the second half of the twentieth century had it not been for its lumber mills (Diamond International and Louisiana Pacific) and *intentional* placement of the "northern"

offices of the Department of Water Resources in the city, and recently, retiree residence.

Red Bluff was the head of riverboat navigation on the Sacramento in pre-railroad days. The past is reflected in the renovated structures downtown and frame cottages in the original city, on bluffs west of the river.

Less significantly than Redding it is a highway junction (I-5, Ca. 99 and Ca. 36) and service functions have importance. The city affords a western gateway to Lassen Park (Ch.11). Considerable retail activity is now located along the highways, including a pseudo false-front "Cowtown". Closure of stockyards and a slaughterhouse reflect a decline of livestock ranching in the surrounding area. In the final quarter of the twentieth century, Red Bluff has attracted retirees from "everywhere" who have a fondness for rural America, especially hunting and fishing. Many live outside the political city.

## THE WEST SIDE

As one speeds along Interstate 5, the casual wayfarer, somewhat cognizant of Great Valley agricultural output, but uncertain of location of more productive districts, may find the several score of miles between Red Bluff and Arbuckle (i.e., the northern West Side) somewhat disillusioning. The red lands, dry-farmed or grazed seasonally, are not the anticipated Central Valley one encounters south of Arbuckle.

Those legendary field of alfalfa, rice and cotton, the peach orchards and the vineyards—where are they? Unless this visitor is observant one may even overlook the narrow strips of irrigated floodplains along Sacramento tributaries that rise in the northern Coast Ranges.

Since the West Side (Map 9-3) lies in the lee (rainshadow) of these highlands, east-flowing creeks tend to be dry during more than half of each year. They provide limited quantities of water in contrast to such East Side rivers as the Feather and the American. This has tended to discourage development of irrigation districts. Much bottomland is watered from pump wells on individual properties.

---

* The attitude of corporate "retail America" is sometimes less than praiseworthy in the case of many communities. In the Central Valley, as elsewhere, city and county officials are "played" against each other—and the *political* city is usually the loser.

Some irrigation expansion has followed construction of west Sacramento Valley units of the Central Valley Project.

Water is diverted from the Sacramento River near Red Bluff and and from Stony Creek near Orland. Already completed is the small *Corning Canal,* 21 miles long. Continuing south is the *Tehama-Colusa Canal* and its southward extension, the *West Sacramento Canal.* These two segments deliver water as far south as Solano County.

Rainfall is sufficient for dry farming, hence landscapes reflect such usage.

The almost-treeless plain of the northern West Side is gently undulating. Properties are large and ranchsteads are scattered. On back roads one can often drive some distance without meeting another vehicle.

Specialized agriculture is restricted to the floodplains of east-flowing Sacramento tributaries (map, 9-3). Here the landscape is richer and the population density higher.

Most West Side communities might be described as "courthouses (or city halls), residences, freight cars and service stations."

North of Woodland in Yolo County, they are "second-generation" California towns, founded in the 1870's along the Southern Pacific's *Shasta* line and evolving in the wheat era. Their current populations tend to be fewer than 5000 inhabitants each.

While they have a settled look, there tend to be fewer shade trees than East Side towns, which are much preferred as residence places.

Relocation of service stations, restaurants and motels reflect traffic flow along Interstate 5. Most of the larger towns are at the junction of east-west roads with this major north-south thoroughfare.

### The Northern West Side

Between Yolo County and the Redding District are four smaller agricultural districts. Population is modest and there is no town larger than 6000.

***The Gerber District*** developed without benefit of reservoir storage and produces such crops as sugar beets, alfalfa and beans.

It has been dependent upon the relatively-high water table along Elder Creek. Cropped land is largely between Interstate 5 and the Sacramento River.

As California's third-ranking olive producer, ***The Corning District*** is unique on the west side.

Prior to availability of C.V.P. water (the Corning Canal) in 1960 irrigation depended upon pumping

**Figure 9-10.** Olive harvest, Corning. The Corning District is a important producer of ripe olives, used for such foods as pizza. (Bureau of Reclamation, photo by B.D. Glaha)

along Thomes Creek and the water table had declined.

Although acreage of the long-lived olive tree has remained constant, changes have occurred.

The *Sevillano,* the most popular variety, is grown as an *eating* olive. Consumption is domestic and much of the processing is done locally. Pizza has provided an additional market but olive import from Spain and Portugal has become a threat.

***Corning*** (6000), the local service place, has grown slowly.

In addition to anticipated farm service and modest trade from wayfarers along I-5, it has olive processing and packing plants.

***The Orland District*** provided a Bureau of Reclamation "model" early in the twentieth century. Current agricultural output is more varied than in the districts farther north just discussed.

Along the floodplain of Stony Creek, the district has long received water from reservoirs (Stony Gorge and East Park). Yet there was insufficient water in drier years until Black Butte reservoir was constructed. Early irrigation development was a testimony to pioneer Will Green, who struggled for half a century to bring irrigation to the Sacramento Valley. The Bureau of Reclamation no longer controls activity.

Traditionally small farms have become larger through consolidation. An exception is corporate Mills Orchard in Hamilton City which produces a variety of crops.

While the district is the leading producer of market milk in the upper Sacramento Valley, output has declined. The district also produces almonds, prunes, and walnuts. Acreage of navel oranges, which ripen here earlier than farther south, has expanded. Ladino clover seed is a specialty of the area.

*Orland* (4700) is a stable crossroads community characterized by modest cottages. Housing is less expensive than in Chico and increased commutation has developed.

The central portion of *Colusa County* is one of the more productive areas of the Sacramento Valley's West Side.

Unlike other West Side districts it lacks an east-flowing stream. Prior to supplementary supply from the Central Valley Project, it was dependent upon pumping of the alluvial strata underlying the Sacramento floodplain.

It occupies the northwestern fringe of the Flood Basins and also has fertile loam (around Arbuckle) upon which almonds are raised.

*Williams* (1800) has gained considerably as a highway junction (I-5 and Ca. 20) that affords a travelers' stop.

*Willows* (6000), with diverse functions, prospers more than some West Side towns.

It is the seat of Colusa County and has a viable central district. It has a little consequence as a G-E-M stop on I-5. There is also a large fiberglass plant on its periphery.

Two neighborhoods, in the southeast (older) and the southwest (newer), are among the most attractive on the West Side. Its "Mexican town" (northeast quadrant) is somewhat unusual for places in the Sacramento Valley.

### The Southern West Side

The southwestern Sacramento Valley, in Yolo and Solano counties, looks like one would expect the Central Valley to look. Virtually the entirety of this area consists of alluvial plains, with extensive and intensive irrigation agriculture.

The population of these two counties is ten-fold that of the two to the north (Colusa and Glenn). They are on the fringes of the San Francisco Bay Area and metropolitan Sacramento. Obviously functions besides agriculture have much importance.

### Yolo County

With highly-diversified agricultural output, Yolo County has long been an agricultural leader in the Sacramento Valley, and is nationally-ranked.

Its fertile alluvial plains are the most extensive of any county in the Sacramento Valley.

Yolo County, as the Santa Clara Valley (Ch. 8) once

**Figure 9-11.** Orland, view to east with I-5 in foreground. "Locals" contend that this peaceful farm town is a "swinging place" on Saturday nights. (dwl)

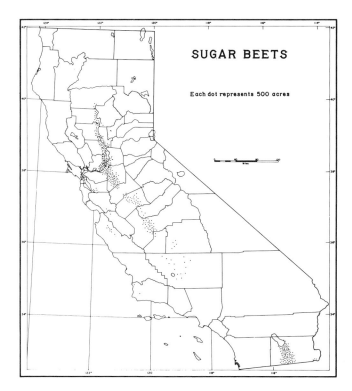

**Map 9-4.** Most of California's sugar beets are grown from the Delta northward into the Sacramento Valley *or* in the Imperial Valley.

**Map 9-5.** Field bean acreage is centered in the southern Sacramento Valley and in the northern San Joaquin Valley.

did, forms a "fruit bowl" with orchards of freestone peaches, prunes, figs, and apricots, as well as vineyards. Its output has been somewhat less than that of the Santa Clara in its "glory years." Import of apricots from Turkey has severely affected production. Local wineries have been established and grape acreage has increased. Also, there are almonds, olives and walnuts. But this is not all—the output of each of ten products exceeds five million dollars annually.

Residents acclaim the county to be "America's sugar bowl", a dubious claim since it ranks only sixth among California counties in beet sugar (Map, 9-4). The beets are favored by by nocturnal flow of cooler ocean air through Carquinez Strait in late afternoon and evening.

Air flow *also* favors tomatoes and Yolo County is one of the nation's leading producers of canning tomatoes (map, 9-6 and Fig. 9-12). However acreage has declined somewhat (due to competition from the huge "food factories" of western Fresno County). But the landscape almost seems to exude bountiful harvests and rural prosperity is much evident.

**Woodland** (40,000),long the Sacramento Valley's largest *farm* town, is is the seat of Yolo County. It has

afforded a service place and and processing center for surrounding agricultural lands. Lately its functions have become more diversified.

This pleasant city, with its tree-shaded streets and attractive residential areas, would long have been a strong candidate for "typical" farm-county seat of California." It was the most representative and the *least* unusual of larger Sacramento Valley towns prior to an influx of Davis and Sacramento commuters. *And,* quite suddenly in the middle 1980's, a new role as a leading Central Valley distribution center.

Food processing *(especially* tomatoes and sugar beets), stockyards, fruit and vegetable packing plants and shipping sheds are noticeable on the east side. Especially during harvest season there tends to be considerable bustle in Woodland.

**Davis** (42,000), university town and liberal "island" amidst the conservatism of the Central Valley, has become one of the more attractive cities in the Valley. It is a "separated" residential outlier of metropolitan Sacramento.

This pioneer farm hamlet (its 1940 population was only 1700) and Southern Pacific rail junction) expanded rapidly after its **University of Califor-**

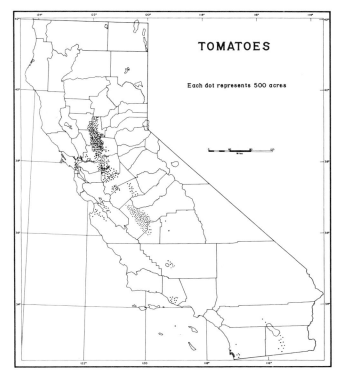

**Map 9-6.** Although the Delta and the Sacramento Valley still important producers of tomatoes, increased output comes from the west side of Fresno County.

**Figure 9-12.** Tomato harvest, Yolo County. Invention of the mechanical harvester and genetic "invention" of firm, square-shaped tomatoes saved a major California crop but displaced many field workers. (Blackwelder Manufacturing Company).

*nia* became "integrated" (i.e., new medical and law colleges and greater emphasis upon liberal arts) in the 1960's. The University for many decades has been recognized a world-class agricultural college. While almost unifunctional, Davis houses many graduates who work in Sacramento or the Bay Area. It also has a tomato processing plant. The central district is small, of course.

While its flat terrain may explain its absence from "best towns" books, it is an attractive place (Figure 9-14) which ranks high in median income and formal education. This is reflected in its residences, numerous shade trees (overhanging wide streets, with bicycle lanes, and parking lots) and well-tended gardens.

Davis has succeeded as well as any California city in promoting orderly growth without sprawl, aided by availability of services in nearby Woodland and Sacramento.

### Solano County

Solano County, providing a transition to both the Bay Area and the Delta Lands, is less typical of the Sacramento Valley than is Yolo County. Its population, twice as large, is also growing faster.

Despite similarities, there are agricultural differences.

Sugar beets are more important and tomatoes less so. Field corn, used as livestock feed, is much more important. Acreage of fruits and nuts is smaller.

Almost all of the Solano cities are affiliated with the Bay Area as noted in the previous chapter. The major exception is **Dixon** (12,000).

"Just outside" of Yolo County, it has meat packing plants. But its recent growth reflects increased importance as a residence place for Sacramento and Bay Area commuters.

### THE FLOOD BASINS

The present-day Flood Basins are located in the south-central portion of the Sacramento Valley, covering land to both the east and west of the Sacramento River (map, 9-3).

Reclaimed in the twentieth century, these lands are now normally "dry" most of every year and throughout drier years *except* for standing ponds in summer in the rice fields.

During periods of high water, they may be inundated to become temporary lakes as tributaries of the Sacramento have overflowed their banks. Dense clay soils have resulted from repeated deposition from standing water.

Flooding in the Sacramento Valley was aggravated in the nineteenth century as result of hydraulic mining (Ch. 10) which raised the level of the blood basins.

McGowan, in his *History of the Sacramento Valley* (New York: Lewis Historical Publishing Co., 1961), relates this anecdote:

Tules, ten to fourteen feet high, covered the land so that farmers who lived all around the rim of the basin were called "rimlanders." It is said that a real estate man once sold 25,000 acres of this tule land to a southern California investor, assuring him that a levee four feet high would be sufficient to reclaim it. However when the buyer first visited his newly acquired property in winter, he exclaimed, "They have sold me the Pacific Ocean!" According to the story the investor held onto his land until he finally sold it for $25 an acre about 1910, thereby making a profit of $500,000 (Vol. 2, p.175).

Concerted flood-control action between 1905 and 1920 was prompted by recurrent disastrous floods.

Levees were built and following establishment of reclamation districts sizable portions were set aside as the *Sutter* and *Yolo* bypasses (although devoid of residential use they are summer cropped).

Normally the heavy runoff occurs during the cool season hence it seldom interferes with cropping, especially since construction of Shasta and Oroville dams. By 1920 400,000 acres of flood-basin land had been drained and were under cultivation.

Since John Sutter raised wheat near present-day Yuba City in 1845 *grains* have thrived on portions of the flood basins.

Repeated cropping of wheat without rotation depleted some soils so severely that farmers sought other crops. Thus rice was welcomed and within a few years had become a major product.

More recently other crops have been added. One,

**Figure 9-14.** Davis, despite flat terrain, is widely regarded as one of California's more liveable cities. The University of California campus is in the foreground beyond I-80. (dwl)

*safflower,* became a million-dollar commodity after 1950. The newest crop is *wild rice,* an import from Minnesota introduced in the 1980's and still sufficiently costly (and unfamiliar to cooks) as to be limited to "gourmet" cooking (see Ch. 2).

*Safflower,* an East Indian composite, was introduced into California in 1949 for use in the paint industry. Its seeds, which mature in a seedhead, produce a colorless oil. Expanded production reflected concern over low-cholesterol diets. The "fad" aspect has disappeared and production has stabilized. Barley drills and rice combines can be used in its production —it offers an ideal rotation crop for the Flood Basins. California is the nation's chief producer. While Fresno and Kings counties have become leading sources the Floods Basins are also important.

California is a major source of *rice* in the United States; the Flood Basins (with a modest contribution from the San Joaquin Valley) provide the Golden State's share (Map, 9-7).

The Sacramento Valley lies near the poleward limit of rice culture; in fact, long-grain Chinese and tropical Asian varieties cannot be grown. Previous attempts at harvesting Chinese rice in the cooler Delta Lands to the south failed.

Even in the Sacramento Valley, nocturnal cooling shortens the growing season and makes production precarious in years with early autumnal rains. Market prospects for shorter-grain varieties do not seem promising and attempts are underway to acclimatize long-grain varieties. Traditionally the modest American market has used short-grain rice mostly in cereals or other rice dishes.

**Figure 9-13.** Woodland, an expanding distribution center. This development represents one of the significant urban changes in the Central Valley in the late 1980's. Interstate 5 in rear. (dwl)

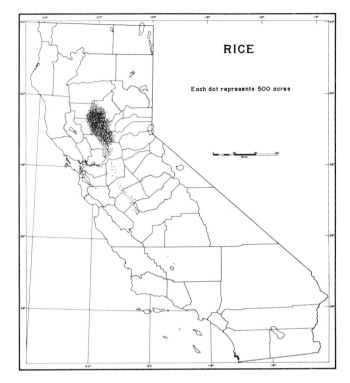

RICE

Each dot represents 500 acres

**Map 9-7.** Notice the concentration of rice in the flood basins of the Sacramento Valley. Acreage of wild rice, a recently-introduced grass from Minnesota, is increasing.

California's *Rice Bowl* is located principally in Butte, Colusa, Glenn, Sutter and Yolo counties.

The rice landscape, principally near the Sacramento River along the lower courses of major tributaries, provides the Valley with some of its most attractive summer scenes. Patterns tend to be fairly continuous and beautifully terraced with both contour and straight check dams. Habitation is limited (growers tend to live in nearby cities) although elevators are conspicuous along rail lines. To fly over this aquatic setting with the soft greens of the rice plants affords an impressive sight.

At the end of the Vietnam war, when production was curtailed in southeast Asia, California harvested a record 525,000 acres acres of rice—it is doubtful if that area *will* be achieved in the future. Previously, the record had been 350,000 acres (in 1954).

Despite the nation's relatively small acreage, United States has ranked third in the world in rice export. Periods of maximum production have been achieved during times of crisis: from World War I through the Vietnam "emergency." In addition to federal subsidies, acreage controls have been tightened to reflect expanded production in countries that prefer long-grain tropical rice.

California rice is raised paddy-style in shallow standing water as in eastern and southern Asia. Because of heavy water demands, the rice is raised upon heavy water-retentive soils. Land gradient is important; there must be enough slope to allow rapid drainage for harvest but sufficient flatness to maintain ponded water.

Valley production represents a "typically" American operation utilizing limited labor while requiring much machinery. Fields are prepared in April and then flooded. For many years plastic-covered checks (field dikes) have been used. Water-soaked grain is dropped from low-flying aircraft; fertilizer and pesticides are also spread by plane.

In the late 1980's the city of Sacramento was strongly objecting to use of chemicals, arguing that the taste of its urban supply was impaired and there was possibly a threat to health. Before insecticides mosquito control in the rice paddies was too expensive to attempt. California has 37 sub-species of mosquitoes, including an Anopheles subspecies that can transmit malaria. Between 1938 and 1947 there were 2298 cases of malaria reported in the state. More recently, an outbreak of the disease has been prevented *only* because of the absence of a suitable vector. Dozens of mosquito-abatement districts have been created.

Harvesting is effected as a single operation with specially-built self-propelled combines that can move through wet ground (Figure 9-15). A three-man crew can accomplish work that once required 100 workers. The rice is taken to dryers and thence to storage silos until marketing.

The Flood Basins form part of the *Pacific flyway* for waterfowl.

Hence the *Sacramento National Wildlife Refuge* was established northwest of Colusa. Each autumn thousands of hunters (and birdwatchers) frequent the Basins for ducks and geese, as well as grouse and pheasants. A number of urban sportsmen have formed private hunting preserves.

## Levee Orchards

Paralleling the channels of the Sacramento River and its chief tributaries, natural levees flank the inner margins of the Basins. Here soils are friable and natural drainage superior.

Extensive strips south of Ca. 32 (between Orland and Chico) have provided long-time sites for or-

**Figure 9-15.** Rice harvest, southern Butte County (northwest of Gridley). Note air conditioned cabs on the machines. (dwl)

chards, especially peaches and plums. Since the mid-twentieth century prunes have been added; the area has become the chief source in California.

**Stagnant Towns**

Most towns in the Flood Basins evolved as ports along the Sacramento and Feather rivers. Briefly the rivers stimulated commerce and natural levee sites tended to be less flood-prone.

Before 1872 the Sacramento Valley depended largely upon river commerce. Particularly during the Gold Rush, most transportation between Sacramento and the Bay Area moved on water. Several river ports had considerable consequence during the zenith of wheat farming.

Railroad competition hastened the demise of the riverboats. Moreover by 1860 effects of hydraulic operations (Ch. 10) were making river travel more difficult.

Most river towns waned long ago and most have vanished from maps. *Tehama* and *Knights Landing* languish. Extant villages house farm person-

nel; there is no sizable "rice town." Grain is usually milled beside rail sidings and moves by rail to the port of Sacramento (Figure 9-18).

Well-shaded *Colusa* (5000) is the largest town between Red Bluff and Sacramento on the river.

**Figure 9-16.** Riparian forest, edge of Sacramento River (fore). This vegetation was more extensive before Anglo settlers arrived in the middle of the nineteenth century. (dwl)

**Figure 9-17.** Butte City, one of a number of stagnant Central Valley farm villages. Don't expect to cash a check at a local bank (although you can buy postage stamps). (dwl)

Bolstered by county government, farm services and residence (by farmers, workers and retired ranchers), it prospers. Income disparities are dramatized by the proximity of handsome homes of landowners and the shanties of farm laborers.

## THE EAST SIDE

The better-watered East Side (Map, 9-3), which achieved importance first during the Gold Rush, remains the dominant area in the Sacramento Valley economy.

It has most of the largest cities in the Valley as well as a series of fertile districts on alluvial fans of perennial west-flowing Sacramento River tributaries.

Away from the alluvial fans, the East Side has extensive acreage on red lands and volcanic flows (from Oroville northward that merge almost imperceptibly into highland foothills on the east). On these unirrigated uplands, dry-farmed grains and seasonal pasturage form the characteristic use.

Long stretches of Ca. 99 *(and* Ca. 70) cross these less-productive surfaces so that the highway traveler does not gain a real impression of East Side agricultural output.

The following districts will be considered: *Los Molinos, Vina, Chico, Feather River Valley* and *Sacramento.*

## THE NORTHERN DISTRICTS

At the north end of the East Side are two small districts. Neither has a community of much consequence. Since Ca. 99 leads across irrigated alluvial fans, the traveler gets less of a feeling of open space than on the northern portion of the West Side along I-5.

The *Los Molinos District* forms the most northerly area of irrigation on the East Side.

Small properties prevail; the district produces poultry, milk and such deciduous fruits and nuts as almonds, apricots, peaches, prunes and walnuts.

*Rancho Los Molinos* in Mill Creek Valley was acquired by Joseph Cone, one of the more-renowned wheat barons, in the middle 1850's. Even-

**Figure 9-18.** The Port of Sacramento. While barge traffic is now negligible, the Central Valley *re-gained* a second seaport with the opening of this facility in the early 1960's. In this view westward the Yolo Bypass is in the middle distance with Davis beyond. (Sacramento-Yolo Port Authority, photo by Sirlin Studios)

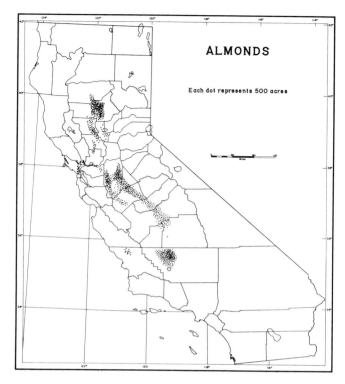

**Map 9-8.** Once the Chico District produced most of the almonds in the United States. While its output has remained steady, there has been an impressive increase in the San Joaquin Valley, *especially* in San Joaquin and Kern counties.

tually Cone acquired 100,000 acres; he was concerned primarily with wheat and sheep although he set out fruit orchards, including Bartlett pears. After his death his heirs established a land company, laid out a townsite and sold small parcels. *Los Molinos* (2000) is a small service point, highway stop and residence town (with commuters to Red Bluff and Chico).

The ***Vina District*** has been associated with some of California's prominent earlier Anglo residents.

In 1843 Peter Lassen acquired Rancho Bosquejo (23,000 acres) along Deer Creek. Henry Gerke purchased a portion of the ranch and introduced quality European grapevines into the Sacramento Valley and by the 1870's had created one of California's finest vineyards.

Senator Leland Stanford bought the Gerke lands in 1881 and added additional acreage so that his *Vina Ranch* included 55,000 acres. Anticipating an expanded market for California wines, he planted nearly 3 million grapevines. But he proved less successful in viticulture than he had been as a railroad magnate.

Stanford deeded the ranch to Stanford University, which sold it as small parcels. Today the Vina

District produces milk, nuts and deciduous fruits. A revival of viticulture may be in the offing. *Trappist* monks hold a portion of the Vina Ranch including some of the Stanford buildings.

### The Chico District

This District, for its size, is one of the more productive agricultural areas in the Golden State. It raises both tree crops and a variety of field crops.

Evolution of the Chico District to its present consequence began with John Bidwell, co-leader of the first overland immigrant party to California (in 1841). He served as Sutter's lieutenant at Sacramento and struck "pay dirt" along the Feather River. Then he purchased two contiguous Mexican land grants, presumably with returns from gold mining. Thus he acquired the fertile alluvial fan of Chico Creek and smaller streams.

While wheat production was the dominant nineteenth-century activity, Bidwell was keenly interested in agricultural experimentation and he left 1800 acres of deciduous orchards. Fruit raising, especially peaches, had already gained local importance but years of low prices prompted orchardists to shift to plums, then prunes and finally almonds.

Almond groves were set out in the 1920's. Once the state leader, the District has dropped to fourth in almond production as acreage has expanded in San Joaquin, Stanislaus and Kern counties (Map, 9-8).

Chico orchards are often small; many "city folk" are "week-end" farmers, dwelling handsomely amidst the trees—farming is indeed a "way of life" here.

*Chico* (35,000) depends on higher education, services, residence, and farm activities (Figures 9-19 and 9-20). Only Davis and Chico, among larger Valley towns, are not county seats—and Chico has a county "center."

Now the largest California urbanized area (70,000 with 175,000 in its S.M.A.) north of Sacramento, Chico began as a dwelling place for Bidwell's workers. Its nineteenth century growth was related to farm service, freighting eastward across the mountains and lumbering.

The future was set with establishment of a normal school (now ***California State University***) in 1887. Older residential blocks have the white frame dwellings and large deciduous shade trees common to East Side towns.

There is modest industry (products include beer,

**Figure 9-19.** Chico—a wooded residence place. Despite the gentle slope of its alluvial fan, there are some interesting departures of street patterns from from cardinal orientation. The oak groves of Bidwell Park extend southwestward into the central district (lower center). Much recent growth has occurred east of the freeway (Ca. 99) in northeast and southeast Chico. (Photo Tech)

stuffed toys and bagels) but Chico is a residence place. Lumbering became less important after Diamond International relocated in Red Bluff.

Functions *modestly* suggest those of Fresno in the San Joaquin Valley. Mid-valley location and attractive setting have prompted residence by hundreds of jobbers, salesmen and affluent ranchers). College growth (the university is *officially* a residential institution), expanding services and retirement residence (hundreds of upper middle-income retirees from Southern California and the Bay) fostered recent growth. The latter is reflected in expansion of eastern fringes into the Cascadian foothills, especially *California Park* with its Canyon Oaks and *Sierra Sunrise* (a resident-owned and operated retirement community suggestive of a small Leisure World in Laguna Hills (Ch.6).

During the academic year there are around 25,000 students and *"hangers-on"*—this number includes many who attend nearby Butte College.

Senior citizens (plus other migrants from metropolitan California) are attracted by the setting. Bidwell Park, with 2400 acres containing oak woodland along Chico Creek, ranks second in size to Los Angeles' Griffith Park among the state's in-limits city parks.

Unemployment in Butte County has been ten per cent or higher for years—this is a dilemma for sundry parts of northern California as many city

**Figure 9-20.** North Valley Plaza, Chico. One of the Central Valley's older regional shopping centers. Except for density of shade trees, this could be any Central Valley urbanized area (dwl).

folk move north without jobs, youth desire to stay and much farm work is seasonal.

### Feather River Valley

Along the lower Feather River, chief tributary of the Sacramento, lies the single most important agricultural district of the northern Central Valley.

For 50 miles this tri-county strip extends between the Sutter Buttes (west) and the foothills of the Sierra Nevada. Conspicuous levees along the Bear, Yuba, and Feather rivers reflect the recurrent threat of seasonal flooding *even* since construction of Oroville Dam (Ch. 10). Miles of gravel heaps along the Yuba and Feather near the Sierran foothills attests to gold dredging in the first half of the twentieth century.

Especially in eastern Sutter County the Valley long ranked among the nation's leading sources of canned peaches—in the 1980's processing declined dramatically.

The long hot summer with low humidity is favorable for *clingstones,* whose firmer flesh is better for canning than *freestones,* hence the former has been the principal type; the mature trees can grow without irrigation. But fruit canning has become an economic tragedy of the late twentieth century

**Figure 9-21.** *Dwarf* orchards, Feather River Valley, with Sutter Buttes. Dwarf fruit acreage is expanding in the Central Valley. (dwl)

and a marked decline in acreage has occurred. One factor has been foreign competition for canned fruit.

*"The peach belt",* or Tri-County district, has reflected the momentum of an early start.

At the time of the Gold Rush John Sutter demonstrated the suitability of the Feather River Valley. But until construction of the first cannery expansion was slow. In the 1890's orchards rapidly replaced wheat fields.

Subsequently the Belt was a leading world producer of canned peaches. Most varieties used in canning originated locally after 1900. Housewives and students from surrounding areas served as seasonal cannery workers.

Since the peach has a relatively-short bearing span (about 20 years), some orchards have been replanted several times. The different varieties ripen from June through August. Orchard management is important as the fruit must be of fairly uniform size and relatively defect-free.

Yields per acre have tripled in the past half century as result of improved cultivation. Production of California clingstones has increased sixfold in the same period, reflecting yield per acre and much acreage expansion *especially* in the San Joaquin Valley. There tend to be a sizable surplus, hence 10 to 15 per cent of the fruit is destroyed annually.

In addition to peaches, the Peach Belt has become the ranking California producer of prunes.

As urbanization has continued in the Santa Clara Valley (Ch. 7) the Sacramento Valley has become a more important source. Orchards have never gained the concentration of the peaches, although much peach acreage has been replanted in prunes.

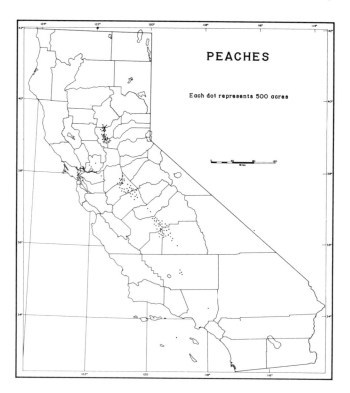

**Map 9-9.** Peach acreage has declined in recent years. Factors include foreign competition and lessened canning of peaches in California.

The upper Feather valley around Oroville is the Sacramento Valley's leading source of olives and oranges. It is also the leading source of pumpkins (used especially for Halloween jack-o-lanterns) in the Central Valley.

### Levee Towns

Excluding the Sacramento conurbation, the Feather River Valley has more towns of consequence than any other portion of the Sacramento Valley.

The three leading communities, all county seats, are "levee towns" along the Feather River. All three was founded during the Gold Rush era.

*Oroville* (11,000) is located at the mouth of the Feather River Canyon (Ch. 10) with residential districts on slopes of Sierran foothills.

Oroville is a lumber town, a farm processing center (olives) and shipping point, a gateway to the "Feather River Country". Hence tourism is important (way stop on Ca.70; Lake Oroville nearby).

Oroville differs considerably from the two larger communities (Chico and Paradise) in its county. The population, which includes the largest black group north of Sacramento in interior California (a legacy of the Gold Era), is strongly blue-collar and conservative. It is somewhat larger than it was during the Gold Rush but growth has been spasmodic. During construction of Oroville Dam (1960's) the town boomed.

Among Central Valley cities only Redding would appear to have a more attractive physical site. Oroville has failed to take full advantage of its setting although a sizable mobile-home village is sited among oak groves and overlooks Lake Oroville.

*Gridley* (4500) relates primarily to agriculture (and calls itself incorrectly the "kiwi fruit capital of the world").

It has processing (including a rice-cake plant) and considerable labor residence.

The twin cities of Yuba City and Marysville plus two satellites house over 50,000 people thus forming the second-largest conurbation in interior California north of Sacramento. This is California's smallest S.M.A.

One survey rated it in last place among standard metropolitan areas. Its last-place position (no. 329) reflected no particular strength but it did not rate last in a single category). Obviously it is *less* truly a metropolitan area than any other in the Golden State.

*Yuba City* (23,000) is a service center, county seat, and residence place with agricultural processing (including the nation's largest prune processing plant).

Conservative, yet more progressive than its trans-Feather twin city, Yuba City is apparently preferred by commuters (to Beale Air Force Base). Not confined by dikes like Marysville, Yuba City has increasingly-outgrown Marysville in the second half of the twentieth century. Its small downtown has not expanded but there has been much increase in retail trade, especially in strip-commercial belts along Ca. 20 (east-west) and Ca. 99 (north-south).

While it was founded in 1849, Yuba City was on the "wrong" (i.e., west) side of the Feather from Gold Rush activities. Hence it remained small until the second half of the twentieth century. Its residential areas are much newer than those of Marysville, with costlier areas in the southwest (residents include many "east" Indians, especially Sikhs) and north. There is a strong pro-growth attitude yet general determination to remain within its sphere of influence, thus averting extreme sprawl. The community houses a significant Hispanic population in the southeast.

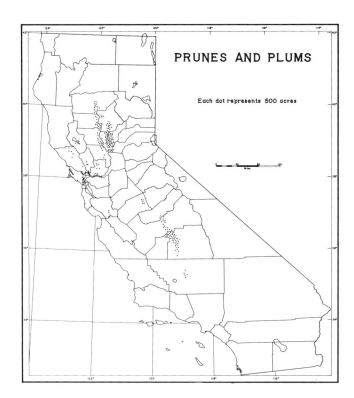

**Map 9-10.** The Sacramento Valley leads California in prune production *and* the Kaweah Delta ranks first in plums.

**Figure 9-23.** Renovation in downtown Marysville. On a small scale it is suggestive of Old Sacramento. (dwl)

*Marysville* (12,000), seat of Yuba County, provides services for a sizable area to the east. One of California's historic places, it began with a trading-post waystop on the California-Oregon Trail in 1842.

For a while during the Gold Rush, as the head of navigation for the Northern Diggings (Ch.10), Marysville was the third largest town in California and was considered as a possible site for the state capital. A rich legacy of buildings remains from from the early days. Its long-decaying central district has experienced extensive urban renewal.

Two contiguous erstwhile "Hoovervilles" occupy the southern portion of the metropolis.

Both are "urban poor" and primarily residential, with many converted mobile homes and a paucity of large shade trees. Both are unincorporated but there has been considerable discussion of incorporation and merger as *Lindhurst*. Extensive flood damage in 1986 reflected insufficient flood-control structures on the Yuba River.

**Olivehurst** (10,000) is almost wholly residential. By contrast neighboring **Linda** (10,000) has more retail activity including the single mall in the metropolis (an economic blunder in view of socio-economic bias), as well as Yuba College.

### Beale Air Force Base

East of Marysville, expansive Beale Air Force Base, a Strategic Air Command facility, provides the "nerve center" for electronic early-warning along the Pacific Coast.

Originally (World War II) it was an Army training camp. Later, it was declared "war surplus" but since 1948 has been used by the Air Force.

### The Sacramento District *

Sacramento County, excluding the Delta Lands and the American River flood basin, is a rolling land dotted with oak woodlands and underlain by the red lands.

Thus, to a lesser extent than in some California urban areas, Sacramento expansion encroached upon fertile agricultural lands cultural areas until the 1980's, with occupance of the fertile Natomas floodplain north of the American River.

Rural land utilization has remained much the same for over a century and seasonal pasturage is extensive. Even the American River Valley, without the attenuated lowland of the Feather River Valley, has only modest agricultural output.

In addition to rice (in the Flood Basin) and dairies and egg farms supplying local markets, hops (east and north of Sacramento), has been a specialty. Decreased use of hops in beer-making has prompted acreage decline.

Focusing upon the junction of the Sacramento and American rivers and extending eastward into the American River Country, the city of Sacramento and its environs forms the pre-eminent conurbation in the Central Valley (Map, 9-11).

Metropolitan Sacramento, approaching Indianapolis and New Orleans in size, has increased fourfold in population since 1950.

Thus it has joined other major California urban complexes in such aspects as major league sports, light-rail transit, university professional (medical and law) schools, service by a number of airlines and cultural events. But another Los Angeles or San Francisco it is not—yet.

While north of the Golden State's geographical center, **Sacramento** (360,000), with a million plus in its S.M.A., is located at the major north-south and east-west route crossings of central California (Map, 9-1).

Unfavorable because of early floods, its downtown site (southeast of the confluence of the Sacramento and American rivers) is only 20 feet above sea level.

Buoyed by government, commerce and manufacturing, trade, military bases, tourism, retail and wholesale trade, the metropolitan population now much exceeds that of the city of San Francisco.

The District formed an *original* area of Anglo settlement in the Central Valley but has become

---

\* This section has been reviewed by Susan Hardwick, C.S.U., Chico and Sandra Karinen, geographic consultant, Davis.

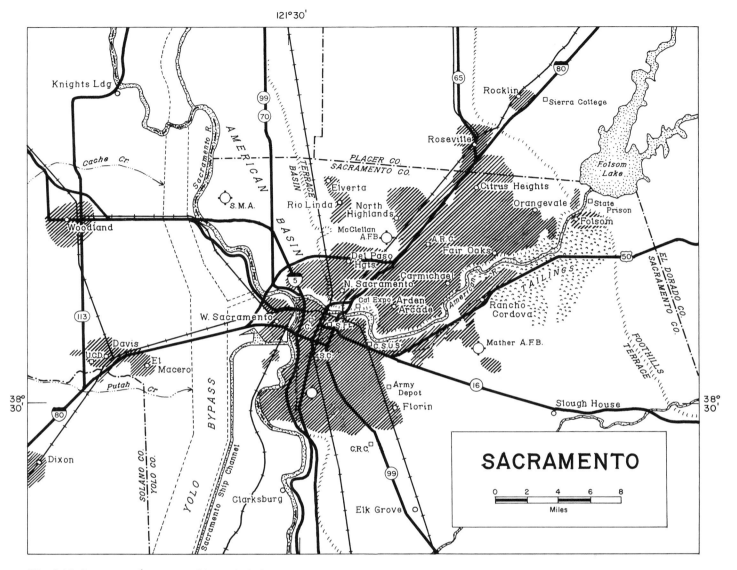

**Map 9-11.** Sacramento is now one of the nation's forty most- populous metropolises. The low downtown skyline (the county jail is one of the higher buildings!), small size of the central district and scatteration obscure this status.

increasingly diverse ethnically in the latter part of the twentieth century.

The American River Country has provided the major transit corridor eastward between central California and the interior West, via Donner Pass, since the 1840's.

Near the site that has become central Sacramento, John Sutter established *Sutter's Fort,* headquarters for *New Helvetia,* the first white settlement in interior California, in 1839—it was two miles east of the Sacramento River and flood-free. James Marshall, his mill foreman, found gold a decade later. Sutter then laid out *Sutterville* on the river, but a squatters' town to the north became Sacramento.

The upstart village promptly acquired thousands of residents. As the principal gateway into the Mother Lode Country (Ch.10) it was the second-largest city in California. With many itinerants it was a boomtown with saloons and gambling houses.

Sacramento experienced early-day disasters. Between 1849 and 1853 there were four serious floods. And much of the city burned in 1852. Meanwhile it had become the capital of California. The legislature convened there in 1852 although the capitol building was not completed until 1874.

Since its founding, commerce has been important in the growth of Sacramento.

Upstream commerce destined for the gold country

was initially important; a rail line was extended to Folsom in 1856.

The *Pony Express* operated west from the Missouri River in 1860-1861; Sacramento served as the western terminus. Then, in 1863, eastward construction of the *Central Pacific Railroad* began at Sacramento, site of its main office. The city's commercial importance was enhanced with completion of the transcontinental linkage in 1869. Forty years later additional revenue was engendered by the construction of a second trans-Sierran railroad utilizing the Feather River canyon.

Although Sacramento was an early-day seaport it lost this status for many years. Finally, in the 1950's, the *Sacramento Ship Channel* was dredged.

Sacramento also flourished as result of agricultural development of the Central Valley, especially the more northerly portions.

While much produce moved to the Bay Area, Sacramento has had continuing importance as an agricultural processing center.

The small downtown (C.B.D.) has evolved eastward from the original townsite, north of Capitol Park (Figure 9-24).

As the two rivers have restricted outward growth to the west and north, the C.B.D. has become increasingly "off center" as the metropolis has grown.

While the C.B.D. contains a few hotels, restaurants and specialty shops, the percentage of retail trade conducted downtown has progressively declined. Planners hoped for a while that the potential trade of large numbers of state employees

**Figure 9-24.** Central Sacramento, view to the northeast. There has been considerable downtown renewal. The small central district is to the north of the Capitol building. Note I-5 (north-south) and I-880 (east-west). Many a visitor has gotten confused at the interchange. (Sirlin Studios, Sacramento).

might revitalize the area but increasingly northside (*Arden Way* and *Sunrise)* and southside (*Florin Avenue)* regional shopping centers have conducted larger trade volumes.

On the northern margin of downtown, near the American River, are the depot and adjoining shops of the Southern Pacific. Also here is the original industrial area.

A considerable portion of *Old Sacramento,* blocks of antiquated brick buildings that formerly extended eastward from the Sacramento riverfront (and merged with the contemporary central district and Capitol Park) was destroyed to permit construction of Interstate 5 and as part of downtown renewal.

*Almost* too late, portions of Old Town west of Interstate 5 were renovated. Before the transition, Old Town formed a socially-submarginal district occupied by many single male transients, lower-income people and ethnics, especially Asians and Hispanics.

Restored Old Town now provides a memento of Sacramento's early years. Together with the adjoining Railroad Museum and rebuilt Chinatown it is one of the city's chief visitor attractions. There are hotel and motel complexes nearby.

State government centers in and around *Capitol Park.*

The capitol and older structures are of classic Greek architecture whereas newer office buildings along Capitol Mall toward the west are of contemporary design. While these edifices form an attractive entry into Sacramento from the west, the functional concrete facades are less imposing than those along the federal mall in Washington, D.C. Many thousand state employees (as well as a considerable number of city and federal workers) provide the metropolis with sizable and steady payrolls.

Capitol Park has some of the nation's most impressive plantings of camellias, as well as other vegetation from around the world.

The city of Sacramento has tended to expand south and east...and lately, north of the American River.

"Close-in", older residential districts retain many nineteenth century frame dwellings. Streets are shaded by large trees and there are suggestions of the Middle West absent in much of California. Thousands of tree-sized camellias are conspicuous among trees and flowers.

Newer residential areas, farther to the east and south, resemble more other large California communities with subdivisions of tract houses.

**Figure 9-25.** Old Sacramento (dwl).

*William Land Park*, while much smaller than Griffith (Los Angeles) or Golden Gate (San Francisco), is the largest of several recreational areas. Nearby are the political city's preferred residential neighborhoods as well as Sacramento City College and Executive Airport.

The metropolis has appreciable status as a cultural, educational, and recreational despite its proximity to the San Francisco Bay area.

**California State University** was established in 1949 and the **University of California at Davis** has broadened its programs. *McGeorge* School of Law (University of the Pacific) offers legal training while Sacramento City, Cosumnes River and American River colleges provide two years of higher education.

Musical and theatrical events have increased. Summer theatre attracts many Valley visitors as does the State Fair (Cal Expo.) The City has a symphony orchestra as well as art galleries.

Capitol Park (with the State Library and gardens), Crocker Art Museum, Sutter's Fort and Old Sacramento provide tourist attractions. The Sacramento and American rivers and Folsom Lake offer opportunities for such aquatic recreation as water-skiing and boating.

Industrial expansion in metropolitan Sacramento has been less rapid than some anticipated.

The older industrial district north of the downtown area was more important for agricultural processing in the past.

Newer firms are involved with soaps, missile fuels and electronics. A rocket manufacturer, Aerojet, which at times employed as many as the several hundred other industrial plants in the district combined, has recently had fewer workers.

**Figure 9-26.** Sacramento's new (1987) light rail and downtown mall. So far the mall has proved a failure. (dwl)

Sacramento has always had importance as a transportation center, located as it is on the state's largest river. Centrality within the Golden State has commended its junction role for north-south and east-west route crossings.

The role of the Port of Sacramento is questionable for container cargo as it cannot compete effectively with Oakland. Earlier, waterborne commerce (particularly agricultural products and petroleum) moved by tug-drawn barges. Today aquatic cargo consists principally of the export of rice and wood chips.

Land transportation has made a signal contribution to the growth of Sacramento.

The city is located on two transcontinental rail routes from central United States into the Bay Area.

The Southern Pacific's *Valley* line links with its *Shasta* division to provide north-south movement between Southern California and the Pacific Northwest.

Highway movement is likewise significant, with two major east-west routes, Interstate 80 and U.S. 50, bisecting north-south Interstate 5 and Ca. 99.

Sacramento has importance for truck and bus lines; understandably there are many motels, especially on the metropolitan periphery.

While Sacramento is less important than San Francisco and Los Angeles as an air center, increasing traffic moves in and out of *Metropolitan Airport*. Flights within California are particularly important because of state government.

Military installations have contributed to the growth of the metropolis for decades.

*Mather Air Force Base* was initiated used during World War I; it has been the principal navigational training center for the Air Force.

*McClellan Air Force Base* replaced inadequate facilities at San Diego in 1936. In recent decades the two bases have employed as many as 27,000 civilians alone and payrolls have reached several hundred million dollars.

The Army maintains a depot in the southern part of Sacramento.

Sacramento is basically a middle-income Anglo city yet it has more ethnic diversity than any other city in the Sacramento Valley.

While its ethnic composition (especially Anglos, blacks and Hispanics) is less representative of the Pacific Rim than is true of some larger Golden State metropolises, it does contain Asians (Chinese, Japanese, Vietnamese, Filipino) and there are others, including Russians, Scandinavians and American Indians.

Since Sacramento is a city of middle-income salaried-office workers, there is a lesser range of wealth and poverty than is found in some larger metropolitan areas.

### The Satellites

Over two-thirds of the metropolitan population resides outside of Sacramento city.

Problems have arisen with fringe-area growth. Despite freeways, rush-hour traffic has worsened. Hopefully the new light-rail transit will alleviate the problem somewhat. As elsewhere in metropolitan California, smog is increasingly serious.

*West Sacramento* (30,000) includes The Port, industry (rice processing) and many older motels.

This is a stable, non-expanding blue collar area. On its northern fringe is *Bryte*, the Russian quarter.

*North Sacramento* (30,000) is also an older residential area. The metropolis has recently expanded to the northwest toward the airport. Here is located *Arco Arena*, site of professional sports.

Urbanization in *North Natomas*, adjacent to I-5 and I-80 is causing some concern about construction too close to the airport flight path and in areas low in elevation.

*North Highlands* (45,000), primarily blue collar, with many modest cottages, has McClelland Air Force Base.

*Arden-Arcade* (94,000), with its large regional shopping center, contains some of the more expensive residences in the metropolis.

*Carmichael* (55,000), to the east, is the locale of American River College.

*Citrus Heights* (120,000) and **Orangevale** (26,000) are on the eastern periphery and are essentially white-collar areas. *Folsom* (20,000), once considered "way out", is on the metropolitan fringe. This is also true of Roseville and Lincoln.

*Roseville* (38,000), traditionally known for its rail yards, now has an expanding computer software industry.

Space shortage within Sacramento accounted for the sizable Southern Pacific facilities at the base of "the hill" (the ascent to Donner Pass). Included are retarder yards (re-assembly of freight cars, with a capacity of 90 trains daily) and shops (freight car repair).

**Lincoln** (6,000) is beginning to experience the effects of commutation.

Its economy has long been affected by local clay deposits and a large clay-products (Interpace) plant.

*Fair Oaks* (40,000), with rolling topography and many native oaks, includes more expensive residential tracts on bluffs overlooking the American River, as well as the Sunrise Mall.

*Rancho Cordova* (55,000), south of the American River, is the locale of Aerojet and Mather Air Force Base; it has sizable blue-collar residency.

*Florin* (30,000), between Ca. 99 and Interstate 5, is an area of more recent expansion to the south. Besides the largest middle-income black populace in the Central Valley, it is the locale of Cosumnes River College. *Elk Grove* too is feeling the outward expansion of the metropolis southward.

The commuter belt has continued to expand into the Foothills of the Sierra Nevada (Ch.10), westward into Yolo County and southward into San Joaquin County.

Thus many Sacramento workers live in Davis, Woodland, Rocklin and even more distant places such as Auburn, Grass Valley and Placerville and Jackson. Less-buildable sites on low ground or hardpan terraces tend to remain agricultural, giving the conurbation an unusually-fragmented rurban pattern.

## THE DELTA LANDS *

At the confluence of the San Joaquin and Sacramento rivers east of Suisun Bay is The Delta Lands. It has been termed "America's Holland"— this area,

like western Netherlands, has been reclaimed yet there are decided differences in landscape.

The Delta Lands lacks the lush greenness of the European land in summer, and the the small properties, dense population, charming old cities and quaint towns.

Moreover, residents of the Delta Lands, despite fear of seasonal flooding, are not constantly plagued by threat of sea inundation.

In a strict sense these rivers do *not* have a delta— the lower course of the Sacramento is an estuary that debouches into the Pacific at the Golden Gate.

Hence the Delta Lands, although it displays some deltaic features, such as *distributary channels* (which merge into a single watercourse downstream at the east end of Suisun Bay), natural levees, islands and marshes (hence it might be called an "interrupted delta") lacks the foreset layers of fresh deposition. It has been likened to the Fens of eastern England.

The Delta Lands is wider on its landward (interior) side, narrowing westward toward Antioch.

Still it has the crudely triangular shape of a delta, with Antioch, Stockton and Sacramento at its apices (map 9-12). On its eastern side it merges almost imperceptibly into the surrounding lowland.

The Delta, about a century and a half ago, was a land of tule swamps and mosquitos, extensively flooded seasonally and little-known except to its Indian inhabitants and a few fur trappers.

Since 1850 it has been polderized to become an area of extreme productivity, both intensive and specialized. It was was among the first deltaic areas to be reclaimed by advanced methods with employment of much machinery.

Earlier-time vegetation, characteristically reeds, was largely replaced at a late pre-occupance time by bulrushes (or tules).

Their residue has created the soil-like mass of partially-decayed organic soil known as peat and muck, intermingled with river silts.

Averaging 18 feet in depth, the peat reaches 40 feet in the west and thins to four to 20 feet in the north. The area underlain by peat is considerably smaller than the entire Delta which also encompasses half a million acres plus the aquatic surface. The northern portion, with more mineral in the soil and less peat, has experienced less subsidence and is more productive.

---

\* The Delta Lands was initially reviewed by Thomas and Marcia (nee McClain) Pagenhart, California State University, Hayward.

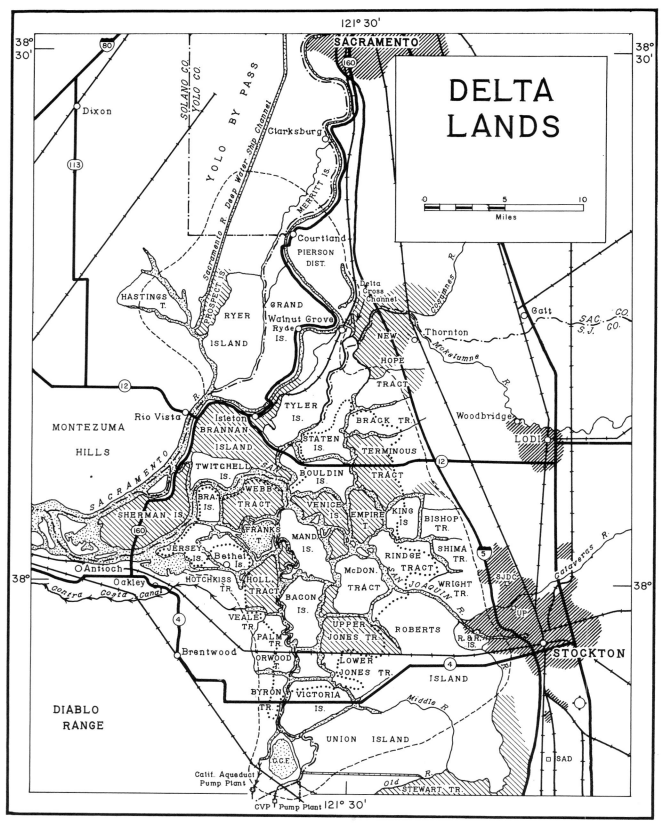

**Map 9-12.** The Delta Lands, despite fertility and high productivity, is a problem portion of California. The dotted line indicates extent of *true peat* and the light cross-hatching areas that were inundated some time between 1950 and 1980. Dashed lines indicate maximum inland penetration of saline water.

Nearly two-thirds of the Delta was being inundated during high tides as late as 1850.

Even since reclamation serious flooding has occurred, more recently in 1928, 1936, 1938,1940, 1955 and 1986.

Post-Indian settlement, which commenced around 1850, originated on the northern edge of the Delta.

As early as 1851 a section of land on Merritt Island was diked but accord between federal and state governments on the extent of swampland was not achieved until 1871. Meanwhile passage of the *Swamp Act* in 1855 led to occupance of additional land.

By 1871 the state had sold virtually all of its swampland. Original parcels, first 320 acres and later 640 acres, had been accumulated in some instances into sizable holdings. Allegedly one person was the transfer agent for some 250,000 acres. Farming methods and reclamation costs encouraged large holdings; this is still true.

Reclamation was a lengthy, costly, tedious and frustrating project. Levees were washed away repeatedly, fields flooded and livestock lost.

Yet there were ample incentives: (1) proximity of markets; (2) good water transportation; (3) ease of irrigation; and (4) inherently fertile land.

Although half of the Delta had been recovered before 1900 and all of it by 1930, as late as 1885 only 8000 acres were completely reclaimed and *relatively* flood-free. Although reclamation districts date from 1861, there was ineffective state regulation until 1911.

Despite setbacks, the land proved unusually productive and diking costs were amply repaid (although many pioneers were ruined financially). Levee construction has always been most tricky on the "light peat" which compresses and "sinks" under the weight of an alluvial levee.

Originally levees represented hand efforts; they were a few feet high and not over 12 feet wide. After 1879 corporation or reclamation district projects became more substantial.

Newer dikes have had a base width of 100 feet and a height of 25 to 30 feet. Chinese hand labor was employed on early dikes but since 1893-1894 the "clamshell" dredger has been used widely. Earlier levees were built of peat sod from the "islands" and many failed; more recently the dredges have utilized river muck ("blue clay").

After construction of Shasta and Oroville dams the threat of winter and spring flooding, as well as summer salinity, was reduced. But salinity has

**Figure 9-27.** Contra Costa Canal and southwestern edge of the Delta Lands. This 48-mile long canal delivers Sacramento River water to farmers and urban users in Contra Costa County. (Bureau of Reclamation, photo by A.G. D'Allessandro).

resulted from tidal inflow of ocean water at times of limited runoff from Central Valley rivers—water released from the dams has regulated Sacramento flow.

Drainage of the islands, whose surface slopes inward from the channels, has been a problem from the early years of reclamation, particularly during periods of winter storms. As subsidence has has continued the problem has worsened.

But since 1920 large electric pumps have been used. Each district maintains one or more pumping stations on pilings above *maximum* flood height. Considerable use is made of siphons, for drainage and irrigation; large-capacity siphons can be started with small pumps to commence the operation. Control of *subirrigation*, through control of the water table, has been widespread.

After reclamation, fire was used frequently to remove tule and weeds from the surface. Burning depth was controlled by maintenance of a high water table.

In earlier years "virgin" unburned peat proved difficult to plow and firing (to eliminate weeds) was more common, even though the humus loss was recognized.

By 1920 the caterpillar tractor, developed locally for Delta use, was often employed in plowing.

Subsidence, the result of burning, accelerated peat decomposition through exposure to air after plowing, and loss through cropping has posed serious problems too. The average depression at the center of the islands is ten feet below mean sea level—and it continues to drop. The center of the Delta has the lowest surfaces and the most difficult drainage and seepage problems.

Climate of the Delta is a modification of the interior dry-summer subtropical (Mediterranean) type associated with the Great Valley.

This modification is especially significant in summer, as there tends to be a fairly- flow of marine air through the Golden Gate and Carquinez Strait. Thus, although summer afternoons may become hot, evenings tend to be cooler than the rest of the Valley. Mid-day relative humidity tends to be somewhat higher than in other parts of the Central Valley— Stockton and Sacramento are likely to *feel* hotter than they are as a result. But ten months are frost-free with a year-round season for hardier crops—the season is somewhat longer than in most parts of the Valley.

## A VARIETY OF CROPS

The Delta raises approximately a tenth of the agricultural output of the Great Valley. Crop yields have been impressive for over a century; the Delta has been a leading California source of tomatoes, pears, asparagus, and field corn.

The physical advantages (mild climate, level terrain, fertile soils and ease of irrigation) have been enumerated. The water-retentive properties of the peat are important too.

Location permitted a shift early from subsistence gardening of Gold Rush days. Even in the 1870's Portuguese, Italian and Chinese tenants gathered bountiful harvests of such crops as beans, onions and potatoes. Wheat, exported via waterways, was a major crop while unreclaimed swamps provided pasturage.

The Chinese were instrumental in converting natural levees into truck patches and fruit orchards. But such recently-important crops as tomatoes, sugar beets, celery and asparagus were not introduced until the twentieth century.

Through the years noticeable land-use transitions have materialized.

Before 1900 much unirrigated land yielded winter grains. At the turn of the century barley was the acreage leader although potatoes were first in value and beans and asparagus were major crops. With availability of refrigerated rail cars, early-season shipment of various products became possible. But only in this century have "brand-name" canned goods and standardized produce become representative.

Mechanized agriculture replaced the hand labor of the Chinese before 1920. New crops gained importance and increasing quantities of fertilizer were being applied. Winter grains have continued to occupy the greatest acreage, followed by asparagus, field corn, and alfalfa. But animal husbandry has declined.

### Tomatoes and Asparagus

Tomatoes have been a major crop of the Delta for over half a century.

With adjacent Yolo County to the northwest (and more recently, Fresno County), the Delta has made California the nation's leading source of processing tomatoes. The Golden State produces about half of the national total—important factors have been high yields (map, 9-6) and mechanization.

Cool nights and deep soils favor late varieties (thus extending the processing season) which are grown on mineral soils rather than peat. Since the mid-1950's most of the crop has been field seeded, thus eliminating transplanting—this change advanced the harvest period about two months.

Canneries have forsaken the Delta and relocated at sites with better labor supply. Thus Delta tomatoes have been trucked to such places as Tracy, Stockton, Sacramento, San Jose and Oakland. Invention of the tomato harvester (Fig. 9-12) is credited with "saving" the tomato in California at a time when the bracero was lost as a labor source in the 1960's. Yet labor spokespeople bitterly complain that mechanization took away *local* non-bracero jobs too.

The Delta has long been the nation's leading source of *asparagus*, the stalk of a perennial lily.

Output, small even for San Francisco markets in the 1880's, became significant nationally in the following decade when "rust" almost eliminated eastern production. Since the 1920's production has remained relatively stable despite local changes of consequence—the Delta produces approximately half of the nation's output.

Asparagus cultivation has been marked by large fields and "cannery" ownership of the crops. Peat soils gave the Delta a long-time advantage in raising "white" asparagus (i.e., stalks growing below the surface in the peat were "protected" from the sun.

Since the 1920's dieticians have encouraged Americans to eat the green stalks. The Delta still furnishes most of the nation's canned white asparagus. It has retained an outlet for fresh green asparagus, particularly in the expanding California markets.

A salient locational shift has taken place within the Delta, chiefly because of *Fusarium* wilt. Afflicted land cannot be successfully replanted in asparagus for many years without expensive fumigation. By the late 1930's, expanded acreage in the northern Delta, center of production, became impractical because of the value of "clean" land for orchards. This situation, coupled with disease, prompted a southward shift to "healthy" land.

### Barley and Corn

There has always been an important spot in Delta agriculture for field crops.

*Wheat*, the first major crop, has been supplanted by barley, whereas sugar beets and field corn have

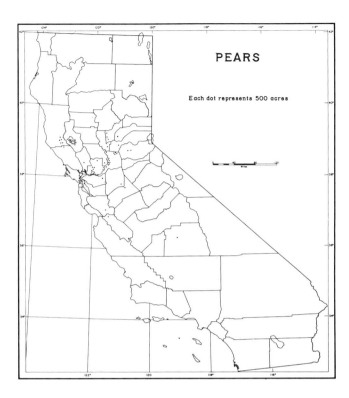

**Map 9-14.** Pear production is concentrated in the Delta Lands, the Sierran Foothills east of Sacramento, and in Lake County.

been important in this century. Some growers always alternate "wet" and "dry" crops to eliminate "wet" weeds or "dry" insects.

*Barley*, a late winter crop used for livestock feed, largely replaced wheat after 1900 (map 9-28).

Barley is planted on peat lands in February, later than is common elsewhere in California. For approximately half a century acreage has remained constant, with about 100,000 acres devoted to the grain annually. Yields are good but lodging has ofttimes been a problem.

For four decades the Delta was the only important producer of *field corn* in California (map 9-13).

Since the 1950's output has expanded elsewhere in the Central Valley, especially in the "cotton belt" of the southwestern San Joaquin Valley.

Corn yields well on the peat—hybrid varieties have yielded record yields. Considerable north Delta acreage previously in asparagus is used now for corn—the landscape suggests central Illinois and leads the Golden State in production.

In the second half of the twentieth century milo has tended to replace corn somewhat, especially on "altered peat" soils. The grain grows well on soils that remain moist later in the season; it is rotated with alfalfa, sugar beets and tomatoes.

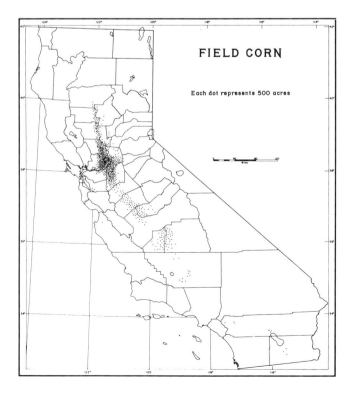

**Map 9-13.** Field corn acreage has increased with development of hybrids better suited to California's dry summers.

The southern segment of California's ranking *sugar beet* belt extends into the Delta; the belt continues northward into the Flood Basins (Map, 9-4).

A good water supply and cool nights are physical assets and yields are high. Acreage has tended to fluctuate less than in the San Joaquin Valley; beets are grown under contract and are shipped to refineries to the north or south.

### Pears Along the Levees

Fruit orchards became commonplace in the Delta by the late 1860's, especially on the natural levees along the Sacramento River.

Recurrent floods and the high water table presumably discouraged production of such "pit fruits" as peaches hence there was a gradual replacement by Bartlett pears. The pears are grown largely on the dikes and near the adjacent outer edges of the northern islands, chiefly around Courtland. The high water-table in central portions of the islands poses a problem for many crops and negates production of trees and other deeper-rooted plants.

### WATERLAND PARADISE

The Delta has become an aquatic playground for boaters, fisherfolk and hunters.

This portion of the Delta economy has gained more importance as the population of surrounding central California has increased.

**Figure 9-28.** Tinsley Island. This small island between Isleton and Stockton, near Frank's Tract, still has a semi-pristine environment that contrasts with Empire Tract beyond (rear). The channel of the San Joaquin River is in foreground and White Slough in the distance. Note the pleasure craft resort. (Aero Photographers, Sausalito)

Much of the activity has developed in the second half of the twentieth century. Although commercial salmon fishing was once important along the lower Sacramento River it is no longer permitted. Long ago some of the canneries were converted to the processing of truck crops.

*Hunting* is restricted within the Delta by posted properties.

Except for the pheasant-hunting spots, most of the desirable places for waterfowl are limited to members of private gun clubs.

For many residents of surrounding areas the chief lure of the Delta is *sports fishing*.

Except for salmon, steelhead and sturgeon, landed less frequently, the fish are varieties introduced from eastern United States: sunfish, crappie, bluegill, catfish and bass. The most popular locale is probably around Frank's Tract, which was not economically reclaimable for agriculture after the flood of 1938 and Bethel Island near Antioch and hence more accessible to Bay Area sportsfolk than most of the Delta. Fishing for striped bass, for which this portion of the Delta is known, is especially popular in spring.

Water sports have increased in popularity. With exception of fishing, boating is probably the most common recreational activity. Boats can be rented at many landings but many visitors bring their own craft. Waters have sufficient depth for the largest yachts along charted channels. Frank's Tract is the focus of much boating. An appreciable amount of waterskiing takes place. Houseboating has also increased in popularity.

Despite its maze of waterways, much of the Delta has limited appeal for swimming. The waters tend to be too murky or too saline except for the upstream portions of the Delta.

Exclusive resorts are absent along Delta waterways.

There are some motels and hotels in Delta towns but facilities available at some California vacation spots are absent. Unlike the Sierra Nevada and the Pacific shore, campgrounds tend to be limited. Visitors either return to their homes or stay in such places as Stockton or Sacramento.

The Delta provides more appeal for scenic touring than most of the Central Valley.

But this is not Netherlands with its windmills and picturesque towns. However, for the motorist willing to take the time, winding Ca. 160, from Sacramento to Isleton to Antioch offers a pleasant trip at almost any season. Multi-lane highways are absent; the peat subsoil discourages construction of wider (and heavier) roads.

## QUIET LEVEE VILLAGES

There are no cities in the Delta—many of its service needs are provided in such peripheral communities as Sacramento, Stockton Tracy and Antioch. Farmsteads are confined mostly to the levees or bordering Delta margins.

The typical town tends to be rather drab, with a minimum of cultural amenities. Dust, humidity, floods and cultural limitations encourage landowners to reside elsewhere.

Before mechanization replaced so much of the seasonal field labor and river transport lost its monopoly, some towns were more populous and more colorful.

The Chinese quarters of some villages, especially *Ryde*, are of interest to the visitor, as are decaying docks and canneries.

The largest communities are found in the northern and western sectors of the Delta along the levees that line the Sacramento River.

*Rio Vista* (3400), the largest town, is the principal community of the lower Delta although it is almost as peripheral as Antioch or Tracy.

It was founded in 1857 but was moved on its present site at the base of the Montezuma Hills after the flood of 1862. Once it was the site of the world's largest asparagus-canning factory.

Rio Vista depends upon Delta agriculture as well as that of the Montezuma Hills to the northwest, recreation (particularly sports fishers) and the manufacture of agricultural machinery. Many landowners reside in the town.

*Isleton* (1000) has been more intimately related to Delta agriculture than has Rio Vista.

Founded in the middle 1870's Isleton boomed in the early twentieth century as an asparagus center; in the 1920's it had three large canneries; now there are none.

Today its economy depends upon retail purchases of field laborers and commuters. Still the home of Anglo farm owners and Hispanic laborers it is less picturesque than in the days when it housed many Chinese.

A series of small towns north of Isleton on Ca. 160, **Walnut Grove**, **Courtland**, and **Clarksburg**, are primarily residential in function. Some of the architectural gems of the Delta (and there are many) are

here, but many of the fine dwellings are found on rural properties.

## THE SAN JOAQUIN VALLEY *

Larger than Belgium and comparable in size to the Netherlands, the San Joaquin Valley occupies the southern two-thirds of the Central Valley—it extends northward from the Grapevine (at the foot of Tejon Pass) to Lodi (map, 9-15).

Despite hot summer afternoons, often too warm for human comfort, its lengthy season, productive soils and available irrigation water have permitted the Valley to become the nation's top-ranking agricultural area. Its three southern counties (Fresno, Tulare and Kern) are the three leaders nationally. Scores of products are grown commercially and only five states match the value of its great agricultural output.

Scenically the San Joaquin is inferior for California and recreation is less consequential in its economy than in either the Sacramento Valley or the Delta Lands.

Yet its position paralleling Interstate 5 and Ca. 99 make *travel* trade important; such facilities as motels and restaurants are conspicuous.

Upon the bases of agricultural history and contemporary land use four areas seem discernible: the ***East Side***, the ***Trough***, the ***West Side*** and the ***South End***.

---

* The San Joaquin Valley has been reviewed by Stanley Norsworthy, C.S.U., Fresno. Originally it was reviewed by James Blick, San Diego State University, formerly at University of the Pacific and Chester Cole and John Crosby of C.S.U., Fresno.

**Figure 9-30.** The Sacramento milkshed is located east of the Delta in the northern Lodi District. (dwl)

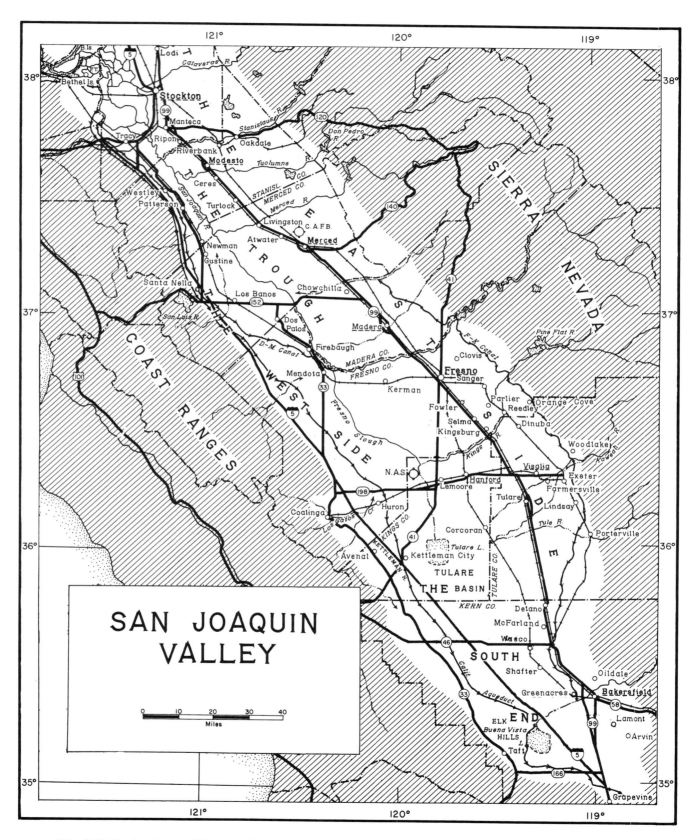

**Map 9-15.** The San Joaquin Valley is traditionally divided into the East Side, the Trough, the West Side and the South End.

## THE EAST SIDE

Extending approximately from the north end of the Lodi District to the southern extremity of the Kaweah Delta, the East Side has had a longer history of irrigation agriculture than other portions of the San Joaquin Valley. It is is less dependent upon the Central Valley Project and distant from the California Aqueduct. Cropping patterns are complex and more varied than elsewhere in the Valley. Many properties are small and the land is usually intensively farmed.

Population density is higher than elsewhere in the San Joaquin Valley—virtually all of the larger cities are located here. In part both agriculture and population reflect the fact that the first railroad (the Southern Pacific's *Valley* line) was constructed along the East Side. The second railroad, the Santa Fe, now with Amtrak service, connects additional places.

Physiographically the East Side consists of the coalescing alluvial fans deposited by the San Joaquin and its major eastern tributaries. The area has a width of 20 to 25 miles. Soil textures become progressively finer to the west where the gradient of the land lessens and there is a merger with the Trough.

Older alluvial terraces at the base of the Sierra Nevada are extensive but less fertile than the recent alluvial surfaces. They approximate the *red lands* of the Sacramento Valley in terrain and use problems. Considerable areas are devoted to livestock ranching and winter grains. Around Galt (north of Lodi) are portions of Sacramento milkshed.

To appreciate the East Side, these subdivisions will be considered from north to south: ***Lodi District, Stockton District, Modesto District, Merced District, Fresno District*** and ***Kaweah Delta*** (Fig. 9-15).

### The Lodi District

Located in northeastern San Joaquin County, the Lodi District, the smallest agricultural subdivision on the East Side, is distinctive for its semi-monoculture. Few agricultural areas in California depend so completely upon a single crop as Lodi does upon the *Tokay* grape.

The Lodi District forms the north end of the vineyard belt which extends almost the length of the eastern San Joaquin Valley.

The belt has particular concentration around Lodi, Turlock, Madera, Fresno, western Tulare County and Arvin (in the South End).

The semicontinuous vineyard belt forms the most ubiquitous aspect of East Side agriculture. It is one of the world's principal concentrations of grape production. Output of table, wine. and raisin varieties exceeds the balance of the North American continent.

Production became significant in the late nineteenth century; for decades grapes have been California's leading fruit crop. Many holdings are still owner-operated and properties tend to be small (by state standards). Many farmers are third or fourth generation Californians whose ancestors came from southwest Asia or Mediterrranean Europe.

Lodi has specialized in the *Tokay*, a red Hungarian grape which is consumed both as a table fruit and as wine.

In the late nineteenth century farmers around Lodi shifted from grain farming to orchards and vineyards with watermelons as a specialty crop. Gradually it was recognized that the Tokay, a finicky variety, is suited to the cooler air drifting through Carquinez Strait which promotes high sugar content and deep red color. Soil is likewise important— vineyards are largely restricted to sandy loam.

Farms are small (many less than 100 acres) and owner operated. Vineyards total less than 40,000 acres. The harvest, commencing in August, is celebrated in Lodi each September by a grape festival prior to the peak picking period.

The Tokay ranks next to the *Emperor* nationally in sales among red table grapes. When the market becomes glutted by the *Thompson seedless*, some Tokays are placed in storage for the holiday markets in November and December.

***Lodi*** (50,000) is an attractive, settled community whose economy has been diversified by local services, grape processing and shipping, commuter and retiree residence and industrialization.

Devoid of shanties or mansions, the tidy town is largely middle-income. Streets are well-shaded and even older houses tend to be maintained well. Lake Lodi Park adds to community appeal.

Ethnic groups were long discouraged from residence here. Now lower income people are deterred by high property prices. The populace includes a small middle-income professional and business black group as well as larger numbers of Asians and long-established Hispanics. Social problems in Stockton (10 miles distance) prompt many to commute from Lodi. Lately the attractiveness of Lodi (which includes a sizable south-end shopping center) has drawn retirees.

Lodi, much more than most Valley cities, has opposed expansion into agricultural lands. This prompted *Measure A* (no growth) in 1981, which the courts rejected. City ownership of utilities has allowed "controlled" growth but the county has permitted fringe sprawl, lessening vineyard acreage.

Food processing, including cereals, is important. A number of wineries are located within the city and its environs. Other manufacturing includes tire-remolding equipment and concrete products.

A number of conservative Russian Germans sold their farms in North Dakota during the drought-ridden years of the 1930's and came to California with sufficient funds to purchase farms in the Lodi District. Money spent by the thousands of visiting North Dakotans who traditionally made this city their "winter capital" added stability to the economy for many years.

### The Stockton District *

Southeast of the Delta, the Stockton District has varied agricultural output. Several dozen commodities, including fruits and nuts, truck crops, nursery stock and market milk, are produced commercially.

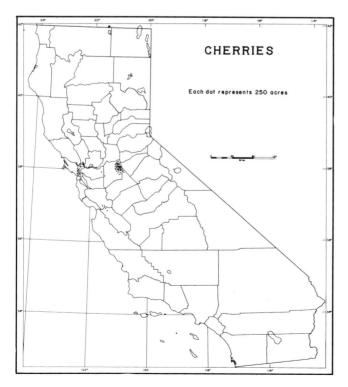

CHERRIES

Each dot represents 250 acres

**Map 9-16.** Cherry acreage in California has decreased somewhat. The principal area is around Linden, east of Stockton.

Intricate patterns are favored by physical factors as well as grower preferences, land values and market accessibility.

A zone of poorly-drained soils is used for pasturage and affords part of the Sacramento-Stockton milkshed.

The area around Linden has long been an important producer of sweet cherries.

Soils and climate are favorable and urbanization in the Santa Clara Valley prompted many growers to relocate here, thus creating the state's leading producer. Virus-caused *quick decline* still discourages expansion.

The District also leads California in production of *English walnuts*.

The major San Joaquin belt continues southward into the Modesto District (map 9-17). With about 90 per cent of the national output, California is the world's leading producer of English *(Persian)* walnuts. The nut ranks with oranges, almonds and peaches among California tree crops.

The walnut prefers deep soils, mild winters and long warm summers. While it is deciduous and can tolerate considerable cold, late frosts in spring can be critical. Until this century it was assumed that the walnut would not grow especially north of the Tehachapi. But new varieties were developed that yield better in central than Southern California. Urbanization was an important factor in virtually eliminating walnuts from Southern California.

The District has also become a ranking source of *almonds* (map, 9-8).

As has happened with other crops in the past, expanded output in California has exceeded market demands abroad, despite increased consumption, particularly since entry of Spain into the Common Market.

*Stockton* (190,000; SMA circa 450,.000), seat of San Joaquin County, is the third largest metropolis of the Central Valley. It is the oldest city and the second largest center (after Fresno) in the San Joaquin. And *now* it has the closest Pacific Basin ties of any Great Valley community.

Founded at the start of the Gold Rush, Stockton served as the debarkation port for the southern portion of the Mother Lode Country. It was in a triumvirate with San Francisco and Sacramento as the largest cities in California. Like other central California towns it experienced a frenzied boom.

---

* This section was reviewed earlier by Roger Barnett, University of the Pacific.

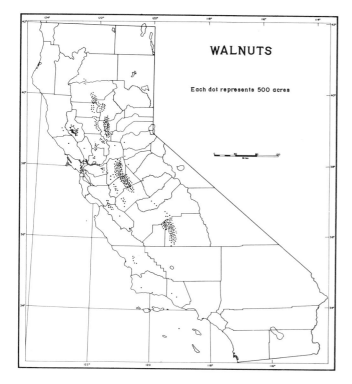

**WALNUTS**

Each dot represents 500 acres

**Map 9-17.** Walnut production, once concentrated in the Los Angeles Lowlands, now occurs chiefly in the Central Valley and Lake County.

Growth of Stockton mirrored the development of the San Joaquin Valley and the Delta Lands.

In the second half of the twentieth century, Stockton, like many other cities, experienced severe downtown deterioration.

Urban expansion has been stimulated by opening of the ship channel, industrial development, military installations (Sharpe Army Depot at Lathrop and Navy Supply Annex at the port), location of the state hospital, higher education and in-migration of southeast Asians.

Stockton was long segregated socially into three units (North Side, South Side and East Side). Now it has a fourth, Downtown, where the other three infrequently meet.

Interaction between the "four" Stocktons is minimal.

Except for governmental agencies, little concern for an united community appears to exist. Neither retail merchants, the university nor agribusiness leaders seem to have been too active. Public transportation, limited to buses as in many California communities, is inadequate.

The metropolis *does* have attractive northside residential areas and parks. But routes of major highways prevent the casual visitor from viewing

most of them.

Downtown Stockton is no longer *the* pivotal retail area.

Decline of the C.B.D. "bottomed out" around 1970 but it has not experienced renewal comparable to such cities as San Jose or Sacramento except on the waterfront (western) edge with a marina, restaurants and motels.

This is the southeast Asian "capital" of central California. Besides Filipinos, there is a considerable number of others (including more than 20,000 Vietnamese). Although the edifice evidence (as in Westminster in Orange County) is absent some street signs are worded in Vietnamese.

The city for many years afforded off-season residence for migratory workers who came to the C.B.D. for "entertainment." Some social derelicts (including mentally-troubled) make the submarginal southern flank "unsafe" at night.

Physical renovation has included street circulation (one-way streets and viaducts over rail tracks) while a downtown parking district has been beneficial. Few corporate outlets have remained and merchants have shown little interest in new quarters ("vacant" lots are conspicuous).

The North Side is the socially-preferred portion of Stockton, especially north of the "Harding Road line" (i.e., north of the Calaveras River).

Closer in are many blocks of attractive older dwellings. Located here is **University of the Pacific**, an Oxonian-type institution, Haggin Museum and the Country Club. Near the rivers (San Joaquin and Calaveras) many residences have backyard dockage for pleasure craft.

Most of Stockton's continuing residential and retail growth has occurred north of the Calaveras River. Hence the several large adjacent shopping centers along Pacific Avenue form the *real* retail core of the metropolis. Here also is the campus of *San Joaquin Delta College*. A local developer has created *Lincoln West*, a self-contained community with marina (and river access) west of I-5. Growth continues to the north, partially within the Lodi School District, so that parents can prevent contact with "those people."

The East Side, largely outside the city limits (and east of Ca. 99), has developed from a "Dust Bowl" tent town.

With its own school district and sewer system, and neighborhood shopping, the East Side tends to "do its own thing." There is limited contact with the rest of Stockton. Residents tend to be largely of lower socioeconomic status with noticeable "red-neckism".

The South Side, with a sizable ethnic populace (blacks and Hispanics) is blue-collar Stockton. This is also industrial Stockton.

Houses, usually modest and on small lots, are commonly older frame structures. There is a pressing need here, as in many American cities, for affordable housing.

Stockton manufacturing (value added) ranks first in the San Joaquin Valley.

Although no major firms have been added recently, products include agricultural machinery and implements, food, paper and containers.

Tomatoes alone have accounted for five canneries. Until construction of a large sewage plant the air "smelled of ketchup" during the processing season.

Stockton has become central California's ranking meat packer since the decline of processing in San Francisco and South San Francisco.

Warehousing is important. Relocation of walnuts in northern California is reflected by the headquarters here of the cooperative Diamond Walnut Growers.

Activity at the Port of Stockton has changed in recent years.

With problems with foreign sale of agricultural products, exports have declined; grain shipment especially has been hurt. Now imports comprise about two-thirds of port tonnage. In addition to fertilizer, imports include manufactured goods, especially from Asia. For example, Stockton is the major place of import of foreign goods for J.C. Penney.

The Port cannot successfully compete against Oakland for container cargo (it is "cheaper" to

**Figure 9-32.** The Port of Stockton with the city beyond; view is eastward. *Northside* is in upper left beyond I-5. The *Westside,* including the downtown area, is in rear east of the port area. (Stockton Port District).

**Figure 9-33.** East Market Street, downtown Stockton. This photo is out-of-date. Since an Asian population (Filipino and Vietnamese) located here, the male derelicts have gone elsewhere. (dwl)

truck merchandise from the Bay Area to Stockton and elsewhere in the Central Valley). The pre-World War II "mosquito fleet" that hauled produce to San Francisco Bay has largely been replaced by trucks.

There is a 77-mile channel, 40 feet deep, between Stockton and San Francisco Bay. The Port, a municipal corporation, is financed by a long-term bond issue and operates profitably. An industrial park adjacent to the port has sundry agricultural processing plants (Fig. 9-32).

On the southern fringe of the District, **Manteca** (44,000) is experiencing much growth as a commuter residence town.

As a secondary highway junction, it has good access to both Stockton and the Bay Area (via I-580). An increasing number of commuters, employed in Stockton, Modesto or the Bay Area, reside in Manteca. Despite its growth the city has been able to effectively control sprawl.

Industrial activity includes diverse food processing (including sugar refining, canning, cheese making) plus machinery, farm implements, and most recently, electronics.

### The Modesto District *

In eastern Stanislaus County, the Modesto District suggests the agricultural Central Valley in microcosm.

Water from the Stanislaus and Tuolumne rivers has for a century provided a basis for "water, wealth, contentment, health," long proclaimed by the sign in downtown Modesto.

The District benefited from establishment of the

two oldest mutual irrigation districts in California.

A local legislator initiated the *Wright Act* and in 1887 two contiguous irrigation districts, Turlock and Modesto, were created. Together they comprise a geographic entity today, the Modesto District. Jointly the two irrigation districts constructed *La Grange Dam* on the Tuolumne in 1891.

By 1910 a shift from wheat to alfalfa (the dominant crop), vineyards and orchards had been effected.

Subsequently the districts cooperated to build *Don Pedro Dam*, upriver from La Grange. Upon its completion in 1923 it was the then-highest concrete dam in the nation. Still more recently the districts cooperated with the city of San Francisco to erect a still higher dam. The districts distribute their own electricity, thus income subsidizes lower-cost irrigation.

Stanislaus ranks among the nation's ten top counties in agricultural output.

Early irrigation development, when costs were lower, has been an important consideration.

Variations in soil texture help explain differing land-use between the two irrigation districts. An apparent transition from loam to sand south of the Tuolumne River is reflected in a change from peach orchards to vineyards, dairies and hay fields.

Favorable environment and early start contributed to the District's rise to number one status nationally in *cling peach* production (map 9-9).

---

* This section was reviewed earlier by Arden Ohl, formerly at Modesto Junior College.

**Figure 9-34.** Residential street east of Modesto Junior College. With its well-shaded streets and handsome older homes, this area is popular with *yuppies*. (dwl)

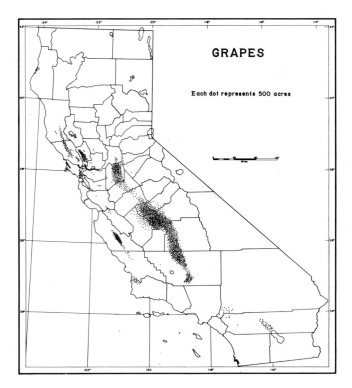

GRAPES

Each dot represents 500 acres

**Map 9-18.** The San Joaquin leads California *and* the nation in extent of grape acreage.

As in other peach districts, there has been an acreage decline (in excess of 50 per cent since the middle 1960's). Meanwhile output of almonds, walnuts, melons (especially honeydew), chickens and milk has increased markedly.

The District is a nationally-ranked center of *chicken* and *turkey* production.

Marketing is primarily local, to such firms as Foster Farms and Swanson. Scattered farms are found on poor soils while local grains are available for "topping off". Due to the popularity of Foster chickens in California, production has doubled within the past two decades and the Modesto District has become the state's leading source.

Like peaches, *grapes* are generally raised for processing.

Table varieties, which ripen two to three weeks later than in districts farther south, would necessitate sale during a period of much competition (Map 9-18). Hence varieties suitable for raisins or wine are grown.

Besides long-established varieties such as Carignane, Zinfandel and Thompson seedless, scores of farmers north and east of Turlock raise such varieties as Chenin Blanc, Ruby Cabernet and Valdepenas.

West of Turlock and around Oakdale *dairying* is of much importance.

Increased California markets for market milk and the migration of dairy farmers from Los Angeles and Orange counties encouraged expansion.

In the Oakdale area farmers shifted from sheep to beef cattle to milk cows. A high water table and poor soils west of Turlock deterred alternative land use.

Productivity of the Modesto District has increased despite stable acreage. Stanislaus County agricultural returns have approached eight hundred million dollars annually.

Cantaloupes and other melons continue to be important on sandy loams around Turlock. Meanwhile improvement of the water situation in the Oakdale area near the Foothills prompted a sizable increase in almond acreage.

***Modesto*** (160,000 with approximately 350,000 in its SMA), is a slightly dubious metropolis.

During much of the second half of the twentieth century its growth has been "out of control." Problems started with incorporation of northside fringe-areas in the 1950's and continued with passage of bond issues for sewer line expansion in the the 1960's. Many long-time residents deplore the disappearance of a small-city atmosphere yet do not feel the metropolitan atmosphere many newer residents sense.

The ten-fold population increase since 1950 reflects a variety of economic supports including industry (*especially* agribusiness), diverse services, and government.

A "watch us grow" spirit prompted rising opposition to continued encroachment into fertile farm lands. Heightened concern followed construction of a regional shopping center with five department stores (and a service area of half a million) on Modesto's northern edge.

Urbanization has proceeded northward for decades (the railroad tracks to the west and the Tuolumne River to the south created barriers). Thus the north-south strip along McHenry Avenue has replaced the central district for retail focus.

Downtown Modesto seems to have adjusted somewhat after several decades of decline. Attempts to maintain this area include a mall, a convention center, a civic center, county library, and high-rise retiree apartments. Thus the C.B.D. has become a daytime *working* area.

Modesto, with scores of industrial establishments, ranks second as an industrial center in the San

Joaquin Valley.

Agricultural processing is important; it includes fruits, nuts, wines, vegetables and oils. The in-limits industrial park in the southeast (Fig. 9-35), coupled with concerted community effort, good transportation and location near the geographical center of California, help explain industrial diversity. Products include cosmetics, lumber, metals, paper containers, soaps, tin cans and wine bottles. Modesto is the site of the nation's largest wine producer (Gallo), whose offices are set in a park-like environment. The emphasis on agricultural processing results in seasonal unemployment.

Transportation services have importance.

Modesto benefits from a crossroads location. It provides a gateway to the central Sierra Nevada and Yosemite National Park and represents a *comfortable* drive from San Diego and Los Angeles enroute north.

Regarded by many as a preferred Central Valley residence place, Modesto is acquiring a modicum of cultural sophistication. Besides long-established Modesto Junior College, with its second (vocationally oriented) campus on the west side, there is a liberal daily newspaper, a symphony orchestra, ballet, little theatre, and local radio and television. Modesto is one of a half dozen Valley cities with a minor-league baseball franchise.

Modesto is more liberal than many San Joaquin Valley towns; it is definitely *not* a "redneck" town.

Upper middle-income residences, many with swimming pools, are especially prominent toward the northern periphery. By contrast, westside Modesto has traditionally housed many lower-income ethnics. While black numbers are modest there is a sizable Hispanic population.

A marked change has been the westside influx of hopefully-upward bound Anglos, many commuting to work in the Bay Area, who have been buying their first "affordable" homes on the westside, assuming they will be able to relocate in the Bay Area after they have acquired a residential equity and their salaries have increased.

*Ceres* (19,000), long an independent village, has become virtually a suburb of Modesto.

It is a residence place with many lower-income Anglos and Hispanics, including many retirees.

*Turlock* (38,000) is dependent upon agriculture, industry and higher education.

Long ago eclipsed by Modesto, Turlock is continuing to grow and has expanded northward to include the once-rural campus of California State University. Like Modesto it houses many commuters to the Bay Area.

Turlock has unique aspects. Ethnically it is a distinctive residence town, home for many Swedes

**Figure 9-35.** The Beard Industrial Tract, the legacy of a pioneer wheat farmer who helped established a traction line (now a short-line railroad). His children converted his farm into an industrial district. Subsequently Modesto has become a leading manufacturing center in the Central Valley. (Greater Modesto Chamber of Commerce, photo by Shoob Studios).

from Nebraska and for Syrian retirees from "all over" America. Also, its central district is about equally divided by rail tracks.

And, like Modesto, Turlock has industrial output. Products include foods (there are three turkey plants), feeds, concrete goods and food-making machinery.

## The Merced District *

The Merced District has more intricate agricultural patterns than the Modesto District.

More modest output, as contrasted with the Modesto District, has resulted from less fertile soils, a more-limited water supply (from the Merced River) and delayed establishment of an irrigation district. Now the District is a "tail ender" for "surplus" water from both the north and south. With expanded storage facilities the supply is adequate.

Agricultural output is represented by dairying (and considerable acreage of alfalfa), grapes, fruits (especially peaches and figs), vegetables (particularly tomatoes and sweet potatoes ) and irrigated pastures. A decline in figs has permitted an in-

**Figure 9-36.** County courthouse, Merced. (dwl)

crease in "almost everything else." The District has the northern limits of cotton production in the San Joaquin Valley.

### Small Farms, Big Farms

Merced County reflects the various types of rural properties that have been representative of the San Joaquin Valley.

Tardily awarded in the 1840's, four Mexican *land grants* were located near the San Joaquin River where conditions favored grazing.

Early American settlement, commenced during the Gold Rush, occurred along tributary stream courses which provided water and grass. West of the San Joaquin, the vast Miller and Lux holdings, discussed later, were accumulated during the cattle era.

Extending its Valley Line south during the 1870's, the Southern Pacific was given *large parcels of federal land*. Other large East Side holdings were acquired early in the grain era when land was cheap. The 42,000-acre Mitchell tract near Livingston affords an example.

The most successful attempts at irrigation development were the lands watered by the Merced Canal, which gained water from the Merced Irrigation District (in 1922). These were *small properties*.

Several *immigrant colonies* in the early 1900's also contributed to expansion of irrigation. Groups of Japanese and Swedes settled on former wheat ranches along the Merced River. Still earlier a Portuguese (Azorean) colony had been established around Atwater.

Another form of landholding was promoted by the state of California as the *Delhi State Land Settlement*, a counterpart of the Durham colony in the Chico District of the Sacramento Valley.

Because of dissatisfaction with real estate operations in farm land, it was formulated in 1917. But before the administration was assigned to the Turlock Irrigation District in 1930, the colony had obviously failed. As elsewhere in the Valley, *real estate operators* also influenced settlement— most sales involved Los Angeles or San Francisco firms.

The *large property*, while commonly associated with the South End and West Side of the San Joaquin Valley, also has characterized over half of the agricultural acreage of Merced County east of the river.

* This section has been reviewed by Wayne Irwin, Merced College.

Such holdings are most prevalent along the Valley Trough— in the second half of this century considerable corporate money has been invested in the District. Despite 150 farms in the county larger than 1000 acres the average size of 3400 farms is less than 300 acres.

Although small farms and a relatively-large rural population density has existed on the East Side, sizable holdings have included the 4000-acre peach ranch of Del Monte and the Cello and Gallo vineyards near Livingston.

Merced County ranks tenth in agricultural output in California. Its East Side portion, the Merced District, leads the state in production of sweet potatoes, fresh *market* tomatoes and Kadota figs (for canning). Additional commodities of importance include almonds, cantaloupes, grapes (for raisins), English walnuts, and peaches (both freestone and clingstone varieties). The Portuguese introduced the well-known Merced sweet potato, grown on lighter soils around Livingston. Output, usually the Puerto Rican Velvet variety, cannot satisfy California markets, hence Louisiana and Texas potatoes are imported. Truck crops (especially tomatoes) and dairies were established by Italians. Recent changes include an influx of dairy farmers from the Bay Area and Southern California. A sizable expansion of almonds, using sprinkler irrigation, has taken place on shallow eastside soils north of Merced (Amsterdam Orchards has been a major supplier for the Hershey chocolate factory in Oakdale).

### Merced Irrigation District

Evolution of this irrigation development has contrasted with those of the nearby Turlock and Modesto districts.

While the Merced Canal, including the main ditches and the distribution system, had been constructed before 1890 by San Francisco developers, the MID was not formed until 1919. When the need for additional water became apparent in the early twentieth century the older group sold its holdings to the irrigation district.

Belatedly, in the 1920's, MID constructed Exchequer Dam on the upper Merced. Prior development of District lands had been delayed by the indebtedness of the MID. This district, like those on the East Side farther north, has not been affected by the Central Valley Project.

The dramatic irrigation expansion that has occurred elsewhere in the San Joaquin in the second half of the twentieth century did not seem possible here. But in recent decades extensive reclamation of alkaline lands east of the Trough, as in Fresno County, has taken place. Landowners have strongly supported such proposals as the *Peripheral Canal*.

### Three Cities

Bolstered by such activities as services, retail trade, government, the military, higher education and manufacturing, **Merced** (52,000 with about 170,000 in its S.M.A.), the principal city, is one of the more attractive San Joaquin urban places. As result of continuing growth, the Census Bureau in the mid-1980's identified it as an urbanized area.

Much recent growth has resulted from an influx of thousands of Hmong (from Laos) and from expansion at the Air Force Base.

A county seat, it was founded beside the Southern Pacific right-of-way in 1870. It is on a highway into Yosemite Park via Ca. 140 (the *All-Year Highway* through El Portal) and was the historic access point to Yosemite for railroad travelers.

There are three well-defined sectors. *South* Merced (south of the railroad tracks and Ca. 99 freeway) is a proud, lower-income area, safe at night, characterized by trim cottages and concerned with good education. Residents include ethnics (second and third generation Hispanics) plus blacks and Anglos. Many Air Force *non-commissioned officers* reside here, as do the Hmong.

*Central* Merced includes the renovated downtown district and older (but still viable) neighborhoods with large trees. The courthouse square and city park are here.

Recent growth has tended to occur in *north* Merced, on terraces (inferior agricultural land) toward the Air Force Base. Along North Bear Creek, adjacent to the city park, is an affluent neighborhood peopled by ranchers, professional people and merchants. Newer housing tracts are found around **Merced College**.

Expanded industrial activity has centered around three types. Products have included bandages, foods, recreational vehicles, computer parts, and plastics.

There has been strong opposition to urban encroachment upon prime farm lands (to east and west). Leapfrogging has been negligible although some merchants have encouraged growth. As in many California counties, a serious city-county schism has existed. Some officials anticipate eventual

**Figure 9-37.** Drying raisins the "old fashioned" way, Fresno District. Early rains in September can pose a hazard yet relatively few grapes are dried into raisins artificially. (California Raisin Advisory Board, photo by Jack Worsham).

coalescence and eventual merger of Merced and Atwater.

*Atwater* 22,000) has importance as a residence place and farm town.

It has been plagued by political difficulties and conservatism but the city has changed. It has been much affected by its proximity to Castle Air Force Base. As noted, coalescence with Merced is eventually anticipated.

**Castle Air Force Base**, a permanent bomber facility, has housed many thousands of resident personnel. It has augmented the population of nearby towns and has raised noise levels by many decibels.

*Livingston* (7000), earlier a farm-labor residence town, has gained food processing plants, reflected in recent growth.

These include wines (Gallo) and poultry. *Foster Farms,* a family firm, is the largest poultry processor in the American West.

Foster Farms discovered that prosperous California residents were willing to pay more for quality. It markets more than a million chickens, processed

in its integrated plant, weekly. Poultry come from more than 60 farms in Merced and Stanislaus counties. Even the offal and the feathers are used (in cat foods).

### The Fresno District

The District, world famous for its grapes (especially those dried into raisins), occupies the heart of California and constitutes the largest East Side subdivision (map 9-20).

Fresno County is the nation's leader in annual value of farm output which is worth several billion dollars. While its East Side (the Fresno District) long has had consequence, top status has resulted from expansion on the West Side, considered later.

Reaching from Kingsburg to Madera, the District occupies the compound alluvial fan created by the Kings and San Joaquin rivers. The diverse agricultural output, permitted by the environment, is representative of the East Side, in contrast with the specialization of Modesto in clingstone peaches and Lodi in Tokay grapes. Deciduous fruits, nuts and grapes have long been the major products of the District.

Within a generation after the arrival of the Southern Pacific, a transition from grains and grazing to small irrigated farms had taken place. Approxi-

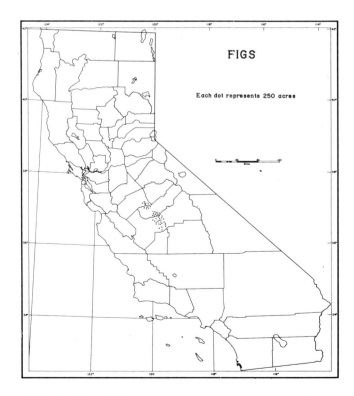

**Map 9-19.** Figs in California are grown principally in the Fresno District. Urban expansion in northeastern Fresno has reduced acreage.

mately 80 per cent of the District remains in small properties, commonly owner-operated, thus cooperative marketing and contract processing has prevailed.

The water supply comes principally from the Kings River and underground aquifers.

Some Central Valley Project water is used in the District, in contrast to more northerly portions of the East Side. The water table, which had been declining locally for several decades, has nearly stabilized since construction of *Friant* (San

Joaquin River) and *Pine Flat* (Kings) dams.

It is possible to drive for miles along some roads and see no crop but grapes; the District comprises one of the world's principal sources and grows approximately five per cent of the entire world production. Output exceeds that in the rest of California (map 9-18).

The subtropical *Vitis vinifera* is raised, as elsewhere in the Golden State, rather than the middle-latitude grapes native to eastern United States. Although suited to hot, rainless summers, the

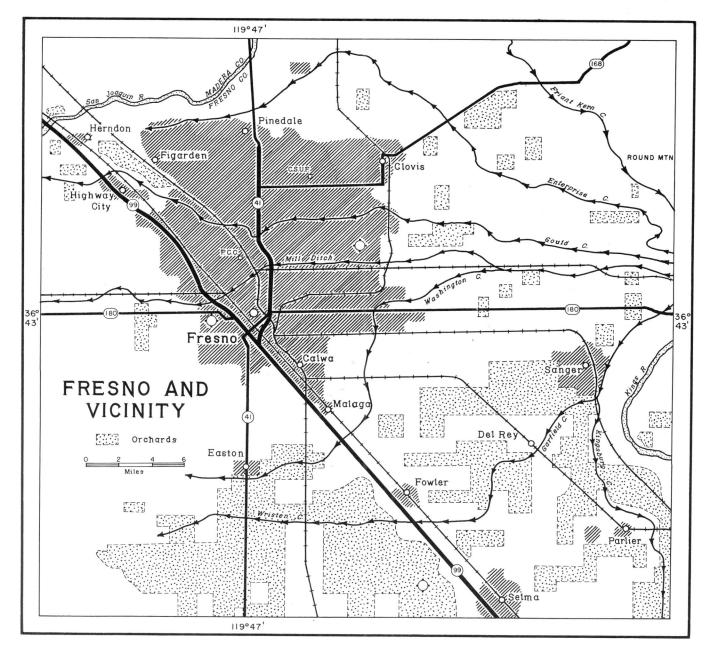

**Map 9-20.** Map of Fresno. Much of the urban expansion is taking place toward the northeast.

**Figure 9-38.** Fig Garden, Fresno—"good life" for a few. (dwl)

vinifera is irrigated here. Plants prefer loose textures but can tolerate a variety of soils. Subsequent to reclamation (lessening of alkalinity) grapes have expanded westward toward the Trough, replacing cotton.

Viticulture beginnings coincided with the arrival of Armenians, knowledgeable in grape culture, in the 1870's. Economic fluctuations prompted formation of a cooperative, *Sun-Maid Raisin Growers.*

The harvest of grapes, between August and October, depends upon the variety—earlier grapes produce the bulk of the raisins. For decades grapes were sun-dried into raisins in the field (Fig.9-37). Now mechanical techniques are employed also.

The Valley has proved ideal for raisins. Farther north, there is a greater chance of rain between early September and October. Initially the *Muscat* variety was raised but it has been replaced largely by *Thompson seedless*, an all-purpose grape; the surplus is sold fresh or converted into wine. Much wine is processed around Fresno although the District does not specialize in varietal grapes. The District is best known for inexpensive "bulk" wines.

Many different vinifera varieties are grown in California; obviously there is much local specializa-

tion, such as the Coachella Valley with its early table grapes (Ch. 5).

Central San Joaquin weather benefits table grapes because of more intense summer heat and earlier crop maturity than in localities even as close as Lodi. California's grape harvest period progresses northward later in the season from the Coachella Valley through Kern County into Fresno County and Lodi.

Half of California's *figs* were grown in the Fresno District until recent decades; expansion of Fresno prompted northward relocation of orchards (map 9-19).

They were found especially on the hardpan (older alluvium) soils north of Fresno. For some decades California vied for second place as a world fig producer after Italy.

The mission priests introduced the fig into the Golden State but it gained commercial importance only in the twentieth century. Expansion after 1900 followed recognition of the need for *caprification* (pollination) of the Smyrna fig by the fig wasp, which had to be imported. The plant was ideal for the water-short San Joaquin—it needs only three irrigations hence does not compete with grapes for "ditch water" in summer.

### Fresno and Environs

California's most-centrally located larger city, **Fresno** (315,000 and S.M.A. circa 625,000) provides services, distribution, shipping and processing for much of the central San Joaquin Valley.

Of the ten urbanized areas in the Central Valley, Fresno, after Sacramento, is probably most justifiably termed a metropolis—population of the built-up area exceeds half a million.

More progressive than most Central Valley cities, it is acquiring status as a cultural center. *Place-Rated Almanac* accords Fresno its highest marks in education, the arts and recreation. Besides its California State University, with an understand-

**Figure 9-39.** Downtown Fresno's third dimension has imparted the feel of a metropolis for decades. (Fresno Chamber of Commerce)

**Figure 9-40.** Convention group. Fresno's central location within California favors a sigificant number of conferences. (Fresno Convention and Visitor Center).

able reputation in agriculture, on a spacious campus, there is Fresno City College. Increasingly, Fresno has become *the* medical center of the San Joaquin Valley.

Fresno has prospered for decades because of the expanding agricultural output of its surrounding District.

Petroleum and cotton, on the Valley's West Side, add to its trade. Also, central location within the San Joaquin recommends it as a residence town for hundreds of sales representatives and traveling salesmen.

Wealth is reflected in many attractive residences, particularly in *Fig Garden* (north) and *Sunnyside* (southeast). The latter developed because affluent Armenians tended to be denied residence in Fig Garden. Northside fringe-area fig orchards have attracted higher-income residents too—some of the costlier new dwellings are found here.

Fresno's downtown area has a noticeable multistory skyline.

Still, despite an attractive mall, renovated Civic Center, and convention center and elaborate freeway structures, the central district has declined as a retail center. There have been gains in banking and retiree residence. The C.B.D. has become increasingly off-center as the city has grown north-northeastward.

There is some suggestion of Los Angeles. After all, the Fresno metropolis is the sixth most-populous in California (and 77th in the nation).

These characteristics include low-density sprawl and traffic flow with attendant increase in smog, and outlying shopping centers. Leapfrogging, particularly to the east, is suggestive of the Santa

Clara Valley (Ch. 8). Fortunately it has occurred on less-fertile soils. Public bus service is hampered by the usual California reluctance to use it.

Too, there is economic disparity. Ninety per cent of the westside housing is occupied by Hispanics, blacks and Asians (among others, Fresno is America's *Hmong* capital); other ethnic groups include American Indians. Much housing is substandard and social problems are acute. The lower-income fringe has pushed westward into prime land.

Fresno derives much income from services rendered travelers and as a place for regional conventions.

It is midway between Sacramento and Los Angeles on Ca.99 and forms a southern gateway into Yosemite Park, reflected by the numerous motels along Ca.41. Highways also lead eastward to Sequoia and Kings Canyon national parks.

The city is the ranking transport center of the San Joaquin Valley.

It has importance as a rail (freight) and trucking terminal and is the commercial air center of the Valley. But the High Sierra barrier to the east denies Fresno a direct overland route into the North American interior.

Industrially Fresno vies with Stockton and Modesto for leading position in the Valley.

Conspicuous among more than 200 establishments is agricultural processing. Major activities include packaging of dried fruits and processing of wine and cottonseed oil. Other products have included ceramics, carpets, plate glass, farm equipment, containers and vending machines. Sun-Maid now has its raisin-packing plant in nearby Kingsburg.

Besides industrial activity the economic base is supported by the regional *Internal Revenue Service* office, an important white collar employer.

Fresno dominates its District completely; there is no other large city (map 9-20).

**Madera** (27,000), seat of its county on the Fresno River, is the third largest city. It is an agricultural-service community; processing includes meats, olives and wine.

There are half a dozen other satellites in the metropolis.

**Clovis** (44,000), in the direction of major Fresno expansion, has many lower-income residents including college students. With continued growth, stronger community identity has developed. The city is proud of its quality schools and its "western image" reflected in downtown facades.

**Reedley** (14,000), an older town, serves as a local agricultural center and houses many commuters. There is a considerable Catholic and Mennonite populace and a community college.

**Sanger** (15,000) is becoming more predominantly Hispanic while **Parlier** (6500) is Hispanic.

**Dinuba** (11,000) and **Selma** (13,200) tend to be more stagnant than some of the satellites.

**Kingsburg** (6000) is unique for its Swedish population, the the legacy of a late nineteenth century colony. It endeavors to maintain heritage atmosphere in its downtown area.

### The Kaweah Delta *

Southeast of Fresno, the Delta might appropriately be entitled the *Kaweah-Tule-lower Kings* District (map 9-15).

Decades ago water limitations prohibited more extensive agricultural development. Subsequently Tulare County has approached Fresno County for first place among the nation's leading counties. When eastern Kings County is added, the Delta is about the most productive subdivision of the San Joaquin Valley. In the late 1980's the farm output of Tulare County alone approximates $1.5 billion annually.

Intricacy of crop patterns is representative of the San Joaquin East Side.

Distinctiveness agriculturally is provided by such major crops as oranges, olives, barley, grapes, cotton and sorghum.

The Delta's assemblage of medium-size farm towns is unparalleled elsewhere in the Central Valley.

**Figure 9-41.** Segment of the student union, California State University, Fresno at noon. (dwl)

**Figure 9-42.** The Friant-Kern Canal. This 165-mile canal, extending south from Lake Millerton (on the San Joaquin River), has a capacity of 4000 second-feet. Shown also is an orange grove near Lindsay. (Bureau of Reclamation, photo by B.D. Glaha).

Visalia, the largest, is now ranked as one of the Great Valley's ten urbanized centers.

Agricultural expansion in the Delta, particularly on the southeasterly and western sides, came after availability of Central Valley Project water.

Inherently fertile when irrigated, these areas utilize much water from the Friant-Kern Canal (Fig. 9-42). Construction of Pine Flat Dam on the Kings provided water which has permitted additional expansion.

Sizable acreages were dry-farmed before the Central Valley Project. Earlier, however, cultivation of upper portions of this coalescing alluvial plain, irrigable from the Kaweah and lesser streams (or with pump well irrigation) developed more intensive utilization.

### *The Thermal Belt*

The eastern segment of the San Joaquin, south of the Kings River, forms an enclave within the Sierra Nevada. Thus the upper (eastern) portion of the Kaweah Delta has crescentric shape.

Winter temperature inversions here create the largest of several *thermal belts* with slightly milder climate, less subject to killing frosts, than

---

* This section has been reviewed by Valene Staley, Porterville College. Previously it was reviewed by James Scofield, College of Sequoias.

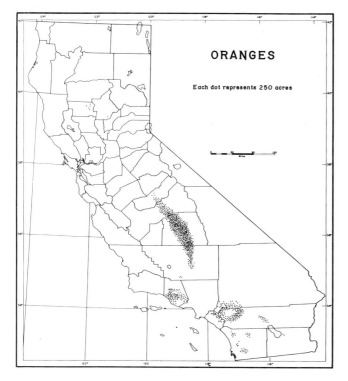

ORANGES

Each dot represents 250 acres

**Map 9-21.** The leading acreages of oranges in California are now found in the Kaweah Delta and the Fresno District.

areas a short distance to the west. This particular thermal belt, extending north-south 55 miles (from Elderwood almost to Terra Bella), attains a width of ten miles.

Despite severe freezes every five to ten years, it was discovered that this locale is suitable for citrus. Some corporate growers have even planted in the "riskier" fringes, anticipating loss some winters. As much as 40 per cent of the output has come from such localities.

Citrus production began in the final decades of the nineteenth century.

One hundred acres of oranges were planted by George Frost, previously of Riverside, near Porterville in 1890. The first carload was shipped east three years later and by 1913 4500 carloads were shipped annually. Particularly disastrous on the fringes of the Thermal Belt, severe frost in 1913 largely defined the limits of production for many years.

The *Washington navel orange* has been the dominant fruit. Because of its consumption fresh, this winter-maturing variety has not suffered the critical competition from Florida oranges that the Valencia variety has since the advent of frozen orange juice (see Ch. 6). Since the fruit is often

picked on the Delta before the likelihood of a killing frost, it is better suited physically here too.*

The Kaweah Delta for several decades has been California's ranking orange producer—Tulare County has about 80,000 acres.

Acreage has stabilized since 1970 but maturation of younger trees has resulted in a near-doubling of output.

Expansion of citrus in the San Joaquin Valley was accelerated by urbanization in the Los Angeles Lowlands. Also, to avert sizable capital-gains taxes, displaced growers reinvested their money in land (Fig.9-43).

Acreage southward into Kern County and northward into Fresno County has been planted in citrus. Low-pressure irrigation sprinklers allow citrus on steep slopes. Other innovations have included considerable grove supervision (by management firms) for absentee-owners and increased mechanization, especially in harvest techniques. Disastrous freezes jeopardize prospects for some groves.

Tulare County leads California in olive production (map, 9-22).

Acreage has expanded in the second half of this century. The Golden State is the single significant source of olives outside of the Mediterranean

---

* The orange *tree* can withstand much lower temperatures for a longer period of time without critical damage than the near-ripe fruit can.

**Figure 9-43.** Orange groves, Tulare County. (Perma Rain Irrigation).

Basin where the long-lived tree is indigenous. Domestic production in the United States does not satisfy the American market. California normally cannot process olive oil sufficiently inexpensively to compete with Spanish and Italian varieties.

Most California olives are dual-purpose varieties, increasingly used as eating olives. Production was enhanced with the discovery around 1900 that olives can be canned. Trees are planted planted in Tulare County both as a primary crop and to provide windbreaks around citrus orchards. The olive is not demanding although the fruit must be picked in November and early December before the possibility of an early frost. Olives will produce without irrigation but artificial watering assures larger trees and better harvests. The tree will tolerate a variety of soils as long as they are well drained and alkaline-free.

The *vineyard* belt of the Fresno District continues southward through Tulare County into Kern County. In the Kaweah Delta grapes are grown west of the citrus (map 9-18).

Since it is deciduous, the grape is not plagued by the threat of frost as is citrus. Soils are suitable and production has been important for some decades. Even in the years before Central Valley Project

water, modest moisture requirement of the vines favored the grape. Once established, grapes can be raised with limited irrigation if the soils are not too coarse.

With delivery of CVP water through the Friant-Kern Canal, grape acreage expanded and water consumption per acre increased. Tulare County now ranks *second* to Fresno County in total grape output but ranks *first* in table grapes. Many viticulturalists at the south edge of Tulare County have Yugoslav ancestors.

Another of California's rapid locational shifts was the rise of the Delta to leadership in production of *plums* (Map 9-10).

In the 1920's California experienced an over-planting of plums, as it has at times with other fruits. A reduction of acreage occurred in the 1930's. Now California grows over 90 per cent of the nation's plums.

Orchards are concentrated now in the southern East Side (Kern, Tulare and Fresno counties), in the Sacramento Valley near Yuba City and in the Sierran Foothills of Placer County. Expansion in the Kaweah Delta reflects rising national consumption and the advantage of earlier ripening than that farther north; now the fruit is largely consumed fresh.

The *peach* belt of Fresno County also continues southward in the Delta.

Currently production of the two counties is comparable. The The former Tagus Ranch has some of the largest orchards in the Valley southwest of Visalia, which is the major peach center.

Other crops, important on the Delta's western edge, include alfalfa, barley, cotton and sorghum.

Tulare County forms an important segment of the San Joaquin cotton belt, discussed later. Its output has lagged behind Fresno and Kern counties. Barley has been dry-farmed for many decades west of Terra Bella.

*Market milk* is an important product of both Tulare and Kings counties. In the second half of this century the Delta has become increasingly-important as a supplier of fresh milk for metropolitan Los Angeles.

Dutch dairymen "fled" urbanization along the Orange-Los Angeles borderland. Capital gains allowed them to establish large "milk factories", with fancy milking parlors and dwellings sometimes suggestive of country clubs (the house is often the "clue" to distinguishing between a newer Dutch dairy farmer and the long-established Por-

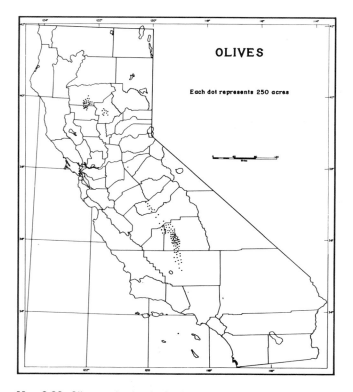

**Map 9-22.** Olive production in California is virtually limited to three centers (Lindsay, Oroville and Corning) in the Central Valley.

tuguese dairyman). The newcomers tended to locate "everywhere" that poor soils, less suitable for cropping, could be found. Dairying previously had been restricted largely to the western edge of the Delta.

*Vegetable* production is likewise significant in the Delta. *Fresh* market tomatoes and green peppers are particularly important.

But a dozen vegetables have significance; acreage shifts with fluctuations in demand. A decline in potatoes reflects inability to compete effectively against other areas. By contrast tomatoes meet a "market gap" in late June and July.

### Cityscapes

The size and productivity of the Kaweah Delta is reflected in the number of its larger market towns.

Other considerations include spacing of parallel rail lines (of the Southern Pacific and the Santa Fe), crop distribution and diversity and inclusion of two counties with the Delta.

City-county relations, in contrast to many California counties, have been relatively good; definite "spheres of influence" have been established. Determined efforts have been made to prevent sprawl into fertile farmlands—this is almost a rarity in the Central Valley—and the nation!

*Visalia* (68,000 with circa 300,000 in its SMA), the principal city, has witnessed much of its growth since 1970. It is regarded by some as one of the more attractive Central Valley cities. Supports include county government, trade and services, and manufacturing.

It is the most important retail and professional services center between Fresno and Bakersfield. Like those two, it is becoming a place for conventions (subregional and statewide). It has long-established *College of the Sequoias* and nearby, county government in a spacious park-like setting. Highway activities reflect its role as a gateway to Sequoia (and Kings Canyon) National Park. These include laundry, food and supply services.

Growth of retail trade and light industry warrant note. Visalia ranks fifth in the San Joaquin Valley as an industrial center with an industrial park near Ca. 99.* The number of branch outlets of San Francisco and Los Angeles retailing firms has increased.

Visalia is a northside-southside city. The northside has the declining central district, the country club and many ethnic residents. The southside has the college, county center, several shopping centers

**Figure 9-44.** South Mooney Boulevard (Ca. 63), Visalia, has several shopping plazas. (dwl)

and much of the newer housing. The southwest quadrant is suggestive of Modesto's McHenry Village. In socioeconomic terms, Visalia ranks second to Modesto among larger San Joaquin cities.

One of the oldest Valley towns (1852), Visalia was an early-day "cowtown." The town refused to bribe the Big Four and the Southern Pacific built south through Tulare instead. Visalia recovered long ago from this setback.

*Tulare* (29,000), strongly supportive of growth and industrial development, is an industrial and residential city with a sizable ethnic population (now including *Hmong*).

It tends to be an eastside (Anglo and central district)-westside (conspicuous Hispanic farm-labor heritage) city. Industrial activity, including

---

* Products include such diverse items as aluminum pipe, batteries, business forms, cotton processing, electronics components, chemicals, milk products, mobile homes, olive processing, plastic irrigation pipes, pumps, pretzels, steel buildings, walnut processing and work clothes!

cotton ginning and food processing, is located along the railroad tracks. Houses tend to be more modest than those in Visalia.

Tulare, in its early years, was a Southern Pacific division point with repair shops. More recent growth has been related to agricultural expansion, especially dairying. In late winter Tulare is the site of the nation's largest farm equipment fair.

*Hanford* (27,000), suitably located as a service center, is the seat of Kings County and has industrial activity.

On the western edge of the Kaweah Delta, Hanford has benefitted from agricultural developments on the bed of Lake Tulare and the nearby Westside of the San Joaquin. It presents a waspish air yet has a sizable ethnic populace (Hispanic and black) on its southern periphery.

Downtown Hanford, with a contiguous community shopping center on the western fringe, remains viable. Hanford, long concerned with services for cattlemen, grain farmers and dairy farmers, now has support from military personnel and cotton farmers as well. *China Alley*, now known for its restaurants, is a vestige of the "early days." Hanford also has the Amtrak service for the Delta.

The important industrial activity includes business forms, dairy processing, oil refining and rubber goods.

Location of a Naval Air Station at nearby **Lemoore** (14,000) represents a transfer of some facilities from Moffett Field. Once known as a farm village with a creamery, Lemoore has much off-base housing for Naval personnel.

*Porterville* (27,000), ranking citrus center of the Delta, has a variety of other functions. Lately it has become a retirement place as well.

The downtown area, adjacent fruit packing sheds and more expensive northside housing suggest the importance of the surrounding Thermal Belt.

*Relative proximity* to metropolitan Los Angeles is reflected in the expanding retiree and Hispanic populace. Like Visalia, Porterville serves as an entry point to Sequoia National Park (from the south). It has two-year Porterville College and a state hospital. A southside industrial park (yarns, sportswear, business forms) has developed adjacent to Ca. 190.

There are socioeconomic problems and considerable unemployment. This is reflected especially in **East Porterville**, once one of the Valley's larger Dust Bowl shantytowns and now increasingly Hispanic.*

**Exeter** (6700) and **Lindsay** (9000), established Thermal Belt towns, have experienced less growth in the late twentieth century than the cities just discussed.

In both towns packing and shipping sheds are conspicuous. Lindsay is California's leading olive processing center. Exeter claims to have more millionaires per capita than any other place in the San Joaquin Valley (and has a new hilltop development with security gates). Exeter ships grapes, other other fruit and vegetables.

## THE TROUGH

The Trough (north-south axis) of the San Joaquin Valley is located west of the Valley centerline since much more alluvial fill has been transported from the Sierra Nevada (than from the Coast Ranges) and hence has elevated the East Side (map 9-1).

The Trough is flattish although it has a gentle slope "downward" (north) toward the Delta Lands. The San Joaquin wanders sluggishly across the Trough; this master stream and its tributaries have created a maze of channels, often abandoned to become *sloughs* with sizable expanses of tule-reed marshlands.

Underlain by compact soils that are often high in alkalinity, the Trough lacks a single sizable community.

This is the most sparsely populated part of the San Joaquin Valley, an area that contains many large properties more often used for grazing than for farming.

In days past, more extensive areas were inundated, generally in late spring, with melting of Sierran snowfields and when streams have overflowed their channels. The problem of flooding has been lessened as additional multi-purpose dams have been constructed in the Sierra Nevada.

Improbable as it may seem today, the Trough might once have been regarded as more desirable than other portions of the San Joaquin Valley.

During Mexican colonial days it was attractive for grazing because it had water when much of the Valley was dry and barren. Accordingly cattle ranchos were established along the Trough. Then the cattle barons, Miller and Lux, acquired vast

---

* A study of California's depression-era *Hoovervilles* over the past half century would make a worthy doctoral dissertation in cultural urban geography. Some, like Bell Gardens, Alisal (now part of Salinas), East Porterville and Weedpatch, have become Hispanic. Others, like Olivehurst and Linda, in the Sacramento Valley, remain Anglo.

acreages here after the middle of the nineteenth century. They purchased thousands of acres as "swamp lands" from the state of California at $1.25 per acre. Later, during the heyday of the wheat farmer, there was a conspicuous absence of settlement in the Trough—the East Side was the preferred area for grain.

In the second half of the twentieth century the Trough has gained more importance as the population of California and the nation has grown.*

Locally there are considerable acreages of sugar beets and rice, crops more tolerant of alkaline conditions and suitable for heavy soils. Much land continues to be used for pastoral purposes to provide forage for beef cattle and dairy cows.

### No Cheese Factories Here

Expansion of dairying along the Trough has produced one of the major agricultural changes in the Central Valley in the second half of the twentieth century.

Pertinent factors have included (1) urbanization in the San Francisco Bay Area and Southern California; (2) continued population growth in California; and (3) conversion of more productive San Joaquin Valley lands into vegetables and fruit sources.

The Trough, from San Joaquin County southward into Kings County, leads the Golden State in milk production (Map 9-24).

Unlike Wisconsin, California is not a leading producer of butter and cheese—milk is consumed fresh in urban areas.

Dairying began on the West Side in the 1890's. Subsequently it has been relocated along the Trough. Many former East Side dairy pastures, too, in the Modesto District, have been converted

into fruit and nut orchards. Others now grow vegetables or raise replacement heifers.

On the East Side, dairies tend to be concentrated in the west portion of the Turlock district, where soils are not suitable for orchards. Many large Southern California dairies have been relocated in the San Joaquin Valley.

Grade A dairies in western Stanislaus County have been relocated east of the San Joaquin River in two belts: (1) in the Trough and (2) on the hillsides of the Oakdale Irrigation District (i.e., in the Sierran Foothills).

"Trough" counties ship considerable milk to metropolitan Los Angeles. Factors that have favored dairy expansion in the Trough have included (1) continued California population growth; (2) central location between San Francisco and Los Angeles; (3) ability of Sudan grass and Ladino clover to tolerate the alkaline "hardpan" (which is not good alfalfa land) (4) adequate water; and (5) sufficient land away from expanding metropolitan areas.

### Paddies Without Coolies

Although the major concentration of rice production in California is found in the flood basins of the Sacramento Valley a smaller output has materialized northward from Mendota in the San Joaquin Valley (map 9-7).

Rice is concentrated in western Fresno County, where it helps reduce alkalinity through cultivation techniques. While the environment is similar to that of the Sacramento Valley flood basins, rice farming has evolved more recently in the San Joaquin. In both areas farming is conducted on an extensive scale with a high degree of mechanization. The longer growing season of the San Joaquin may afford it prospects if a satisfactory long-grain rice variety can be developed in California.

### A Place for Beets

Increased water availability under the Central Valley Project permitted increased sugar-beet cultivation in the Trough, especially in Fresno County (Map 9-4).

In contrast to such leading California counties as Imperial, Yolo and San Joaquin, production re-

**Figure 9-45.** South Dos Palos. (dwl)

---

* In 1958 Professor Chester Cole estimated that reclamation of alkaline lands, including leveling, application of gypsum, installation of irrigation works and fertilization, would cost several hundred dollars an acre. Alkalinity has resulted from salts concentrated in the upper layers of the soil as result of (1) lateral migration of groundwater; (2) evaporation after overirrigation; and (3) "ponding" of flood waters in natural depression.

mains relatively low. As elsewhere, beet pulp has been used for cattle feed.

### Just Little Towns

Towns in the Trough are small, have fewer trees, have less affluence and look less settled than the East Side cities.

They provide residence for farm workers as well as shipping facilities for surrounding areas. Although some trade is engendered locally, many workers conduct their retail trade in the larger East Side county seats.

**Mendota** (5500), founded on a spur rail line from Fresno in 1895, has grown with vicinal agricultural expansion. It is the site of a sugar-beet factory.

**Firebaugh** (4000) has shipping sheds and agricultural processing plants (including rice and alfalfa dehydration).

**Dos Palos** (4400) began with a rail station (in 1889) and grew with location of an agricultural colony nearby three years later. Like other towns in the Trough it remains a farming community. Comparison with nearby **South Dos Palos**, a black residence village, would make an interesting sociological study.

### THE WEST SIDE *

Between the Trough and the Diablo-Mt. Hamilton Range, the West Side has been transformed. This change has resulted from a major thoroughfare (Interstate 5) coupled with availability of "outside" water from the Central Valley Project and the California Water Project.

This area extends southward from the Delta to the South End (Kern County) and includes the floor of old Lake Tulare (see Map 9-15).

Irrigation agriculture developed here relatively late.

For decades after the East Side was a land of vineyards and orchards, much of the West Side remain grazing land, seasonally parched.

A climatic map (Overview A) reveals why irrigation agriculture was delayed in this portion of the San Joaquin. In the lee of the southern Coast Ranges, the West Side is either semi-arid (north) or a desert (south).

The intermittent streams that flow eastward from the Diablo Range have small volume, in contrast to their Sierran counterparts on the East Side and have produced smaller alluvial fans. During months when water is critically needed for agriculture their beds are dry washes.

Relatively early in the colonial period the Spanish became acquainted with the West Side.

A "short-cut" mission bypass, *El Camino Viejo*, was established between the Los Angeles Lowlands and the San Francisco Bay Area.

It might seem illogical that several Mexican ranchos were awarded on the West Side.

But this portion of the Valley was closer to occupied land in the Central Coast. Moreover the ranchos were located upon alluvial fans of larger streams—the remainder of the San Joaquin remained in its pristine state.

### Cattle Kings

During the Mexican period the San Joaquin never became a significant source of beef cattle. With the Gold Rush, however, the West Side gained importance as a source of beef.

The firm of *Miller and Lux*, dominated by one-time German butcher boy Heinrich Kreiser (Henry Miller) became the "greatest cattlemen of them all."

Miller and Lux acquired thousands of acres between Tracy on the north and the San Joaquin "bend" west of Fresno.

They obtained an option on part of Rancho Santa Rita in 1857. Eventually they acquired 247,000 acres in Merced County alone.

Land was gained in various ways: (1) direct purchase of rancho property from Mexican owners. Sometimes this was done as it was in Southern California and in the Central Coast— loans at ruinous rates were followed by foreclosure; (2) Considerable land was gained through purchase of land script, at perhaps 50 per cent of value, that had been given to veterans of the Civil War and Indian wars; (3) Miller and Lux encouraged their employees to take out homesteads which were then purchased at low prices; (4) A vast acreage in the Trough was acquired under the *California Swamp Act*—marshlands could be purchased at $1.25 an acre.

Allegedly upon his death in 1916 Miller held 161,000 acres in Merced County alone. Chester Cole, in his dissertation on Fresno County, reported that "A common saying in the San Joaquin

---

* The West Side has been reviewed by Jerry Williams, C.S.U., Chico and Donald Forth, West Hills College.

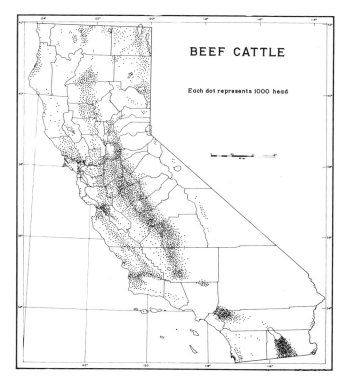

**BEEF CATTLE**

Each dot represents 1000 head

**Map 9-23.** The Central Valley leads California in production of beef cattle although other areas have importance.

Valley was that Miller made three fortunes...one for himself, one for his partner and one for his attorneys" (p.144).

Miller and Lux were indirectly responsible for the major portion of earlier irrigation development on the West Side.

After a San Francisco firm had constructed its *San Joaquin and Kings River Canal*, Miller and Lux demanded their riparian rights and forced the canal builders to sell them the ditch for one third of its cost. Able to water 150,000 acres, it was one of the nation's largest schemes at the time. The canal provided the stockmen with surplus water, used partially to reclaim alkali lands along the Trough.

**Beef, Grains and Settlers**

Occupance of the West Side proceeded more slowly than along the East Side.

Besides the holdings of Miller and Lux, additional deterrents were dryness and the absence of adequate transportation (prior to the Southern Pacific's construction of its West Side line in 1890).

Other than livestock, dry-farmed wheat constituted the principal source of livelihood in the late nineteenth century. In his thesis dealing with

Merced County, Graham estimated that during the grain-farming days the "typical" non-irrigated West Side acreage experienced three successive occupances, reflecting inability to obtain an adequate livelihood in a land with such limited precipitation.

Before the railroad era Los Banos, center of Miller and Lux operations, was the single West Side town. While the federal government granted the Southern Pacific rights to alternate sections around Los Banos, the railroad never assumed title. Thus this land became available for homesteading around 1885.

Sundry groups of European immigrants settled on the West Side. Basque families, who began to come to California at the time of the Gold Rush, located at the base of the Diablo Range as sheepmen. South Italians were imported by Miller and Lux in the middle 1870's as laborers on their ranches. Some gradually purchased small holdings from homesteaders and bought water from Miller and Lux. They sold vegetables to Miller and Lux employees and other residents of the West Side.

Following opening of the railroad in 1890 smaller farms appeared on the West Side. Another factor was the death of Lux in 1887; Miller had to sell some of the partners' lands to satisfy the demands of Lux's heirs. Accepting changing times, Miller constructed an "upper canal" and sold some of the water from his own operation. But extensive sale of Miller lands was delayed for a decade after his death; in 1916 the corporation formed by his heirs began to dispose of his remaining holdings, which covered 530,000 acres in 1926.

As much acreage was obtained from Miller for colonization in the 1890's Dos Palos, Gustine and Los Banos became foci of more intensive land-use.

Accordingly, after 1900, Portuguese dairymen bought tracts, usually of 20 to 40 acres. Many Portuguese, who were oft-times impecunious upon arrival, rented for a while.

Much of the West Side remained untilled until the 1930's. Cotton farming, discussed later, was a corporate operation that demanded pump wells often more than 2000 feet deep and individual pumps able to provide water for an entire section (640 acres) of land.

Distinctive subdivisions have evolved on the West Side, even as they did on the East Side.

Partially because the period of irrigation agriculture has been shorter, land-use patterns have become less intricate than on the East Side, hence

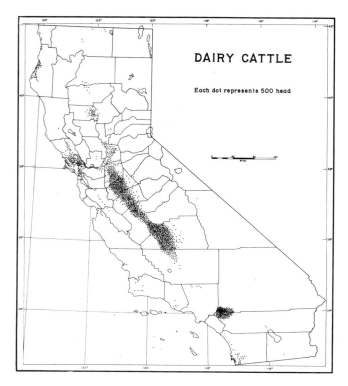

**Map 9-24.** The San Joaquin Valley now leads California in production of milk.

a subdivision into Northern and Southern sections seems sufficient.

### The Northern West Side

The northern West Side extends southward from the Delta Lands to Los Banos (map 9-15).

There are several basic differences between the northern and southern West Side. Relative to the northern area: (1) annual rainfall totals are higher; (2) cotton is absent—the season becomes shorter and the threat of early autumnal rains too risky; and (3) there has been a longer history of irrigation agriculture.

Precipitation, between 10 and 15 inches annually, tapers off southward. In some years the southern West side receives no more than five inches.

Partially because precipitation was heavier and also because of better market access in the prerailroad era (before 1890), the northern West Side produced considerable dry-farmed grains. Over sizable portions of the entire San Joaquin Valley, shipping costs tended to be a determining grain factor before the railroad, except for districts near the lower San Joaquin that could ship down the river.

Despite their personal interest in beef cattle, Miller and Lux indirectly fostered the rise of irrigation agriculture.

In addition to sale of water from their San Joaquin and Kings River Canal, they constructed roads. The quantity of their livestock marketing was a major incentive to the South-Pacific to build its West Side line.

Most irrigation agriculture developed after construction of the railroad although alfalfa had been introduced previously. General farming and dairying continued until mid-century. Subsequently specialized agriculture has prevailed.

### Farewell, Brown Cow

For several generations dairy farming was a major rural activity in the northern West Side.

Full-time dairying followed the arrival of a Swiss dairyman in 1892. Many early dairy farmers were former Miller and Lux employees; others came from the Central Coast or directly from Europe. Eventually there were hundreds of Italian-Swiss. Meanwhile, Azorean Portuguese who generally started out as hired milkers gradually established dairies. Distance from market favored processing.

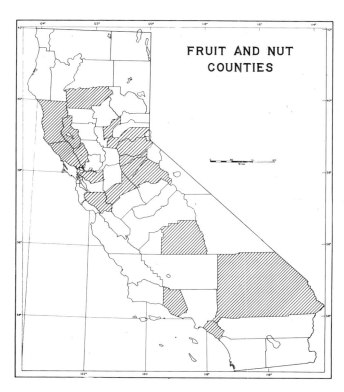

**Map 9-25.** Counties where production of fruits and nuts has dominated agricultural activity.

The Great Central Valley 393

Bay Area distributers began trucking fresh milk to city markets in the 1920's. Cole (in Soil Survey of the Newman District, 1938), estimated that the area between Crows Landing and Newman had more milk cows per acre than any other dairy belt in the nation. As the Bay Area population increased, a marked shift from manufactured to market milk took place, quality of cows improved and milk output increased. By the 1940's the metropolitan areas insisted upon Grade A milk.

Except in San Joaquin County dairies have almost disappeared from the northern West Side.

Dairymen who elected to continue generally relocated along the Trough, as indicated previously. In the decade of the 1950's between 1400 and 1500 dairies in western Stanislaus County alone were converted to fruit or vegetable farms. One still sees decaying dairy barns about the landscape.

### Orchards and Garden Patches

The rural landscape of the northern West Side in the late twentieth century reflects a transition typical of the dynamic economic geography of the Golden State.* On a limited scale fruit orchards were planted south of Tracy as early as the 1920's. Even then, some dairymen began to shift to production of beans, enticed by a comparable return for less effort—when the bean market "softened" they went back to dairying. By mid-century, costs of converting the many small dairies to Grade A milk output was almost prohibitive.

It has long been recognized that the northern West Side is suitable for fruits and vegetables (maps 9-24 and 25)—sundry factors prompted a land-use shift.

(1) Earlier this area was unable to compete well against the Santa Clara Valley in such fruits as apricots—the Santa Clara had the advantages of early start, location and packing facilities; (2) Urbanization of the Santa Clara prompted some of its orchardists to follow the example of Southern California citriculturalists who moved to the Kaweah Delta; to avoid excessive capital-gain taxes they invested in West Side orchards. Land, formerly relatively cheap, increased rapidly in price; (3) West Side dairymen willingly sold their farms and bought less expensive land in the Trough which enabled them to develop the larger farms necessary to operate Grade A dairies; (4) The Central Valley Project made water available through the Delta-Mendota Canal and new irrigation districts were established. The Tracy-Patterson district alone has thousands of acres of tree

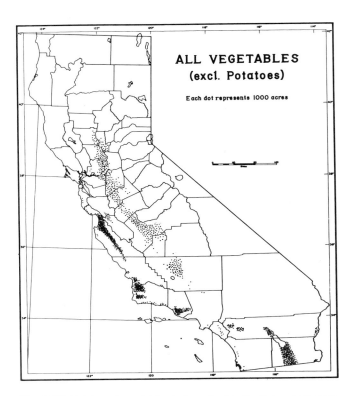

**Map 9-26.** Raising of vegetables is important in the Colorado Desert, Southern California, the Central Coast and the Central Valley.

crops; apricots, almonds and walnuts have been acreage leaders.

Originally treeless, the northern West Side now displays groves of eucalyptus, Lombardy poplars and cottonwood as windrows (Fig. 9-46).

Fields are usually leveled to grade and fences tend to be limited. Decaying milksheds, mechanized harvesters, open-sided implement sheds, orchards and fields of truck crops have become commonplace. Despite the shift from dairying alfalfa is still a common rotation crop. There is an impressive variety of vegetables which are trucked to such market towns as Tracy, Manteca and Modesto.

### Still-Small Places

Metropolitan California has not reached the northern West Side. The typical community is the farm town beside the Santa Fe Southern trackage *rather than* along I-5.

Communities tend to be at least a generation younger than those of the East Side. There are

---

* Slightly elevated above the Valley along the base of the Diablo Range, the section of I-5 in western Stanislaus County, designated a *scenic highway*, affords some of the most pleasing vistas in the Central Valley.

**Figure 9-46.** Land preparation near Patterson. (Caterpillar Tractor Company)

fewer shade trees and less evidence of growth—this is analogous to the contrasting East Side and West Side towns of the Sacramento Valley noted earlier in the chapter. But increasing commutation to Bay Area jobs has occurred.

*Tracy* (22,000) is the largest and least-typical West Side city. It is a service place for the southwestern Delta Lands as well as the northern West Side. Increasingly it has become a Bay Area outlier.

Tracy has been important as a Santa Fe Southern rail junction. Older than most West Side towns, it was founded as a railroad station in 1878.

Although there is diversity, Tracy's industries emphasize foodstuffs: vegetables (especially tomatoes), sugar, dairy goods and wines. Assumedly H.J. Heinz relocated its plant here (from Berkeley) because of lower taxes, available land, good transportation and local availability of tomatoes. Shipping of agricultural products is also important.

Nearby are the pumping stations of the California Aqueduct and the Central Valley Project, which "lift" Sacramento River water (brought by the Delta Cross Channel) into south-flowing canals (the Aqueduct and the Delta-Mendota Canal).

*Patterson* (5000) is a growing community with a number of ranch-style residences.

It has an unique circular street pattern in its central district. Indicative of changing land use is a frozen-foods processing plant opposite a creamery.

Smaller places include **Gustine** (4000), a longtime dairying center now surrounded by orchards and

truck farms, and **Newman** (2500), another dairying-farming town.

At the south end of this area, *Los Banos* (12,000), second largest of the northern West Side towns, provides various functions.

Older than most West Side towns, it began as the headquarters of Miller and Lux. The third largest town in Merced County, it has persisted as a ranching and milk-handling place. Recent growth has reflected California Water Project, freeway construction and the need for additional workers in vegetable patches.

### The Southern West Side

Essentially western Fresno County, the southern West Side extends from Los Banos to the northern edge of Lake Tulare. It has had a land-use development different from the area just discussed.

In this latitude most of the Miller and Lux holdings were farther east in the Trough. South of the northward bend of the San Joaquin River at Mendota, surface water for irrigation usage has been inconsequential. Thus pastoral uses continued through the first third of this century.

The southern West Side, along with the adjacent South End, contains the largest tracts of noncultivated land in the entire San Joaquin Valley today.

Locally, especially around Coalinga, petroleum mining encouraged population growth early in the twentieth century (petroleum is considered with discussion of the South End).

Southern West Side agricultural development has not been typified by small farms and colonies.

Attempts at homesteading in the nineteenth century often failed; by 1870 much acreage was being

**Figure 9-47.** This *was* downtown Coalinga prior to the devastating earthquake of May 2, 1983. (dwl)

accumulated by large companies which established livestock operations. Fallowing was usually necessary to assure a good barley harvest except in the wettest winters. Since 1900 the account of farming in the southern West Side has been primarily the evolution of the giant cotton farm. Such operations are not suitable for the "faint-hearted" or for the person unable to obtain financing.

The southern West Side ranch contrasts strikingly with the typical East Side farm and even with many on the northern West Side of the San Joaquin.

It is not esthetic—farming here has been a business, not a way of life. Ranches are large, commonly entailing many hundreds of acres and sometimes many thousands of acres. Chester Cole (dissertation) found that over 60 properties in southwestern Fresno County averaged over 4000 acres. The capital investment for an individual property is often multi-million dollars. Understandably this is a land of corporate farming. Around mid-century, "raw land" was relatively inexpensive (i.e., $50 to $100 an acre) for the Golden State. But the cost of development has been sizable, particularly land leveling, purchase of equipment and installation of an irrigation system.

The critical factor in land development in the southern West Side has been water.

Initially, without imported water or stream flow, it was necessary to pump. For a generation approximately 600,000 acre-feet were "mined" annually.

The water table declined 15 to 20 feet annually after 1940. By the early 1960's the average pumping depth exceeded 600 feet. Subsequently the water table has declined approximately 100 feet (much water is *now* imported). Before the availability of water from the California Aqueduct much of the pumped water had been connate ("fossil") water, sealed within the earth by overlying strata of clay and thus not a renewable resource. Moreover, the clays form a deep dike along the Trough which prohibits westward movement of water percolating underground from Sierran streams.

Pumping has resulted in local subsidence, particularly between the Kettleman Hills and Los Banos and principally on alluvial fans. Subsidence and soil compaction have damaged pump wells and made construction of irrigation canals more difficult.

The pump wells, often capable of providing water for an entire section (640 acres) with a single unit, vary in depth from 400 to 4000 feet; some of the largest well employ 300 horsepower motors or diesel engines and may lift water 800 feet. Even at mid-century 800 of the 1000 wells on the West Side were more than 500 feet deep. Such wells cost scores of thousands of dollars each to drill and case. Because of corrosion (due to minerals in the water) they have had a life expectancy of about ten years.

Crops in the southern West Side include alfalfa, barley, cotton (discussed later), field corn and safflower.

In the past half century there has been an impressive expansion in acreage of these crops. This combination makes steadier use of the land, rebuilds soil and provides "filler crop" substitutes when cotton acreage quotas have been reduced. There has also been a noticeable increase in acreage of melons and vegetables—this area has become the nation's leading source of cantaloupes.

The largest town between Bakersfield and Los Banos, *Coalinga* (8000), serves an extensive, still sparsely-populated portion of the West Side.

For decades it has grown slowly. The central district (*and* much of the community) has been rebuilt after considerable earthquake damage in 1983.

Oil was a dominant factor in the economy of Coalinga (and *still* remains important) for nearly half a century. Oil became the chief support in 1896. Later, in the 1920's, spectacular oil development occurred in the *Kettleman Hills* to the southeast. Coalinga had 10,000 people as early as 1910; for a time it was California's largest oil town.

In recent decades the economy of Coalinga has been affected too by agricultural development of the "middle" West Side. It is the site of West Hills College, which serves western Fresno County. Although it is nine miles west of I-5, no rival to Coalinga has materialized along the freeway.

**Avenal** (4300), a petroleum town and way point on Ca. 33, likewise does not appear to have suffered because of location off the freeway.

### Westlands Irrigation District

Established in 1952, this development involves 600,000 acres of land; three quarters is irrigated. It is corporate-owned and was established to take advantage of "cheap" water from the Central Valley Project. During arguments over the 160-acre limitation in the late 1970's it was controversial.

The District, extending north-south from Kettleman City to Mendota and east-west from I-5 to the Valley Trough, forms the largest single unit receiv-

**Figure 9-48.** Interstate 5, the "dreary stretch" northwest of Bakersfield where extensive areas remain uncultivated. Farther north it is a scenic highway. (dwl)

ing water from the Bureau of Reclamation. It produces about three dozen crops worth hundreds of millions of dollars annually—the leader has been cotton.

Critics charged that large landowners (including Anderson, Clayton and Santa Fe Southern) violated the "spirit" of the Reclamation Act. Ranches in the District *average* 2000 acres.

Prior to irrigation development, much of this area had been of slight value, used for dry grazing. Following completion of the *San Luis Canal*, the District built an 1100-mile distribution system and irrigated acreage spiraled, increasing sevenfold within a decade.

### Where are the People?

There was considerable anticipation that construction of Interstate 5 through the West Side, coupled with additional water (from the California Aqueduct), would prompt a sizable population growth in the southern West Side.

Some rashly predicted a land rush larger than that into Indian Territory (Oklahoma) about a century ago. Oil company officials and others anticipated evolution of several "intersection cities". One writer boldly predicted several cities as big as present-day Fresno. Highway services are increasing; the way-station of **Santa Nella** near Los Banos has the largest concentration.

Many farm owners seemingly reside in East Side cities and many field workers in towns along Ca. 33.

### FIELDS OF COTTON

Expanded acreage in the San Joaquin Valley has brought additional crops rather than replacement of older crops. Thus cotton appeared in localities that had not been watered previously: (1) the South End; (2) western segments of the Kaweah Delta; (3) the southern West Side; and (4) less alkaline portions of the southern Trough.

In the past half century three sources of water have been available for the rapidly-expanded cotton acreage: pump wells, Friant-Kern Canal (Central Valley Project) and California Aqueduct (California Water Project).

California's cotton saga has had several chapters. Presumably the earliest cotton was grown on the colonial missions.

Late nineteenth efforts were discouraged by unfa-

**Figure 9-49.** Cotton harvest. The mechanical harvester replaced hand picking around mid-century. Prior to harvest a defoliating chemical is sprayed on the plants. (Greater Bakersfield Chamber of Commerce).

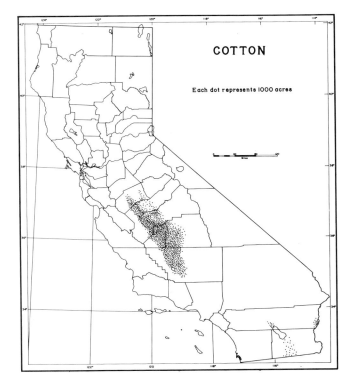

**Map 9-27.** Cotton in California is raised in the San Joaquin Valley, the Palo Verde Valley and the Imperial Valley.

miliarity with irrigation culture, competition from other crops, high production costs, insufficient markets and labor shortage. After 1900 output in California increased, particularly in the Imperial Valley during World War I (Ch.5). In the early 1920's a major handicap was the problem of a suitable variety; attempts to raise long-staple cotton had not been too successful. The state College of Agriculture experimented with different varieties.

By the middle 1920's it was realized that *upland* rather than *long staple* would prove the most successful.

Varieties from Asia and Africa, as well as native American cotton, were tried. By 1924 it seemed apparent that native American upland types (Acala, Durango and Pima) offered considerable promise. Acala supporters obtained legislative action in 1925 that restricted production in the San Joaquin Valley and the Colorado Desert to that variety.

Through continuing experimentation an improved *Acala* strain has been developed and yield per acre has continued to rise. It produces medium bolls with one to 1 3/16th inch fibers of considerable strength; it is suitable for mechanical picking and it can be harvested early. Yield has more than

**Figure 9-50.** Barley harvest in Kings County. California has led the nation in some years but production has declined in recent decades. Fields and farms are some of the largest in California (United Aerial Survey).

doubled in the past half century and record output now exceeds 1100 pounds per acre. The San Joaquin has become the largest single-variety producer in the United States.

Since 1949 cotton has often been California's most valuable crop (but *third* commodity after beef and milk). A large acreage expansion occurred in the 1940's (map 9-27).

The net return in good years has approached half a billion dollars. Boll-weevil damage and crop diversification in southeastern United States, federal price supports (from the 1930's) and World War II cotton demands led to expanded San Joaquin output.

In the five counties of the southern Valley (excluding Merced County) cotton has been the leading crop and has contributed significantly to making Fresno, Tulare and Kern the three top-ranking counties nationally in total value of farm products. A maximum 1.4 million acres was planted during the Korean emergency in the early 1950's. Besides culture on newly planted land, cotton partially replaced alfalfa, melons and grains.

While ranking between fifth and seventh in acreage nationally, California has achieved second place (after Texas) in total output. Yields far higher than those in the Southeast account for production higher than that of most traditional Cotton Belt states.

Cotton raising in the San Joaquin is a big-time operation.

Fields and farms are large; extensive use of machinery (including harvesters), much application of fertilizer (soils tend to be nitrogen deficient) and irrigation characterize this type of farming.

Sprinkler irrigation (including center pivot) is widespread. Although there is no standard rotation scheme crops generally rotated with cotton include alfalfa, barley* and potatoes (Maps 9-27, 9-29 and 9-30). While differences in soil texture do not noticeably affect cotton yield, production declines if soils are too saline.

Unlike many crops grown in California there is no correlation between population growth in the Golden State and cotton acreage since the state does not have a cotton-fabrication industry. Following local ginning, the cotton is shipped to mills in Asia or in eastern United States. Subsequently some of the cloth is returned to California for use in clothing manufacture.

The role of the federal government in California cotton production has long been recognized.

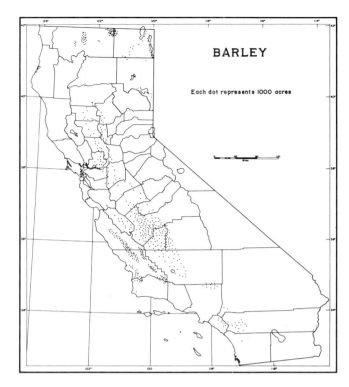

**Map 9-28.** Barley is widely grown but the largest acreage is in the Central Valley.

Cotton prices have been maintained artificially since the middle 1930's through price supports. Following the Korean emergency United States produced a cotton surplus and the Secretary of Agriculture applied marketing controls nationally. Because allotments were based upon long-period records, western states (Arizona and California) were cut back more severely than states in the southeast.

When acreage has been restricted, farmers tend to raise cotton on their best land, apply much fertilizer to increase yields (thus profiting from high federally-supported prices) and place other acreage in alternative crops.** Long-range prospects

---

* California leads all states in production of barley even though the Middle West is the leading region (Fig. 9-50). Long ago barley replaced wheat as the state's leading cereal grain. It is consumed principally as livestock feed locally although an appreciable amount of grain from the Tulelake Basin, western Sacramento Valley and northwestern San Joaquin valley is used for brewery malt making. Approximately half of California's barley is grown in the San Joaquin Valley with western Fresno County the leading producer. Cotton farmers help amortize high "capital" (investment) costs by raising barley as a winter crop.

** Other considerations exist. For example, a combination of unsatisfactory weather and a "bad" year for insect damage caused cotton production in Kern County to drop a third in one year in the middle 1960's. The pink boll weevil became a threat in the 1960's also. "Control" techniques have included use of a lure and earlier (in September) "termination" of the crop.

anticipate expanded acreage in the San Joaquin. Conceivably, without acreage controls, California might become the nation's leading producer.

## THE SOUTH END *

The South End of the San Joaquin Valley, principally within western Kern County (third largest within the Golden State), approximates the population center of California. Yet it is physically subpar, even for the Central Valley (map 9-15).

Physiographically the South End encompasses the bulk of the **Tulare Basin**, an area of internal drainage. Hottest and driest portion of the entire Valley, this arid land receives the natural discharge from the Sierra south of the Kings River as well as part of the Kings River.

Since construction of Pine Flat on the Kings River and Lake Isabella on the Kern, Buena Vista Lake, southwest of Bakersfield, and Lake Tulare in Kings County, upon occasion sizable water bodies before white settlement, have almost disappeared.

Economically, the South End has differed from various other sections of the Valley, especially the East Side.

Its rural countrysides were long typified by extensive grazing lands and dry farming, with large uncultivated tracts as well as oil fields. The Kern River was used for irrigation but without large storage reservoirs, only limited acreages were watered. Such an environment favored the large property; the corporate farm has been a representative feature of land use in the South End.

### Petroleum

"Black gold" converted the South End away from an economy wholly dependent upon cattle and grains, long before the sensational expansion of irrigated acreage. The San Joaquin Valley, last of California's six oil-producing "Tertiary Basins" to be discussed, has ranked second in total output to the Los Angeles Basin.

These two areas together were largely responsible for making California the nation's leading petroleum producer between 1900 and 1936 and second-ranking producer until 1958.

| Leading Oil Fields of California | | | |
|---|---|---|---|
| Area | Field | Recent Year Rank | Cumulative Rank |
| Los Angeles Basin | | | |
| | Huntington Beach | (4) | (4) |
| | Santa Fe Springs | | (6) |
| | Wilmington | (1) | (1) |
| Ventura | | | |
| | Ventura Avenue | (7) | (5) |
| Central Coast | | | |
| | San Ardo | (5) | |
| South San Joaquin Valley | | | |
| | Belridge, So. | (8) | |
| | Buena Vista | | (7) |
| | Kern River | (3) | (11) |
| | McKittrick | (10) | |
| | Midway-Sunset | (2) | (2) |
| West San Joaquin Valley | | | |
| | Coalinga | (9) | (8) |
| | Kettleman, North Dome | | (9) |
| Offshore | | | |
| | Dos Cuadras | | (6) |

Source: California Division of Oil and Gas

Presence of petroleum beneath the surface of the San Joaquin Valley has been known for over a century.

But production did not become important until the opening of the McKittrick field (1887) and the Kern River field (1899) east of Bakersfield.

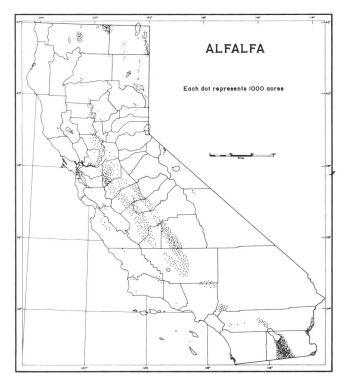

**Map 9-29**. Alfalfa is grown extensively in the Central Valley. Much is used for feed.

* The South End has been reviewed by John Lyman, Bakersfield College.

More than a score of fields have yielded petroleum worth billions of dollars.

As oil men have sought deeper into the earth, some of California's deepest wells have been drilled. At some fields, such as the Kern River, peak output was achieved in the first decade of this century. For others, the peak came in the 1920's and 1930's.

*Midway-Sunset* has been the most productive field; especially spectacular was the *Lakeview gusher* in this field which came into production in March 1910. In a brief "lifetime" of 18 months it yielded nine million barrels of crude oil.

Probably no portion of United States has been more intensively explored. Despite a continuing search, there has been no major new field in some decades.

A secondary technique, *steam recovery*, has prompted renewed production from such low-gravity fields as Kern River and Midway-Sunset.

The technique has been employed since the late 1960's and geologists estimate that the southern San Joaquin may yield petroleum for another 60 years or so. A precipitous drop in world oil prices in the mid-1980's led to a marked slowdown. An attempt was made to operate minimally until prices went higher. Currently around 10,000 wells are being "steamed."

Petroleum from the San Joaquin is generally marketed elsewhere.

While Bakersfield has been a modest local refinery center, much more crude oil is delivered by pipeline elsewhere in California.: (1) across the Tehachapi and Transverse ranges into the Los Angeles Lowlands; (2) the Oil Coast (San Francisco Bay Area); (3) Estero Bay near Cayucos; and (4) Avila on San Luis Obispo Bay.

The San Joaquin Valley has been spared the wasteful "town-lot" drilling as did some parts of the Los Angeles Basin. Still, conservation appeared belatedly.

The **Kettleman Hills,** where production has been dominated by Chevron on leases of federal land, has been a good example of well-spaced wells. A valuable U.S. Navy reserve in the *Elk Hills* was "saved" for many years, pending a future national emergency. By presidential order, the field is now being pumped.

### Water and Land

For decades, additional water, increasingly imported, has been altering utilization of the South End.

Earlier, expanded acreage was achieved by drilling of deep pump wells and evolution of sprinkler irrigation. Subsequent construction of Lake Isabella on the upper Kern and the Friant-Kern Canal, a major Central Valley Project unit, have had much impact.

Still more recently a county water agency has been created and a *Cross Valley Canal* completed to regulate distribution of C.V.P. and C.W.P. (from the California Aqueduct) water. While the South End has contracted for one-fourth the *entire* flow of the California Aqueduct, it is felt that additional imported water may be necessary (to flush out salts, for example). Problems related to water include alkalinity threats and subsidence on the western side of the South End.

In a single decade, 1939-1949, cultivated acreage in Kern County alone almost doubled.

Subsequently there was expansion into the 1970's, reaching more than 800,000 acres. Acreage has now stabilized. Meanwhile the gross value of the county's agricultural output increased from $26.4 million (1939) to $1.2 billion annually in the late 1980's.

### A Lot of This and That

South End commodities, like those of the Kaweah Delta, tend to reflect the general agricultural picture of the San Joaquin Valley.

But despite more than a score of crops yielding multi-million dollar returns, the South End is still "field crop country." Cotton is a major commodity; alfalfa is important, as are grains (now the "new" Mexican wheats have replaced much barley).

Cropping has become more permanent, with more fruit and nut acreage.

Extent (of fruits and nuts) has increased from 32,000 (1961) to more than 240,000 in the late 1980's. Especially dramatic are almonds, oranges (with a big gain on the west side), grapes (overplanted)—*Barbera* leads among the new varietals. Acreage of olives and pistachios has expanded. A promising new crop is the *Granny Smith* apple, used in wine cooler mixes.

Area in truck crops has been relatively steady for a quarter of a century although shifts have occurred.

Potato acreage is down while lettuce and melons are up. Lettuce has been important since the early 1970's. The South End tries to "hit the market" between late (autumn) Salinas and early Imperial output.

A distinctive newer activity is the growing of rose bushes commercially. Wasco now claims to be the "rose capital of the world."

Leading Kern County Farm Products

| | Value Rank |
|---|---|
| **Field Crops** | |
| lint cotton | 1 |
| alfalfa hay | 2 |
| rose plants | 3 |
| cottonseed | 4 |
| wheat | 5 |
| barley | 6 |
| sugar beets | 7 |
| dry beans | 8 |
| corn | 9 |
| irrigated pasture | 10 |
| sorghum | 11 |
| **Livestock and Products** | |
| market eggs | 1 |
| poultry | 2 |
| market milk | 3 |
| cattle and calves | 4 |
| sheep and lambs | 5 |
| **Vegetables** | |
| potatoes (white) | 1 |
| carrots | 2 |
| lettuce | 3 |
| onions | 4 |
| watermelons | 5 |
| cantaloupes | 6 |
| Fruits and nuts grapes (all types) | 1 |
| almonds | 2 |
| oranges | 3 |
| pistachios | 4 |
| peaches | 5 |
| plums | 6 |
| olives | 7 |

Source: Agriculture Commissioners of Kern County

### The Vanishing Potato Patch

Potato farming in the South End first achieved importance in the early 1930's—the market for *spring* potatoes was stolen from southeastern United States.

For decades the single important variety was the all-purpose *White Rose* or California Long White. Recently there has been a shift to *Russets*.

Traditionally the "potato belt", underlain by sandy soils, extended from Shafter past Bakersfield into the Arvin District (Map 9-30).

Initially expansion, which began in 1931, resulted for low prices for competitive crops. Although Kern County potatoes continue to find a "new potato" market in California, many years of relatively-low potato prices led to a widespread shift to orchards, especially almonds and pistachios.

### The Corporation Farm

Like the Trough and the southern West Side, the South End has long been a land of large rural properties.

The small operator in the South End was handicapped from the beginnings of extensive grain farming in the 1880's until the advent of the Central Valley Project. Low yield (for dry-farmed grain) and aridity negated much success for the average homesteader. In the twentieth century the cost of well drilling and land reclamation have continued to discourage the small farmers.

Several advantages for large-scale farming have prevailed in the South End.

Included have been: (1) land that was inexpensive; (2) availability of cheap labor and development of large machines that tended to "perpetuate" the system; and (3) state and federal land that fostered the large property here.

Through homesteading the federal government encouraged settlement but the low return from such arid land soon prompted homesteaders to sell "for a pittance." The state government, through the Swamp Act, virtually gave away large tracts subject to seasonal overflow (i.e., Tulare and Buena Vista lakes).

Large ranchers have had their origins in (1) expansion by more successful homesteaders; (2) the "Swamp" lands; (3) several Mexican ranchos; (4) railroad grants; (5) combination of tracts obtained with Veterans (Civil War) Script; and (6) school lands.

**Figure 9-51.** Harvest of Irish potatoes near Shafter. Much acreage formerly devoted to potatoes in the South End is now used for almond orchards. (Tenneco West).

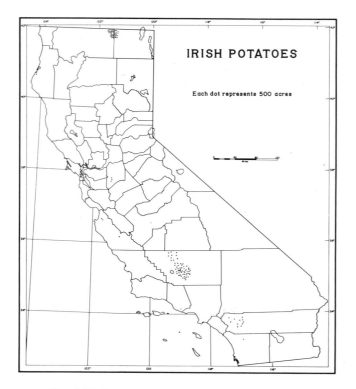

IRISH POTATOES

Each dot represents 500 acres

**Map 9-30.** Potato production in California is localized.

In his thesis Wills identified five types of large holdings in the southern San Joaquin Valley.

These included (1) the land-and-cattle company; (2) the bonanza wheat farm; (3) the "factory" farm; (4) the "indirect" landholder; and (5) the miscellaneous operator. He might have added oil company holdings.

Representatives of the land-and-cattle companies have included such firms as Tejon Ranch (Ch. 10), Miller and Lux and Kern County Land Company (*now* Tenneco).

Significant in the nineteenth century, the bonanza *wheat farm*, tended to survive longest on the rough lands of the foothill perimeter and the bed of Lake Tulare, subject to recurrent flooding. Represented by a few firms in all parts of the Valley, the "factory" farm is a twentieth-century phenomenon; the largest one in the South End was DiGiorgio Fruit Company in the Arvin District.

### A Type Example: Superior Farming Company *

Superior Farming Company is a former subsidiary of a Los Angeles petroleum corporation.

It was founded in 1968 and took over the parent company's (Superior Oil Company) scattered holdings in Kern County, previously acquired in connection with mining for oil. Earlier the oil company

had been sharecropping its lands. Management of Superior has been directed by half a dozen agricultural specialists with diverse prior experience.

Superior holdings include 22,000 acres of former Kern County Land Company property purchased from H. Roberts in 1972. Roberts had planned "syndication farming" but the Securities and Exchange Commission forbade interstate sale.

The company is divided into five departments to provide maximum efficiency. Application of water-conserving and labor-saving methods are employed. For example mainline water supply is underground. On each of its 44 "farms" there is a central water control house; the land is watered with an automatically-controlled system.

Most of the land is in permanent crops (almonds, citrus, stone fruits and grapes). The remainder is devoted to vegetables. Commodities typify South End agriculture—in all, about 40 different crops are grown.

### The 960-Acre Limitation

An issue since the beginnings of the Central Valley Project has been the maximum size of individual landholdings that can receive water under large-scale programs in the Central Valley (there is no limitation under the California Water Project).**

For three-quarters of a century after its formation in 1902, the United States Bureau of Reclamation *assumedly* followed a policy of water distribution to provide the "greatest good for the greatest number", or a maximum of 160 acres per person (or 320 acres for husband and wife).

The large corporations of the South End and elsewhere are either not subject to or have subverted the intent of the 160-acre restriction. In older districts, landholders with their own facilities (such as Modesto or in areas developed by such means as deep wells (South End and West Side) have not been curbed. Water users dependent upon the flow of the Kern and Kings rivers success-

---

* The two examples used previously are not longer applicable. In return for C.V.P. water for ten years, DiGiorgio Fruit Company made agreements made with the Bureau of Reclamation to divert itself of 10,000 acres north of Arvin. It *appears* that operations may have been similar to those in the Westlands District (West Side). Tenneco, whose operations seemingly have been quite different, acquired Kern County Land Company.

** There is some feeling that the Bureau of Reclamation has served its usefulness in California and should be removed from future water development in the Golden State. Most recently controversy has concerned the Auburn Dam, still unbuilt, and the East Side division of the C.V.P.

**Figure 9-52.** Vegetables and oil wells, Kern County. (Greater Bakersfield Chamber of Commerce)

***Bakersfield*** (165,000 and SMA circa 460,000) has been one of the Central Valley's fastest growing metropolitan areas in the second half of the twentieth century.

Between 1950 and 1990 the city *alone* quintupled in population. Major factors have included the momentous growth in agricultural output coupled with increased services plus the petroleum industry. The doubling of county population reflects gain principally in metropolitan Bakersfield.

Through the decades varied activities have promoted growth.

Bakersfield was a dusty cattle town at the time of the Civil War. In the next decade its physiognomy began to change with the arrival of the railroad.

The economy was altered with expansion in the petroleum industry . And since the middle 1900's, much change has resulted from agricultural growth.

Present functions of the metropolis include agribusiness, trade, finance, government, manufacturing, higher education, the petroleum industry, tourism and conventions and a host of other services.

An important highway crossroads, Bakersfield "guards" the approaches to Tejon (Ca.99-I-5) and Tehachapi (Ca. 58) passes. Motels, restaurants and service stations are conspicuous.

With its low skyline Bakersfield does not suggest a traditional metropolis.

fully circumvented the 160-acre limitation when Isabella and Pine Flat dams were constructed *primarily* as flood-control facilities by the Army Corps of Engineers.

Provision for additional water to the western and southern San Joaquin prompted renewed dissatisfaction with the 160-acre limitation.

One complicating issue was the construction jointly by the state of California and the Bureau of Reclamation of *San Luis Reservoir* west of Los Banos. Water is stored there for both the C.V.P. and C.W.P..

A number of political leaders and larger landholders, from California and other western states, opposed the 160-acre limit. Farmers who received water from the C.W.P. paid more than landholders whose water was provided by the C.V.P., with larger holders being assessed a surcharge above the base rate. There has also been conflict in philosophy between differing governmental agencies. For example, the 160-acre limitation and commodity acreage controls were not compatible.*

In the early 1980's the 160-acre limit was changed to 960 acres.

Obviously large landholders have been delighted. Conceivably the change may hasten the disappearance of many smaller acreage operators in the American West.

---

* An illustration: If the owner of 160 acres could plant his land entirely in cotton, he would need one set of machinery. But if he had a 20-acre cotton allotment and comparable small allotments of other crops, the multiple costs of several sets of equipment, along with other costs, could be prohibitive.

**Figure 9-53.** Taft, a *different* California town. Oilfield service establishments border the railroad line (lower left). (dwl)

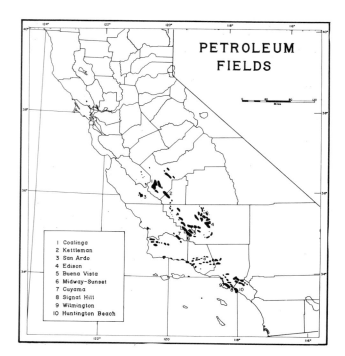

PETROLEUM
FIELDS

1 Coalinga
2 Kettleman
3 San Ardo
4 Edison
5 Buena Vista
6 Midway-Sunset
7 Cuyama
8 Signal Hill
9 Wilmington
10 Huntington Beach

**Map 9-31.** Production of "landbased" petroleum in California continues to decline. Increased output occurs offshore, not indicated.

One still feels the relaxed atmosphere of a smaller city. Like many California communities, there is much sprawl and scatteration with considerable open space. But much more than Redding or Yuba City, Bakersfield residents are becoming aware of metropolitan status, especially during rush hours. Sundry districts and neighborhoods can be found.

At mid-century Bakersfield was essentially a northside-southside town, divided by rail tracks. More recently it has become more of an eastside-westside city, with Cal. 99 freeway providing a divider.

Downtown Bakersfield looks relatively new—it was extensively rebuilt after an earthquake in 1952.

Despite its Civic Center and convention complex, it has lessening trade, facing competition from Valley Plaza to the south, a newer eastside mall and neighborhood centers.

Northeast Bakersfield is an attractive, mature residential area with many houses overlooking the Kern River valley.

*Bakersfield College* is located here—its sizable stadium reflects community enthusiasm for sports. On the extreme northeast fringe, adjacent to *Kern River County Park* is the *Rio Bravo* neighborhood with expensive newer homes.

But it is the growing southwestern quadrant of the metropolis, the *Stockdale District,* that has the most affluent neighborhood, adjacent to the country club.

In addition to the spacious campus of still-small *California State College,* this area has the headquarters of Tenneco plus other corporate and professional offices. In this area too is *Kern City,* popular with retirees.

**Figure 9-54.** Downtown Bakersfield. Extensive rebuilding followed a disastrous earthquake in 1952. (Greater Bakersfield Chamber of Commerce, Rorex photo)

**Figure 9-55.** The wayfarer on Ca.99 misses the opulence of westside Bakersfield but cannot avoid the poverty of smaller Kern County towns. (dwl)

Closer-in, southeast Bakersfield has many lower-income residents, including numerous blacks and Hispanics.

Towards the fringes, in county territory, are modest newer-housing areas.

Two disparate communities occupy the northern fringes. On the east (of Ca. 99 and near the airport) is *Oildale*, a lower-income Anglo satellite.

This is the locale for "country western." West of Ca. 99 is found industrial activity, especially agribusiness. Limited residential growth has occurred here.

Culturally, Bakersfield has gained a reputation as the California center of "country western music."

It is perhaps more suggestive of southeastern United States than any other California community. The dichotomy between enthusiasts of country western and lovers of ballet and symphony is obvious—many lack enthusiasm for the former.

Bakersfield is probably the most conservative larger city in the Central Valley—support for the "American way of life" is strong (one sees American flags flying "everywhere"). People here, while they read the Los Angeles *Times* and support baseball's Dodgers do *not* feel they reside in a distant satellite of Los Angeles. *

Social unrest tends to be subdued despite sizable Hispanic and black groups and increasing numbers of Asians.

Strong leadership is seemingly lacking among the ethnic groups. Presence of lower-income ethnics in-limits and higher-income Anglos in county territory is reflected in relatively-low income statistics in the city (and obscures the wealth of the

metropolis). Bakersfield affluence is in agriculture. Oil executives tend to be middle-level managers who have never dominated the city socially.

**Oil and Farming Towns**

The urban landscape of the South End differs somewhat from other parts of the San Joaquin Valley.

A major reason is the existence of the petroleum towns (Maricopa, Taft, and McKittrick) on the west side of the Valley.

Water was long a precious commodity in this desert land (prior to the California Aqueduct). Trees and lawns are limited. Also there tends to be a temporary air to mining towns, even longtime petroleum producers.

Elsewhere the "typical" town is the local farm center. Some, housing numbers of farm workers, are among the least prosperous-appearing communities in the Central Valley.

***Delano*** (20,000) has continued to grow as the agricultural center (farm service, shipping sheds, processing) of northern Kern County.

Like many towns along California 99, it evolved with the arrival of the railroad. Viticulture, which developed after Prohibition, has been a growth factor. Delano acquired notoriety in the 1960's as a focus of *the* grape strike. Hostilities now are less open; there is a United Farm Workers' retirement home west of Delano.

This is distinctly an eastside-westside community. The ethnic group (60 per cent Hispanic and five per cent Filipino) reside on the lower-income westside. The central district plus Anglo and Japanese residents occupies the east side.

Not all towns in the South End are growing. And some, east of Ca. 99, house second-and-third generation "Dust Bowlers".**

***Wasco*** (11,000), a Dust Bowl community, has become a center for the growing of roses bushes.

***Shafter*** (9000) has quadrupled in population since mid-century.

A number of westside landowners live here and the town has profited from the effects of California Aqueduct water to the west; many farm laborers

---
* A common attitude is "This is Southern California? Come on, guy, you are putting me on. Those dudes live on the other side of the Tehachapi."

** Many of the original migrants have died. Those who have acquired status tend to retire to coastal Cayucos or Grover City. Others have gone back to Oklahoma or Arkansas where they have status as "Californians."

**Figure 9-56.** A segment of Kern County Museum, Bakersfield.(dwl)

shop here. Also, the town has grown also because of surrounding almond orchards.

*McFarland* (6000) is basically agricultural. The headquarters for Roberts farms is east of town.

*Corcoran* (6500) is a "company-dominated" agricultural community without much evidence of middle-income residents.

It is on the northern edge of the South End in Kings County and has benefitted from agricultural expansion on the floor of old Lake Tulare. The farm labor group is sizable and there are a few landowners. Machine shops, a cotton gin, feed lots and grain elevators reflect its reliance upon surrounding farms.

Southeast of Bakersfield several erstwhile Dust Bowl towns have experienced ethnic shifts. Many of the Great Plains people have left and a conspicuous migration of *established* Hispanics from metropolitan Los Angeles is occurring.*

*Arvin* (9000) had its origins as an agricultural colony early in the century. Its growth as a farm-supply point has been promoted since Kern River water was brought to its environs. It is now a Hispanic-majority community (some stores downtown have Spanish-language names).

*Lamont* and *Weedpatch* (circa 8500) unincorporated farm workers' towns nearby, were the site of a prominent migrants' camp in the 1930's. Both are now conspicuously Hispanic and have improved physically in appearance.

*Taft* (6500) is the biggest western Kern County oil town.

No other community in California is so suggestive of western Texas. Taft gives the impression of having been transported from the southern Great Plains.

It boomed early in this century with the petroleum industry. The town has a settled drabness, accentuated by the paucity of large shade trees, a reflection of the desert setting. Fringe-area population gives a total of around 13,000. Like most of the oil towns, Taft is stagnant.

The sectional importance of Taft is reflected in its community college (as in Texas, sports are big here). While it gained notoriety briefly in 1975 as a "redneck town" when young Anglo *toughs* chased some black college students out of town, this attitude has "softened." While a town of modest white-frame dwellings on small lots, Taft does reveal community spirit.

Nearby *Maricopa, Fellows* and *McKittrick* are much less consequential.

## NEEDED: ONE GOOD CRYSTAL BALL!

Despite its rural setting, the Central Valley is essentially urban in terms of human residence.

The population of the Valley is comparable to that of the entire state of Connecticut or Iowa. Nine of its 13 counties are are classified as urbanized areas by the Census Bureau. But it tends to be conservative in outlook and agricultural in viewpoint. Some functions represent a "spill-over" from metropolitan Southern California and the Bay Area.

Urban functions tend to be less complex than those

---

* This trend does not yet appear to be reaching too far northward in the Central Valley, in contrast to the on- going northward migration of Anglo Southern Californians which began around mid-century.

**Figure 9-57.** Retirement residence for United Farm Workers west of Delano. (dwl)

of the more populous conurbations. A number of Valley cities are striving to attract industrial plants to gain economic diversity. Fresno, Modesto, Stockton and Sacramento have been more successful than some of the others, partly because they are more or less situated between California's two major population concentrations. Yet even in these more "industrialized" communities there has not been a spectacular increase in manufacturing in the last several decades.

It is easy to become intrigued by the prodigality of the Great Valley, which yields much of the agricultural wealth for which California's Heartland has long been renowned.

But much of the output is grown with expensive irrigation water. Few of the scores of products (such as kiwi fruit, peaches and nuts) are those items which the spiraling ever-hungry population of the world basically needs to survive. To raise the essential items at price poor Third World customers could afford would doubtless necessitate federal subsidy. Some products (especially peaches) are being overproduced. And there is concern that others, such as almonds, rice and oranges, may be grown in surplus in the future.

So far, in contrast to the Southern California and the Bay Area, where much of the fertile lowlands have been overwhelmed by urbanization, production in the Central Valley has increased.

Countless thousands of acres can probably still be placed under irrigation by future California Water Project and Central Valley Project programs. Expansion is most probable on the west sides of the Sacramento and the San Joaquin and in the South End of the San Joaquin. But there is increasing opposition to additional public programs. Also, farming is increasingly a corporate affair.* There is concern over availability of water to flush salts from the soil, especially in the drier southern San Joaquin. Of current concern is the Kesterson drain proposal.

Future farming will assumedly become more highly mechanized, new crops will be introduced, cultivation will become more intensive and farm labor will decline.

Some significant shifts have already taken place, such as the decline of dairying on the northern West Side of the San Joaquin and the citrus expansion in the Kaweah Delta. Crops such as rice and cotton, which have been dependent upon federal policies and foreign markets, could be affected by changes.

**Figure 9-58.** This vanished sign reflects the Arvin *that was* before it became a Hispanic community. (dwl)

Among subregions of the Heartland, the Central Valley has lesser residential appeal than some.

While technologic advances make summer heat tolerable indoors, or in an air-conditioned automobile or a swimming pool (for those sufficiently unconcerned about the world fuel situation), the Valley is plagued for some months each summer when *some* afternoons "do not have too much edge on hell!"**

Considerable numbers of senior citizens, ordinarily local residents, are spending their retirement years in Central Valley communities. And more attractive cities, such as Redding, Chico, Modesto and Visalia, are luring many from coastal portions of metropolitan California.

There are unresolved problems, even as elsewhere in California and the nation.

Crime has increased. While much of the Valley has been spared from severe earthquake damage (some are less assured after the Oroville earthquake in 1975) experienced in some parts of the Heartland, floods have not been entirely eliminated (evidenced at Yuba City in 1964 and Linda in 1986). Steadily, year by year, the pall of smog worsens—too little local concern is seen yet. The long-range effects of fertilizers and pesticides pose another problem. And what will the displaced farm labor do as mechanization continues?

The Central Valley, as elsewhere in the Heartland, has sundry other problems of a cultural nature.

---

* Much of the Nader volume, *Politics of Land* (Grossman, 1971 and 1973), edited by R.C.Fellmeth, concerns the Central Valley.
** The Valley is *not* that continuously hot in summer. Extreme heat periods tend to be broken by milder weather while early mornings and evenings are often pleasant.

The fringes of central districts have sometimes deteriorated. Ethnic groups, will still less numerous than in larger metropolitan centers, are understandably dissatisfied. Meanwhile too little intelligent planning has been implemented on urban fringes, so that some of the richest farmland has been taken needlessly for urban sprawl. An acute problem is the antagonism that exists too often between county and city officials, "almost" everywhere. The former (especially the supervisors) tend to be elderly (and often retirees), conservative and rurally-oriented and more or less oblivious to the urban problems.

Cultural amenities tend to be fewer than in California's "big" metropolitan areas.

But as populations in the Valley increase, the disparities are decreasing. Many outdoor enthusiasts in metropolitan Southern California and the Bay Area visit friends and relatives, especially in the more northern reaches of the Sacramento Valley, and yearn for employment opportunities that would allow them to escape their own urban congestion. Too often they fail to realize that inmigration is creating the conditions from which they wish to escape.

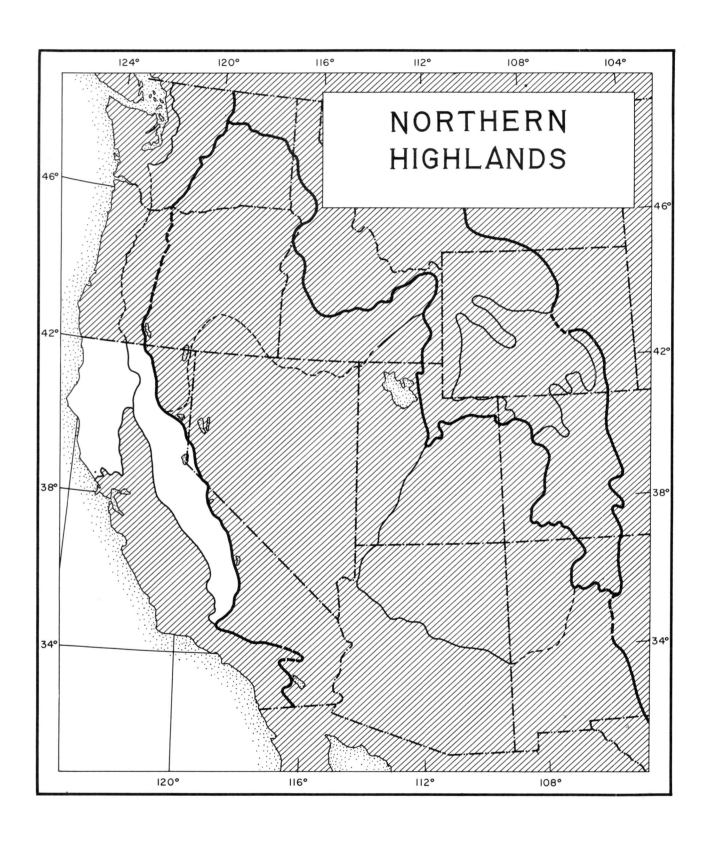

# PART THREE

NORTHERN
HIGHLANDS

# THE
# NORTHERN
# HIGHLANDS

The Northern Highlands, surrounding the Heartland of California in the shape of an inverted letter "U", is peripheral to much that happens in the state.* It encompasses a fourth of the state's area and half of the state's 58 counties, entirely or partially. Yet its largest city, Eureka, is not among the fifty largest cities of California, and its residents comprise less than a tenth of the population of the Golden State.

Mountains provide the most salient features on the surface of the earth. In North America few ranges excel the Sierra Nevada, the Cascade and the Klamath for scenic loveliness and dramatic landscapes. Many sojourners have thrilled to the impressive spectacle of Mt. Shasta from I-5 (Fig. 11-1) or the awesome east wall of the Sierra Nevada from U.S. 395 (Fig. 3-5).

The Klamath and the Sierra Nevada share a certain physiographic similarity; it would be difficult to find a companion range more unlike them in structure than the Cascade. In their present form all three, of course, are of recent geologic evolution. The name of the latter range has in fact been given to the orogeny, the Cascadian Revolution, that uplifted most of the majestic mountains of this earth. Without its more prominent cones, Lassen Peak and Mt. Shasta, the southern Cascade of California would not belong in such queenly company. These peaks rise thousands of feet above the surrounding tablelands. The Sierra Nevada, by contrast, is one of the world's most-renowned fault blocks, while the Klamath is known more for its deep canyons although it too has some alpine summits scoured by ice. The northern Coast Ranges, generally higher than the southern Coast Ranges, are well wooded but lack the grandeur of the Sierra, the Cascade and the Klamath. Their membership in the association results from location, resources, and nature of utilization.

The Northern Highlands has multiple uses. From its snowfields come the rivers that provide domestic water for Los Angeles, San Francisco and a host of smaller cities. Increasingly, through the Central Valley Project and the California Water Project, its surplus waters are utilized in the Heartland. The Great Central Valley, without the water that accumulates in these mountains, could not be a great agricultural empire. Redwood, fir, and pine from the montane forests have built cities while hydroelectric power from falling water has fostered industrial growth. To the mountains for health, relaxation and pleasure, go numerous thousands of Californians and many visitors, to hike, ski and fish—or merely to relax amidst the splendor of alluring summits.

California is divided into two realms by the eastern segments of these Highlands (i.e., the Southern Cascade and the Sierra Nevada). To the west are the Heartland (Chs. 6 to 9) and the Northwest (Ch. 12), which benefit from the influence of moisture-laden Pacific air masses. To the east are the dry Intermontane lands (Chs. 2 to 5), hampered by rain-shadow location. The Highlands still form multiple barriers to surface transport. Only a relatively few passes carry heavy traffic flow. Substantial populations serve, and are supported by, interstate highway and rail movement through the Highlands. Yet the largest gateway or pass-site functions tend to occur in more amenable adjacent lowlands (at such points as Bakersfield, Sacramento and Redding).

Some inhabitants within the Highlands (and beyond, in the Intermontane Region) have felt themselves so apart from California's Heartland that upon occasion they have talked of secession; in some quarters lowlanders are tolerated rather than welcomed. Some highlanders look askance at expanding recreation-oriented trade even when it is the single source of income apart from pensions. Nor are water resource developments always supported enthusiastically even when there are concomitant benefits such as tax revenue, flood control, constructional monies or vacation facilities. In brief, isolationism is favored by the types of residents who remain in, or migrate into, the Highlands. This is a realm where native-born Anglo-Saxon Californians are particularly dominant.

---

* Authors of Anglo-American geography texts have associated these Highlands with the lower-lying land to the west and south (i.e., The Heartland) in a single region. While there is merit in delineation of extensive portions of the earth as regions, the physical contrast alone between these loftier mountains and the plains of the Heartland seems sufficient reason to give them separate status within the study of a single state.

**Figure 10-1.** Many alpine enthusiasts consider eastern Kings Canyon National Park one of the most scenic parts of the Sierra Nevada. Seen here are Lower Rae Lake with Dragon Peak and Mt. Rixford. (Joseph Wampler)

Chapter Ten

# THE SIERRA NEVADA*

* This chapter has been reviewed by Bruce E. Bechtol, California State University, Chico. It was reviewed earlier by the late John E. Kesseli, University of California, Berkeley.

# THE SIERRA NEVADA

The Sierra Nevada is sublime. When the gods bestowed on these mountains such attributes as Lake Tahoe, one of the world's lovelier alpine lakes; Mt. Whitney (14,495 ft.), long the nation's highest summit (Mt. McKinley is higher, of course); Yosemite Valley, acclaimed by some as the prime beauty spot of the hemisphere; the giant trees of Sequoia Park; a dozen deep chasms; and some of the most awe-inspiring examples of valley glaciation known to man—they dealt lavishly. This is a mountain range whose appeal and charm usually increase with one's knowledge. Full appreciation of the Sierra comes slowly, for much of the area is inaccessible except afoot or by pack animal.

A tremendous highland block, the Sierra Nevada extends more than 400 miles from Tejon Pass (in Los Angeles County) to the steep wall that rises above the southern borders of Lassen Park (map 10-1). Its width approximates 70 miles; near Lake Tahoe it is more than 80 miles but in the south less than 50. The range encompasses more than 27,000 square miles. On the west, the approach from the Great Central Valley into the Sierra foothills is sufficiently gradual that the stranger may be well into the range before he becomes aware of it. But on the east, its walls rise precipitously above three of California's four Intermontane lands (Part One).

## THE ARRANGEMENT

In introductory geography and geology classes the Sierra Nevada is often identified as a "textbook" example of the fault block (Chart 3-1).

Such elementary description fails to convey the intricate history of this complex highland, which includes a long background of sediment deposition, folding and faulting, volcanism, glaciation, uplift and erosion.

### Development

The genesis of the Sierra Nevada began with deposition of thousands of feet of sediment into a geosyncline. These particles came from the wearing away of the ancient highland mass. In succession over a long period of geologic time the following changes then occurred.

(1) Forces within the crust buckled the sedimen-

tary strata upward into folded layers; the deformation was accompanied by violent faulting. Evidence is seen today in the north-south parallelism of foothill terrain (reflected in the twisted shape of many reservoirs and highway routes).

(2) A major event in establishment of this ancestral Sierra was the intrusion beneath the sediments of a vast molten mass—it cooled to become several batholiths of impressive proportions. Now this light-hued granite, which forms the bulk of the range, imparts the gleaming "range of light" surfaces. Emplantment of gold within the Mother Lode also resulted at this time. These initial mountains were much lower than the contemporary Sierra; its creation was followed by a long period of calm, as if Mother Nature had been so wearied by the strain of her labor as to need a renewing of strength.

(3) Through millions of years the upfolded ridges, which were separated by downfolded troughs and fault basins were worn so low that the presently-dry lands of the Intermontane Region (Part One) were exposed to much more rain falling from Pacific-borne air masses. Prior to the wearing down of the highlands, however, their northern end was buried by lava flows. Thus we find evidence of past times in the quite-level interfluves and plateaus (Fig.10-5), such as the surface into which Yosemite Valley has been cut.

(4) The upbowing of the batholith, deprived of much of its sedimentary cover, commenced in the Eocene. As erosion continued the higher elevations were etched out to produce mountainous terrain. Uparching and erosion and volcanic activ-

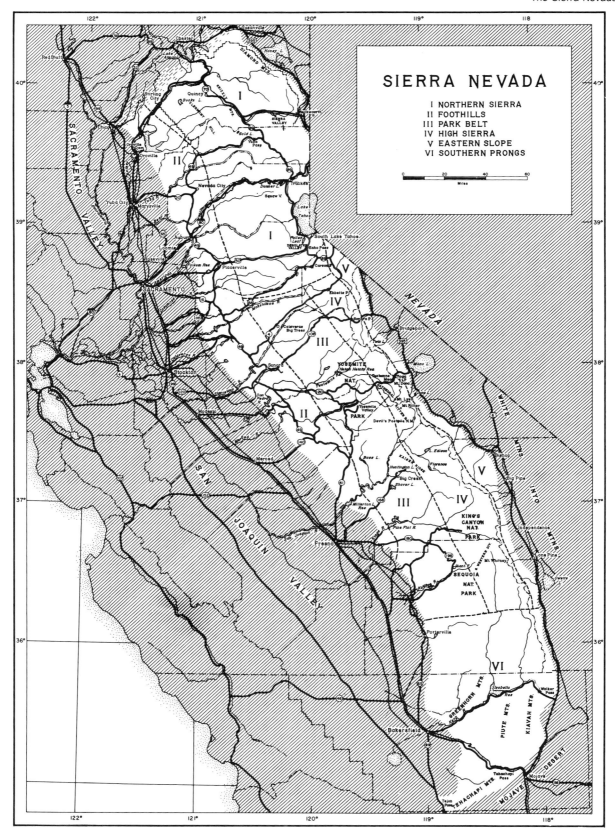

**Map 10-1.** The topographic and geologic Sierra Nevada extends from Los Angeles County northward to within sight of Lassen Peak. All but a single ridge (the Carson Range) is within California.

ity, largely restricted to the northern Sierra, continued intermittently during much of the Tertiary. Today the flows give color and variety to the terrain; they include the many flat-topped interfluves in the Foothills. Several are known as Table Mountain (several features are identically-named).

(5) Near the close of the Tertiary, the maximum uplift took place, concentrated in the east, so that the range began to assume its present unsymmetrical tilt. As this deformation ended, large-scale faulting occurred, coupled with the dropping of Owens Valley, to create the dramatic east face of the range. The uplift caused rivers to cut deeply into the subdued upland, thus creating contemporary stream canyons. Placer gold was deposited in the stream valleys. Present-day fault blocks and escarpments developed.

(6) Finally came the ice sculpture discussed next. Glaciation was caused partially by the increasing wetness and cold produced by the uplift.

## Ice Carving

The Sierra Nevada would be impressive even without the glaciation of the Great Ice Age. Because of ice sculpture there are the deep broad-floored canyons (Fig. 10-14), serrated summits, scores of lakes, spectacular waterfalls and other features that contribute majesty to the "range of light."

Most of the Sierra was not greatly affected by the repeated advances of the ice tongues down the canyons.

In the north, where summits were between 6500 and 7000 feet, only small cirque glaciers formed. But from Donner Pass southward into the canyon of the upper Kern, a distance of nearly 300 miles, glaciers filled scores of canyons. Some were only 10 to 15 miles long but others attained lengths of almost 60 miles. Around the crest between Lake Tahoe and Cathedral Range in Yosemite Park a small ice cap formed.

## Domes and Serrated Ridges

Today's Sierra Nevada is a complex fault-block that retains some vestiges, particularly around headwater areas, of ancient trellis drainage patterns associated with the ridge-and-valley character of its ancestral highlands.

Remnants of its earlier orogeny are also found in superimposed ranges, generally with northwest-southeast trend. The better known of these seg-ments are the contiguous Ritter and Cathedral ranges in the Yosemite area, Kaiser Ridge and the Great Western Divide.

The east wall rises, with en echelon fault facets, to the highest summits in the High Sierra around Mt. Whitney. At the northern end of the range, faults and differential tilting have produced three parallel blocks with east-facing scarps. From east to west there are the *Diamond* (Carson) Mountains, *Grizzly* Mountains and *Clermont Hill.* Although the eastern Sierra contains a maze of faults, they are often obscured by erosion and by alluvial deposits at the base of the range.

The Sierra Nevada contains only small remnants of the folded sedimentary rocks of the ancestral range. Granitics are far more widespread.

Sedimentaries are commonly found in the western foothills or the superimposed ranges mentioned above. The bulk of the exposed bedrock of the Sierra consists of granitoidal rocks. Weaknesses in the granitics, produced by faulting and other causes, have been responsible for the ease with which water and ice have etched out certain segments of the batholith. Elsewhere, lack of jointing accounts for such impressive monoliths as Half Dome, Tehipite Dome and Moro Rock. In the northern Sierra lavas and schists are responsible for darker rock colors.

The Sierra varies considerably in elevation.

Summits are generally under 7000 feet in the north; too, elevations seldom reach 6000 feet in the Greenhorn, the Piute, and the Tehachapi in the south. Seven out of the eleven peaks whose summits exceed 14,000 feet are found in proximity to Mt. Whitney.

Complemented by the work of valley glaciers, water has gouged deeply into the Sierra's gently inclined western slope.

The 14 major rivers* have produced a series of canyons that vary in depth from 1500 to more than 6000 feet in extreme instances. Whereas the slight tilt of the Sierran block is readily appreciated from interfluve ridges, the marked degree of dissection tends to obscure elsewhere the gentleness of the westward inclination throughout much of the range.

---

* From north to south, they are: Feather, Yuba, Bear, American, Cosumnes, Mokelumne, Calaveras, Stanislaus, Tuolumne, Merced, San Joaquin, Kings, Kaweah and Kern.

## FOOTHILLS TO ALPINE SUMMITS

With intricacy of surface, the greatest relief within the 48 conterminous United States, and length through 5 degrees of latitude, the Sierra Nevada is distinguished by considerable variation in weather and climate, which is reflected in its vegetation contrasts as well.

Relief is the principal determinant of vertical zonation. Other controls produce such effects as *ubac-adret* (sunny slope-shady slope) and a descending timberline northward.

### Rain Storms and Snow Flurries

The typical California pattern of moist winters and dry summers exists in the Sierra Nevada. Variations and extremes tend to be more exaggerated than in most of the state, of course. And as expected, a decrease of temperature with altitude takes place. Distribution of moisture is even more impressive than temperature gradient.

Less than three per cent of the annual precipitation falls in summer; three-fourths comes during the winter half year. Southward migration of the Hawaiian High permits an invasion by cyclonic storms from the north Pacific. The fronts usually pass to the north (as elsewhere in California) hence much of the moisture comes from the warmer tropical Pacific air masses within the warmer portion of the storms.

Close to the heaviest snowfall within the United States occurs in the upper reaches of the northern Sierra in the vicinity of Donner Pass—annual amounts fluctuate between 200 and 700 inches.

The maximum precipitation season, which lasts longer in the northern Sierra, usually occurs from November through April. The belt of heaviest snowfall (a north-south zone about 80 miles long), which has registered more than 30 feet in one month, lies between 3000 and 6500 feet elevation on western slopes. January is likely to receive the maximum; but with continued low temperatures, the snowpack commonly increases in depth through February. The deep pack is heavy, necessitating supported steep-roofed buildings, snow-sheds (on the Southern Pacific), and employment of much snowfighting equipment on main highway and rail lines. The weight of snowbanks at Blue Canyon in 1914 so bent a fence whose rails consisted of two-inch locomotive boiler flues that they fell out of their posts.

Vernal river flood stage generally is caused by rapid rise of spring temperature, accelerating the melting of snowbanks; violent thunderstorms are uncommon in the Sierra.

The worst winter floods usually occur in late December or January although their occurrence is infrequent.

Then warmer Hawaiian storms bring rain to higher altitudes. This is most likely if there has been unusually heavy snowpack earlier in the season (November and December). Although summer precipitation totals are limited, orographic storms are sometimes accompanied by lightning, which may cause fires in the dry forests.

Climatic zones in the Sierra vary with altitude; the several types inevitably display summer drought (Map, A-5).

The semiarid subtropical type, restricted to the lower reaches of more southerly stream canyons, has the hot dry summers typical of the southern Central Valley. The warm-summer subtropical (Mediterranean), representative of the Sacramento Valley, extends southward along the lower foothill uplands, narrowing southward. A broader belt of cooler-summer subtropical (not identified as such in Overview A) prevails in the upper foothills. Much of the forest land lies within the dry-summer middle latitude belt. Winters are colder but temperatures are seldom below zero at 5000 feet. That portion of the High Sierra that lies above timberline is described as alpine or tundra. Its mid-summer temperatures are akin to those of the arctic slope of Alaska but winter temperatures are not comparable. Unlike the Arctic there is no period with many weeks of continuous darkness.

### Pines and Chaparral

The natural vegetation of the Sierra Nevada reflects elevation and various climatic ramifications which result from its bulk and dissection (map C-1). The vegetation has been grouped into several zones: foothills, montane forest, subalpine forest, alpine meadows, and eastern slope.

In addition to other controls, the Foothill Zone is the product of repeated fires. Vegetation is principally grasses, shrubs and pines.

The zone begins at the eastern edge of the Great Central Valley and attains its upper limits around 4000 feet (lower in the north). Its lower portion is grasslands, parched during the dry summers in seared hues of straw-yellow (Fig. 10-13). Scattered

**Figure 10-2.** The open and sunny Montane Forest. Note the natural regrowth. (U.S. Forest Service).

amid the grasses are groves of interior live and Valley oak as well as numerous herbs and wildflowers.

The middle portion (between 1000 and 4000 feet elevation) contains chaparral with its various ceanothi and manzanita; chamise is especially common. This dwarf evergreen "forest," quite mixed, is generally found on rocky well-drained slopes. Most plants are markedly drought tolerant. The higher foothills, clue to transition into beautiful forests of higher elevation, contain an open digger pine-blue oak woodland, common between 3000 and 4000 feet (in the south). The digger is a shaggy tree, hardly fit company on the bases of foliage and coloring for the lordly pines of higher elevations.

Between 3000 and 7000 feet (north) and between 5000 and 7000 feet farther south is the Montane Forest. It is a southward continuation of the luxuriant coniferous forests of the Cascade Range, yet it seems a different forest—more open and light (Fig. 10-2).

While most of its trees are conifers, it includes such broadleaf as Kellogg oak, bigleaf maple, dogwood, and western azalea—most conspicuous in autumn when the leaves turn. The dogwood leafs, for example, become an almost dazzling red. Incense cedar, Douglas fir, and the pines especially the sugar, jeffrey and ponderosa (western yellow), are conspicuous at lower elevations. The ponderosa particularly flourishes on drier slopes and at lower altitudes. The Douglas fir, more abundant in the northern Sierra, prefers north-facing slopes. The white fir becomes a dominant at higher elevations. The Montane Forest includes the giant Sierra redwood, Sequoia dendron, whose groves are apt to contain ponderosa, sugar pine, and incense cedar.

The Sequoia is found only in the southern Sierra; it is sometimes confused by strangers with mature incense cedar. This Forest with its many variations, includes many different trees, shrubs, and herbs. It is decidedly a cone-bearing forest; sometimes, because of the prevalence of the ponderosa it is called the "yellow-pine forest." Glades and treeless slopes have numerous shrubs. Moist treeless slopes are particularly popular with such plants. Wet swamps and meadows support water-tolerant grasses, herbs and shrubs (Fig.10-3).

The Subalpine Forest rises from 5000 feet (8000 feet in the south) to timberline (Fig. 10-10).

The red fir, often in heavy stands, is perhaps the most characteristic tree. Other conifers include such pines as western white and lodgepole, mountain hemlock, and white fir. The aspen, most conspicuous in September, when its trembling leaves turn golden, is common. Yellow-green lichen are common on tree trunks. Significant modification takes place toward timberline. The pines (whitebark, foxtail and limber) are still representative, and the Sierran juniper is often prominent at timberline. Lodgepole pine and mountain hemlock flourish. At timberline the oft-contorted juniper and the whitebark pine offer evidence of deep snow and strong winds.

Above the forest, the Alpine Meadows are found generally from about 9000 feet to summit ridges and peaks (Fig. 10-5).

Besides grasses, they afford a garden of elfin plants and constitute one of the delights of a high-country visit. Two blue favorites are gentian and Palemonium. Whereas heather adds its purple, the Indian paintbrush red—there are many hues from snow white to deep blues and purples. Even

**Figure 10-3.** Sheep on summer pasture in northern Sierra. Grazing of animals in the range has declined in the twentieth century. (U.S. Forest Service)

such trees as pines and hemlock exist as stunted little sticks not over a foot in height. These plants must grow rapidly— the season is short. Green shoots appears before all the snow has melted. July brings a riot of color; late August seed pods and dried plants. The discerning eye finds plants wherever there is a bit of soil and a trace of water.

A badly fractured reproduction of the westside slopes, the Eastern Slope, tends to have narrower zones.

The montane forest reaches higher and is more open than on the west side (Fig.10-8). Jeffrey and ponderosa pine are conspicuous dominants. At its base, pinyon and juniper are found, often associated with cottonwoods and such vegetation from the east as sagebrush. And, especially in Mono County, the famed fall-color aspen. Because of steeper gradients and sparser cover than the western slope, the vegetation of the eastern slope seems more dissimilar than it actually is. The effects of thin soil, drought, and wider extremes of temperature contribute to the feeling of difference between east and west.

## SETTLEMENT

### Places of Refuge

Members of three aboriginal families occupied the Sierra Nevada. These were the *Penutian* (west), *Shoshone* (east) and *Washoe* (a Hokan people who lived in the Tahoe Basin and Carson Range). Little information remains regarding these pre-European inhabitants. Their numbers, their mode of life and even their migrations are uncertain.

In their lower reaches these highlands afforded relatively favored environments and held a much larger proportion of the pre-European populace than the subregion does of current California population.

Permanent abodes were commonly in the canyons, warmer than the uplands and better supplied with fish, game and water. Despite the rugged terrain, there was less cultural diversity than in such subregions as the Northwest. The summit of the range posed less of an economic or political barrier than it does today.

The Sierra provided varied resources for the Indians.

There was an abundance of acorns; the Foothills generally constituted a more attractive habitat than the floor of the Great Central Valley. Hill

tribes tended to be stabilized with limited need for migration in quest of food. The eastern Sierra provided the Shoshone with a more favorable residence than that of their relatives to the east in the Great Basin.

Mountain areas often have formed places of refuge for weaker people—this was the case with the Sierra Nevada.

For example the Washoe (Hokans) were apparently "senior residents" of the Golden State who had been driven into higher country by later arrivals. With the exception of Southern California, the Northwest and the Intermontane areas more reservations have been established in the Sierra than in other parts of the state.

### Fur Trappers, Then Pioneers

The Spanish did not know the Sierra Nevada; they had neither the economic necessity nor the numerical strength to penetrate so far from the coastal missions.

Even the present name of the range was given initially to the Coast Ranges around Monterey Bay. It has been assigned to the Sierra only on maps constructed since 1848. The Spanish had no influence upon later utilization of the range; even the names they assigned some rivers, as *Rio de los Reyes* (Kings), *Rio de las Plumas* (Feather) and *Rio de los Americanos* (American) have been Anglicized so that the Spanish origin is no longer apparent.

The Sierran passes (see section on Transportation) that became significant later in the economic growth of the state were first discovered by the fur trappers.

Jedediah Smith, after presumably camping along the Kings, first failed in a midwinter crossing from the west but later successfully crossed the Sierra en route to Salt Lake in 1827. The outstanding early exploration was achieved by Joseph Walker, who apparently crossed the range from the east via tributaries of the East Walker River in 1833. Most fur trappers were not literary; only limited records, usually diaries, remain of their travels.

Emigrant parties followed the fur trappers in the 1840s.

Their goal was not within the range itself but the lowlands to the west. Their guides sometimes were men who had gained knowledge as fur trappers. Some earlier groups utilized passes previously unknown to Americans. Thus the Bidwell party, the first company, used Sonora Pass in 1841. The first traverse of Donner Pass in 1844 is described in *The Opening of the California Trail*, edited by G.

R. Stewart. The name of this famous crossing, however, is derived from the tragic Donner party, which used it in 1846.

Efforts to objectively examine the Sierra Nevada began with the Fremont expedition of 1843-1845, guided by Joseph Walker and Kit Carson.

This group visited such places as the Tehachapi Range, Lake Tahoe and Kings Canyon. The official expedition map was published in 1848 and was the first to show such features as Carson, Walker and Kern rivers, Owens and Bonpland (Tahoe) lakes. During the later 1840's specific attempts were made to find the best routes for emigrants.

The extent and general features of the Sierra were known at the time of the Gold Rush.

Foothills settlement, a quest for more feasible transportation routes and appreciation for the High Sierra came afterwards. Knowledge was expanded by two federal railroad surveys: the Williamson survey of 1853 in the south and the Beckwith survey of 1854 in the north. Yosemite and Kings Canyon were appreciated by the early 1850s; Yosemite has been used for vacations since 1855.

Geologic investigation of the Sierra came relatively early and amplified the knowledge of cattlemen and miners.

California Geologic Survey parties explored and mapped the range for a generation, gaining knowledge of the High Sierra in 1864. Although specific areas had been mapped in the previous decade, orderly survey of the Sierra started in the 1890's. Since 1890 the United States Geologic Survey, the Sierra Club (following the efforts of John Muir and others) and the National Park Service have contributed much to the knowledge of the physical geography.

## Miners and Tourists

American settlement came to the Sierra with precipitous suddenness. Within two years after Marshall's discovery of gold on the American River in January 1848 there were perhaps 50,000 working miners in the range.

Many miners soon forsook mining for more certain livelihood, frequently outside the Sierra. But the effect of the Rush was momentous. California statehood was hastened and speedy urbanization of San Francisco, Sacramento, Stockton and Marysville materialized. Economic development was accelerated: banks, retail establishments, lumber-ing, transportation facilities, ranching and industry (especially in San Francisco).

Widespread creation of governmental agencies and services, as well as cultural activities, took place.

These activities included formation of mountain counties. Schools, theatres, churches, and newspapers materialized. Surely the Gold Rush left a legacy of artistic and literary richness.

By 1880 most of the Sierra was experiencing post-Rush population and economic decline.

Initially the boom camps commonly consisted of tents and rude shacks, often forming narrow ribbons along stream canyons; many were plagued by repeated fires. Within a generation some had vanished and many were crumbling. Most contemporary Sierran towns had their beginnings during the Rush. But many towns and entire counties have never reacquired the population they had in their early years.

Originally an adjunct of mining, lumbering has been a persistent source of livelihood.

As in the Northwest and the Southern Cascade, the history too often has been one of "mining" the forest. Like gold camps, some lumber towns have withered and vanished.

The steadiest source of livelihood in the subregion has been livestock ranching, which also had an early start.

Yet it has never been responsible for assemblage of sizable populations. Transhumance started in 1864, a drought year when cattle were taken to high meadows near the source of the San Joaquin River. Ranching, much more than mining, has stabilized the economy of the Sierra for nearly a century and a half.

The Gold Rush necessitated a hasty establishment of transportation facilities.

Crude trails across the Sierra were in regular use by 1850 and in the Foothills mostly, ferries were operating across rivers. For more than a century the subregion has had rail routes. Through commerce, like ranching, has continued to be an important factor in settlement stability.

The contribution of early recreation, albeit modest, was significant.

Lake Tahoe and Yosemite gained popularity during the late nineteenth century. Hydroelectric development also has tended to be a twentieth-century stimulant.

## LOCOMOTIVES AND AUTOMOBILES

Transportation has contributed much to utilization of the Sierra. Despite use since Gold Rush days and notwithstanding technological improvements, the range remains an impediment to east-west surface travel.

Conditions that contribute to this barrier effect include (1) continuity of summit height; (2) canyons (i.e., eroded surfaces, especially on the west side); (3) steep slopes; (4) winter storms (especially deep snow and heavy rains followed by landslides) and (5) ownership, especially federal land control. While the Sierra presents handicaps, its position athwart routes between Los Angeles and the Central Valley (i.e., the Tehachapi Mountains) and between central California and interior United States results in much surface traffic across the Sierra.

### Steam Horses and Diesels

The Sierra has been crossed by rail lines since the Southern Pacific (initially called the Central Pacific) extended its line eastward into Nevada.

This remained the single rail route eastward across the mountains (north of Tehachapi Pass) for the remainder of the nineteenth century. Although this line has been hampered by steep grades and heavy winter snowfall, which necessitated miles of snowsheds, it has been favored by its directness between the Bay Area, Sacramento and interior United States.

The Southern Pacific extended its second line across the range in the 1870's when it built its Sunset Route southward through the San Joaquin Valley and across Tehachapi Pass in 1876. This traverse, unhampered by deep snow or high elevation, was made difficult because of faulting and steep slopes on the northwest face of the Tehachapi (Fig. 10-11).

The feasibility of the Feather River Canyon for an east-west crossing was recognized in the 1860's. But the tortuous nature of the Feather canyon seemed to impose impossible construction problems. Hence it was not until 1909 that another company, the Western Pacific, made a crossing of the Sierra at Beckwourth Pass. Its line is not handicapped by heavy snow as at Donner Summit, but rain sometimes leads to landslides (Fig. 10-31). The Western Pacific (now Union Pacific), shortest trackage of the major western rail systems, connects central California with the Middle West via Salt Lake City.

### Wagon Trails, Even a Few Freeways

The Sierra is crossed by ten east-west highway routes but only half of them are kept open throughout the year. Generally these passages were discovered before 1850 and long were used as crude wagon trails.*

Routes tend to ascend rapidly the steep eastern slopes of the Sierra, then descend the west slopes gradually, following the relatively gentle interfluves. Much improvement has occurred since the Model T days of the 1920's but most highways remain winding two-lane roads with steep grades. Such major crossings as Interstate 80, Ca. 58 and Interstate 5 have become freeways; only portions of U.S. 50 have achieved this expressway status.

East-west travel across the southern half of the Sierra is hampered because many of the state highway routes, utilizing higher passes, are seasonally blocked by snow (Fig.10-9). In midwinter no highway between Carson Pass (Ca.88) and Ca. 178 ( Walker Pass) remains open all winter. In fact there is no highway between Tioga Pass (Ca. 120) and Ca. 178. In this portion of the range lies the High Sierra, including California's largest wilderness area, discussed later. Residents of the San Joaquin Valley around Fresno complain about the absence of a direct route east.

Justifiably most of the commercial carriers as well as the majority of private vehicles utilize relatively few highways. In the north, most of the traffic follows Interstate 80 or U.S. 50 and in the south Interstate 5 or Ca. 58.

### The Crossings

Extremely low-elevation passes are absent, although Tejon (4183 feet), Tehachapi (3988 feet) and Walker (5250 feet) are sufficiently low and far enough south that they are seldom closed by snow even briefly. **

---

*The Feather River highway was not opened until 1937. This arduous engineering achievement in places involved lowering of workmen into the canyon with ropes. Previously, travelers from the adjacent Sacramento Valley took the old wagon road across the uplands to Quincy; this way was closed by heavy snow in winter.

** California passes tend to be appreciably lower than those in the Colorado Rockies, where paved roads reach the summits of Mt. Evans (14,260 feet) and Pikes Peak (14,110 feet). However the base of the Sierra lies thousands of feet lower than the base of Rocky Mountain ranges. The highest pass in California is Whitney (13,500 feet), crossed by the foot trail to the summit of Mt. Whitney.

422 The Northern Highlands

California's highest automobile pass, Tioga (9941 feet), seasonally forms the eastern entry into Yosemite Park; until recent decades a 22-mile stretch of Tioga Road represented a modified wagon trail of the 1880's. Passes northward from Tioga to Echo (U.S.50) are higher: Sonora (9626 ft.), Ebbetts (8731 ft.) and Carson (8573 ft.). From Echo (7382 ft.) northward they tend to be lower: Donner (7089 ft.), Yuba (6701 ft.) and Beckwourth (5221 ft.). Heavy snows necessitate the use of large motorized equipment to keep most of these latter crossings open in winter.

The remainder of this chapter will be concerned with subdivisions of the range. These units will be considered successively: (1) **High Sierra**; (2) **Eastern Slope**; (3) **Southern Prongs**; (4) **Park Belt**; (5) **Foothills**; (6) **Northern Sierra** (see maps 10-1, 10-3, 10-4 and 10-5).

## THE HIGH SIERRA

The true alpine country, the High Sierra, is a paradise for the nature lover; it is a relatively unspoiled wilderness uncrossed by major highway. Yet with continued population growth within California the area is, as one writer has expressed it, an unspoiled wilderness "only by courtesy." Only the efforts of organizations of sportsmen and outdoors enthusiasts have prevented ravishment by commercial interests such as the group that has proposed a freeway running the length of the High Sierra.

### Sky Country

While the High Sierra lacks definite geographic limits, for its advocates it has positive meaning: it is the alpine wilderness.

It can be defined as the alpine belt above the continuous forests—the central one third of the Sierra. It extends from Sequoia Park (south) into Alpine County (north). It is, according to description, the area that was covered by a Pleistocene ice cap and where summits exceed 12,000 feet (Fig. 10-4)—in short it includes all of California's 14,000 foot peaks except Mt. Shasta and White Mountain Peak.

### Polished Rock and Snowbanks

The High Sierra represents one of America's finest examples of scouring by mountain glaciers.

Hence there are over 1200 lakes and tarns; pater noster (bead-like chain) arrangement of lakes along its U-shaped canyons is common. There are scores of rapids and cascades along its streams but few waterfalls. Today the High Sierra glistens with cleanswept granite of lighter hues—ice re-

**Figure 10-4.** Mt. Lyell and environs in winter. Scalloped and serrated crests in the High Sierra are suggestive of the Swiss Alps. (San Francisco Public Utilities District, photo by Marshall Maxom).

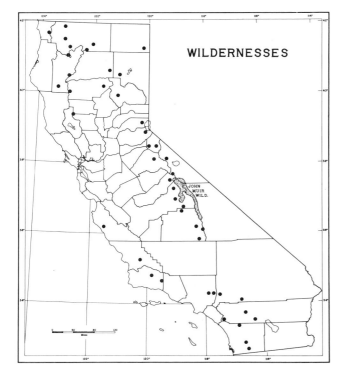

**Map 10-2.** While wildernesses are found in all of California's loftier highland areas, the amount of the High Sierra thus protected is impressive.

moved much of the loose or broken rock. The "Little Ice Age" of recent centuries left a few dozen glacial remnants. Vistas include serrated ridges and glacial-grooved canyons (Fig.10-4), capped by skies whose blueness seems unmatched in populated portions of lowland California.

The High Sierra, climatically, presents striking seasonal contrast: wintry blasts as opposed to the serenity of clear summer skies.

But in summer there are severe thunderstorms at times while frost is a threat even in July or August. Snowfall tends to be less than at lower elevations in the range—summits are sometimes swept clear by strong winds. Yet along north-facing slopes and in canyons snow lingers so long that banks can be found in sheltered places even in August.

Trees are apt to be stunted, even prostrate.

Their number is limited; dense stands are uncommon. Tree-line varies from 10,000 feet (north) to over 11,000 feet (south). Vegetation characteristically consists of herbacious plants—perhaps a third are indigenous to California. Various sedges and grasses prevail in wet meadows.

Fauna are found only in small numbers— the High Sierra is a harsh environment.

Animals include the alpine chipmunk, cony, marmot and mountain sheep (but only a small number of sheep remain). Birds are seasonal residents save for the rosy finch, which flitters about even in winter.

### The Wildernesses

The High Sierra is a public domain.

Nearly half of it is contained in the back country of three national parks (Sequoia, Kings Canyon and Yosemite). The remainder is under the supervision of the U.S. Forest Service, including all or parts of six national forests.*

The Service has long recognized the desirability of keeping portions of national forests as unspoiled wilderness and thus established primitive areas. Renamed "wildernesses", they now exist in a number of California mountain areas (see Chs. 2, 6, 7, 11 and 12).

The Forest Service began establishing primitive areas in 1930.

In time 78 such areas were established in the nation, including about a twelfth of the total national forest acreage. Within these realms commercial lumbering, roads, wheeled vehicles and landing of aircraft have been prohibited. The primitive areas are intended to provide aesthetic, mental and physical values for their visitors. On the deficit side their use has been limited to the hardy few, while the nation loses their potential lumber, minerals and waterpower.

Eventually Congress recognized the wilderness concept through enactment of the Wilderness Act of 1964.

This legislation provides that the wildernesses (i.e., primitive areas) will be administered so as to keep them unimpaired for future use and enjoyment. However, the Act forbids the designation of wilderness except through congressional approval, which makes additional areas harder to establish than in the past. But once confirmed by

---

* There is a basic difference in purpose and philosophy behind national parks, national monuments, and national forests. The National Forest Act of 1891 allows the President to establish a national forest by proclamation. Later legislation expanded the purpose and scope of the forests. Supervision of the forests is based upon the concept of multiple use (i.e., lumbering, mining, grazing, hydroelectricity and recreation). The concept appears simple but it is difficult to apply because of contradictory interests and pressure groups. National parks are more singular in purpose—they are created to preserve scenic value for public enjoyment. Congressional approval is necessary to create a new park. By contrast, under the Antiquities Act of 1906 the President can decree land as "national monuments" to protect historic relics and physical wonderlands.

**Figure 10-5.** Great Western Divide (horizon) and the Kern Plateau westward from Mt. Whitney reveals an area of limited dissection despite the Kern Canyon. Contrast with Fig. 10-4. (U.S. Forest Service)

Congress, wilderness areas enjoy freedom from exploitive pressures that once threatened them.

Under the legislation the thirteen previously-established California wild and wilderness areas became *"Wilderness System Charter Areas."* These contain 1 1/4 million acres. Nearly all of these had originally been set aside in 1931 as primitive areas, then reclassified in the 1950's and 1960's as wild or wilderness areas according to their size. Charter Sierran Wildernesses included *John Muir, Mokelumne, Hoover, Minarets,* and *Dome Land.* A sixth, *Desolation,* was added later.

The (federal) California Wilderness Act of 1984 added million acres to the state's designated wildernesses.

Most of this acreage lies within Yosemite, Sequoia, and Kings Canyon national parks in sectors that might otherwise be subject to road construction and other "defacements" of the natural environment. Besides enlargement of some existing reserves the Act created 23 new wildernesses, almost half of them in the Sierra Nevada. Counting segments of the three national parks, wildernesses now form a near-continuous swatch between Carson and Walker passes.

California's largest wilderness, the John Muir, contained 504,000 acres prior to 1984. An additional 81,000 acres is now included.

This reserve, which is mostly bare rock country, encompasses much of both sides of the main Sierran crest from the vicinity of Mammoth Lakes southward to the eastern boundary of Sequoia National Park near Mt. Whitney.

**Now A Winter Playground Too**

The High Sierra long served only as a summer playground. Winter sports were limited by isolation and the absence of lodges and other facilities.

Hiking, mountain climbing, fishing and "packing in" (from lower elevation pack stations) are still principal forms of recreation. Most of the visitors are merely nature lovers who come individually or as couples, families or groups to "escape" civilization in this serene setting—a lesser number are fishers or rock climbers. During the summer when the lower Sierra is parched, the high country is still spring-like, with blue skies and green meadows, shimmering lakes, fresher air and scenic grandeur. But in the past several decades increased winter cross-country skiing has taken place.

While transmontane High Sierra highways are lacking, numerous approach roads permit the rapid hiker to gain alpine summits within hours after leaving his vehicle.

A score of roads westward from U.S. 395 bring the visitor much closer to the summits than do the western approaches which number slightly more than half those from the east. Because of the absence of highways across the High Sierra residents of Southern California have a near-monopoly on eastern approaches. Western approaches tend to be used by people from central and northern California as well as some from southern California.

**Figure 10-6.** Enroute to Palisade Glacier. Up the trail through Bigpine Canyon, past the chain of seven pater noster lakes. This glaciated landscape is accessible afoot or on horseback. (U.S. Forest Service)

**Figure 10-7.** The many lakes of the High Sierra are the home of the golden trout, California's "state fish." One is curious, "Did the lady have all the luck?" (Joseph Wampler).

A network of lateral walking trails from the canyons laces the High Sierra.

Most of the westside trails were constructed by stockmen in the nineteenth century.

The 13-mile *Mt. Whitney Trail* was opened in 1904; the present crest-crossing via Whitney Pass was completed in 1930. The 48-mile *High Sierra Trail,* built by the National Park Service in 1930-1931, extends from the Giant Forest Highway in Sequoia Park across the Kern-Kaweah Divide to join the Muir Trail.

The *John Muir Trail* is the stellar High Sierra pathway, completed in 1932.

Envisaged by a pioneer member of the Sierra Club (T. Solomon) its construction was directed by the State Engineer, with the assistance of the Forest Service and the Sierra Club. The route across lofty Forester Pass (13,200 ft,) was not finished until 1938. Extending 212 miles from Yosemite Valley to Mt. Whitney, the Trail is jointly maintained by the Forest Service and the National Park Service. The Muir Pass-Mather Pass portion (west of Bishop) is conceded to be one of the most scenic sectors, vying with the Sequoia Park portion, which includes the highest pass (Forester) as well as the Kings-Kern Divide and Mt. Whitney. Access to the Muir Trail is provided by 38 laterals that connect it with automotive routes.

The principal mode of travel in the High Sierra is hiking; for shorter jaunts a person can travel virtually unencumbered by a pack.

Yet so popular has the area become that numbers are limited by permits. The high country has a varied appeal and offers 50 trail passes and 350 miles of improved paths above 10,000 feet elevation.

July and August are the best months in the high country. By July streams are low enough to ford and the early wildflowers are abloom. August is the most popular month; there are late flowers. Of the thousands who signed the register atop Mt. Whitney in a recent summer, hundreds did so on Labor Day alone!

Combined hiking-camping pack trips have popularity with groups.

A rate of 1 to 2 miles an hour is possible with pack animals. The problem of grazing by pack animals is of increasing concern. Suggested methods of grass protection have included fencing, signs, meadow reseeding, restricted grazing, time limits, rotated meadow use, route planning for larger groups and feed importation. Since three fourths of the High Sierra lies west of the principal crest, most camping is on that side. Only a few thousand (2000) pack and riding animals are available for high country trips during August, usually necessitating reservations months in advance.

Rock climbing is restricted to the more agile and

physically fit. Some find challenge in climbing the maximum number of high summits; others are satisfied with climbs that provide the maximum vantage of alpine scenery.

This lofty land is a paradise for the fly-fisher.

It offers snow-fed creeks and lakes with sufficient brush to shade the water, abundance of fish, and relatively few fishermen.

This is trout country: land of the rainbow, golden, cut-throat, Lock Leven and Eastern. The bright-hued golden, California's state fish, has its home in the timberline water bodies (Fig. 10-7). In *Waters of the Golden Trout Country* McDermand lists over a hundred high-country trout lakes and indicates the types of fish in each. There are 1200 lakes an acre or more in size above 10,000 feet. Among the streams, the Kern has long been famous for its trout.

### Winter Wonderland

The High Sierra is a snowy land, still visited by relatively few for eight months out of every year.

It is exciting to enter this winter wonderland, entirely blanketed by a white coat save for the green hues of the conifers and barren rock out-crops. Unobstructed by man, nature in the High Sierra maintains a balance between the hunters (coyotes, hawks and owls) and the hunted (rabbits, mice and rats).

Snowshoes once provided solution for winter travel for those few who had to go to the High Sierra as those Southern California Edison power crews to Florence Lake. Now cross-country skiing has gained popularity with the venturesome hardy.

Winter in the High Sierra was described by O. Bartholomew in the Sierra Club Bulletin (Vol.15). Bartholomew stored 11 caches of food during the autumn, then in the winter of 1929 skied from Lone Pine to Yosemite, using special skis and a six-pound tent. He experienced no temperatures be-low zero above 11,000 feet during his trip and nowhere found snow more than four feet deep. In January he found the summit of Mt. Whitney barren; strong winds restrict snow depth around the heights and account for the relatively "high" temperatures encountered. Even above 10,500 feet, he found many flowing creeks. He concluded that with a knowledge of mountaineering and with proper clothing the High Sierra poses no great hazards for winter travel.

### THE EASTERN SLOPE

Often considered to be a straight, precipitous fault face, the Eastern Slope rises abruptly from the desert country to the east (Fig. 3-5). This is almost true southward from Bishop; north of Bishop the eastern front becomes more complex.

In such places as the Carson Range and the Sweet-water Range (north of Bridgeport) it includes a series of re-entrants. Canyons of the two larger streams, the Walker and Carson rivers, tend to have a lesser gradient eastward.

Coupled with proximity to U.S. 395, the abrupt-ness of portions of the eastern Sierran front makes it accessible to those many more outdoors folk who like their rugged country in easier doses than the High Sierra.

Accordingly it is a much frequented vacation land for those who tour by automobile. A score of well-maintained lateral access roads, varying in length from three to 20 miles, makes some scenic country available from U.S. 395. Some locales become congested (especially during summer and winter holidays).

### Camping, Fishing—and Sprawl

The Eastern Slope is one of the more frequented highland areas in the West; tourism has become "big business" here.

Varied recreational use prevails, with concentra-tion in canyons, upon lakes and along streams. Visitors are far more numerous here than in the High Sierra. Many resorts and small communities depend upon tourism.

Sports fishing in this part of the Sierra suffers from too many fisherfolk. Few trout streams in the nation are more heavily fished; despite heavy annual stocking, the individual catch compares unfavorably with the High Sierra.

A limited number of water bodies are available for boating. These include Twin, June, Mammoth and Sabrina lakes. Swimming is popular at most of these spots on summer afternoons.

Many thousands visit the Eastern Slope on sum-mer weekends and facilities become congested.

There are numerous facilities. Much of the area is within national forests and many camping spaces are available. Considerable use is made of house trailers and even more of recreational vehicles. Mammoth Lakes, Twin Lakes, the Reversed Creek (June Lake) Area and Lone Pine Creek are espe-cially favored.

**Figure 10-8.** Camping beside Rush Creek. Many Californians, as well as out-of-staters, take advantage of the accessibility of national forest campgrounds along the Eastern Slope of the Sierra. (U.S. Forest Service)

**Figure 10-9.** Alpine County, acclaimed the "Switzerland of California," is the least populous of the 58 counties. Seen here is the locale of Carson Pass (8573 ft.) on Ca. 88, now kept open except during the most severe winter storms (Mary Hill).

A score of commercial packers have ranch head-quarters at the base of the eastern front.

They reflect the significance the area has as an outfitting center for high-country trips. The "pack train express" is less expensive—a pack train from a larger station follows a regular daily route. Thus it sometimes possible to have camping equipment delivered at a specific spot while the individual goes afoot without burden.

Use of the Eastern Slope has much accelerated for winter sports.

Adequate snow is more assured here than in Southern California mountains. Forty years ago *Mammoth Mountain* was unknown. Now this 11,000-foot peak is the most-frequented ski spot in the nation. Facilities include lodges, several double chair lifts and a ski school.

Recreation has created two foci of permanent settlement.

***Mammoth*** and ***June Lake*** each now has a "year-round" population of 2000, swollen "in season" (especially holidays, both winter and summer, by many thousands). "Sprawl", suggestive of a miniature Paradise or Clear Lake (Ch. 12) describes both communities.

### Alpine County

The economic problems that have afflicted some of the Sierra Nevada for decades are dramatized in Alpine County.

During decades when California's population was increasing rapidly, some Sierran counties were either stagnant or even experiencing actual decline. But since 1970 Alpine County has doubled its population (to 1000!).

Settlement of this portion of the range commenced with the Gold Rush.

Alpine County was formed in 1864 when mining was the principal source of California income; thus establishment of this remote entity seemed valid. There was a silver boom south of present-day Markleeville and the original county place, Silver Mountain City, had a population of 3000. After the boom collapsed, county population dwindled. Briefly, Alpine forests supplied timbers for the Comstock Lode in Nevada.

Superlative scenery and pleasant summer weather are not sufficient compensations for geographic isolation.

Despite access eastward to U.S. 395, much of the county is secluded half of each year from California hence its residents must look eastward to Nevada for many goods and services. While recreation is an important seasonal source of livelihood, mining, lumbering and livestock ranching also contribute to local incomes.

***Markleeville*** is the diminutive county seat. It is a one-street town of less than a hundred people in a tiny pine-sloped basin at 5500 feet elevation. Its small one-story courthouse suggests a rural

**Figure 10-10.** Pine Creek Mine near Bishop. This operation has been the major tungsten producer in the United States. (Union Carbide Nuclear Division of Union Carbide Corporation, photo by B.Carl Huddleston).

schoolhouse. The county has no doctor, dentist, barber, movie theatre or practicing attorney. Nearby *Grover Hot Springs,* however, provides recreational opportunities.

## Power From Falling Water

East-flowing Sierran streams are small in volume but have the advantage of steep gradients along their upper reaches within the Eastern Slope. Thus there is waterpower potential.

Rights to the flow of numerous creeks belong to Los Angeles Department of Water and Power, which has constructed plants also in Owens Gorge east of the Sierra and southward along the Los Angeles Aqueduct (Ch.3).

North of the area of Los Angeles activity, private power companies have long utilized the gradient of several creeks and of the Truckee River.

Energy development has been consolidated into two firms, California Electric Power Company and Sierra Pacific Power Company. Sierra Pacific supplies the larger communities of western Nevada with power generated along the Truckee. California Electric originated with the demand for electricity at gold-boom Tonopah (in 1904). But for many years its principal markets have been in southeastern California. *

## Tungsten but No Gold

The Sierra Nevada has proved a major source of few minerals save gold from its Foothills. As exception is Pine Creek Mine north west of Bishop, the nation's chief source of tungsten (Fig. 10-10).

Since the mine is high (above 11,000 feet) on the Eastern Slope, ore is trucked to the modern mills at the base of the range via spectacular switchbacks.** Elsewhere, the Leviathan Mine in Alpine County has produced sulphur, which has been used in smelting copper ore at Yerington, Nevada.

## THE SOUTHERN PRONGS

Extending southward from the High Sierra to Tejon Pass, the Southern Prongs links the Sierra with the Transverse and Coast ranges (map 10-1 and B-1).

For many Californians this lower portion of the range with its pastoral scenes does not conjure the usual image of the Sierra Nevada. Although two of the four principal Sierran crossings (Tehachapi and Tejon passes) are here, elsewhere much of the Southern Prongs is little known.

As noted earlier, the Sierra Nevada is not a "simple" fault block. At both the south and north ends of the range parallel blocks replace the single mass. The units of the Southern Prongs are : (1) *Greenhorn* (west); (2) *Piute* (middle) (3) *Kiavah*— this is the continuation of the High Sierra main crest (4) from Tehachapi Pass southward the blocks merge into a single anticlinal structure, the Tehachapi Range.

Summit elevations of 5000 to 9000 feet are typical; the Southern Prongs is appreciably lower than the High Sierra. The whole landscape has been eroded into a maze of slopes with many craggy ridges. Besides the principal canyon, the Kern, there is also a series of little intermontane basins.

The Southern Prongs is drier and lower than more northerly portions of the Sierra. The altitude of timberline is higher here than the summit hence montane forests ascend ridgetops and alpine meadows are lacking. Groves of valley oak are typical on the western slopes of the Greenhorn and the Tehachapi. Chaparral is widespread whereas desert vegetation, rising upon eastern slopes, is particularly prevalent in the Kiavah. Spring is the verdant season, as elsewhere in California. Seared countrysides occur during the long drought period—dust prevails until late fall. Some winter moisture comes as snow, but a considerable portion falls as rain.

Briefly, due to a gold rush in the middle 1850's, the Southern Prongs formed the economic center of Kern and Tulare counties.

Mining was focused along the Kern River and in the Greenhorn Mountains. Kernville was the principal camp. After the rush subsided many residents moved into the southern San Joaquin Valley and Southern Prongs towns languished.

---

* California Electric (now an affiliate of Southern California Edison) was earlier called Nevada-California Power. Beginning in 1905 four generating plants were constructed along Bishop Creek. Lake Sabrina is the largest of three artificial reservoirs that regulate flow. Plants are so staggered along the creek as to permit maximum hydrostatic head between each successive generator; the steep gradient of the Eastern Slope is helpful. To assure a post-gold boom market, local firms in the eastern Los Angeles Basin were absorbed. Its market area now includes a portion of western Nevada, eastern Los Angeles Basin and the Colorado Desert. An interlacing transmission system joins various communities and a number of steam plants supplement power from water-driven generators.

** Markets for tungsten expanded with the growth of the aerospace industry and its use of heat-resistant steels. Wolframite, the common tungsten ore, is usually found in low concentrations in granitic rocks. Another important source has been northeast of Bishop in the Benton Range, where production has been less regular than at Pine Creek. The Bishop District has collectively yielded tungsten worth $100 million.

The Prongs' modest population (about 15,000) is supported today by sundry activities—hillside grazing, mining, much through commerce, a little farming in the basins, recreation, lumbering and hydroelectricity.

Cattle ranching is more common on western slopes; much livestock is moved seasonally to irrigated alfalfa fields in the San Joaquin Valley. The drier Kiavah has limited use. There has been a little lumbering; Johnsondale near the Kern was once a company-owned pine producer.

An important contribution to the Southern Prongs economy is made by water, particularly along the Kern. Both Southern California Edison and Pacific Gas and Electric generate hydroelectricity.

Construction of Isabella Dam (see Ch.9) led to a Kern boom based on recreation. Now there is much boating, fishing, and camping; the Southern Prongs is relatively accessible to the millions in Southern California. An assemblage of lodges and cafes has appeared. Sports fishing centers on the Lake and farther north along the Kern. Summer cabins have been erected within the montane forest belt, especially by residents of the area around Bakersfield who desire refuge from San Joaquin summers.

Residents of the southern San Joaquin ski in the Greenhorn if snow permits. Likewise real estate ventures to entice Southern Californians are conspicuous—terms such as "hideaway" and "speculative rural acreage" have been employed.

Use of the Tehachapi tends to be distinctive for the Sierra.

Besides traffic flow across Tehachapi and Tejon passes (Fig. 10-11) there is ranching (beef and grains) in Tehachapi Valley as well as the manufacture of cement at Monolith.

Originally designed to provide cement for the construction of the Los Angeles Aqueduct, the plant has been a long-time producer. A second plant now operates near Gorman.

Much of the Range is a vast private domain, Tejon Ranch, used for livestock ranching and grain farming (Fig. 10-13). These operations tended to negate recreational development, now being considered, to include summer homes. The Tejon, a quarter-

**Figure 10-11.** An engineering miracle of the 1870's, the Tehachapi Loop utilizes 28 miles of trackage to ascend 2735 feet in 16 "air miles." This route enables two transcontinental railroads entry into central California (Santa Fe Southern Company, photo by Dorman).

**Figure 10-12.** Dwarf fruit orchard, Techachapi Basin, from Ca. 58. View west. (dwl).

**Figure 10-13.** Beef cattle grazing in the Tehachapi Mountains. These grasslands are part of the sizable Tejon Ranch (Tejon Ranch Corporation).

million acre estate (partly owned by publishers of the Los Angeles *Times)* was assembled from several Mexican ranchos in the mid-nineteenth century. Other ranch products have been petroleum and irrigated crops (part of the property is in San Joaquin and Antelope valleys).

Southern Prongs towns are typically hamlets. But *Tehachapi* (5000) has importance as a tourist stop and a center for localized farming (grains, potatoes and orchards). But the leading source of local employment is the state prison. Following construction of Lake Isabella, the surrounding canyon of the Kern has acquired a larger population cluster. Thus Lake Isabella and *Kernville* are recreation-oriented.

## THE PARK BELT

The central portion of the Sierra Nevada along its western slopes within the montane forest, where stream-cut canyons have deepened by ice into tremendous chasms, is the Park Belt.

Its boundaries are nebulous. Essentially it lies above the Foothills and below the High Sierra, but the three national parks "overlap" into these higher and lower elevations.

This portion of the range, like the High Sierra, is singularly devoted to recreation (Maps 10-1 and 10-4).

Besides the national parks there are less-renowned beauty spots.

## Yosemite National Park

This park and the Tahoe Basin are doubtless the best-known portions of the Sierra Nevada.

Yosemite encompasses nearly 1200 square miles and contains the two impressive ice-deepened canyons of the Merced (Yosemite Valley) and the Tuolumne (Hetch Hetchy Valley or The Grand Canyon of the Tuolumne) as well as the uplands surrounding these gorges plus some spectacular examples of alpine glaciation (within the High Sierra).

Yosemite Valley presumably was "discovered" (from an Anglo perceptive) in 1851 during a punitive expedition against the Yosemite Indians. Later, fame of the Valley was enhanced by *Discovery of the Yosemite,* written by a member of the expedition (L.H. Bunnell).

Recreational development of Yosemite began shortly after its discovery.

James M. Hutchings led the first "tourists" into the Valley in 1855; soon trails and horseback roads had been constructed. By 1874 12,000 tourists from many lands had journeyed into the Valley by horseback. The next year three wagon roads (Coulterville, Big Oak Flat and Mariposa) had been extended into the Valley. Although a rail line was operated from 1907 to 1937, the automobile rapidly became the principal means of twentieth century conveyance.

Governmental wardship for Yosemite began in 1864.

Initially the federal government gave the Valley and its surrounding uplands to the State of California. But through the efforts of John Muir and others, the state reserve (including the Mariposa sequoia grove) became a national park in 1890 and the Park Service took control in 1916. Its personnel have been repeatedly plagued by problems of too many visitors, too limited funds and insufficient staff. *

The tragic "theft" of the Park, the "raid" of Hetch Hetchy Valley, was achieved by the city of San Francisco in 1913.

After a five-year struggle in Congress, Hetch Hetchy, the somewhat smaller, less favorite "twin" of Yosemite Valley, became the site of a metropolitan reservoir. As numbers of park visitors increase, the seriousness of the loss of the Hetch Hetchy region for public use becomes more evident

---

* A "master plan for the park was announced in 1980 (after a public uproar over a franchise-holder proposal for a convention center in the Valley). In the 1980's more than 20,000 daily and 50,000 on holiday weekends visit the Valley. The Plan will reduce auto parking spaces, campsites and overnight accommodations. Such "clutter" as tennis courts and golf courses will be removed. Already much housing for Park Service personnel has been relocated. But unfortunately for the Plan, the Reagan administration did not provide funds.

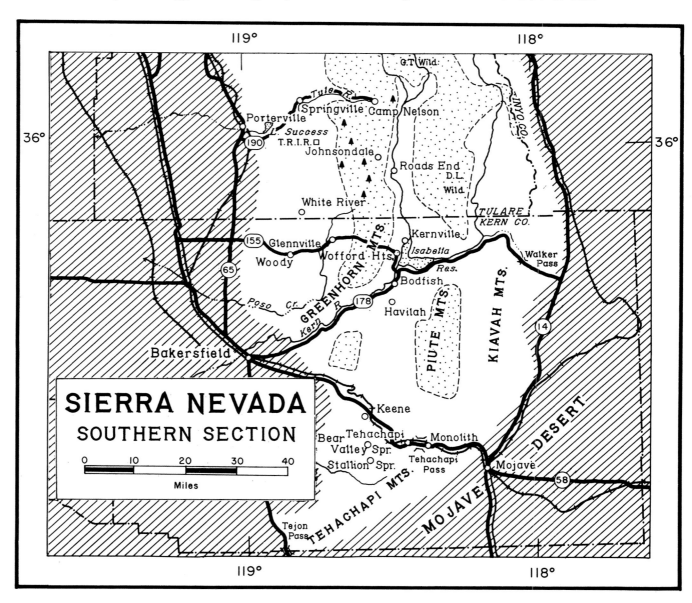

**Map 10-3.** Although the Southern Prongs of the Sierra is not the most scenic portion of the range, it is crossed by two major highways (I-5 and Ca. 58) and is quite accessible to the millions in Southern California. Stipled areas indicate extent of forest and tree symbol indicates grove of Sequoia.

(Fig. 10-15). In retrospect it might well have been "cheaper" to have built a more expensive storage facility elsewhere.** In 1988 the Secretary of the Interior proposed elimination of the dam and its reservoir.

Yosemite Valley, for many visitors, is a synonym for the Park. Lamentably its over-use reflects its siren-call appeal (many have acclaimed it one of the world's wonders).

Many tourists see no other parts of the Park—most visitor facilities are concentrated here: Government Center (including museum and hospital), campgrounds, luxurious Ahwahnee Hotel, Yosemite Lodge and more spartan Camp Curry. Its natural attractions include the Merced Valley (the river flows more slowly here) and its Happy Isles, Mirror Lake and the vegetation. Marginally, Valley walls, rising 4000 feet, possess spectacular (especially in spring) waterfalls and great granite domes (Fig. 10-15).

Several roads connect the Valley with other portions of the Park.

Southward from the Valley Wawona Road (Ca.41) has a turn-off past *Badger Pass,* known as a winter ski area, to *Glacier Point,* affording impressive views of the Valley and of Little Yosemite Valley (to the southeast) with its waterfalls (Fig.10-15). Ca. 120 ascends the north wall, then continues eastward across the High Sierra via Tioga Pass to connect with U.S. 395 (Ch.3).

From the Valley hiking trails lead to Glacier Point, the falls and the High Sierra. To give isolated backcountry portions of the Park more access (and hopefully lessen congestion in the Valley) five hikers' camps, approximately 10 miles apart, were constructed in the High Sierra (they too require advance reservations).

## Sequoia National Park

At the south end of the Park Belt is smaller (half the size of Yosemite) Sequoia Park.

The eastern portions (in the High Sierra) of the parks are similar, with alpine landscapes. But Sequoia was established because it has more than a score of groves of Sierran redwood.

Led by Indians, an early San Joaquin Valley resident "found" Sequoia in 1858.

His discovery fascinated botanists but more than a generation passed before efforts were made to establish a national preserve. In the interim thousands of cattle and sheep were grazed in this part of the Sierra Nevada. It was the founding of the Kaweah Cooperative Commonwealth Society (a socialistic group), with the intention of taking timber from Giant Forest that caused local conservationists to hasten establishment of a national park. A road into Giant Forest was finally completed in 1914. After construction of the groves linking *Generals Highway,* which made the largest trees accessible, the number of visitors increased. Expanded visitation in the past third-century reflects the marked growth of California population.

As contrasted with Yosemite and Kings Canyon, it is the big trees rather than topography that attracts visitors' attention in Sequoia.

Most visitors concentrate in the *Giant Forest.* It is situated on the much-dissected upland between the canyons of the South Fork of the Kings River and the Middle Fork of the Kaweah River, which rises from 5000 to 7000 feet.

Park officials have been able to avert a carnival-like atmosphere despite ever-increasing numbers of visitors.

Activity is centered at Giant Forest Village. In summer emphasis is upon strolls through the forests, visits to Moro Rock with its views of the Great Western Divide, drives along the Generals Highway (Fig.10-17) and evening campfire lectures. In winter there is the appeal of winter sports and of the Sequoias underlain by snow.

The Park's chief attraction of course are the groves of Sierran redwood.

The Sequoia, among the oldest (and bulkiest) of living forms, is more limited in distribution than the Coast redwood. These related species constitute the remains of a vegetation formation that was widely distributed in the northern hemisphere in past geologic ages. Fortunately, the Sierra sequoia within the park is reproducing its kind so that extinction of the species in the protected groves does not seem imminent. Besides bulk, heights (exceeding 200 feet) and great age (in some cases exceeding 3000 years), the species is impressive with its thick, fire-resistant bark. On the southern edge of the Park at *Mineral King* plans to develop an "Alpine Disneyland" were abandoned after much controversy following the merger of the area into the Park. A major objection of conservationists resulted from plans to develop a major access highway through a segment of the Park.

---

* Yosemite vies with Yellowstone and Rocky Mountain among western parks in volume of visitors. The Park Service, long plagued by low salaries and too few personnel, was aided materially during the Eisenhower presidency by the ten-year program known as Mission '66.

**Figure 10-14.** The ice-scoured trough of the Marble Fork of the Kaweah River, viewed from Pine Ridge in Sequoia National Park. Great Western Divide is on the skyline. (National Park Service, photo by Stagner).

**Figure 10-15.** The headwall of Yosemite Valley, Half Dome. Ice tongues flowed into the Valley from Tenaya (left) and Little Yosemite (right) canyons. In the rear is the High Sierra. (dwl)

**Figure 10-17.** This road (Highway of the Generals) in Sequoia National Park is kept open throught the year. (National Park Service, photo by Stagner)

### Kings Canyon National Park

Created in 1940, Kings Canyon, located north of Sequoia Park, resulted from a lengthy (half century) effort by nature lovers to protect one of the most scenic portions of the Sierra as a preserve of "wilderness."

While the Sequoia groves of the former General Grant National Park are within its limits, such groves are more characteristic of Sequoia Park. Much of Kings Canyon lies within the High Si-

erra—truly it is an alpine park. While less well-known than those of Yosemite, Kings Canyon has some of the outstanding granitic domes and glacial topography of the Sierra.

Very little of the Park is accessible by road—Kings Canyon is "wilderness."

A continuation of Ca. 180 reaches into a portion of the South Fork of the Kings Canyon—it terminates near Cedar Grove just within the western limits of the Park. A glance at a highway map reveals why many residents of Fresno and vicinity wish to have this road extended eastward to a junction with U.S. 395.

The alpine landscapes of Kings Canyon compare favorably with those of Yosemite—John Muir recognized this long ago.

While the *South Fork of the Kings Canyon* is neither as deep or wide as Yosemite Valley, it is several miles long. But it lacks both the number of granite domes and waterfalls. The Park encompasses other precipitous canyons as well. Along the Middle Fork of the Kings is isolated *Tehipite Valley*— larger than Yosemite with loftier walls. Its great Tehipite Dome is one of the remarkable granitic knobs of the Sierra. Lengthy segments of Tehipite and Kings River canyons remain outside actual Park limits—they were excluded to appease advocates of future reservoir construction, subsequently built, with others still being considered in the late twentieth century.

Kings Canyon will probably disappoint the tourist seeking creature comforts; facilities of the type

**Figure 10-16.** One solution for human congestion in Yosemite Valley has been use of free shuttle buses. (National Park Service).

found in most national parks are absent. But this Park delights the hiker, camper, or fisher to whom overcrowded Yosemite Valley is frustrating.

### Bass Lake

Bass Lake, south of Yosemite Park, does provide the comforts of city life.

Accessible by good paved road (and near Ca. 41) Bass Lake is an man-made water body behind a Pacific Gas and Electric storage dam. Because of its accessibility, warm water (for swimming, boating, water skiing) and public campgrounds, the site is frequented by families and becomes congested. Despite its attractive sylvan setting (and such urban conveniences as newspapers, postal service in Bass Lake village, and fresh milk delivery) some feel there is not adequate compensation for the resultant congestion (for example, boats must cruise in a counterclockwise course!).

### Huntington Lake Country

Situated in the montane forests (from 5000 to 7000 feet elevation), the Country is a delightful portion of the Park Belt.

It has long been frequented by residents of the San Joaquin Valley (but is not well-known to out-of-staters) and more recently by Southern Californians. Within the Sierra National Forest it is approachable via Ca. 168. It includes segments of the San Joaquin and Kings drainage basins.*

The Huntington Lake Country is one of the attractive playgrounds of the Sierra.

Its artificial lakes (constructed for hydroelectric development) look deceivingly-natural (except at the dams) (Fig. 10-19). The weather is cool, the water clear, and there are campgrounds amidst conifers (plus too many summer homes in some places). Lower (5370 ft.) and warmer than most reservoirs in the Big Creek Project, *Shaver Lake* is used for swimming and boating. *China Peak* ski area, with its lodge and double-chair lift, has become one of the more-frequented winter resorts in the Park Belt.

Elevation variations within Huntington Lake Country favor diverse recreation usage.

The area reaches up into the High Sierra at Florence Lake, a departure point for high-country trips. *Huntington Lake,* favored for fishing, weekend homes and camping, is sufficiently high (6950 ft.) that its water is too cool for swimmers. Dinkey Creek is lower; (besides its warmer waters at *Honeymoon Pool)* the stream is popular with fishers; its campgrounds become congested.

The *Big Creek Project* forms the major hydroelectric development in the Southern California Edison system (Fig. 10-20).

Since 1911 more than $220 million has been expended by this utility company; it has constructed 14 dams, 10 tunnels and eight powerhouses along the upper San Joaquin and its tributaries, using and reusing the force of falling water. Such projects do not lessen the flow of rivers downstream, unlike the federally-built Friant Dam, designed to divert water for irrigation. Florence Lake and Lake Edison, in the High Sierra, form the easternmost units.

Completed in 1911, the basic project included 15-foot Ward Tunnel (drilled under Kaiser Ridge through 13 miles of solid rock to transport water from Florence Lake to Huntington Lake), Huntington Lake (a regulatory body) and *Shaver Lake.* Mammoth Pool reservoir (at 3100 ft.) forms the lowest (and newest) storage facility. Big Creek, a "company" town which contrasts with many abandoned mine and lumber camps, is the focal point. The utility sends 690,000 kilowatts generated by the project 250 miles to metropolitan Los Angeles.

Farther south Pacific Gas and Electric completed its *Kings River Project* in 1962 west of the national park.

A pioneer (A.G. Wishon) of the California electric power utility had discovered that the Kings River drops 7000 feet in 20 miles! The project (on the North Fork of the Kings River) initially generated 313,000 kilowatts for use in central California. It was expanded in the 1980s with addition of the *Helms Pumped Storage Project.*

### THE FOOTHILLS

Flanking the Great Central Valley on the east, from the Kern Canyon northward to the Feather River Country, the Sierran Foothills has been the most intensively utilized portion of the Range since the Gold Rush.

Elevation varies from less than 1000 feet above sea level in the west to approximately 4000 feet in the east. The *interfluves* (uplands) slowly ascend eastward while stream canyons deepen progressively. Grasslands, with groves of valley oak and digger

---

* *Devil's Postpile National Monument,* an interesting formation of columnar basalt, *Rainbow Falls* and *Reds Meadows* are situated in the headwaters area of the San Joaquin. Since they are reached by road across the main Sierran summit from Mammoth Lakes these attractions are probably best considered as Eastern Slope recreation spots.

**Figure 10-18.** Bass Lake, deceptively montane for its low elevation (3400 feet), is mid-way between Fresno and Yosemite Valley via Ca. 41. (Pacific Gas and Electric Company).

**Figure 10-19.** Huntington Lake was created to provide regulatory storage as part of the Big Creek Project. Located at 7000 feet, it looks deceivingly natural. Water from the South Fork of the San Joaquin River is diverted through Ward Tunnel (under Kaiser Ridge). The north shore of the Lake now has a continuum of weekend cottages. (Southern California Edison Company).

pine, cover the countryside; in places the earth is heavily mantled by thickets of chaparral.

Climatically the Foothills is a favored portion of California.

Lower elevations are warm in summer but less hot than the Central Valley. The high fog of coastal areas and the wintry "tule fog" of interior lowlands are absent. Seasonality is definite but winters are not too cold; storms tend to bring rain rather than the heavy snows of higher elevations to the east.

Economic pursuits have included mining, ranching, through transportation, recreation, residence and lumber processing.

### The Mother Lode Country

The Mother Lode Country is the heart of the Foothills.

As identified here it extends from Sierra City on the north to Mariposa on the south; *strictly*, as a gold-producing area and *not* in terms of contemporary use, it does not include the *Northern Diggings*.

Approximately 15 miles wide and tributary to Ca. 49, this attenuated belt has yielded the bulk of California's gold. Over two billion dollars worth of gold has come from its eight counties. * Yet today there is a somnolent air contrary to Gold Rush days and much of contemporary California. The geologic *Mother Lode* proper, the discontinuous zone of Jurassic quartz fissure veins outcropping

from Mariposa to Georgetown, has smaller dimensions, with a north-south length of about 120 miles.

The social, political and economic consequence of the activity promoted by the Gold Rush has far exceeded the value of the gold.

California's growth was hastened by some decades. During the second half of the nineteenth century California gold made the nation the world's leading producer. Save for the new Argonauts, production had virtually ceased until the 1980's.

The major surge of goldseekers began in 1849. It was more than a year after Marshall found gold in the mill race of Sutter's lumber mill that the big rush took place. *Local* excitement materialized during the summer of 1848. In the next several years possibly 100,000 came into the Mother Lode Country from many parts of the world. A number soon went elsewhere, usually without anticipated riches; thousands remained in California to help build a state.

Most of the gold has been recovered by three techniques (placering, lode and dredging). While all three were adapted early, maximum return came at different periods.

---

* The two billion dollars represents a near-forgotten price of an ounce of gold.

**Figure 10-20.** The Big Creek Project's Powerhouse No.I, one of eight plants utilizing the South Fork of the San Joaquin River. which accordingly is called "the hardest working water in the world." (Southern California Edison Company).

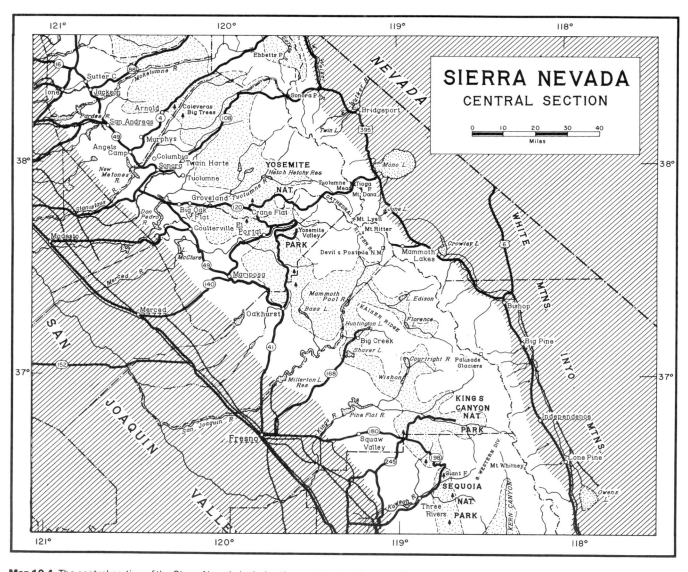

**Map 10-4.** The central portion of the Sierra Nevada includes three national parks as well as extensive wilderness and a segment of the famed Foothill Gold Country. See Map 10-1 for meaning of the dashed lines.

The early mining commonly entailed washing of the stream gravels (i.e., *placering).*

It employed the bulk of the miners and was often done with crude equipment. Placering took place in a belt 50 miles wide and 150 miles north-south; before 1880 it was the chief means of recovery. Recovery of gold worth $1.3 billion was achieved in this way. It began in the alluvial deposits of stream beds, bars and adjacent benches. Such deposits represented the reconcentration of Tertiary gravels (originally laid down in streams of the ancestral Sierra) into such contemporary rivers as the Feather, Yuba and American. Although the richest nuggets were recovered the first year, production gained for several years as the miner influx continued—per capita recovery declined.

Gold seekers soon began investigating the long-abandoned Tertiary stream gravels (now found on hillsides). Drift and hydraulic techniques were employed.

Tunnels into the deposits was essential for *drift mining;* this process was often expensive—it demanded *shoring*; it was also risky (due to threat of cave-in). Running water to cut into the old gravels was adopted quickly; *hydraulicking* (directing a stream of water, under high pressure, from a nozzle at the end of a pipe against a hillside) began in 1853. Speedy and inexpensive, this process was used widely until the courts issued a permanent injunction against hydraulicking. It had led to choked river channels, increased flood threats in the Central Valley, destruction of farm lands through silting (which also occurred in San Francisco Bay).*

Fremont's Mariposa Grant was the initial site of *lode mining*.

At first it was believed that quartz veins were widespread through the Sierra. Gradually there came awareness that the gold-bearing country rock was limited largely to the elongated Mother Lode with its separate and discontinuous fissures. The wealth acquired by hard rock mining has come from scores of mines. In time, mining techniques, necessary knowledge of ores and suitable machinery evolved. Lode mining became the chief means of recovery after the placer decline and persisted into the 1950's. Half the vein gold of the Mother Lode came from a single 10-mile strip in Amador County. Leading mines there, each of which is thousands of feet deep, have yielded gold in excess of $10 million each.

*Dredging* was the principal recovery technique in the earlier twentieth century. It was concentrated along the western edge of the Sierra from Butte County southward into Merced County.

Large-scale operations obtained hundreds of millions of dollars from deposits uneconomical to mine by other techniques. In some instances floating bucket-dredges weighing several thousand tons each have been employed. Too often, unfortunately, such mining has ruined the land for grazing— soil is replaced by cobblestone and gravel as result of dredging.

Generally considered apart from the Mother Lode to the northwest is the **"Northern Diggings"**, centered on Grass Valley, Nevada City and the nearby Allegheny District.

Much mining here, beginning in 1852 and surviving until the late 1950's, tended to be of the lode type. For some years Nevada City, North Columbia and North Bloomfield were also foci for hydraulic mining. Ores averaged of sufficient value that vein mining was resumed for a decade after World War II.

California gold output made a progressive decline after 1852.

Annual yield ranged in value between $15 and $25 million from the mid-1860's; decline occurred after World War I. A spectacular but temporary increase followed passage of the Gold Reserve Act in 1934. Then issuance of Regulation W led to cessation during World War II. After the war the higher costs of mining versus the low price of gold prevented many mines from reopening. Subsequently most gold was recovered through dredging in the north. Even this activity has almost ceased. Currently hundreds of "new argonauts" are reworking streams (Fig. 10-21)—some make a fair return from their "hobby."

A resurgence of corporate mining of gold took place in the 1980's. It was prompted first by the high price of gold in the 1970's followed by other factors such as international uncertainties in South Africa and the Middle East. Approximately a dozen operations have taken place. The major one is the Sonora Gold Company's open-pit near Jamestown.

For several decades in the latter half of the twentieth century production of cement in Calaveras and El Dorado counties exceeded the economic importance of gold.

The plant at San Andreas (Genstar Cement) expanded its output several times after its establishment (in 1926). Its several hundred employees have contributed significantly to the economy of a mountain county. However in the 1980's foreign competition made the future problematic.

---

\* A good example of one-time hydraulicking is Cherokee, near Ca. 70 north of Oroville. Activity necessitated 100 miles of ditches and pipes of 30-inch diameter. One pipe crossed the North Fork of the Feather 900 feet above the stream! At its zenith, 18 monitors (nozzle heads) were being directed against the ancient stream channel. Each nozzle could blast a stream of water 400 feet. By the time the gold supply was exhausted in 1883, $10 million had been recovered. A larger operation, *Malakoff Diggings*, on the Yuba River northeast of Nevada City, is now a state historical park.

**Figure 10-21.** A late-twentieth century argonaut "vacuum" sweeping for gold in South Fork of the Yuba River. (dwl)

The geologic *Ione formation*, principally around Ione, has been a major source of clay for refractory use. The formation also has been a source of silica for the California glass industry.

Divers other mining operations in the 1980's included montan wax from lignite in Amador County, limestone and dolomite in Tuolumne County, asbestos at Copperopolis and tungsten in Madera County.

### Oranges and Chickens

Foodstuff production in the Foothills began with the Gold Rush—markets then were almost wholly in the camps.

Early yield was often on a subsistence basis—a miner planted some crops for his own needs. When mining declined Foothills farming stagnated—markets were almost absent and transportation poor.

Ranching in the Foothills is both hampered and favored by the environment.

Terrain is often a major disadvantage—sizable areas are handicapped by slopes and rocky soils. Summer drought made irrigation difficult before sprinklers and drip irrigation. Temperature is an asset—intermediate elevations have a long season. Rainfall at higher elevations may permit ranching without irrigation. If topography was more suitable numerous Sierran streams could have provided irrigation water even though stream regimes (periodicity of flow) would have demanded reservoirs. Now much water is allocated elsewhere. Sometimes there is land-use conflict between forestry, grazing and recreation.

Livestock ranching forms the most extensive land-use in the Foothills.

Beef production started during the Gold Rush; as accessible forests were cut, areas suitable for grazing were expanded. Overgrazing and repeated burnings have lessened the value of some pastures while chaparral has engulfed many abandoned farms. Many smaller Foothills ranches are combination year-round feeding-grazing properties with production of dry-farmed grains and hay where the environment permits. The importance of the Foothills for beef production increases as the population of California rises—for some years the state has been a "meat-deficit" producer. A unique development near Sonora is the establishment of llama farms.

Pasturage has had greater relative value in the

economy of the southerly Foothills (from Mariposa through Amador counties).

Transportation handicaps in these counties before the automobile era, plus much terrain unsuited for cropping (especially before sprinklers) and less moisture than farther north, favored livestock. Considerable San Joaquin Valley livestock were pastured here in late spring in the course of transhumance to higher grasslands.

Marked expansion of irrigated pasture lands followed adoption of the practice half a century ago. Topographic problems were lessened with adaption of overhead sprinklers and more recently drip irrigation.

Extension of commercial agriculture into the Foothills came long after the Gold Rush.

Abandonment of hydraulic mining provided some ready-made irrigation systems. Two examples of mining era antecedents are the *Paradise* and *Oroville-Wyandotte* irrigation districts (Butte County). Many locales initially farmed during the Gold Rush reverted to second-growth forest or chaparral.

Specialized aspects describe Foothills agriculture; poultry farming and fruit growing are important.

There are part-time subsistence farms, adjacent to major communities and principal transportation arteries. Climate permits a variety of crops, especially in the so-called "thermal belt" (generally between 200 and 1200 feet). In the northern Foothills, interfluves provide farm land; farther south steeper slopes are a handicap. At least half the Foothills is too rocky or too steep for farming.

Thermal belt mildness, with limited frost, has permitted oranges in the north near Oroville and in the south near Porterville.

The climatic advantage was not fully appreciated until the damaging California frost of 1879-1880, which encouraged establishment of commercial orchards. Oroville is on the fringe of the Sacramento Valley; the adjacent citrus belt extends eastward into the Foothills. While larger acreages are found on the Kaweah Delta, oranges are grown in small coves and valleys and on the lower slopes within the Foothills of Tulare County. The thermal advantage has permitted both areas to make their heaviest shipments in November, before the large post-Christmas shipments farther south. Through marketing agreements the large growers have virtually eliminated orange production in Butte County. Both of these counties have been important olive producers, which are processed locally.

Sometimes olives are grown on thin soils not too well suited to citrus.

Deciduous fruits, at elevations between 1000 and 3000 feet, have been produced in Placer and El Dorado counties since the Gold Rush. Pears and plums tend to have the greatest value. There has also been increased production of grapes and apples near Placerville.

Plums are found between Loomis and Auburn (at lower elevations); spring months are virtually frostless and plums mature earlier than elsewhere in California. But output has never fully recovered from overplanting and subsequent decline in the 1930's.

These counties, long known for their pears, have become one of the nation's centers for this fruit. Although pears can tolerate more frost than some deciduous fruits, they are grown on sloping, well drained soils. The thermal advantage has permitted marketing later. When urbanization eliminated Santa Clara Valley orchards, additional Foothills acreage was planted. For a time in the 1960's pear decline ("red death") threatened orchard destruction.

Paradise (in Butte County) historically was a secondary apple-producing locale; grapes were also grown and fruit was often marketed at orchard stands. Urbanization has nearly eliminated fruit production.

Production of poultry, both chickens and turkeys, is a major agricultural development in the Foothills.

Poultry are especially important in the rural economies of Placer, Tuolumne and Mariposa counties. Turkeys, more difficult to raise than chickens, are usually grown farther from urban areas. Expanded California markets and improved transportation has helped expand poultry in these counties. In Tuolumne County a number of farms are connected with Foster Farms in the San Joaquin Valley at Livingston.

### Boating and Touring

Tourist expenditures have considerable value in the Foothills economy.

An appreciable local income derives from services to trans-Sierran travelers (especially on I-80 and U.S. 50) and vacationists utilizing higher portions of the Sierra. Cafes, motels, garages and service stations in such communities as Auburn, Placerville and Sonora gain much income from wayfarers. Likewise Yosemite-bound vacationists bring much business to Mariposa and Oakhurst.

Visitors, commonly Californians, follow Ca. 49, the *Mother Lode Highway,* to "re-live" Gold Rush times.

Some search for sites of such once lively camps as Hell's Hills, Hoodoo, Lake City or Frenchmen's. Far more visit the mill site on the American River (now a state park) where Marshall discovered gold in 1848 and also inspect the locales of placering, the pockmarked Mother Lode itself, or famed lode mines like the *Argonaut.* Tourists visit the slope towns with their plain pre-Victorian white cottages, ailanthus-lined streets, weathered brick business blocks with their sagging iron shutters and overhanging balconies. Perhaps a dozen Gold Rush era hotels have been restored for overnight stays. Much-frequented **Columbia** maintains the atmosphere of the boom years—it is a state park. Although the town is "protected," its environs have experienced much sprawl, including a community college.

Between the well-populated Central Valley and higher portions of the range, the Foothills have become increasingly popular for weekend outings, for summer youth camps, for vacation cottages of lowland dwellers, and for retirement residence. Spring is delightful, with green hillsides and wildflowers. There is also a particular appeal to autumn, when the leaves are turning and after the High Sierra has become snowbound.

Storage reservoirs have become increasingly popular as recreation sites.

Near Fresno, and frequented by many boaters and fishers, is *Millerton Lake.* well suited as a recreation area (Fig. 10-23). Crammed with campers and boaters throughout the summer is *Turlock Lake State Park.* Lakes behind Pine Flat, Folsom, and Oroville dams, as well as lesser-known reservoirs, are utilized increasingly.

### Flumes and Logging Trucks

Wood processing continues as a basic source of contemporary Foothills employment. Elevations above 2000 feet in the north (and higher in the south) are often forested but most of the logs now come from elevations above the Foothills.

Wood processing gained importance with the Gold Rush; emphasis has shifted in recent decades. Initially lumbering was conducted near mine camps. When mining declined, lumber output declined also. Still, the more accessible forests had been cut before 1900. Before the motor truck *flumes* (inclined channels made of wood) provided

**Figure 10-22.** Lake Millerton, Friant Dam and the Friant-Kern Canal. This multi-purpose unit provides water for irrigation in the southern San Joaquin Valley plus flood control and recreation. (Bureau of Reclamation, photo by A.G. D'Alessandro).

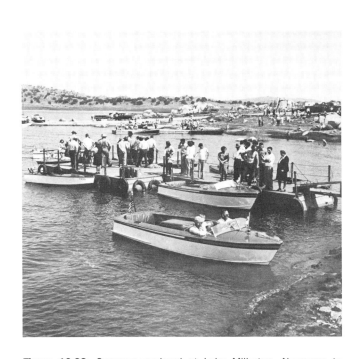

**Figure 10-23.** Summer weekend at Lake Millerton. Nearness to metropolitan Fresno and other places in central California makes this a popular place. (Bureau of Reclamation, photo by B.D. Glaha).

**Figure 10-24.** The gold camp of Columbia has been restored, beginning with the California statehood centennial. It is now a state park in the Foothills, much-visited. (California Division of Beaches and Parks).

an important means of transportation although some logging railroads were established.

Recently, the "Tree Rush" has experienced considerable changes from earlier Sierran lumbering. Once ponderosa pine was the dominant species; it has declined relatively and increasing amounts of true fir and Douglas fir have been logged.

Traditionally the cut came from private lands; now much of it comes from the public domain. The ponderosa, at lower elevations, has been held by smaller owners. The large companies tend to have reserves at higher elevations, owning fir forests. Mechanization, such as chain saws and power loaders, has permitted logging in less accessible areas with rugged terrain.

Some tree farming is developing. However exploitative forestry continues; the montane forests are well suited to selective cutting.

In the national forests marketable timber is sold on a contract basis and cutting operations are checked by the Forest Service. Some private owners want an immediate cash return and cut as much of their holding as state law allows. Others value their properties for residence or recreation and permit no cutting. Much acreage was cleared quickly to provide grazing land. For several reasons much potential forest land is not well stocked with timber. However much acreage of once-cropped land, abandoned before 1900, reverted to forest and reached marketable size by mid-century. Much of this forest, chiefly ponderosa pine, has been cut hence forestry has declined.

Woodworking remains an important contributor to the Sierran economy with greater local importance than in the past.

**Figure 10-25.** Mariposa has a diversity of supports. It is a county seat, highway stop on the "All-Year Highway" into Yosemite National Park, and a local support place. (dwl)

Actual processing usually occurs in the Foothills or in Central Valley towns. Total employment numbers some thousands; each of a dozen mills employ more than 100 workers. The sub-region ranks second to the Northwest, ahead of the Southern Cascade. El Dorado and Tuolumne counties are the leaders but forestry is the chief source of income in most counties. Now mill workers are family men who operate ranches or semisubsistence farms on the side. Sierran lumbering is seasonal, with winter closure due to snow hence annual incomes are not adequate without supplement.

### Hydro Power and Water Storage

Like timber, falling water first became an important Foothills resource during the Gold Rush.

Early water rights were associated with placer and hydraulic mining. With the demise of mining, ditches and other works were available for other uses. Topography tended to discourage use of water for irrigation over much of the Foothills; also, market limitations tended to discourage farming in the nineteenth century.

Development of Foothills water resources in this century has been threefold: hydroelectric power, irrigation and urban consumption, with recreation and flood control as important adjuncts.

Some works have had multiple functions, as hydroelectricity and then downstream, irrigation; or irrigation coupled with flood control.

The principal firm to utilize water for hydroelectric development in the Foothills has been Pacific Gas and Electric Company, (P.G.and E), a San Francisco amalgamation.

This corporation, possessor of one of the nation's three leading private power transmission systems, was established in 1905 through consolidation of smaller companies. By the late nineteenth century hydroelectricity had been devised as the solution for power needs in fuels-poor central California; waterpower development was well established before petroleum became available as fuel.

Now this giant corporation generates electricity at scores of powerhouses in the western Sierra, from the drainage basin of the Kern northward to the Feather basin. Power distribution is effected throughout the Bay Area, the Central Valley, the Central Coast, and northwestern California. Hundreds of Foothills residents are employed by this utility, which pays more than half the taxes in

**Figure 10-26.** San Andreas. Some of the gold towns that survived most successfully tended to be county seats that became road crossings (Ca.49 and east-west highways). Like other camps, San Andreas was located in a stream valley. (dwl)

several counties. In some instances P.G. and E. uses water "belonging to" irrigation districts; after its use for power production the water is available for agricultural purposes.

Domestic power is obtained in the western Sierra Nevada by the city of San Francisco as well as the communities of East Bay.

At the approximate time that Los Angeles began its aqueduct southward through Owens Valley (Ch 3). San Francisco also sought Sierran water by making a water filing within Yosemite National Park. Its plans were opposed by such interests as San Joaquin Valley ranchers, the Sierra Club and others. After some years Congress passed the Raker Bill, which was signed by President Wilson. Construction of *O'Shaughnessy Dam* in Hetch Hetchy Valley began in 1913.

Now water from the reservoir flows down the Tuolumne for 12 miles before it is diverted through the intake into the main 150-mile aqueduct which carries water to the Peninsula south of San Francisco. Near Moccasin advantage is taken of a 1400 feet drop in elevation. There the City constructed Moccasin Powerhouse. Unlike Los Angeles, San Francisco does not have its own distribution system, so it sells power to P.G. and E.. Completion of the *Hetch Hetchy Project* was achieved in 1934 with construction of Crystal Springs reservoir near Palo Alto. Now, in the 1980's, San Francisco aspires to construct another Sierran reservoir.

Alameda County cities have followed the San Francisco example.

They organized East Bay Municipal Utility District ("East Bay M.U.D.") in 1923. There were fewer complications than San Francisco experienced with Hetch Hetchy. The District built Pardee Dam on the Mokelumne River and in 1931 completed an aqueduct to deliver water from the Foothills into reservoirs in the Berkeley-Oakland Hills.

Sierran waters for irrigation has been used in varied ways.

Spectacular activity has included *Friant* (on the San Joaquin and *Folsom* (on the American) dams of the Central Valley Project, *Pine Flat* (constructed on the Kings by the Corps of Engineers, and *Oroville Dam* (on the Feather) under the California Water Project (Fig. 10-37). Before the Central Valley Project, water users of the Turlock and Modesto districts constructed *Don Pedro* reservoir on the Tuolumne downriver from Hetch Hetchy. Other older structures include Exchequer on the Merced and Melones on the Stanislaus.

Actual water use within the Foothills itself is on a far less grandiose scale than the big dams would suggest.

Within the Foothills irrigation works evolved from ditches built by early mining interests. With growth of commercial agriculture in the twentieth century, several irrigation districts were formed.

In recent decades P.G. and E. has devised a "partnership" with some districts. It underwrites bond issued and gains long-term contracts to purchase power. In return the irrigation districts acquire "cost-free" facilities, including enlarged dams and new delivery systems. Still, as in the early days, water in many localities is sold on the basis of the "miner's inch."

### Some Camps Still Live

The Foothills is the residence of much of the permanent population of the Sierra Nevada.

The percentage of native-born Anglos tends to be appreciably higher than in California's conurbations. Also there is residential dispersion which has prevailed since the Gold era. There is much scattering of non-farm dwellings apart from towns, albeit along roadways. Hence many towns almost imperceptibly merge with the open countryside. Thus the usual community census understates considerably the actual urban-oriented population. Thus the four leading urban-rural conglomerations appear to be Auburn, Grass Valley-Nevada City Alta Hill, Placerville and Sonora, each of these is about 30,000.

**Figure 10-27.** Central Nevada City. The seat of Nevada County, at the junction of highways 20 and 49, has much appeal. (dwl)

Almost without exception, Foothills towns originated as gold camps. Thus they share many common attributes.

Many are situated in canyons, often clustered in groups, with "shoestring" patterns and narrow winding streets. Most towns experienced destructive fires in their early years yet the unadorned pre-Victorian style of architecture is conspicuous in many wooden cottages with white siding. Business blocks are often of stone or brick—in most towns at least a few buildings are more than a century old. Thus Foothills towns, with mature shade trees, look more settled than many California towns elsewhere of comparable size. Some

have experienced recent growth, so that large plate-glass windows and neon signs and incongruously contemporary designs are common.

But most Mother Lode camps were born and declined within the span of a few years.

Often no physical evidence remains to indicate where numerous miners once gathered. Of the villages which survived, many are small and tranquil, with slight hint of growth or prosperity. Elderly, lifelong residents are representative; many have less formal education and lower incomes than is typical in California—these people do not go to the city to seek their fortunes. A new type of resident is the *earth person*—many of these young people are single parents including unwed mothers, refugees from urban California, often on welfare.

Several *northern Foothills* towns have grown moderately large for the Sierra.

An important factor is good access to Central Valley cities which allows easy commuting.

**Paradise** (26,000), the largest Sierran town, has gained a statewide reputation as a retirement spot "in the pines."

Half its residents are retirees (many are former business and professional people from Southern California or the Bay Area). It is one of a growing number of retirement centers apart from urban California (others include Yucaipa, Clearlake and Atascadero). Incorporated finally (on the third attempt), Paradise is a rambling assemblage of

**Figure 10-28.** Paradise is a commuter (to Chico) and retirement town on the extreme northern edge of the Sierra Nevada. Its four-lane main street The Skyway winds for miles across The Ridge. (dwl)

attractive residences and some shanties (Fig. 10-28). Twelve miles from Chico by four-lane highway, it lacks some services that might be expected for its size.

With better-defined central districts, the twin cities of Nevada County, **Grass Valley** (9000) and **Nevada City** (2600) virtually fuse along a low-density "umbilical cord" (the Ca.20/49 freeway).

Grass Valley continued into the 1950's as a hardrock gold camp; meanwhile it had become the county's major retail center. It has acquired commuter residents (employed in the Central Valley) and retirees. Both towns have lumber mills while Nevada City, one of the Sierra's most charming communities, is also the county seat.

In the past several decades urbanization has become apparent in the *central Foothills* towns from Auburn to San Andreas.

To a varying degree there is freeway access to *greater* Sacramento, Stockton and even the Bay Area (via I-80 and U.S. 50). Housing tracts, suburban shopping developments and new schools have materialized. Except for Ione and Sutter Creek, the major towns are county seats.

**Ione** (2800),was never a gold camp even though it was known as Bedbug. It has remained a center for livestock ranching and has a state correction institution for boys.

**Sutter Creek** (2000) was long sustained by the Central Eureka Mine. A one-time favorite residence place for miners, this charming town with several antique shops now attracts urban retirees and vacationists. There is a sizable fringe-area mobile home community.

**Auburn** (9000) and **Placerville** (7400) rank among the faster-growing towns in the entire Sierra.

Actually much of the growth is in unincorporated fringes. Both have higher average-income levels than most Sierran communities and both are surrounded by agricultural districts. Each can be semi-bypassed on freeways by Tahoe-bound vacationists.

Auburn, on I-80, has grown more dramatically; it is popular with Sacramento commuters. An unique feature is the contrast between *Old Town* and *New Town*. Nearby *Rocklin* is the site of of Sierra College, one of three collegiate institutions in the entire subregion.

Placerville, with apple and pear-shipping sheds, several wineries and nearby lumber mills, has sundry governmental facilities.

**Jackson** (3800), popular with tourists and retir-

ees, represents the epitome of the persistent hardrock camp. Its narrow main street is flanked by old business blocks and overhanging balconies. Initially less prosperous than some gold camps, its deep-shaft *Kennedy* and *Argonaut* mines brought continuing wealth after many places had vanished. It has a Slavic populace hence the only Orthodox church in the Gold Country.

**San Andreas** (1600) survives as Calaveras County seat; it also has a cement plant. Unlike most viable Foothills towns it is not a gateway on a trans-Sierran highway.

The *southern Mother Lode* towns (Angels Camp to Oakhurst) tend to have less productive hinterlands. More distant from major Central Valley cities, these towns usually experience less commuting.

Except for Tuolumne the principal towns are Sierran gateways; several benefit from Yosemite vacation clientele. Two (Sonora and Mariposa) are county seats.

**Tuolumne** (1400), terminus for the lumber-shipping (and tourist hauling and movie-filming) Sierra Railroad, has the subregion's largest single lumber mill.

**Angels Camp** (2500), a gateway to Calaveras Big Trees State Park, is sustained by ranching and lumbering. The town remembers the writing of Harte and Twain each spring with its jumping frog festival. Many enjoy the Gold days charm and quietude of **Murphys** (1200) to the east.

**Sonora** (4500) no longer has to vie with nearby Columbia as the metropolis of the "southern mines." Its economy is bolstered by lumbering, tourism, limestone quarries, local trade and retirement residence. Much of its populace resides outside city limits.

One of the more attractive Sierran towns, at the junction of Ca. 49 and 108, it is a gateway to *Twain Harte, Dodge Ridge* and *Sonora Pass*. The long-needed highway bypass of its central district is projected.

*Mariposa* (300) is a diminutive county seat that benefits as a stopping point at the junction of Ca. 49 and Ca. 140, the All-Year Highway into Yosemite. It is situated in a relatively sterile area. Nearly stagnant, it lacks the numerous newer structures of larger Foothills towns and thus retains more feel of yesteryear.

**Oakhurst** (2000) is becoming a "second" Paradise. At the junction of Ca.49 and 41, it affords a "way stop" for Fresnoans and Southern Californians bound for Yosemite. It is a "lengthy" commute to Fresno.

### THE NORTHERN SIERRA *

North of the High Sierra, the Northern Sierra blends into the Foothills (on the southwest). It has distinctive features that tend to set it apart from the rest of the Sierra Nevada.

North from Echo Summit (U.S.50) elevations of prominent peaks are markedly lower than to the south. While individual summits exceed 9000 feet around Lake Tahoe, farther north they lie between 7000 and 8000 feet. Except where glaciation has stripped surfaces to bedrock, the Northern Sierra is forested across its summits; the alpine zone of the High Sierra is absent. Snowfall is generally heavier and isolation, apart from major trans-Sierran crossings, has been a persistent winter characteristic (Fig. 10-31). Another distinctive feature is the terrain.

The Northern Sierra, like the Southern Prongs discussed earlier, consists of three offset blocks separated by two depressions.

The easternmost block, the *Diamond Mountains,* continues southward as the *Carson Range* in Nevada. The middle block to the west is the *Grizzly Mountains* while the westernmost block, *Clermont Hill,* is less well defined and lower. The Feather River, which has cut its canyon through Clermont Hill and the Grizzly Mountains, like the Kern River is suggestive of an antecedent stream. Sierra Valley and the Tahoe depression lie west of the Carson-Diamond mass whereas small basins like

---

\* This section was reviewed by Brad Cullen of the University of New Mexico.

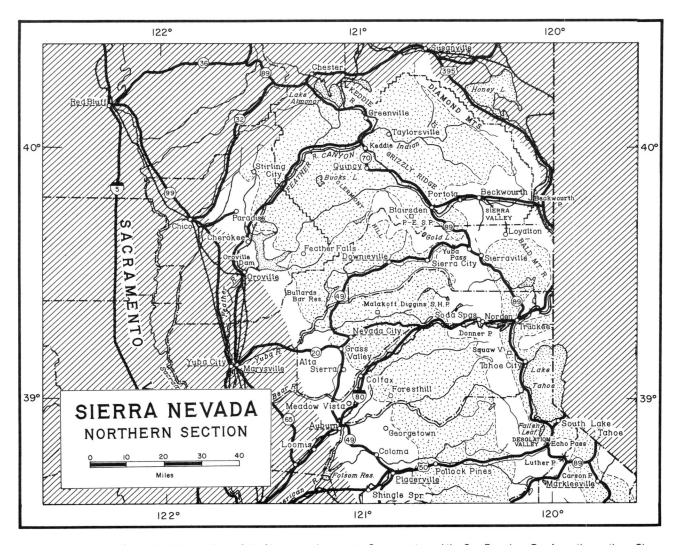

**Map 10-5.** With three of the principal crossings of the Sierra, good access to Sacramento and the San Francisco Bay Area, the northern Sierra is much frequented and more populous than other portions of the range. Stipling indicates extent of forests.

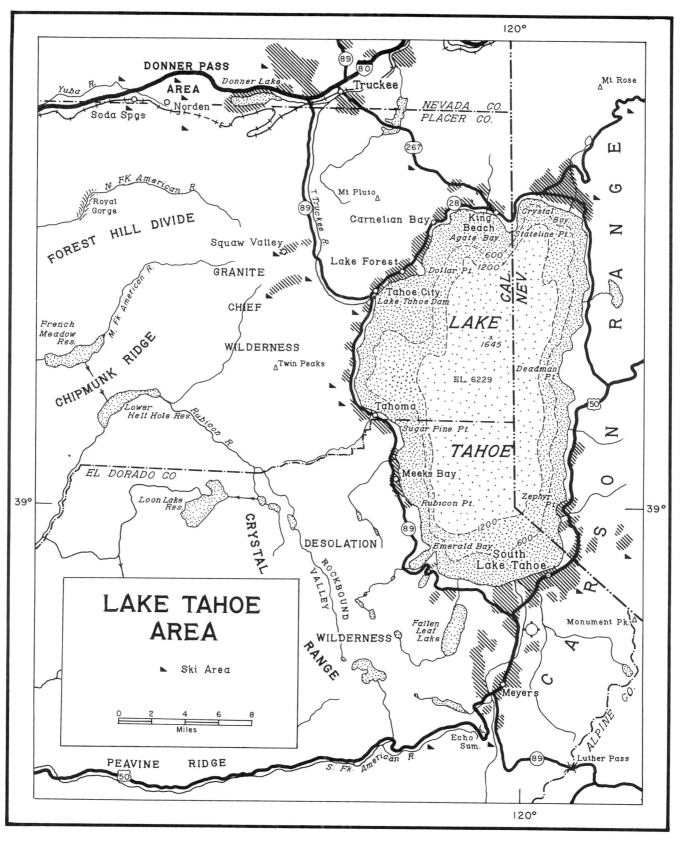

120°

DONNER PASS
AREA
*Yuba R.*
Soda Spgs
Norden
*Donner Lake*
Truckee
89 80
NEVADA CO.
PLACER CO.
△ Mt. Rose
267
89
*T Truckee R.*
Mt Pluto △
Carnelian Bay
28
King Beach
*Agate Bay*
*Crystal Bay*
*Stateline Pt.*
*N. Fk American R.*
Royal Gorge
FOREST HILL DIVIDE
Squaw Valley
Lake Forest
600
1200
*Dollar Pt.*
*M. Fk American R.*
GRANITE
CHIEF
Tahoe City
*Lake Tahoe Dam*
LAKE
CAL.
NEV.
R A N G E
French Meadow Res.
CHIPMUNK RIDGE
WILDERNESS
△ Twin Peaks
× 1645
EL. 6229
*Deadman Pt.*
50
Lower Hell Hole Res.
*Rubicon R.*
Tahoma
*Sugar Pine Pt.*
TAHOE
EL DORADO CO
Loon Lake Res.
Meeks Bay
*Rubicon Pt.*
*Zephyr Pt.*
C A R S O N
39°
39°
CRYSTAL
DESOLATION
ROCKBOUND VALLEY
1200
600
*Emerald Bay*
South Lake Tahoe
LAKE TAHOE
AREA
► Ski Area
WILDERNESS
RANGE
*Fallen Leaf Lake*
Monument Pk. △
ALPINE CO.
0   2   4   6   8
Miles
Meyers
*Echo Sum.*
89
Luther Pass
PEAVINE   RIDGE
50
*S. Fk American R.*
120°

**Map 10-6.** Lake Tahoe and environs. One of the most populous and most visited portions of the Sierra Nevada.

American and Big valleys (in the Feather River Country) are between the Grizzly Mountains and Clermont Hill.

Other than recreation, water resources and transportation, there has been limited modification in utilization of the Northern Sierra since the Gold period.

It shared in the mining activity but with less success than the Mother Lode Country. Ranching and lumbering developed early and still form important adjuncts of the economy. Some localities have shown little population gain in more than a generation but more change generally has occurred in the past several decades.

Five subdivisions of the Northern Sierra will be discussed: **Donner-Tahoe Area, American River Country, Sierra Valley, Yuba River Country,** and **Feather River Country**.

### The Donner-Tahoe Area*

The Donner-Tahoe Area, and the American River Country to the west, provide many visitors from the east their first glimpses of California—few Sierran locales could make a more impressive introduction.

While less spectacular than the High Sierra,** the Area still has high summits and hints of the ice sculpturing that is conspicuous farther south. There is sharp contrast between the Nevada desert and the forested Sierran slopes.

The Donner-Tahoe Area provides the most important corridor into central California from the Western interior.

This crossing has been used by humankind in growing numbers since the Gold Rush days. Railroad construction across Donner Summit, previously noted, took place over a century ago. Major highways, U.S. 50 and Interstate 80, provide broad paved ribbons whose generally-easy gradients make the Sierran transit a motoring pleasure.

The Area, accessible to the population of the San Francisco Bay Area and the Central Valley, has relative assurance of snow, which has made this district one of the leading winter-sports centers of western America (Fig. 10-29).

Snow sports became important in the mid-20th century, although a little skiing occurred during the Gold Rush. Long-time limitations included absence of lodgings and transportation facilities. Renewed interest in skiing came from Europe after World War I; early foci were Yosemite Park and Truckee. In the early 1930's the principal impetus came from the university campuses in Palo Alto

**Figure 10-29.** Higher in elevation than many of the Sierran ski places, Mt. Reba has more powdery snow, thus it has particular popularity. On the western edge of Alpine County and of the Mokelumne Wilderness it also on the southern fringe of the northern Sierra. (dwl)

and Berkeley when ski clubs were organized. The Sierra Club was also an important force.

The Donner-Tahoe Area has become one of the nation's most frequented ski centers.

Its advantages include diverse facilities and good highway access. **Donner Summit**, with its Sugar Bowl, Soda Springs and Boreal Ridge, has long been a much-utilized winter sports locale. Depending upon winter snowfall, the ski season usually lasts from late November into May. A series of Aleutian storms, bringing the dry powdery snow that delights the skiing enthusiasts, is considered ideal. By contrast, central Pacific storms, which

---

* The Donner-Tahoe Area has been reviewed by John James, University of Nevada, Reno
** Lamentably Bay Area news media have elected to call this land the High Sierra. Assumedly *Desolation Valley* might qualify but not Lake Tahoe.

tend to bring mushy snow, makes for unsatisfactory skiing. Open forest slopes and the customary depth of snow add to skiing enjoyment, as do the relatively mild weather and abundant sunshine.

Millions of dollars have been spent to make **Squaw Valley** one of the nation's ranking winter sports areas.

Six miles north of Lake Tahoe, the Valley was unknown until a New York socialite acquired 640 acres in 1948. After the Valley was awarded the winter Olympic Games in 1960, the state spent $20 million developing facilities that became a state park. Added millions were expended on nearby private lodges, restaurants and dwellings adjacent to the park and in nearby *Alpine Meadows*. In the 1980's an additional $200 million was expended to create an Alpine village suggestive of Zermatt (Switzerland) or Vail (Co.).

More recently another winter-sports area has developed near **Echo Summit**.

Best known of several sites here is *Heavenly Valley* on the state line with "runs" in both states. Farther south, other other developments have taken place along some trans-Sierran highways. These include *Dodge Ridge, Bear Valley-Mt. Reba* and *Kirkwood*.

Resort operators in the Donner-Tahoe Area are plagued by periods of uneven tourist activity.

The Tahoe Basin is primarily a summer vacation land; still, lodges along Interstate 80 and U.S. 50 gain considerable year-round business with wayfarers and winter-sports enthusiasts. Yet, there remains the problem of weekend congestion followed by limited mid-week activity.

**Truckee** (approx. 2500) serves as a lumbering, railroad and California gateway point and highway junction.

It benefits from services to winter sports enthusiasts—a change from its beginning as a lumber camp (nearby hillsides have long since been denuded) even though a lumber mill continues to operate.

**Lake Tahoe**, situated in a setting of breathtaking beauty, has been enjoyed over many decades by millions.

Among San Francisco socially elite, "I am going to the Sierras," has long meant the Tahoe Basin.

The Lake lies in a structural basin at an elevation of 6225 feet, rimmed by ice-sculptured summits rising above conifer-forested slopes. Tahoe is more than 20 miles long and covers 193 square miles (partly within Nevada). Ice, flowing from the south, deposited a mass of moraine across the depression thus detaching Tahoe from shallower *Fallen Leaf Lake* to the south.

Like Yosemite Valley, Tahoe and its Basin has fallen prey to its own beauty; it has become one of the more frequented highland recreation areas in the American West.

Thousands of Californians and numerous outlanders visit the Tahoe area, especially in summer, to enjoy the superlative setting and escape from hot lowlands to the west (Fig.10- 30). Lake-encircling highways add to its accessibility; there are also daily jet flights from Bay Area airports. On summer weekends and winter snow sports periods,

**Figure 10-30.** Emerald Bay. This cove on the west side of Lake Tahoe on Ca. 89 is a state park and is popular with swimmers and boaters. (Link Studio, Stateline, California).

traffic congestion becomes as annoying as on many winding city streets. This (coupled with thousands of fireplaces and wood stoves) has led to worsening smog periods. It gets particularly noxious during fair weather with high barometric pressure—pollutants get trapped in a shallow inversion only hundreds of feet deep. Scores of private resorts, lodges and cottages front the highway; except for *Bliss* and *Sugar Pine* state parks and a few other public campgrounds and beaches, desirable waterfront sites have long been privately owned (and some lots sell for "six figures"). Hiker congestion has spread upward into *Desolation Valley Wilderness.*

The lesser permanent population belies the summer hordes. But **South Lake Tahoe** (23,000) has challenged Paradise as the largest Sierran city; **Tahoe City** (circa 4000) is much smaller.

South Lake Tahoe is an elongated and gaudy array of vacation facilities and blatant billboards. Much of its growth is related to gambling casinos on the Nevada side of the lake. U.S. 50 is congested for miles throughout the year (a freeway bypass is planned). Tahoe City, focal point for nearby summer estates, has a municipal pier that provides an aquatic parking lot.

Utilization of the Tahoe Basin has experienced much change in the past century.

Californians began to recognize the resort potential early; relaxation as well as fishing and hunting lured pioneer visitors. After Tahoe City was surveyed (1863) a hotel was built. Between 1860 and 1900 the wooded slopes were logged; subsequent regrowth has occurred. Gradually better-appointed lodging was erected. Nevada water-users for a time considered lowering the Lake level to obtain more water (than the Truckee River provided).

Horse-drawn vehicles brought visitors who stayed a week or so before the automobile era. With use of automobile stays shortened. Weekend visitation has expanded to create the present-day congestion.

A wide range of summer outdoor recreation is available plus winter sports (at Mt. Rose and elsewhere).

The shallower (and warmer) waters of *Fallen Leaf Lake* and *Emerald Bay* are preferred by swimmers to the chilly waters of Tahoe's main body. The gambling casinos on the Nevada side have become the principal attraction. Virtually all other facilities, including dozens of motels, are on the California side, nearer central California.

Concentration of the tourist trade in summer adds to the problems of the resort operators.

The multitudes are so large who now frequent the Basin that only with careful planning and restriction can the beauty of the Lake and its environs be saved. A generation ago the San Francisco *Examiner* (April 6, 1961) noted the problem with con-

**Figure 10-31.** Donner Pass and the northern Sierra receive much snow in winter. Since the days of the tragic Donner Party, deep snow has hampered transit across this 7000-foot pass although railroad and highway crews usually manage to keep routes open. (Santa Fe Southern Pacific Railroad Co.)

cern: "Coney Island at Tahoe?" The Nevada legislature took steps in time to prevent a continuum of shoreside cottages. But Nevada has been reluctant to stop casino construction. The two states created a California-Nevada Interstate Compact Commission (in 1961) to apportion water shared by the two states (including Lake Tahoe and the Truckee, Carson, and Walker rivers). But there is not yet adequate protection otherwise for the Tahoe Basin.

The Basin has become more and more frequented by winter-sports enthusiasts.

Besides Mt. Rose the centers now include *Heavenly Valley* at South Lake Tahoe and *Incline Village*.

The Tahoe Basin has acquired the largest permanent population concentration in the entire SierraNevada region.

It approximates 50,000, with anticipation of 75,000 in the near future. With transients summer population approximates 300,000—water importation into the Basin may be necessitated. With rising population sewage contamination threatens the Lake despite disposal plants. Hillside housing may spill silt into Tahoe while industrial development is a threat. Tahoe Keys (at South Lake Tahoe), a $100 million waterfront development where every lot has its own dockage, has caused shoreline erosion. Yet some some business interests would support additional casinos. The Tahoe Region Planning Agency, a bi-state group (with a federal representative), was formed several years ago, charged with regulating Basin development so as to maintain the natural beauty and future activities. The consensus is that the Agency has had only limited success.

### Sierra Valley

Sierra Valley is a flattish, crudely circular plain nearly a mile above sea level.

It occupies the north end of the Tahoe depression, separated from the Basin by a rolling, much logged volcanic upland.

Settled early, the Valley forms the economic core of Sierra County.

Despite Ca. 70 and the main line of the Western Pacific Railroad (now Union Pacific) which skirts its northern edge, Sierra Valley has been apart from main travel routes.

The Valley is the principal ranching basin within the Sierra Nevada.

A number of early occupants were Italian-Swiss dairymen. Land use has changed only slightly in more than a century. Cattle ranching and summer haymaking, pioneer activities, remain the an important base of the economy despite expanded recreational use. The Valley center, with extensive marshes, contains a source of the Feather River; it is used by local ranchers and Sacramento Valley cattlemen for summer grazing. Both group also utilize slopes surrounding the basin. Hardier field crops, especially grains (barley, oats and wheat) are grown on Valley fringes; short season and frost negate many crops. With improved transportation facilities, dairying declined in the 1950's. Butter was formerly shipped to the Central Valley; now milk is brought from the Sacramento Valley at less cost than Grade-A milk can be produced locally. California markets for beef prompted a shift to beef cattle. Recent changes include land purchase by a large corporation, a turf farm and application of center-pivot irrigation.

Population is concentrated along the highways (Ca. 49, 70 and 89) that encircle the Valley.

Rural properties are large; buildings (white two-story farm houses and large barns) have steeply-pitched roofs which reflect winter snow. Towns such as *Sierraville* and *Loyalton* (1600) traditionally served local ranchers. The latter still has a lumber mill. Now there are a number of commuters to Reno, including Mormons (who do not want their families "exposed" to the gambling activity). *Calpine*, once a lumber camp, now houses retirees.

### American River Country

The Country (especially if one includes the Foothills portion of the American River basin with Auburn and Placerville) has been important since Gold Rush days.

It is traversed by two important trans-Sierran highways (I-80 and U.S. 50). I-80, paralleling the original *Central Pacific* (now Santa Fe Southern) rail line, follows a ridge; transportation services and commuter residence are significant. U.S. 50 lies in the canyon of the South Fork of the American River; many urban residents of central California have summer cabins here.

Much of the uplands area, within a national forest, has produced timber. The watershed also yields considerable water, from which Pacific Gas and Electric and Sacramento Municipal Utilities District (Sacramento M.U.D.) generate electricity.

### Yuba River Country

This Country reaches eastward from the Foothills to Sierra Valley.

This was a portion of the *Northern Mines* (see Foothills)— nowhere else did gold mining extend so far eastward into the Sierra with as much success as it did here.

Hillsides are dotted with evidence of gold mining; the western portion, in the Foothills, contains conspicuous evidence of hydraulic mining as well as the famed lode mines of Grass Valley.

Within the Yuba River Country, present-day economic activity is centered along the North Fork, which is followed by Ca. 49.

Many consider this landscape more attractive than the Feather River Canyon to the north, which is better publicized. For many years P.G. and E. has generated power at *Bullards Bar Dam.* Upstream lumbering has had continuing significance but on a scale more modest than in portions of the Foothills.

An increasing contribution to the economy of the Yuba River country is made by tourism.

Besides motels and lodges there are a series of picnic spots and campgrounds along the North Fork. Trout fishing attracts many vacationists. The canyon is accessible to residents of the Bay Area and the Sacramento Valley especially. For some weekend gold mining is a hobby that sometimes is profitable.

**Downieville** (circa 500) is the only town of consequence in the Yuba Country east of the Foothills. The village is invitingly sequestered at the base of pine-covered slopes (Fig. 10-33). It is supported by county government, lumbering, vacationists and local trade. Residents include a few senior citizens, refugees from urban California (there is no hospital but helicopter "ambulance service" to Sacramento Valley cities is available). Its tortuous main street, flanked by nineteenth-century buildings and overhanging balconies, has provided a setting for "western" movies. **Sierra City** (circa 300) up-canyon, another vacation spot, lingered as a mine camp long after boom days—gold came from a quartz ledge at the base of the *Sierra Buttes.*

The Yuba Country has been discovered by increasing numbers of central Californians.

A generation ago a venturesome capitalist might have bought the entire hamlet of Sierra City for $20,000. In less than a decade individual lots were sellings for some thousands of dollars each.

### The Feather River Country

The Feather River Country forms a heartland for the extreme Northern Sierra.

It is traversed by the main line of the Western Pacific (now owned by the Union Pacific), noted previously as a spectacular engineering feat (Fig. 10-32). Ca. 70, not too well known until the 1950's, provides a scenic crossing of the range.

**Figure 10-32.** The Feather River Canyon. Although this trans-Sierran crossing's eastern summit is half a mile lower than Donner Pass, the precipitous canyon walls long delayed (until the twentieth century) railroad and highway construction. Heavy winter rains lead to slides and washouts (Ca. 70 was closed for many months in 1986). The now-historic California Zephyr made its final run in 1970. (Union Pacific Railroad).

**Figure 10-33.** Downieville, the seat of Sierra County. This gold camp, at the confluence of the Downie and North Fork of the Yuba rivers, exudes color. Many of its residents are retirees. (dwl)

**Figure 10-34.** Indian Valley, once a "resting area" on the "way west", has long been used for livestock ranching. Now this little rift, between the Diamond and Grizzly mountains, is attracting retirees, some from Southern California. (dwl)

**Figure 10-35.** Caribou Powerhouse in the Feather River Canyon. The energy of falling water in the Feather is used and re-used to generate hydroelectricity. (Pacific Gas and Electric Company).

In recent decades the Feather River Country has become more frequented and better known for several reasons.

Its western portions formed the northern edge of the "Northern Diggings" during the Gold Rush, but much of the Feather River Country remained a quasi-wilderness until late in California history. It has since become better known and more frequented as a playground, as a producer of hydroelectricity and lumber, as a commercial passage and as a water source for drier lands to the south.

Upon occasion in winter, Ca. 70 gains more importance as an *entryway* into central California when U.S. 50 and Interstate 80 become snowbound.

The crossing is relatively low (*Beckwourth Pass* summit is 5221 ft.) which explains construction of a wagon road in 1851—it could not follow the deep narrow canyon below Portola and hence veered off to the northwest.

Later than some portions of the Sierra, much of the Feather River Country was covered with virgin forests of Douglas fir and ponderosa pine.

Exploitation was encouraged with construction of the Western Pacific Railroad in the early twentieth century. In the second half of the century expanded consumption of lumber in California prompted construction of access roads away from Ca. 70. Widespread lumbering prompted cutting of some of the state's finest remaining softwoods; milling places included Quincy and Indian Valley. Heavy winter snowfall prompted logging in summer hence seasonal unemployment was a local problem, as in other northern California locales.

The Country formed the northern end of the Sierran gold belt.

Shortly after discovery of gold farther south, Foothills portions of the Feather River Country were being worked. Miners progressed rapidly up the canyons.

Such places as *Bidwell Bar* (now beneath waters of Lake Oroville), Big Bar and Rich Bar were sites of some of the more spectacular placering. The hydraulic operation at Cherokee was noted previously. *Plumas-Eureka* (farther east near Johnsville) was the best known lode mine.

Largest stream in the Sierra, the Feather River has become a major focus of hydroelectric development (by Pacific Gas and Electric).

Great Western Power (merged later into P.G. and E.) erected a dam in 1917 to create **Lake Almanor**, a regulatory body covering Big Meadows. Downriver (along the North Fork) P.G. and E. uses and reuses falling water (Fig.10-35) at six powerhouses to generate 712,000 kilowatts. Recently several city-owned utilities tried to acquire these plants. There are additional plants on the West Branch and three more power houses have been constructed on the South Fork in connection with Oroville-Wyandotte Irrigation District construction. P.G. and E. desired to construct generating facilities on the less accessible Middle Fork; there was strong opposition from conservationists and fishers—the Middle Fork is now a wild river. In addition to Lake Almanor, another artificial lake, *Bucks*, is used for water sports plus adjacent summer cabins.

Ranching is relatively inconsequential in the Country although uplands and basins are sometimes used.

The two principal basins, other than Sierra Valley already noted, are *American Valley* around Quincy and *Indian Valley*, a dairying area before World War II, now devoted to beef cattle (Fig.10-34) and retiree residence.

**Figure 10-36.** Keddie, once a division point on the Western Pacific Railroad, did not succeed too well as a resort. Now it houses commuters to Quincy and elsewhere. (English Properties, photo by Eastman's Studio, Susanville).

**Figure 10-37.** Lake Oroville is the key storage unit for the California Water Project. Oroville Dam, at the time of its completion in 1967, was the world's largest earth-fill dam. It rises 770 feet and is a mile long. The lake, like Shasta Lake farther north, has become a leading center for aquatic recreation in northern California. (California Department of Water Resources).

The Feather River Country is being used increasingly as a summer vacation land despite distance from major centers.

The appeal of the *North Fork Canyon,* where most of the resorts are located, alone makes it attractive for outings (Fig.10-36). Sports fishing is popular while winter sports have local patronage.

The Country is located less advantageously than Mammoth Lakes or the Donner-Tahoe Area. Yet the beauty of **Lakes Basin Recreation Area** (in the Grizzly Mountains near Sierra Buttes) lures campers, fishers and hikers. Nearby **Plumas- Eureka** mine is the focal point of a 5600-acre park that is considered one of the more inviting in the California state system. Most skiers come from nearby towns. Second homes and golf courses are found around *Graeagle,* once a lumber camp.

Feather River communities are both small and older towns.

Their slow growth reflects economic limitations of the Northern Sierra. There are a number of abandoned lumber towns and ghost mine camps.

**Quincy** (6500 with fringes), an unincorporated county seat, affords a service point for a sizable, if sparsely populated, area.

This one-time gold camp lies snug against the southern edge of American Valley. It has had lumbering and there is a community college. Governmental activities include the headquarters of a national forest. With its older frame dwellings and white marble courthouse it suggests a Vermont village. Highway services are conspicuous.

**Portola** (2000) depends upon the railroad, tourism and highway services. It began as an early twentieth century railroad division point. Now highway services have importance. Mormons and others also commute to employment in Reno.

### Looking Ahead

This largest of mountain ranges in the 48 conterminous states has provided California a magnificent inheritance. How much of this legacy must be squandered by selfish individuals who with callous disregard for future residents, assert that "this land is mine?" With continued population growth in the Golden State, ever-increasing utilization of this lofty mass is anticipated. As a barrier, its significance has been lessened by technological advances. Present-day federal and state highways and rail lines have diminished the effectiveness of its mighty wall. Accelerated population growth indicates expanded utilization for recreation. Summer congestion in the Tahoe Basin and Yosemite Valley will doubtless be duplicated elsewhere. Attractive cabin sites on water have become expensive. Despite higher gold prices it is doubtful if mining will ever again have the moment it did during the Gold Rush. Yet for generations to come, the Foothills should be frequented by those who wish to visualize the atmosphere of that tumultuous period in Golden State history. Water resources will have more demand and need for conservation more urgency; additional dams are anticipated but will continue to be opposed by "white river" enthusiasts and other preservationists. Increased forest conservation is overdue; tree farming should in time wholly replace forest mining. An interesting question pertains to the future: Locked in federal preserves, can it remain a virgin wilderness— or like Lake Tahoe and Yosemite Valley, will it be opened to the masses with construction of paved highways, resorts and other lures? Trends in Auburn, Paradise and Tahoe Basin intimate bigger cities yet sizable urban centers still seem improbable. There is slight evidence for much industrial development.

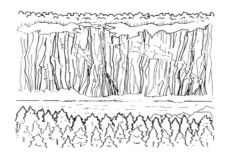

**Figure 11-1.** "I think it is only the Californian's love of superlatives that allows him to mention Mt. Whitney, while dwelling in the same state with Mt. Shasta. Whitney's claim to fame is merely that it is the highest peak in continental United States..as a mountain it is nothing to look at...Shasta, but a few hundred feet shorter of stature...rises grand and solitary above a vast volcanic plain, dominating the landscape for a hundred miles... Shasta, then, is the real thing..." (Quotation from Charis W. and Edward Weston, *California and the West* (Duell, Sloan and Pearce, 1940, p. 97). Copyright 1940 by the Westons. Reprinted by permission. (dwl)

Chapter Eleven

# THE SOUTHERN CASCADE *

*This chapter has been reviewed by Ladd Johnson, California State University,Chico and Phillip Tincher, Shasta College. Previously it had been reviewed by Arthur Carthew, Los Angeles City College and John Carthew, Pierce College.

# THE SOUTHERN CASCADE

There is almost a surfeit of natural loveliness in the Golden State. As the state's population expands by additional millions and as beauteous spots near its urban clusters yield to human modification, it is a blessing that the major mountain masses of California, too sizeable and too steep-sloped to bulldoze into plains and too perdurable for natural wastage within the human time scale, can provide places of brief relaxation and respite apart from urban life on increasingly-crowded lowlands.

The Southern Cascade has less fame than its sibling highlands to the south, the Sierra Nevada, despite its verdure, ever-flowing streams and several snow-tipped cones. Yet the Cascade has mountains which Californians can enjoy.

Most of the Cascade lies north of the Golden State (it extends from southern British Columbia to Lassen Peak). Still California possesses two of the better-known summits, Mount Shasta and Lassen Peak. Similar in size to the Colorado Desert (Ch. 5), the California Cascade approximates 4000 square miles, hence qualifies as one of the two smallest subregions of the state. Still its population (about 50,000) exceeds that of the adjoining *Northeast*, (Ch. 2) which is twice as large.

Physical boundaries of the California Cascade are difficult to define precisely.

Somewhat blurred is the eastern border—the Modoc Plateau of the Northeast *also* has scattered cinder cones. To the west the Sacramento Gorge and Shasta Valley provide a depression between the Klamath Mountains of the Northwest (Ch. 12) and the Cascade. There is a southerly transition from the western slope of the granitic Sierra to the volcanic landscape around Lassen Peak—it is convenient to draw a line between Susanville and Chico. For humankind the northern boundary is simple—it is the Oregon-California line.

Sociopolitical delimitation is more difficult.

From Nevada to Pacific shores residents of far northern California have similar local interests—and disinterest in many international and national issues. In one Congressional election, a candidate, queried about "issues", replied in frustration, "What issues? Nothing besides legislation related to fishing and hunting, water, timber and ranching seems to concern most of these people."

## THE PHYSICAL REALM

The earth, as elsewhere in California, often seems to form the basis for geographic subdivision.

In a sparsely populated land like the Southern Cascade, terrain becomes particularly conspicuous (Fig. 11-1). The Cascade, in the recent geologic past, was the locale of some of Vulcan's best displays of natural fireworks.

The Southern Cascade consists of a dissected tableland of basaltic sheets, mudflows, and ash, topped by volcanic cones.

This is the only California subregion so completely dominated by volcanic features. South of Mt. Shasta the range is rather poorly defined with numerous small cinder cones; besides better-known Lassen Peak prominent summits include *Crater Mountain* (7148 ft.) and *Burney Mountain* (7871 ft.). Northward from Shasta the area is more typically Cascadian with larger volcanoes rising more impressively above their surroundings. The most noteworthy in California, aside from Mt. Shasta, are *Whaleback* (8536 ft.) and *Goose Nest* (8289 ft.).

Encompassing the largest single diameter in the *entire* range, *Mt.Shasta* (14,162 ft.) is considered by many California's most impressive summit.

This majestic peak rises almost two miles above its surroundings to completely dominate the locale. It is actually a double cone; its younger "twin," *Shastina*, attains 12,336 ft.. Shasta wears a tiara of valley glaciers whose dimensions have been reduced appreciably since the Little Ice Age. More-

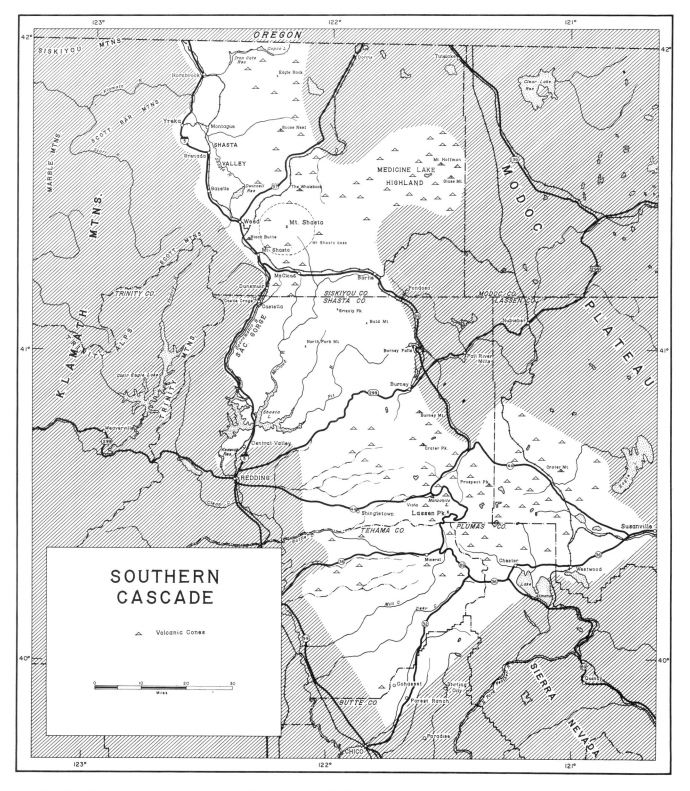

**Map 11-1.** Most of the Cascade Range is within Oregon and Washington—but how fortunate California is to have a small portion.

over, the volcano is not completely extinct; its crater is still "hot."

Northeast of Shasta the *Medicine Hat Highland* contains scores of small cones rising above a shield base. While the highest of these, *Mt. Hoffman* reaches 7928 ft., *Glass Mountain*, an obsidian pile, is nearly as high (7649 ft.).

Much of the *Lassen Volcanic Ridge* (Fig. 11-2) lies within the national park—it forms the range's southern limits.

With hundreds of small cinder cones, the Ridge was once dominated by an ancient stratovolcano, *Mt. Tehama*, which collapsed internally. *Lassen Peak*, a *plug* volcano, arose from its core late, as did Cinder Cone (6913 ft.) to the northeast. A few hundred years ago Chaos Crags likewise arose from the northwest base of Lassen. From 1914-1917 Lassen was "mildly" active; hundreds of explosions occurred. Some of these "eruptions" resulted from the contact between hot lava and snow meltwater. Since the St. Helens "showoff" of 1980, Californians, even overlooking activity in Hawaii and Alaska, cannot claim Lassen as the single area of recent American activity.

Two depressions, the *Sacramento Gorge* and *Shasta Valley* form the western periphery of the California Cascade, thus creating a separation from the Klamath Mountains to the west.

Oval-like Shasta Valley, 15 miles wide (east-west) by 30 miles long, has a highly irregular surface at about 2500 feet elevation; its western portion consists of floodplains and alluvial fans, with volcanic features in the south.

Beyond Mt. Shasta to the south of Shasta Valley, the Sacramento, fed by streams from the Northeast and swollen with meltwater from the slopes of Shasta, has cut its impressive *Gorge* into the eastern prong of the Klamath Mountains.

The *McCloud Country*, east of the Gorge, is also a portion of the geologic Klamath Mountains. Because of their location, both these features are included within the Southern Cascade.

The subregion has deep defiles, such as those formed by the Klamath, McCloud, Pit and Sacramento, yet they seem less awesome than the major canyons of the Sierra Nevada.

Because the continuously high crest and the abrupt eastern wall of the Sierra are absent, east-west Cascadian travel is less difficult. Two west-flowing rivers, the Pit and the Klamath, completely breach the California Cascade.

This subregion, like the remainder of California. experiences summer drought.

Perhaps more important is the effect of varying altitudes, which create vertical zones and climatic complexity.

Shasta Valley is *semi-arid middle latitude,* a reflection of its *rainshadow* location east of the Klamath Mountains. Eastward, lower portions of the tableland grade into *dry-summer middle latitude*, more extensive in the Northeast (see Ch.2 and Overview A). A *tundra* zone exists above timberline (about 10,000 feet) on Mt. Shasta (Fig.11-1) and Lassen Peak.

Elevation becomes a major factor when Pacific storms cross northern California in winter. Lower

**Figure 11-2.** The Lassen Volcanic Ridge. Near its southern limits the Cascade Range is ill-defined. A cluster of volcanic cones rise like giant scoops of ice cream above the surrounding basaltic tableland. View south with the town of Burney. Seen here are Burney Peak (7871 feet) and Lassen Peak, on the horizon (rear). (dwl)

lands receive moisture as either snow or rain (annual snowfall varies between 50 and 100 inches). But the southwestern slopes of the volcanic cones receive considerably more precipitation; between 20 and 30 feet of snow falls annually on Lassen Peak.

The Cascade is a land of much-cut forests, principally pine and fir.

Dominated by sugar pine, yellow pine, white fir and Douglas fir, an open conifer forest typifies elevations between 2000 and 6000 feet. Known as the montane zone (or Sierran transition) it forms a continuation of the Sierran westside belt and has been the focus of commercial lumbering. The understory is often a carpet of green meadows, chaparral shrubs or flowers.

There is a timberline zone of hemlock and whitebark pine above the pine-fir forests on the slopes of Lassen and Shasta. It is replaced by alpine meadows higher up, with dwarf trees, lichens, daisies and penstemons.

Shrubs and brush are locally prominent—forest cover is not ever-present.

Shasta Valley has sagebrush and rabbitbrush; there is also appreciable grassland. Chaparral is elsewhere too. A belt of this "elfin forest", manzanita-dominated, surrounds the base of Mt. Shasta.

## YESTERYEAR

Sparsely populated in pre-Spanish days, the Cascade remains one of the less-inhabited portions of the Golden State.

The mountain "spine" through the center of the subregion has appreciably reduced its human utilization.

The *Shastans*, members of the Hokan tribe, were the aboriginal residents of the area.

They occupied lower elevations, in Shasta Valley and Scott Valley (in the Northwest—Ch.12) and along the Pit and the Klamath. Their dread enemies, the Modoc, were on the northeastern fringes. Hunters and fisherfolk, the Shastans also gathered acorns and manzanita berries. Diet was based mainly upon salmon from the rivers and deer and bear. Yet these peoples were among the more culturally backward California Indians, especially the Yurok.

The Cascade was beyond Spanish California.

Captain Luis Arguello led an exploring party in 1820 that skirted the southwestern fringe of the subregion and assigned the name Mt. Joseph to Lassen Peak.

British and American fur trappers visited the California Cascade between 1827 and 1845.

**Figure 11-3.** Yreka, county seat, service center, highway junction, lumber producer—the ranking city of the southern Cascade. Separated from Shasta Valley proper by the Killdall Hills (right), this Gold Rush camp continues to prosper. (Yreka Chamnber of Commerce, photo by Yreka Studio and Camera Shop).

Some of the trails they followed became routes of pioneers who came later.

The central passage of the *California-Oregon Trail* is now the general course of Interstate 5.

It connected the Willamette and Sacramento valleys via the Southern Cascade. The several segments of the Trail provided logical routes which doubtless had been employed by Indians. One route went west of the Sacramento Gorge, up the Trinity River, thence into Scott Valley. The central Gorge branch was followed early by Hudson Bay trappers. It was used to drive cattle northward from Mexican California into Oregon in the late 1830's and in the 1840's. In 1854 a deviant wagon road circled east of Mt. Shasta into Shasta Valley, avoiding the Gorge.

By 1860 stagecoaches were operating between Sacramento and Portland; trips continued until the arrival of the railroad in 1887. Early east-west routes across the range included *Lassen's Trail* and the *Emigrant Trail*; the latter wound past Cinder Cone and Manzanita Lake (now in Lassen Park).

The volcanic Cascade has not favored too much mining.

Quest for gold brought the granitic periphery of the subregion into brief prominence in 1851 although more activity occurred in the Klamath Mountains to the west (Ch. 12).

Oregonians scurrying to the Sierran gold fields overlooked Shasta Valley. It was other miners, working eastward up the gravel bars along the Klamath, who "found" Shasta Valley. Additional strikes occurred around Yreka; although mining endured for several years gold production never reached the levels of other centers. Much later Bully Hill, whose smelter at Kennett is now beneath Lake Shasta, was important as a source of copper. Calaveras Cement operates northeast of Redding and prospects for an iron mine in the area have been investigated. These activities occur in the sedimentary-metamorphic extension of the geologic Klamath Mountains.

A modest number of gold miners became ranchers in the Southern Cascade but widespread settlement has never occurred.

The subregion suffered isolation in the pre-railroad era. Completion of the Shasta Line of the Southern Pacific favored increased utilization.

Between 1890 and 1920 forestry became a late occupance force.

Gold mining did not persist long enough to create a local lumber market, as took place in the Sierra. Before the railroad the California Cascade was too inaccessible to justify extensive lumbering—good stands of trees were more available elsewhere. Hence some lumber-oriented towns were not established until the late nineteenth or early twentieth century.

## FORESTRY AND OTHER PURSUITS

During the twentieth century the Cascadian economy has been modified.

Lumbering, commerce, use of water and recreation have developed or expanded. But agriculture and livestock ranching existed before 1900.

### The Way to Oregon

Through commerce is a basic source of livelihood in the Cascade.

The *Shasta Corridor* follows the course of the California-Oregon Trail through the Sacramento Gorge and across Shasta Valley. It forms a portion of one of three major north-south routes into Oregon (others are the coastal, or Redwood, and the Intermontane passage through Susanville and Alturas). Way stations, established in the days of freight wagons and stage coaches, eventually become railroad stops; some developed into towns.

The Shasta Route has provided the single rail corridor between central California and Portland and

**Figure 11-4.** Logging operations east of Redding. The power saw, the motor truck, the Caterpillar Tracavator, sometimes *even* helicopters, have replaced the logging railroad , handsaw and donkey engine of days long ago. (Caterpillar Tractor Company).

Puget Sound since 1887.

A branch line from Black Butte (near Weed) to Klamath Falls was completed in 1909; it has replaced the Ashland-Medford segment as the "main line" of the Shasta Route.

Interstate 5, successor to U.S. 99 as the "mainstreet of California," follows the old Gorge trail.

The Gorge remained a vexatious impediment until freeway completion (Fig. 11-7). Impressive excavations were needed to create the multi-lane highway in the vicinity of Dunsmuir. Highway services is an important activity in route towns.

Cascadian terrain is more negotiable for east-west travel routes than Sierran topography, *except* in areas of much dissection.

For example, the dissected tablelands south of Ca. 36 (southwest of Lassen Park) have some of the least-passable in the state. Several east-west highways link the Intermontane Region east of the Cascade with Interstate 5.

U.S. 97 parallels the railroad between Weed and Klamath Falls. The eastern portion of Ca. 299 crosses the range between Lassen Peak and Mt. Shasta. Ca. 44 and Ca. 36, farther south, likewise serve as gateways to Lassen Park; Ca. 36 is also an important year-round crossing past Chester to Susanville. Ca. 36, with increasing traffic, has been improved. Mechanical plows have lessened periods of winter closure due to deep snow.

East of Interstate 5, Ca. 89 (Mt. Shasta city-Lassen Park-Tahoe Basin) is the single north-south highway within the range; it crosses I-80 at Truckee. Ca. 44-A21 skirts the higher country within Lassen Park, thus is suitable for winter travel.

### Beef—Not Milk

Ranching has provided the most constant mainstay of Cascadian economy since the Gold Rush days.

Rugged terrain, thin rocky soils and extensive timberlands have restricted agriculture. While livestock ranching is more extensive, holdings are scattered—Shasta Valley is the single sizable area.

Because of its rolling volcanic topography **Shasta Valley**, approximately 500 square miles in extent, does not resemble the usual intermontane basin.*

The eastern half, *The Scablands*, is almost without farm value except for Little Shasta Valley. In addition to terrain and poor soil, the Valley is hampered by limited water, short growing season and distance from major California markets.

There were extensive grasslands in the western Shasta Valley; here extensive areas were plowed under and planted in wheat.

Although some land was eventually homesteaded, there were extensive properties too. Before the Forest Service (early 1900's) mountain range seemed sufficient; transhumance had significance. Before the railroad arrived cattle were trailed south to Redding. Irrigation began in the 1870's and alfalfa introduced; in recent decades sprinklers have tended to replace flooding of hay meadows.

While promoters established several "colonies," rural land-use has experienced modest changes in the twentieth century.

Short seasons and limited markets impede many crops found in the Central Valley although such row crops as beans and onions are raised.

Dairying, which became important in the 1920's, has declined since the 1950's, as in Sierra Valley (Ch. 10). As urbanization continues around Watsonville (Ch. 7) some feel there could possibly be relocation of apple orchards into Shasta Valley. The raising of summer-ripening apples in the Central Valley makes this less likely.

Beef cattle remain the principal product of Shasta Valley despite the demise of transhumance.

The "typical" cattle ranch encompasses about 6500 acres; properties on rough lands are even larger. Herefords (or Aberdeen Angus) are usually shipped to the Sacramento Valley for fattening before delivery to slaughter houses.

### Forest Products: A Troubled Industry

Lumbering remains an important economic pursuit in the California Cascade but has become a troubled industry.

The subregion has been one of the state's primary sources of pine lumber, ranking after the Northwest and the Sierra Nevada. There are extensive private holdings as well as three national forests (in Shasta County acreage of private land exceeds national forest lands).

Despite much change, forestry is still of moment in the local economy.

Accelerated cutting nearly half a century ago reduced stands on private lands; many small

---

* The wayfarer on I-5 misses much of the Valley. The highway veers west through Yreka Creek Valley, separated from the remainder of the basin by the Killdall Hills. Residents of Yreka do not consider their re-entrant Yreka Basin a part of Shasta Valley.

("gypo") mills closed as such sources were diminished. Operations then stabilized for a decade or so, as activities were dominated by large corporations. But with changing techniques, some corporations appear to have closed older mills to take advantage of tax write-offs. With purchase of supplemental logs from public lands (especially in the Klamath National Forest) a sustained-yield basis may be achieved. Some firms retain sizable tree plantations.

Large tracts have been accumulated in different ways. One method employed the *Timber and Stone Act* (1878). More recently some corporations acquired holdings through purchase. For example, Diamond International, which processes its wood in the Sacramento Valley (Ch.9) began accumulating its 220,000-acre tree farms in the southwestern California Cascade (paralleling Ca. 32) with purchase of Sierra Lumber Company. Sierra in turn had been created in 1878 out of individual operations in eastern Butte County that originated in 1866. Diamond in turn was acquired in the 1980's by a British financier who has dismantled it.

Various methods of removing logs have been employed.

Use of oxcarts, obviously slow, began early. Later in the nineteenth century much footage was transported into the Sacramento Valley by flumes, some as long as 25 miles. They carried impressive loads; the last one was built east of Anderson in 1886. Subsequently logging railroads were built. The McCloud River Railroad connects the Southern Pacific at Mt. Shasta with the Burlington Northern at Big Valley (Ch.2). Diamond International's Butte County Railroad (now dismantled) went eastward from the Southern Pacific mainline at Chico. In recent decades additional mechanized equipment has been employed, including trucks and diesel tractors (Fig. 11-4). Some firms constructed their own logging roads.

Large forestry operations in the Cascade began in the late nineteenth century.

McCloud Lumber Company (no longer operating) established its company town, McCloud (east of Mt. Shasta city), before 1900. As noted above the firm built a logging railroad. Even after its purchase by Champion International it employed 750 men and cut 130 million board feet annually, operating two sawmills, a planing mill and five bandsaws. The operation was closed in 1979 and the plant has been dismantled. Closure surprised some, since the firm had acquired cutting rights to a billion board feet of timber from Fruit Growers

**Figure 11-5.** Weed—lumber town, highway stop, college town. At the south end of Shasta Valley, its *reduced* lumber operation (once Weed Lumber, then Long-Bell, then International Paper and now Roseburg Lumber) survive a bit precariously. (Weed Chamber of Commerce.

**Figure 11-6.** College of the Siskiyous, the *single* institution of higher education in the Southern Cascade, not founded until 1957, has a superlative setting near the northwestern base of Mt. Shasta (College of Siskiyous, photo by Bauer)

Supply (an affiliate of Sunkist) after that firm closed its Westwood operation.

Another major producer, International Paper, sold its operation in Weed and the plant has been closed partially.

Antecedents began at the turn of the century when Abner Weed established Weed Lumber Company, with 70 employes, and laid out the town of Weed (Fig. 11-5). A box factory was built in 1900, a sash-and-door mill in 1907 and the second-oldest plywood plant on the West Coast in 1911. Sold in 1913, the plant was acquired by Long-Bell Lumber (merged with International Paper) in 1956. Long-Bell had cut timber extensively northeast of Mt. Shasta; dirt roads still follow its erstwhile logging road grades. Recently the operation has been acquired by Roseville Lumber, an expanding Oregon firm; despite mill closure, some logging and finishing activities continue.

A Minnesota firm, Red River Lumber Company, developed one of the largest forest operations in the Southern Cascade.

It obtained large holdings east of Lake Almanor and commenced activities at the company-owned town of Westwood in 1913. The town for several decades was the largest community in the subregion. Little changed, it was a "typical" company town with unpaved streets, wooden plank sidewalks, unpainted frame houses and a company commissary. After World War II the operation was acquired by Fruit Growers Supply (Sunkist affiliate), which later suspended operations. In 1956 the mill was torn down.

Some of the largest private tracts of Cascadian timber have been held by Shasta Forests, Inc., a family holding-company owned by heirs of T.B.

**Figure 11-7.** Dunsmuir and the Sacramento Gorge. The narrow defile posed a highway traffic barrier for a long time. The solution (right) still creates problems during wet winters. (Caltrans)

**Figure 11-8.** Hydroelectric plant on the Pit River. The utility has constructed a chain of powerhouses along this stream, as well as many others farther south on the Feather, Yuba, American, and Kings rivers. View shows Pit No. 5. (Pacific Gas and Electric Company)

**Figure 11-9.** Lassen Park and Lake Manzanita. Although it is not the most awe-inspiring of national parks, Lassen has geologic interest and provides cool open space for camping and hiking, as well as fishing and winter skiing. Since 1974 the environs of Manzanita Lake has been declared "geologically hazardous." (National Park Service)

Walker, one of the wealthiest men in America when he created the Westwood operation. Sundry operations are still conducted, albeit much reduced, in the Sacramento Valley and the Northeast; affiliated firms have included Paul Bunyan and Ralph Smith.

### Hydro Power: At Capacity

With portions of two of the Golden State's three largest rivers (Sacramento and Klamath), the California Cascade is an important supplier of hydroelectric energy.

Activities include the single-largest power operation (at Shasta and Keswick dams) in California (Fig. 11-11).

Most of the power generated in the subregion is transmitted elsewhere, particularly to the San Francisco Bay Area and the Central Valley, since local population is small and industry limited.

Activity early was undertaken by California-Oregon Power Company (now part of Pacificorp of Portland). With limited demand in the Southern Cascade much of the energy goes to Oregon. The hydro plants are east of I-5 on the Klamath and there is an interchange with Pacific Gas and Electric (P.G. and E.).

Hydroelectricity has been developed by P.G. and E., major supplier of power to northern and central California, on Hat Creek and at several plants along the Pit River.

P.G. and E. added three additional plants along the McCloud in the 1960's so that the 733,400-kilowatt output of the Pit-McCloud plants exceeds that of the firm's Feather River operations (Ch.10). *Shasta Dam* constitutes the first major storage unit in the Central Valley Project (Ch. 9).

The structure was erected by a group of California contractors who took the name Pacific Constructors, Inc.. It is 602 feet high and 3460 feet long and contains more concrete than Hoover Dam; it retains a reservoir with a capacity of 4.5 million acre feet. Heightening has been proposed to nearly treble storage capacity. Power is sold to various city-owned utilities and to P.G. and E..

### Hikers and Fishers

The California Cascade in near-entirety provides a vast natural playground, still little frequented; it should achieve greater value as California population increases.

The Cascade, with adjacent portions of the Northeast (Ch.2) and Oregon, has been identified locally as the *Shasta-Cascade Wonderland.* Encompassing 2.5 million acres, this inviting land, includes a national park, three national forests (with several wilderness areas) and California's largest man-made lake. Despite improved highways in recent decades, much of the area remains accessible only by pack horse or by hiking.

Least-frequented of California's four Cascadian-Sierran national parks, **Lassen Volcanic National Park** is also the smallest.

**Figure 11-10.** Winter sports at Lassen Park. In winter the Lassen Loop Highway (Ca. 89) is closed for many months although it is kept open (from Ca. 36) to the ski area. Skiers come mostly from Redding, Red Bluff and Chico. (National Park Service)

**Figure 11-11.** Shasta Dam, Shasta Lake and Mt. Shasta. Shasta Dam, 602 feet high and 3460 feet long, is the *key* unit the Central Valley Project. Built without widespread publicity during World War II, it produces hydroelectricity, provides recreation, regulates the flow of the Sacramento River, afford storage for irrigation and has reduced flooding in the Sacramento Valley. In the 1980's there have been proposals to heighten the dam and thus double the storage capacity. (dwl)

Its establishment in 1916 followed volcanic activity that began in 1914, with ashes and vapor rising as high as 40,000 feet.

The chief attraction is Lassen Peak, ascended by a 2.5 mile trail that allows a good view of the surrounding tableland (Fig.11-9). There are other volcanic features, as well as forests, lakes and meadows.

Most summer visitors follow the *Lassen Loop Highway,* a segment of Ca. 89, possibly stopping to visit Lake Helen (at the base of the peak trail) or Bumpass Hell. The latter is the most impressive of three areas with sulphuric fumes and mud pots. The park remains greener, cooler and less dusty than the three Sierran national parks. Lassen continues to be a "camper's choice"; facilities are modest—and nearby lodges are few.

Eastern Lassen Park, accessible chiefly by trails, is a rolling land of conifer forests, lakes and meadows. It is a satisfying country for the fisher and the hiker, with cross-country skiing in winter.

A portion of Shasta National Forest, *Mt. Shasta Recreation Area* lacks the highways and other facilities of Lassen Park.

Shasta has been regarded as the most impressive summit in the Golden State by naturalist John Muir and many others (Fig.11-1). Muir's views that the peak should be a national park have not received sufficient local support.

A difficult climb for the "average" hiker, Shasta is climbed far less often than Lassen. Hikers usually depart from Mt. Shasta (city) and drive to the end of the Everitt Memorial Highway at 7703 feet. In *Steep Trails* Muir described what can await one who endeavors to ascend the peak in early spring. A one-time Ski Bowl lodge burned; it has been replaced and and the ski lift (to 9212 feet) is again in operation. The snow supply is excellent but the locale is distant from large urban areas.

After completion of Shasta Dam (in 1944) **Shasta Lake National Recreation Area** was established (Fig.11-11).

There is a 365-mile shoreline around the 47 square-mile water body. Even before construction of the reservoir the Sacramento and its tributary streams had already gained popularity with sportsmen. The lower McCloud canyon especially has been used for summer cottages and for camping for many years. Much of the McCloud Country has been a private preserve of the Hearst family for generations. Unlike San Simeon the family's *Wintun Lodge* is surprisingly unknown even in northern California.

The California Cascade contains two state parks.

Actually within the Klamath Mountains but adjacent to Interstate 5, *Castle Crags* is a granitic mass suggestive of a miniature Sierra Nevada. It overlooks the Sacramento Gorge. *McArthur-Burney Falls*, north of Burney on Ca. 89, has as its outstanding feature the double 165-foot falls of Burney Creek, which plunges into a pine-surrounded pool (Fig. 11-12).

**Figure 11-12.** McArthur-Burney Falls Memorial State Park. The waterfall is the highlight of the 485-acre park on Ca. 89. Nearby Lake Britton, a P.G. and E. storage reservoir, affords water sports and fishing. (California Division of Parks and Beaches).

Within Lassen National Forest two wildernesses flank the national park.

They are more attainable than most wild areas in the Golden State. *Caribou Peak*, with 16,000 acres southeast of Lassen Peak, provides excellent sports fishing. *Thousand Lakes*, northwest of the park is small (15,000 acres) and visited infrequently despite an attractive camping and hiking setting with many little lakes and access from nearby highways.

In a lovely conifer setting, **Lake Almanor** has become a popular recreation destination in northern California.

It is located along the "border zone" between the Sierra and the California Cascade. Like some of the storage reservoirs mentioned in the previous chapter it looks deceptively natural. Its shores offer appealing vistas of Lassen Peak. Much use is made of the lake for water sports and fishing. Since highway improvement (Ca.32,36,89 and 70) and population growth in central and northern California, a number of summer homes have been built, especially at *The Peninsula* and along the west shore. Land prices demonstrate that there is no "free" waterside land in northern California!

## QUASI-STAGNANT VILLAGES

There is a modest number of smaller communities, generally time-worn and often languishing, within the Cascade.

Apart from the Northeast and the Trans-Sierra, no California subregion has so few consequential towns. Those along Interstate 5 tend to be more active and "closer" to life in the rest of California.

Customary functions include local services (such as groceries and gasoline), way stops for highway travelers, shipping facilities (for ranchers and lumber firms) and residence for a small number of city-refugee retirees. Shasta Valley has the principal concentration of hamlets; elsewhere villages tend to be scattered.

The single "pseudo-metropolis" is **Yreka** (6000).

This is the oldest town (Gold Rush beginnings) in the subregion and through the years generally has been the largest. It functions as the service place for Shasta Valley and Siskiyou County (it is the county seat), I-5 highway stop, and lumber processor (its several non-corporate mills are rather unique today in California).

Some business blocks along Miner Street (principal east-west avenue) and frame cottages along locust-lined streets sometimes date from the gold years.

On the southern periphery of Shasta Valley, **Weed** (3000) has somewhat different functions than Yreka.

Its lumber camp roll has declined (especially since closing of the mill). But this legacy is reflected in the greatest ethnic diversity (especially Italian and Southern black) in the subregion. At the junction of U.S. 97 and I-5, the travel function is important. It has in College of the Siskiyous the single collegiate institution in the California Cascade.

The highway function looms large in **Dunsmuir** (2200), the only important town along the Sacramento Gorge.

For decades its major function was as as railroad division point at the south end of the volcanic uplands between the Rogue River Valley of Oregon and the Sacramento Gorge. That activity lessened with the railroad's shift to diesel locomotives. Despite an attractive but steep-sloped setting, the future seems limited.

**Mount Shasta** (2800) city, spectacularly sited at the base of the peak, functions chiefly as a residence place and outfitting point for sportsmen who frequent the Mount Shasta Recreation Area.

Its lumber processing function has declined but it remains a preferred retirement community for Italian lumbermen (and others) which explains the unique cuisine of some downtown restaurants.

A "place of widows" might describe **McCloud** (2100), formerly a company lumber camp.

After an investment company bought the town in toto in 1966 and sold dwellings individually, many retiring lumbermen remained. Many houses have been refurbished, and some conceive of McCloud as the future "Paradise (see Ch.10) of the Southern Cascade."

Should **Burney** (2200) lose its forest products mill, the future could be precarious.

Status as a northern gateway to Lassen Park affords some support and there is some retiree residence.

**Central Valley** (2400) is a lower-income northern outlier of Redding (Ch.9).

Founded as a residence place for Shasta Dam construction crews (many came from the Great Plains), it has a noticeable dearth of business executives and professional people.

**Chester** (1500) has grown as a waystop on Ca. 32 (and southern entry point to Lassen Park), as the service place for Lake Almanor and environs and a lumber processor.

Demise of its mill could lead to economic decline. Attractively situated beside Lake Almanor on the North Fork of the Feather, the town probably has a better future than some in the subregion. Its airport is popular for "fly-ins" of visitors to Lake Almanor and Lassen Park.

The hamlet of *Mineral*, farther west, which "seems" to stretch for miles along Ca. 36, is *also* a Park gateway as well as the headquarters for Lassen Park.

**Westwood** (1800), another former lumber camp, a town that "would not die", now functions as retirement place with many commuters.

It began as a Red River Lumber camp in 1913 and became the largest Cascadian town (circa 4000). After milling ceased in 1956, a Los Angeles firm bought the entire town for dismantling. It was soon evident that many residents desired to stay and the houses were sold individually—many became vacation dwellings. Now there is much commutation to Susanville (including a number of ex-urban youth who ride by "free bus"—Ch.2) and Chester. Primarily blue collar and cohesive, Westwood has many single parents; about a quarter of its residents are retired.

### Suburbia

The Southern Cascade lacks a north-south highway comparable to the Sierra's Ca. 49 through its western fringes. And in the Sacramento Valley north of the state capital there are only two incipient metropolitan areas, Chico and Redding. East of these two cities there are "hints" of urbanization based on commutation.

East of Chico along Ca. 32 **Forest Ranch** (1500) in the pines is vaguely suggestive of Paradise (Ch. 10), several ridges to the south. Northeast of Chico along a county road is **Cohasset** (circa 2000). Both of these unincorporated hamlets are water-short but gaining in population.

East of Redding, along Ca. 44, are **Palo Cedro** and **Shingletown**. Farther north, along Ca. 299, is **Bella Vista**. "Softer" terrain and water near to the surface, as well as a north-south county road, is permitting "suggestions" of an earlier-day Paradise or Atascadero with "week-end gardener" agriculture including viticulture and horse ranches.

## THE FUTURE:
### Perhaps Not Promising?

Examining the future in California can be risky. While the population of the Golden State continues to grow, the decades ahead portend uncertainty for the Southern Cascade. For several decades geologists have warned that future eruptions of volcanic cones can occur—Mt. St. Helens suggest need for concern about Shasta and Lassen. Obviously residents of Cascadian California need be well prepared for such an eventuality.

The future for the subregion seems closely aligned with recreation. Presently Yreka and possibly Chester seem to be "coming communities." Some others, especially those concerned with lumbering and ranching, are either stagnant or have waned. Modest numbers of city folk are retiring to some of these mountain communities.

Overall, the economic prospects do not appear bright. The hydroelectric potential is largely developed now. Lumbering has crested—much acreage has been cut over and regrowth will be needed. A few large corporations have "tree farm" plantations but have not yet achieved sustained yield. Older mills appear to have prompted some firms to take tax write-offs and cease operations. Possibly agriculture in Shasta Valley *could* become more intensive in the future with an influx of farm "money" driven from urban California—that prospect does not appear imminent.

**Figure 12-1.** This is a gold mine! *The McLaughlin Mine,* on the border of Napa, Lake and Yolo counties, opened in 1986. This state-of-the-art open-pit operation had to resolve around 300 environmental controls. It has become the largest employer in Lake County. (Homestake Mining Company)

Chapter Twelve

# THE
# NORTHWEST*

* This chapter has been reviewed by Joseph Leeper, Humboldt State University. Previously it was reviewed by Harold Jackson, also of H.S.U..

# THE NORTHWEST

The Northwest is that portion of California west of the Southern Cascade and the Sacramento Valley and beyond the northern reaches of Bay Area urbanization. Culturally and physically the Northwest (to some "The North Coast") provides a transition between Oregon and the California heartland.

Its climate has most aspects of dry-summer subtropical yet is suggestive of the cooler wetter lands to the north. On the southern periphery agricultural activity is distinctly Californian yet over much of the area lumbering has been more characteristic—this is an economic aspect more representative of western Oregon and Washington than of the Golden State.

The earth affords a congeries of slopes—its forests, from numerous promontories, seem to spread across the land like a green coverlet atop an unmade bed.

The Northwest has fewer inhabitants than San Jose (or perhaps four per cent of the state's total) though a tenth of the area of the Golden State is here.

The single larger city, Eureka, is not among California's 100 biggest urban places.

Apart from lumbering the Northwest has made a limited contribution to California's economy.

Livelihood is closely allied with the earth—recreation, lumbering, ranching and fishing form principal pursuits.

Water there is, sometimes in surplus. Heavier than in most of California, in wetter spots precipitation exceeds 100 inches annually.

As California population spirals upward, the subregion may perforce become a major exporter of water and hydroelectricity to drier, more populous portions of the Golden State. Such development as dams on the Klamath, Eel and others would "hurt" the subregion, lessening its appeal and jeopardizing residence.

The Northwest, especially its interior and northerly sectors, has remained isolated.

Along with terrain, location is the principal handicap—the subregion is apart from major passageways. Economic basis for subsidization of through transport is lacking. U.S. 101 is the single important north-south highway. Coupled with decline of domestic sea commerce, coastal contacts have been hampered by the paucity of good harbors. Commercial air service is limited to the Humboldt

Bay "metropolis" which is the also the northern terminus for the single outlet rail line.

Much of this area remains unknown to many Californians and little visited.

Many inhabitants are suspicious of everything in California south of Santa Rosa. It has much scenic appeal but must compete with the Sierra Nevada and is often the loser.

Urban people from the San Francisco Bay Area, the Sacramento Valley and elsewhere, whether weekend visitors, summertime residents, retirees or entrepreneurs, have an increasing impact. Tourism continues to expand, prompting renovation of long-somnolent places. Second homes and retirement abodes of urbanites are increasingly-conspicuous, especially in the southern reaches of the Northwest. Meanwhile a recent rural pursuit, the growing of *Cannabis* illegally, has benefitted from the isolation that has hampered other activities in this part of California.

## CANYONS, RAIN AND CONIFERS

A rough land, generally of moderate elevations, the Northwest has a constricted coastal ledge (Fig. 12-5). For California, rivers are sizable; their canyons afford east-west travel routes though the streams themselves are non-navigable. Drainage is almost wholly westward into the Pacific.

The Northwest contains two landform provinces, the Klamath Mountains and the northern Coast Ranges. They meet along the impressive South Fork Fault Zone, which is followed by segments of the Smith, Klamath and Trinity rivers.

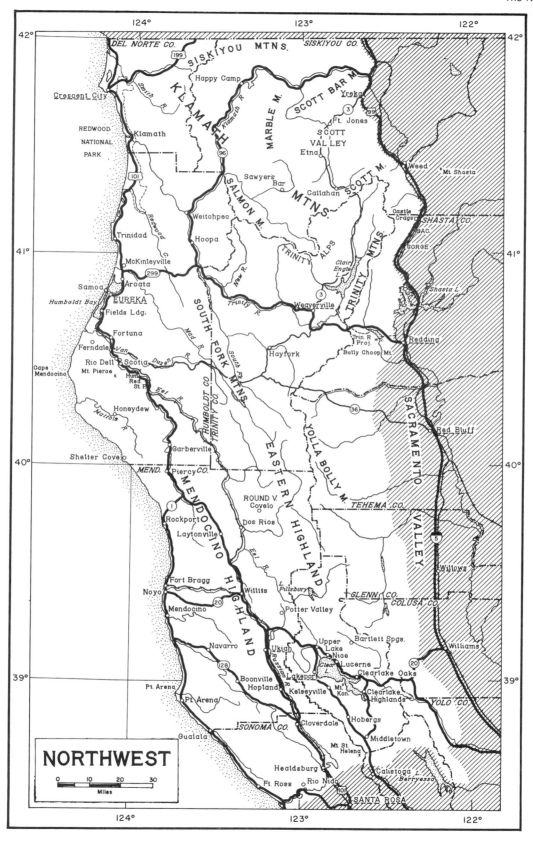

**Map 12-1.** The Northwest, unfortunately sometimes referred to as *The North Coast* (the Klamath Mountains is hardly coastal), includes the Klamath and the northern Coast Ranges.

An ancient mass worn down to what some consider a peneplain, the **Klamath Mountains** was uplifted with much reverse faulting. The Klamath contains some of the most rugged terrain in California.

While moderately-even ridgelines are widespread around 6000 feet, higher summits rise above 8000 feet.

Deep steep-sloped canyons of the Klamath River and its principal tributaries separate the uplands.

The Klamath has cut its gorge across the width of these mountains. By contrast all of the other rivers within the Northwest originate within the subregion.

Higher portions of the Klamath Mountains were glaciated during the Great Ice Age.

Thus they display serrated summit ridges, U-shaped valley and little lakes (Fig. 12-15). Rock outcrops, usually metamorphic, are conspicuous.

Collectively the Klamath provides a name for several distinct units that are known by individual names such as Scott Bar Mountains and Trinity Alps.

In the northwest, extending into Oregon, is the *Siskiyou Mountains* whose summit ridge separates the watersheds of the Smith and the Klamath. Farther south the *Marble Mountains* is impressively rugged. Still farther south, drained by the Salmon, New and Trinity rivers, is the much-dissected *Salmon Mountains*. The *Trinity Alps Range* includes some glaciated terrain. On the eastern periphery of the Klamath, Bully Choop Mountain and Castle Crags provide conspicuous landmarks. Where the Trinity and **Scott** ranges converse, with headwaters of the Sacramento and Trinity rivers, is Mt. Eddy (9025 ft.), the highest point in the Northwest.

There is a bewildering complexity of drainage patterns.

It results from several periods of mountain building as well as the influence of lithology and faulting. Structural basins tend to be small; the most significant is *Scott Valley* in the northeast.

Several features representative of the California Coast Ranges in their entirety are found in the **Northern Coast Ranges**.*

The striking linear arrangement of the southern Coast Ranges is less apparent in the northern ranges.

This is especially true in the north, despite the 150-mile ridge extending northwest from the Yolly Bolly Mountains to the Oregon border. Particularly conspicuous from the air, this ridge has such local names as *Rattlesnake* and *South Fork*—it forms a distinct boundary between the Coast Ranges and the Klamath Mountains.

The *San Andreas Fault* does not reach the length of the Northwest.

It continues westward from Punta Gorda for more than 1500 miles along the *Mendocino Fracture Zone*. Overall the faults have the same northwest-southeast orientation as south of San Francisco Bay despite less regularity of trend. Streams tend to flow along the fault depressions; a trellis drainage is characteristic.

*Franciscan* sedimentary series are even more widespread in the northern Coast Ranges than farther south.

Sandstones, shales, conglomerates and altered layers are commonplace. There are local lava flows and much serpentine. Landslides are frequent during the rainy season; they reflect high clay, fault-ruptured materials, ancient slide terraces and road construction. Thus frequent winter highway closures result.

As elsewhere along the California coast *marine terraces* are often conspicuous.

Those a thousand feet above sea level suggest recent mountain building; lower ones reflect sea level changes during the Great Ice Age. As farther south too, submarine canyons extend outward beneath the ocean floor.

There are two basic highland units in the northern Coast Ranges.

(1) Paralleling the Pacific is the Mendocino Highland (*or* Plateau), while (2) east of the structural depression occupied by the Russian and Eel rivers is the larger Eastern Highlands.

The **Mendocino Highland**, a westward-sloping, maturely dissected plateau, reaches a width of twenty miles.

Less rugged and lower than the Santa Lucia Range, its coastal counterpart in the southern Coast Ranges, it is nearly breached by the valley of the Navarro River. Farther south the water gap of the Russian River traverses its entire width.

To the east, the **Eastern Highlands** provides more complexity and elevations which exceed 7000 feet in *Black Butte* and *Snow Mountain*.

There are three somewhat parallel ranges separated by structural depressions—Clear Lake lies

---

* Too frequently the terms *Coast Ranges* and *Pacific coastal mountains* are confused. The *Peninsular* and *Transverse Ranges* of California are *coastal mountains* as are the Olympic in Washington and the Coast Mountains in British Columbia. The *Coast Ranges* of California include the southern and northern in California and the Oregon Coast Range. The northern Coast Ranges of California extend from Marin County to the Oregon border.

in the rift between the two more westerly uplands. Generally there is a maze of hills and small structural basins, less well defined than the features of the southern Coast Ranges.

A relatively-youthful volcanic area extends from San Francisco Bay to Clear Lake; it includes *Mt. Konocti* and *Mt. St. Helena*. The many hot springs are related to volcanism, as is the geothermal power development at *The Geysers*.

## Winds, Fog and Rain—even Snow

Much of the Northwest experiences a dry-summer subtropical (or Mediterranean) uplands climate.*

As noted earlier the Northwest forms a transition between the cooler, moister climes of Washington and Oregon and the warmer dry-summer lands to the south (see Overview A).

The Pacific (Hawaiian) High exerts less influence here than it does farther south; the Northwest experiences the effects of more storms out of the north Pacific basin. Rainfall tends to be heavier and the wet season longer and storms more frequent than farther south. Still, as elsewhere in the Golden State, precipitation varies widely from year to year. Precipitation decreases towards the east and south.

Winters are wetter than elsewhere in California; the forest floor is often saturated.

San Francisco averages 22 inches, Eureka 39 and Crescent City receives an average of 74. Rain falls on twice as many days annually in Eureka as in San Francisco. Despite a paucity of highland records, exposed uplands in Del Norte County apparently receive more than 100 inches annually.

Higher summits in the Klamath and in the Eastern Highlands carry a snow cover much of the winter.

Over most of the subregion however precipitation falls as rain.

The North Coast littoral is windswept, often overcast and it can be damp even in summer.

Throughout the year coastal residents of Del Norte and Humboldt counties can anticipate dense fog at least once a week. The fogbanks, reaching thickness of 1500 feet, form when warmer maritime air drifts eastward across that great ocean-river of the eastern Pacific, the *California Current*. Advection fog becomes more commonplace in summer when winds blow continuously from the northwest as the Hawaiian High shifts north with the sun.

Besides cooling of air flowing across the California Current *upwelling* of colder water from the depths close to shore further cools the air. Upwelling

causes lower surface temperatures than along the coasts of Oregon and Washington. Even when summer skies are clear, the cloud banks rise over the nearby ocean, hanging ominously and ever-threatening to move inland. Rising midday temperatures usually cause the fog to "burn off" the land; the banks remain offshore within 10 to 20 miles of the coast. There is close correlation between the fog and the "redwood belt." Interior valleys, beyond the fog, sometimes become quite warm in the summer.

## Redwoods, Other Conifers, Chaparral

The Northwest, particularly in its more northerly portions, tends to be a realm of conifer forests (chiefly redwood, Douglas fir, yellow pine) plus oak woodlands and even chaparral.

Interior valleys tend to have a mixed conifer and broadleaf woodland interspersed with considerable grassland. Grasses are also found on many interior Coast Range ridges.

The *coast redwood* is restricted to a belt within approximately 20 miles of the ocean.

Drip from summer sea fog helps reduce temperature and provide moisture throughout the long drought season. These magnificent trees, tallest of North American plants, attain heights of 100 to over 300 feet in virgin stands; diameters often exceed 10 feet.

There are scattered groves northward into Oregon and southward into the Santa Lucia Mountains (as well as widespread ornamentals elsewhere). But the coast redwood is restricted largely to northwestern California. Its heaviest stands are along stream flats where it produces a prodigious board footage per acre. Often growing in pure stands trees create cathedral-like groves in which the sunlight filters down softly; there is often a covering of mosses and ferns on the forest floor (Fig. 12-8). On slopes Douglas fir, white fir, western red cedar, hemlock, California bay and wax myrtle grow frequently amidst the redwoods.

The *Douglas fir forest* is inland from the redwood belt. Like the redwood, it forms even-aged stands

---
* In introductory geography classes students learn that the dry-summer subtropical climate (Koeppen's Cs is found on west coasts between 30 and 40 degrees latitude. Small-scale world maps show the *temperate middle latitude* (marine west coast), extending southward virtually to San Francisco along the coast. Coastal Eureka has low precipitation locally, but with orographic lifting eastward precipitation increases markedly.

where density has invited loggers and repelled ranchers.

In the northern half of the Northwest this association reaches eastward across the Klamath. Eastward it tends to become more open and there is more undergrowth. Such plants as bay, bigleaf maple, madrone and tanbark oak grow in the association.

Farther eastward and often at higher elevations is the *yellow pine forest*. More characteristic of the Southern Cascade and the Sierra Nevada, this forest type is the most extensive in California; it reflects colder winters and hotter drier summers.

Particularly in the Eastern Highlands of the northern Coast Ranges, *chaparral* forms an extensive cover.

*Chamise* creates dense thickets towards the Sacramento Valley, especially on south-facing slopes. Denser vegetation includes California laurel, scrub oak, various ceanothi, manzanita and may contain such conifers as Douglas fir and yellow and sugar pine. In spring the redbud is covered with magenta-hued blossoms while in autumn the red berrries of the toyon make a colorful addition to the landscape.

## FROM SALMON FISHERS TO MINERS TO LOGGERS

There has been a longer history of occupance in the Northwest than its modest present-day population might suggest.

There have been appreciable numbers of Native peoples and even today, descendants of pre-Columbian Indians are proportionally more numerous than in most of California. Never consequential to Spanish and Mexican colonials, the subregion was one of the first areas to be settled by Anglos in California.

### Native American Potpourri

Specifically toward the west and the north the Northwest constituted a more favored habitat for American Indians than did most of California.

Salmon and other fish were abundant in the perennial streams. The more southerly valleys provided many acorns. Besides a variety of berries, nuts and seeds there was much small game. There was not the continuous effort to avoid starvation that prevailed in more niggardly habitats. Such tribes as the Yurok placed more emphasis upon materialism than was typical of California Indians.

Transitional between the Pacific Northwest and the California heartland, the Northwest has had more ethnic diversity than any other subregion in the Golden State.

Athapaskan, Algonquin, Hokan and Penutian linguistic groups were represented.

Apparently the four *Athapaskan* tribes had been longtime Californians.

These North Coast hillfolk resided seasonally along streams during the salmon runs. The *Hupa*, residents of the lower Trinity Valley, probably have survived more successfully than most California Indians because of their isolated habitat; there is still a Hoopa Valley reservation.

The *Algonquin* were coastal people.

They achieved the highest cultural levels of California Indians and were quite materialistic. Skilled as wood craftsmen they built plank houses and redwood dugout boats.

The *Pomo* occupied an environment well favored for hunter gatherers.

Their homeland included the Mendocino Highland, the Russian River Valley and the Clear Lake Country. Pacific shores provided fish, mussels and sea lions. Clear Lake, perhaps focus of the largest population, supplied waterfowl, fish and young tule shoots.

Materially inferior to their neighbors were the *Yuki* (Yukians), mountainfolk of the upper Eel Basin.

They were less skilled as fisherfolk than some of the Northwestern Indians. In fact they did not construct boats. Their habitat was one of the most niggardly portions of the entire subregion.

Between 5000 and 6000 Indians still reside in the Northwest.

Half live on or near the 40 reservations (some are miniscule *rancherias* which cover 200 square miles; about 3000 acres are cultivated by the Indians. Possibly a thousand are townsfolk—there is even a *Pomo Women's Club* in Ukiah.

### The Colonials: Russians, not Spanish

To the western world the Northwest was an "empty" no-man's land between England's western outposts and Russian America to the north and New Spain to the south. Czarist seafarers visited Humboldt Bay in the late 1700's and established an outpost along the Sonoma Coast in 1809.

Their settlements in southeastern Alaska needed foodstuffs and the Russians grew a little wheat in California. They were more successful in obtaining pelts of the numerous sea otter. When the Russians abandoned California in 1841 their property was sold to John Sutter.

The Spanish seemingly ignored the Northwest prior to establishment of Ft. Ross by the Russians.

Concern over Russian encroachment promoted Spanish exploration and led to the founding of Mission Sonoma in 1823.

During the Mexican period more activity developed than had transpired during the preceding Spanish era.

More than a score of land grants were ultimately awarded; as in the Central Valley most were made in the 1840's. Indian opposition discouraged early settlement attempts in the Santa Rosa Valley.

Most of the Northwest thus remained in Indian possession until the Gold Rush began. It was quite distant from Los Angeles, much less Mexico City; Spain and subsequently Mexico had too infirm a hold to expand activities so far. San Francisco Bay

formed a decided transportation barrier. The numerous Indians too discouraged penetration. And the rugged, forest-covered terrain had little appeal to Hispanics.

**Miners and Loggers**

Exploration and occupance of less accessible portions of the Northwest was triggered by "gold fever."

Gold was discovered on the Trinity River in 1848; within a year thousands were examining sand bars in Klamath Mountain canyons. Foci included the Trinity canyon around Weaverville and Scott Valley farther north. For years a mine northwest of Weaverville remained one of the world's larger hydraulic operations.

Mining prompted establishment of seaports along the North Coast.

*Trinidad*, the first harbor, was in use in 1850. Soon thereafter Humboldt Bay was "re-discovered" and

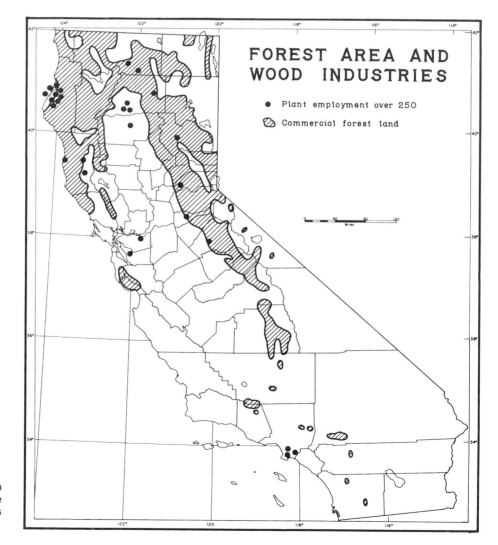

**Map 12-2.** The number of lumber mills in California has declined four-fold since 1950. Most of the remaining operations are corporate owned.

**Figure 12-2.** The "Cat" is skidding a large log to the landing area near Cloverdale. Then the log goes to mill by truck. (Caterpillar Tractor Company)

Eureka was established, as was Crescent City farther north.* Opening of several traces was prompted by the need for overland transportation. Besides the *California-Oregon Trail* (the chief interior way), wagon trails were extended along the Klamath Canyon from Trinidad and eastward from Humboldt Bay to Weaverville. Red Bluff was the shipping point on the Sacramento River (Ch. 9).

Many disillusioned miners sought other pursuits. Agriculture promptly developed around the flanks of Humboldt Bay. Ocean transportation to San Francisco provided a market for butter and cheese. Even in more remote Lake County good arable land was tilled by 1860.

Redwood lumbering likewise had beginnings early.

There were soon seven mills in operation at Eureka; forests approached the strand of Humboldt Bay. Yet the Northwest did not lead the state in lumber in the 1850's; in part this was due to available timber much closer to San Francisco and to Sierran gold camps. Yet by 1869 75 million board feet of redwood was processed around Humboldt Bay.

## FROM FORESTRY TO TOURISM

Most of the basic foundations for the present-day economy of the Northwest existed over a century ago.

While lumbering, ranching and fishing remain important, in the late twentieth century recrea-

tion has increasing importance. By contrast mining is only locally important.

### Forestry

Lumbering remains a primary source of livelihood in the Northwest—the whine of the saw, the smell of newly-cut wood and the ashy gray wisps of smoke from the trash burner were long commonplace. **

To the ever-present threat of a logging truck around the next backroad bend has been added the "menace" of speeding woodchip haulers on main highways.

As California's chief source of wood products the Northwest has provided a major reason why the Golden State vies with Washington for second rank nationally (after Oregon) in lumber products.

Far more of the Northwest is forest-covered than any subregion except the Southern Cascade. Humboldt County leads the state in reserves of standing saw timber and for many years has led the state in wood products output.

As elsewhere lumbering boomed in the Northwest around mid-century.

Small operators from the Pacific Northwest came into northern California to produce lumber for the post-World War II housing market; many became inactive within a few years. After the "choice of the forest" had been cut subsequent production was

---

* Yankee captain Jonathan Winship in his *O'Cain* had visited Humboldt Bay in 1806. Subsequently it was "lost" whereas Trinidad was a known site.
** The acrid odor of sulfurous compounds has replaced the clouds of wood smoke. Waste products are now converted into chips at Samoa and shipped to Japan for further processing. According to local lumbermen, "We use everything but the cry of 'timber-r-r'."

more modest. Factors included alternative building materials, competition from other forest products areas and several periods of slowdown (most recently in the early 1980's) in home construction.

Disease, fire, insects and especially man, collectively continue to consume the forests more rapidly than regeneration occurs.

Despite a century of heavy and often wasteful cutting, considerable stands of timber remain. National forest lands retain much "virgin" cover. Actually rapid cutting, with sufficient precaution, has been one way of achieving balanced growth-and-drain conditions; much standing timber has been old growth, which yields less new wood annually than younger trees.

The forest products industry has pulsated with the state's housebuilding demands.

Markets out-of-state, while secondary, are more important for redwood and yellow pine than for other species.

Most of the annual timber cut becomes lumber.

Sawing and planing, which dominate the industry, provide more employment than all logging and nonlumber products combined. There is an increasing output of other products, especially plywood; manufacture of pulp too has increased.

Many erstwhile smaller logging and sawmill operations have disappeared.

Remaining plants have become larger as forest industries have become more concentrated and automated under corporate control.

Efficient trucking of logs and processing complexities reduce the advantage of milling near the stumpage site. Thus mills are found east of the Sierra-Cascade, in the Central Valley, the Russian River Valley and even within major metropolitan areas.

As concerns the varied major forest types of the Golden State the Northwest contains most of the redwood and Douglas fir, and an appreciable portion of the pine—these three associations vary in appearance and exploitation.

## The Redwood Belt

The coast redwood forests have been logged longer and more thoroughly than other Northwestern forests.

Traditionally redwood lumber was shipped from Eureka and smaller ports and landings to San Francisco where it was highly valued for siding and for shingles. Forests have been high in quality with long branch-free boles and trees of great size

that have yielded 25,000 to 300,000 board feet per acre.

Present-day operations are conducted mostly by a few large corporations which operate on a vast scale and "more or less" practice scientific forestry with tree farms.

The great mills of Samoa, Arcata, Crescent City, Eureka, Fort Bragg and Scotia form the largest redwood operations. Douglas fir is also trucked in from forests toward the east. The Mendocino Coast, once the leading producer (before World War II) now ranks a weak second to Humboldt County; its virgin stands have been much depleted. While over 90 per cent of the total virgin forests have been cut, third-growth redwood is now being used as corporations endeavor to achieve sustained yield. Marketable redwood can be produced in 40 to 70 years.

## The Douglas Fir Realm

The Douglas fir forest is inland from the redwoods; it reaches eastward into canyons and bordering slopes at elevations of 3000 to 4000 feet.

Douglas fir tends to grow in more open stands than the redwood yet stands can be relatively dense. It grows widely elsewhere in California too, including the Cascade and the Sierra.

Out-of-state markets are less important than for the redwood and pine since much Douglas fir is used for rough construction.

Douglas fir also constitutes the principal raw material in plywood, which uses veneer "unrolled' from giant peeler logs.

Lumber industry dispersal inland from accessible tidewater into the rough interior of the Northwest came late.

Extensive logging of the Douglas fir forest materialized in the second half of the twentieth century. In terms of annual cut, standing volume and yearly regrowth Douglas fir has become the leading species in the *entire* state. Most of the logging still takes place in first-growth forests; typically it represents "clear cutting" of large tracts. This technique hampers regeneration less than it would with some California species since the seed disperses readily and seedlings grow best as even-aged stands in full sunlight.

## The Pine-Fir Belt

The interior Coast Ranges and the eastern half of the Klamath Mountains present more climatic ex-

**Figure 12-3.** Fort Bragg and coastal redwood mill. With its unincorporated fringes, this popular vacation spot is about three times as large as its listed population. (Georgia-Pacific, Inc., photo by Clyde Sutherland)

**Figure 12-4.** The Skunk, an unique train. Daily service, at least in summer, is maintained by *the Noyo Chief,* alias The Skunk, so named because of the flumes from its diesel engine. A larger train, pulled by a steam locomotive, is also operated. (Georgia-Paicific, Inc., photo by Ed Freitas)

treme and rougher terrain than farther west. Hence pines are more widespread.

Although Douglas fir predominates in many canyons, elsewhere it is replaced by yellow or sugar pine in more adverse areas such as the Siskiyou-Trinity border zone, by true firs (white and red).

Because these mixed forests were less accessible than in the Cascade and the Sierra, they tended to remain in the virgin state much longer. Isolation was also instrumental in holding many Klamath pine-fir forests in the public domain thus isolation was instrumental in delaying their cutting in contrast to the privately held redwood stands. Most of the current logging is occurring within national forests, with firms bidding for cutting rights. Governmental policy relative to allowable cuts and construction of logging trails are fervently debated.

Other than Happy Camp and Hayfork no Northwest processing places currently exist in the pine and fir belts of the Klamath Mountains.

Thus many logs have been trucked to Yreka, Redding, Weed and Eureka. Considerable pine and fir timber has been trucked to Oregon mills—observant travelers are impressed with the volume of logs that have moved north on U.S. 199 and Interstate 5.

### Flounder and Shellfish

Traditionally the North Coast (Map 12-1) ranked below the central and southern costs in both commercial and sports fishing.

The continental shelf is narrower here than farther south and fishers tended to remain near shore. As boats became larger, with more freezing capacity, fishers tended to make longer trips. Foreign competition, here as elsewhere, led United States to establish a "200-mile national limit" (without supporting the international law of the sea). Without sizable vicinal markets much seafood is trucked elsewhere in California.

Fishing in the Northwest differs in several respects from areas farther south.

One difference is in the varieties taken. The North Coast is California's leading source of flounder (sole); rockcod, salmon, sablefish, thornycod, herring, and tuna are also caught.

The North Coast is the state's leading producer of shellfish with over a third of the state catch; crab and abalone are important and there are oyster beds in Humboldt Bay. Fishers have tended to be of Scandinavian or Italian origins. Eureka (with

approximately 500 commercial boats), Crescent City and Noyo (Ft. Bragg),ith its new sea urchan processing, are the principal centers.

### Sheep and Cattle

Pastoral activities are widespread in the Northwest; operations tend to be extensive rather than intensive.

Cattle and sheep have both been important, although different times and in dissimilar parts of the subregion. Livestock is logical here—climate, slope and isolation favor animals over crops. There is much grassland and cutover forest suitable for grazing.

The northern Coast Ranges have been a major California producer of sheep for a century, *especially* west of the Russian-Eel corridor (path of U.S.101).

Ranches tend to vary from 1000 to 20,000 acres; two to five acres per sheep are needed annually. Distance from the ocean significantly influences moisture—the cool climate and wet winters has favored production of long-staple wool.

Mild winters allow grazing on hillsides hence lambs can be produced outdoors on the range and shipped to market in late winter when there is less competition from other parts of the United States. Reduced sheep numbers have reflected weak mutton demands, substitution of synthetic fibers for wool and overgrazing. Some sheepmen specialize in production of rams and use frozen semen. Besides expected locations sheep have long browsed within Sonoma County orchards.

Cattle ranching too is a widespread rural activity in the Northwest although considerable forest areas are not grazed.

The principal foci for many decades have been the northern Klamath Mountains and the Eastern Highlands (i.e., east of U.S.101). Over much of these areas terrain is rugged and valley lands for ranch headquarters (with fields for supplemental feeds) are relatively small and dispersed. Much land is now within national forest preserves. As elsewhere in the West, the U.S. Forest Service has reduced steadily the number of livestock that can be taken to mountain meadows in summer.

### Quicksilver and Gold

In a few sections of the Northwest mining had importance historically but for decades the subregion did not make a significant contribution to California's total mineral output. That condition may be changing in the 1980's.

In the past $150 million in gold was removed from the Klamath Country. The early mining did stimulate such subsequent activities as settlements, transport routes and seaports, as well as providing historic sites for contemporary tourism.

Historically Sonoma and Lake counties ranked after New Almaden and New Idria (both in the Central Coast) as California sources of quicksilver.

Output tended to be erratic since California has been unable to compete successfully against Spain during peaceful periods. Between 1850 and 1950 less than a tenth of the California output came from the Northwest; few mines have operated since 1950.

In the 1980's it appears that the Northwest may again become a significant producer of minerals—*now* chromite and gold.

## "Skunks" and Back Roads

Transport media are less completely developed in the Northwest than in most parts of California.

Rugged terrain, heavy winter rains coupled with landslides and limited population form major impediments.

Ocean commerce remains locally significant.

Eureka (Fig. 12-6) and Crescent City currently are the leading seaports. Before 1940 considerable lumber was shipped from Noyo (Ft. Bragg). The once-important passenger traffic has vanished. Through the years the bulk of the tonnage has consisted for wood products for export.

No through rail lines (either north-south or east-west) cross the Northwest.

In fact Del Norte, Lake and Trinity counties lack any rail facilities.

A single rail line, now Eureka Southern (formerly the Southern Pacific's Northwestern Pacific line), once extended from Marin County (San Francisco Bay) to Eureka. Now it hopefully operates between Willits and Eureka although in 1987 it was in a state of bankruptcy and operations were suspended.

Through service to Eureka first became available in 1915 after completion of the roadbed through slide-prone Eel River Canyon. Recurrent floods and landslides make the future of the line problematic.

The *California Western Railroad*, 40 miles in length, was initially constructed to transport lumber between Ft. Bragg and Willits. For many years passenger service, provided by the *"Skunks"* (both diesel and steam), has been popular with tourists especially in summer.

Difficult to construct in much of the Northwest, highways have remained inferior generally to those in more populous parts of the Golden State.

Westernmost of the state's three principal north-south arteries, U.S. 101 is an exception. Before the year 2000 and after the expenditure of hundreds of millions of dollars, most of it will have freeway status between the San Francisco Bay Area and the Oregon border.

Along the coast segments of scenic Ca. route 1 have been widened and straightened.

Yet segments remain narrow, winding and comparatively slow (adding appeal for the leisurely traveler). Landslides sometimes block both Route 1 and U.S. 101 as well as other roads.

There are only three adequate east-west roads in the Northwest.

U.S. 199 follows the Smith River as it extends from Crescent City across the Siskiyou Mountains into southwest Oregon.

Ca.96, with a southwesterly course along the Klamath River, has been paved and improved but does not connect U.S. 101 directly with Interstate 5.

Considerable portions of Ca. 299, the principal thoroughfare of northernmost California, have been upgraded; it links Redding (on Interstate 5) with U.S. 101 at Arcata.

Ca. 36, westward from Susanville (in the Northeast) to U.S. 101, is now paved but narrow winding stretches remain.

Much work needs to be done if Ca. 32 will reach U.S. 101— portions in the Northwest are not even designated a state route and remain unpaved and tortuous.

Farther south Ca. 20 has become an important route from Interstate 80 (in the Sierra Nevada) past Clear Lake to Ft. Bragg.

Commercial air service has been limited. Only the Humboldt County Airport at McKinleyville offers daily commercial flights.

Private planes help lessen isolation and in recent years helicopter service has been available into some remote locales. "Local" firms provide service eastward into Central Valley cities.

## Weekenders and Backpackers

As the California population has continued to increase, portions of the Northwest have had increased recreational usage.

They offer a variety of scenic areas—the seashore, redwood groves, highlands, lakes and perennial streams. As yet development has been modest. Accessibility is still limited in many areas and facilities inadequate if not non-existent. One can imagine the popularity of the subregion with its amenities if located in Illinois or Texas, for example. More reachable portions of the Northwest have long been utilized by residents of the populous San Francisco Bay Area and the hot-summer Sacramento Valley.

Visitor congestion, basically a summer-weekend phenomenon, takes place especially around Clear Lake, as well as attractive stopping points along U.S. 101 and Ca. Route 1, where lodges, food establishments and campgrounds north to the Oregon border become taxed.

Fewer numbers visit the northern interior Northwest.

They tend to be hikers, fishers, hunters, campers, rafters and sundry "outdoor" types who do not need freeways or elaborate facilities. In fact they may be seeking refuge from such development.

Outdoor recreation benefits from public preserves that occupy forty per cent of the Northwest.

Most of this area lies within four national forests (and associated wildernesses), mostly within the Klamath Mountains and the higher Coast Ranges.

Farther west the land is held primarily in ranches and corporate timber holdings.

Yet a series of state parks exist along Pacific shores among the forests near highways Ca. 1 and U.S. 101. They augment the attenuated Redwood Na-

tional Park, as does the *King Range National Conservation Area* with its 25 miles of coastline near Shelter Cove.

## THE *REAL* NORTH COAST *

The North Coast has long been the principal focus of human activities in the Northwest.

It was available early because of ocean transportation and the Gold Rush. Later the Eel-Russian corridor, now followed by U.S. 101 and the Eureka Southern Railroad, added to its accessibility. The "southern shore", followed by gradually-improved Route 1, has several highway linkages eastward to U.S. 101.

Many feel the Coast resembles northeastern Anglo-America (i.e., New England and the Maritimes) more than it does the remainder of California.

Some visitors envisage in Mendocino the epitome of a small New England village—this is not too strange because the town founders came from that area. Others find the shoreline with coves, elevated terraces, stacks and rocky strands a near-replica of Canada's Gaspe Peninsula. Again, with its frequent fogs this Coast resembles northeastern North America. Some find that the setting around Cape Mendocino especially, with its ferns,

---

* Some identify the entire Northwest as "North Coast". The Klamath Mountains and the Eastern Highlands hardly fit such delineation.

**Figure 12-5.** Small wonder the summer-cool Mendocino Coast has so much popularity, especially with residents of the Sacramento Valley and the San Francisco Bay Area. (dwl)

its sheep and its windswept bleakness, is suggestive of the Scottish Highlands.

Much of the Coast is abrupt with sheer headlands. Steep escarpments rise in places from the water's edge.

Habitable land tends to be rather restricted. Even the loading of lumber in the past at some places challenged the more skillful block-and-tackle men.

Human occupance is concentrated within three county sectors; (1) **Mendocino Coast** (2) **Humboldt Bay Littoral** and (3) **Del Norte Coast.**

### The Mendocino Coast

The Coast consists of a seaward-tilted, dissected uplands with perennial west-flowing streams. There are no broad plains nor an anchorage comparable to Humboldt Bay (despite a long-projected deep-water port at Noyo-Ft. Bragg).

The Russian River has cut its water gap across this western Coast Range block on the southern periphery.

Occupance is largely restricted to wider terraces, principally around Ft. Bragg and Point Arena.

Despite some much-improved strips with Scenic Views (roadside pullouts) the Shoreline Highway (Rt. 1) is not an expressway.

The strand, consisting of rolling terraces, varies from a few hundred yards to a mile or so in width. * Only near Point Arena is there much farming. Land is devoted to dairying and other livestock.

The earth is blanketed in grass, soft green or straw-colored according to the season. In spring there are numerous clusters of wildflowers in assorted hues.

Notwithstanding some changes the land retains a settled look. White frame farmhouses impart a hint of New England.

The ubiquitous redwood fences, assorted styles, have been stained by rain, salt, sun and wind. The "plain" (terraces), dissected by narrow wooded ravines, has an outer border of seacliffs, a hundred feet or so high. Along the scalloped shore (Fig. 12-5) one finds narrow strips of sand, sea stacks, and waves pounding against bare rock.

Despite its picturesque shore, the Mendocino Coast is less visited than the more southerly (and more populous) sections of the California coast.

Many partake of sports fishing but more visitors come to savor marine landscapes and vernal displays of rhododendrons.

Villages tend to be small and slow-changing. Some have rustic charm. Catering to the visitor has become important.

**Mendocino** (1200) where it was once difficult to find a ready cup of coffee, has become an artists' center. This "Carmel of the North Coast" has cafes (some insist that a place here serves the best breakfasts in all of California!), gift shops, and art galleries, motels (and bed-and-breakfast spots), and even a stock brokerage office.

**Fort Bragg** (circa 12,000 with fringes) has become the leading tourist center of this coast.

It now has dozens of lodgings and restaurants. Services are available for farmers, fisherfolk, lumbermen and others. The Louisiana-Pacific mill is a ranking redwood producer (Map 12-2). Contiguous **Noyo**, once a lumber-shipping point has seafood restaurants as well as sports and commercial fishing (and sea urchanprocessing) facilities.

The **Mendocino Highland** proper, inland from the terraces, is devoid of significant towns and is covered extensively by somber redwoods.

During storms the Highland is water-saturated; in summer moisture is provided by fog drip. Its natural (and expanded!) pastures have long been one of California's major sheep ranges; climate favors year-round pasturage. But past overgrazing coupled with foreign competition and synthetic fibers, have contributed to the decline of sheep here, as elsewhere in the Northwest.

The Mendocino Coast, extending south into Sonoma County, has achieved popularity as a summer vacation land (despite chilly ocean waters).

At its southern end the lower **Russian River Valley** around **Guerneville**, has long served the Bay Area for weekend outings. Recently it has been known as a rural retreat for San Francisco homosexuals. The warm river water in a cool forested setting has much appeal. At times weekend congestion imparts an amusement park air. In winter the mouth of the Russian River is frequented by sports fishers. *Armstrong State Park.* among the more southerly of the Northwest's sequoia preserves, is much visited, as is rebuilt *Fort Ross* with its reminders of Russian colonials.

### The Humboldt Bay Littoral *

For almost 150 years the Humboldt Bay Littoral has been the principal hub of activity in the "upper"

---

*Some observers feel that recent human-built structures threaten to make this coast an "imperiled" shore unless the Coast Plan (Ch. 7) can prevent further desecration.
* This section was previously reviewed by Richard Harm, formerly at College of the Redwoods.

**Figure 12-6.** Eureka and Humboldt Bay. While the U.S. Census Bureau does not identify Humboldt County as a M.S.A., Eureka *seems* more metropolitan than some *urbanized places* in California. (The Greater Eureka Chamber of Commerce)

Northwest.

As the commercial, governmental, educational and lumbering center of the entire subregion it is unrivaled in population. Over 80,000 people reside along this portion of coastal California.

**Humboldt Bay** provides one of the outstanding natural embayments of the Pacific Coast between Puget Sound and San Francisco.

With a maximum width of four miles (Fig. 12-6) and a length of 14 miles it is well sheltered by two sandbars (kept apart by constant dredging) and reinforced tetrapods. Due to a sparsely populated hinterland, ocean commerce has largely been restricted to imports of petroleum and manufactured goods and exports of forest products, fish and dairy products.

Along with the south and north flanks of Humboldt Bay the lower **Eel River Valley** forms a ranking farm area in the Northwest.

This rural landscape evolved during the initial Anglo settlement; by the 1850's the better lands were occupied. A cool foggy climate and abundant grasses for pasturage proved ideal for dairy cattle; this use has prevailed for nearly a century and a half.

The land tends to be locally owned. Except for retiring dairymen there has been a reticence to sell. Some owners are descendants of the "original" Italian-Swiss farmers; later arrivals have included Danish, Irish and finally Azoreans.

Marked changes have occurred in recent decades, especially on the *Arcata Bottoms* and the *Mad River Floodplain* northeast of Humboldt Bay. Growth of Arcata has absorbed some choice acreage. A number of older farmers retired and less than a dozen dairies remain west of Arcata. Much land is now rented for beef pasturage. Consequently dairy barns have decayed and in some cases farmhouses have been rented to youthful communes.

Approximately 50 dairies are concentrated along the lower Eel River south of the Bay; dairy herds range from about 50 to 280 cows.

Dairysteads tend to be located on "higher ground" and thus are safe from "little" floods. A critical flood problem for dairymen is to receive accurate high-water forecasts in sufficient time to move their cattle.

Three-fourths of the dairies in the Littoral are Grade B (there are two large powdered milk processing plants here). It appears that the Littoral will be the "last mainstay" of Grade B dairies in California. Humboldt County has the lowest feed costs in the state yet a third of the milk sold in the Littoral is "imported" by supermarket chains despite an adequate local supply of milk.

The ranking "metropolis" and leading seaport of the Northwest, **Eureka** (25,200) is the seat of Humboldt County as well as the site of College of the Redwoods.

The city sprawls along the tidal flats and lower terraces of the Bay (Fig. 12-6). Despite its street grid pattern, the visitor may be confused because U.S. 101 generally follows shoreline curvature.

Eureka is the Northwest's chief retail and wholesale center and is an important tourist stop *(especially in summer)*.

Its northern (waterfront) sector is dominated by sundry seaside activities including fish docks (and a famed seafood restaurant). Located here is the *Carson House*, regarded as a gem among America's outstanding Victorian structures. "Old Town" renewal included new shops and restaurants as well as in moving of a number Victorian dwellings from the anticipated U.S. 101 freeway corridor through Eureka.

Near Old Town is the central district, long confronted solely with competition from a "junior" shopping center and hence still viable. Motels are much in evidence. A large regional shopping center was opened in the late 1980's.

Along the bayshore to the south are lumber mills and veneer plants. *Ft. Humboldt* has an "outdoor" museum whose exhibits depict the evolution of local lumbering. Additionally Eureka has a sizable redwood preserve in its *Sequoia Park*.

**Arcata** (15,000) has grown as an university and lumbering town.

Thus it is "tied" to Eureka by commercial establishments along U.S.101. Arcata is a westside-

eastside (Humboldt State University and allied residences) town. The university, which gained its reputation with programs in forestry, natural resources, oceanography and sciences, attracts students from other parts of California, especially the major metropolitan areas.

Contiguous, unincorporated **McKinleyville** (circa 12,000) has evolved as a "do your own thing" residential place.

Many of its occupants are offspring of lumbermen who originally came from the Dust Bowl areas of the Great Plains. Some refer to it as "Oklahoma by the sea."

There are several smaller communities southeast of the Bay.

**Ferndale** (1500), whose shops and handsome Victorian houses attract many tourists, and **Fortuna** (8500) are settled dairy towns. **Rio Dell** (3100) provides an "overflow" residence place for lumbermen employed at nearby Scotia.

### The Del Norte Coast

Except for the low lagoon strip between the mouth of the Smith River and Crescent City (map, 12-1), the Del Norte Coast is craggy. This small area contains virtually all of the farmland in Del Norte County. The remainder of the County consists of Coast Ranges which rise abruptly from the Pacific Ocean.

In this foggy environment there are less than 50,000 acres in farms. Dairying forms the chief activity and processed products are necessitated by distances from large urban centers and small nearby markets.

The hybrid Easter lily is a local agricultural specialty.

Developed locally in the late 1930's it acquired popularity during World War II when Japanese bulbs were unavailable. Despite Japanese competition Del Norte growers have been able to maintain domestic markets.

The Coast has adjusted to the collapse of redwood lumbering.

The decline followed overcutting in the 1950's and 1960's. During subsequent years many of the lumber people returned to Oregon, whence they had come. County population is comparable to that in 1950. Only a single corporate firm, endeavoring to maintain sustained yield, remains. Third generation regrowth should permit the firm to expand its output in the 1990's.

In the late 1980's per capita incomes were the lowest of any county in California. The statistics

**Figure 12-7.** On the trail to *Lady Bird Johnson Grove*, Redwood National Park. (dwl)

are somewhat misleading; a considerable number of migrants from the Bay Area and Oregon receive welfare support. In any event payrolls at a new state prison southeast of Crescent City should bolster local incomes.

The Coast forms the north end of the California redwood country. Seasonally the economy is stimulated by summer vacationer visitation.

Besides some magnificent old-growth redwood groves (including the national park and three state parks) there is sports fishing at the mouth of the Klamath River.

The Save-the-Redwood League has proposed a Smith River National Park but there is vociferous local opposition. Many feel that government has too much control of Del Norte County now. The Park Service rejected the proposal in 1987.

On a crescentric south-facing harbor, **Crescent City** (3800) is the only significant community in its county.

The town experienced extensive rebuilding near the waterfront after a *tsunami*. Its harbor, protected by a rock breakwater with tetrapods, has separate facilities for lumber shipment and commercial fishing. The economy is bolstered by trade from the surrounding area, government offices (including headquarters of the national park), highway services and its Oregon "gateway" function (via U.S.101 and 199).

**Redwood National Park.** established in 1968, has matured and is visited by hundreds of thousands, chiefly in summer.

Park attractions include headquarter displays, the visitor center (near Orick), magnificent *Gold Beach*, the nature trail to *Lady Bird Johnson*

*Grove* and the relatively-accessible *Tallest Tree Grove*. Shuttle bus service is provided from Orick. A sizable Park addition (in 1978) includes the *Redwood Creek* watershed, which contained much cutover forest. Rehabilitation (including extensive planting of redwoods) has obscured most of the loggers' despoilment and protects downstream groves.

Nearly a third of the ultimate 100,000-acre reserve will necessitate incorporation of three California state parks *(Jedediah Smith, Del Norte Coast,* and *Prairie Creek)*. Pending arrangement with the state of California, Redwood consists of non-contiguous segments. Camping facilities are found only in the state parks.

Completion of a 23-mile strip of ridgetop freeway (the most expensive contract made by Caltrans) on U.S. 101 east of Prairie Creek will eliminate soon a long-disputed highway "bottleneck."

The four-lane corridor, with grades as much as seven per cent, may prove costly to maintain. However it will hasten through traffic and allow use of the old two-lane road through Prairie Creek to function as a scenic byway.

## REDWOOD HEARTLAND

The Eel River Valley in Humboldt and northern Mendocino counties forms a natural core for the coast Sequoia realm that once had a north-south reach of 450 miles.

Until the late 1800's cutting remained sufficiently modest to balance regrowth. Introduction of the

**Figure 12-8.** Crescent Beach, Redwood National Park. Obviously the park offers more than giant trees! (dwl)

**Figure 12-9.** One of the great redwood mills, Scotia. Conservations are apprehensive about future production plans of the new owners. (Pacific Lumber Company)

*donkey engine* and accompanying wire cable dragout favored complete "logging off". Thus by 1920 half of the *Sequoia sempervirons* were cut.

### Save-the Redwoods

Some conservation-minded individuals and groups became concerned over redwood destruction.

The *National Geographic Society* and John Muir and his *Sierra Club* were among the leaders. Even before incorporation of *Save-the-Redwoods League* (1918) such groves as *Armstrong, Big Basin, Bohemian*, and *Muir Woods* had been set aside farther south in the state. Initially the League favored a national redwoods park but instead adopted a policy of seeking sanctuary for groves along U.S. 101 as a nucleus for the entire California state park system. Active more as a community interest organization than as militant conservationists, the League and its supporters, relying upon philanthropic donations, have created preserves in excess of 70,000 acres.

### Gazers, Campers and Marijuana Growers

The majesty of the giant trees has appealed to sufficient Americans to assure protection of some magnificent groves. Thus the Redwood Heartland is one of the prime tourist lures of northern California.

But a flight over this area or travel along a byway from U.S. 101 makes one realize how much of the total forest has fallen prey to the axe and saw.

The Heartland is a land of recreation—and of forestry.

Pacific Lumber Company (formerly a San Francisco firm) has at Scotia the world's largest redwood mill—and there are also smaller firms. "Palco", operating out of its company town (Scotia) had the best record of forest maintenance prior to an "unfriendly take-over" in 1986. Its 220,000-acre holding contains about 40 per cent of marketable redwoods; the firm's claim to be on sustained yield will probably vanish under the new ownership.

Tourism is highly seasonal.

Queried on a quiet December morn about local activities, a service station attendant replied, "In summer we live off the tourists, the rest of the year off each other." Winter unemployment may exceed 20 per cent.

A myriad of sundry attractions (such as fish ponds, "You catch 'em, we fry 'em") are scattered along U.S. 101. One marvels that there is sufficient business to warrant such activity until one drives along this route on a summer weekend.

Basically tourism consists of driving along the highway, perhaps sauntering along shady trails within the groves. The Save-the-Redwoods League

**Figure 12-10.** The Redwoods of Dyerville Flats. View of forest floor in Humboldt State Redwood Park. (California Department of Parks and Recreation, photo by Tom Myers).

**Figure 12-11.** U.S. 101 freeway through the Redwood Heartland has allowed the old road to become *The Avenue of the Giants,* permitting the nature lover to proceed leisurely through the groves. Farther north, another bypass of groves through Prairie Creek State Park is being constructed. By the year 2000 through travelers and loggers should be able to drive from Marin County to the Oregon border with few "bottlenecks." (Caltrans)

won a partial victory in 1956 when it was agreed that the freeway would bypass the groves and the old highway would become a scenic drive through the groves (Fig. 12-11). Thus one finds marked contrast between the 13-mile *Avenue of the Giants* (old U.S. 101) whose bordering groves convey a pristine atmosphere, and the freeway route which reveals the extent of redwood logging.

The focus of the Heartland is 38,000-acre *Humboldt Redwoods State Park*, with a linear series of groves (Fig.12-10).

It includes Bull Creek Flats, acclaimed the "world's finest forest," despite flood damage in 1955 and 1964 that was undoubtedly accelerated by earlier logging outside the park.

A number of other redwood state parks are outside of the Heartland. Collectively the parks form a discontinuous 350-mile belt between Jedediah Smith on the north and Henry Cowell, the southernmost preserve (near Santa Cruz).

Additional "renown" for the Heartland has come with the illegal growing of marijuana, reputedly among California's few billion dollar "crops."

Allegedly established by earth people ("hippies") from cities, it has provided cash income in areas where livelihood is difficult and it gained a measure of local sympathy. An "emerald triangle", focusing on southern Humboldt County, received international publicity. Repeated raids has prompted dispersal into Oregon and even northeastern Washington. In California cultivation seems to have flourished from Santa Cruz northward. Statistics are lacking but Humboldt may rank first, then Mendocino County, with Butte County possibly third.

There is no single urban concentration in the Heartland.

A series of small communities exists along U.S. 101. **Willits** (4500) is actually south and east of the redwoods. This pleasant town, a lumbering, traveler sojourn and ranching place, provides a gateway to the Heartland and an entry place (on Ca. 20) for the Mendocino Coast. It is the eastern terminus of the California Western Railroad.

Farther north are the companion towns of **Garberville** (500). a highway stop with a high school and hospital and **Redway** (1600), essentially residential.

The company town of **Scotia** (1100) is concerned exclusively with lumbering—it is the locale of the world's largest redwood mill.

**Round Valley**

Sequestered in northeastern Mendocino County, Round Valley remains quasi-isolated from "everywhere."

It is northeast of Willits and hence east of the Redwood Heartland. With about 2000 people, Round Valley is a land of livestock ranches (and even a few orchards) amid white oak groves (local residents contend that the *Henley Oak* is the world's largest). Cattlemen (Anglos) arrived even before an Indian reservation (multi-tribal) was established. Thus much of the Indian land is lo-

**Figure 12-12.** The highlands of southern Lake County. Mount Konocti(4100 feet) and the eastern end of Clear Lake are seen here. (dwl)

cated in surrounding highlands.

**Covelo**, a tranquil ranching town, has experienced modest twentieth century change. It escaped inundation (as part of the California Water Project) when plans for a reservoir (holding Eel River water for Southern California) were abandoned.

## RUSSIAN RIVER BASINS *

The Russian River flows southward toward the Santa Rosa Valley through a series of elongated structural basins that are one to three miles wide.

These basins are separated by low ridges across which the river has cut gorges. Finally, south of Healdsburg the Russian turns westward and crosses the forested Mendocino Highland to reach the Pacific.

Despite winter precipitation averaging 35 to 40 inches annually this agrarian portion of the Northwest suggests drier parts of central California. Slopes are covered with oak woodland and landscape become noticeably seared in summer.

Once the railroad reached Ukiah (in 1889) market outlets, generally absent in the interior Northwest, were afforded for farm and lumber products.

Wood processing depends upon forests to the west and north.

Farming in the Russian River basins is suggestive of lowlands to the south on the northern periphery of the San Francisco Bay Area.

Products include truck crops (for local markets), grapes, deciduous fruits and livestock (including riding horses).

Some of the most fertile alluvial loams, in strips near the Russian River, have been lost to freeway construction and urban expansion. For nearly a century the basins formed a major California source of hops. In the second half of the twentieth century they have been replaced by grapes and pears.

The Ukiah Valley has become a focal point for Bartlett pear orchards. But with the decline of fruit canning, acreage has lessened by half.

A dramatic transition in recent decades has been the expansion of viticulture.

The Russian River basins now rank with Sonoma and Napa counties as important producers of varietal grapes for premium wines. Cultivation has also expanded westward into *Anderson Valley*, within the Mendocino Highland, which is known also for its production of apples.

The urban landscape is dominated by two communities, Ukiah and Healdsburg; there are smaller towns as well.

**Healdsburg** (9000), long agriculturally-oriented, also has lumbering, as well as highway services. Publicity stresses "bed and breakfasts" and other "Wine Country" amenities.

**Ukiah** (14,000) is one of the principal communities of the Northwest.

It is the seat of Mendocino County, has an important service function and is a popular waystop on U.S. 101. There are several lumber mills and wood products (plywood and masonite) plants. A county community college (Mendocino) and a Hindu university (on the former site of a state hospital) have accounted for some of its growth. There are increasing numbers of retirees as well as commuters to the northern portion of the San Francisco Bay Area.

## LAKE COUNTY

To most visitors, "We are going to Lake County" means *southern* Lake County. And in the closing years of the twentieth century, the south half of Lake County is increasingly atypical of the Northwest.

Although it has the oldest population in the Golden State, the median age is dropping. In contrast to near-stagnancy in many parts of the Northwest, Lake County has the highest per cent of population increase in the state. Economic bases are broader than is common in counties to the north...and the tax base better than in much of rural California.

The heart of the county is Clear Lake, the largest natural body of fresh water *entirely* within the state.

While it has an area of 85 square miles, its average depth is less than 20 feet. Some writers have likened its setting to the English Lake District, an analogy more appropriate in April than in September.

### Land of the Pomo

Archeological evidence continues to mount that in prehistoric days Lake County was (and is today) a choice part of California for its Native American inhabitants.

* This section has been reviewed by Robert Wallen, Mendocino College, and George Smart, geographer-land appraiser, Ukiah.

This is one of the milder portions of California. And in addition to timber and water, there have been fish and game and nuts and grasses.

While the Pomo lost most of their land to the white man soon after the Gold Rush, they retain five rancherias.

A tribal headquarters has been located in *Nice* and new dwellings built. An adjacent bingo parlor offers some employment for its Pomo owners.

The Pomo have had difficult times, but the future is beginning to show some hope.

For decades employment has been chiefly in agriculture. A tribal "sense of direction" is appearing and additional employment opportunities may develop.

**Figure 12-13.** Lakeshore residence in Nice. The appeal as a retirement area is obvious. (dwl).

### Yesteryear

The County has had many aspects representative of the entire Northwest: quasi isolation, sparse population, narrow economic base and limited outside contacts.

Despite early settlement by Gold Rush Anglo-Saxons, Lake County remained a land of semi-self-sufficiency in the late nineteenth century—livestock and grains were important.

Quicksilver mines made an intermittent contribution. Recreational significance for San Franciscans developed early. The County was less than 100 miles from "The City", cooler than the Central Valley, and most important, had mineral springs.

By the 1880's three early resort centers had developed: Cobb Mountain and its surrounding volcanic areas, upland springs north and east of Clear Lake, and springs west of Upper Lake. Health seekers sought the medicinal values of mineral waters. With medical advances and improved roads to more distant vacation spots, the springs were doomed.

### Boats, Pears and Gold

Clear Lake itself gained popularity (from the 1920's) for sports fishing, bathing, boating, and more recently, water skiing.

Popular areas are adjacent to Lakeport and around the eastern shore. The lake is pleasantly warm in summer but becomes murky later in the season—partly because some of its water is dispatched (via Cache Creek) to Sacramento Valley fields. Pollution has been slowed by restrictive measures (as control of septic tanks). Still, some visitors prefer the smaller Blue Lakes to the north-

west.

For decades, especially in summer, Lake County has been a week-end place for growing numbers of middle-income residents of central California, especially the Bay Area.

Many city folk have cabins, especially near the eastern shore of Clear Lake (evening breezes have tended to dispel the gnats). Where waterfront construction has been possible, blocked lake views are suggestive of the Malibu Coast near Los Angeles (Ch.6).

*Cobb Mountain*, whose mineral spas amidst pine forests once attracted Bay Area collegians to dance to the "big bands" now lures golfers and commuter-residents.

Although arable land is scattered, agriculture in Lake County is quite viable, in contrast to some areas where it has been troubled in the late twentieth century. Such products as walnuts, pears and wines do not depend on foreign markets.

"Small landscapes" appropriately describes the tilled patches—more than a dozen small basins, chiefly near the Lake, are farmed. For many decades market access was a problem.

Early in this century deciduous fruits and walnuts became important. By the 1920's walnuts have largely replaced prunes. Too much wetness during the pollination period has discouraged almond growing.

Post-1950 urbanization of walnut producing areas in Southern California encouraged expansion in Lake County, especially on hillsides near volcanic *Mt. Konocti*.

In season supermarkets in metropolitan California advertise "Lake County pears." Reputation for quality fruit (some can now be stored for weeks), especially Bartletts, justifies costs of shipping. Acreage is stabilized but yields per tree increased with improved disease control.

More belatedly than in the Napa Valley nearby, Lake County farmers returned to grapes. Much of the varietal wine (mostly Cabernet), produced by descendents of earlier-day vintners, is sold "on the farm."

The ranking agricultural area is *Big Valley* around Kelseyville.

Vineyards have replaced some irrigated pastures but acreage-wise, pears are the ranking crop on better soils.

Lake County has attracted many retirees from the Bay Area and Southern California. A number came from modest "blue collar" backgrounds; shabbiness describes many older dwellings.

Lake County gained the *McLaughlin* gold mine in 1985.

The nation's largest firm, Homestake, has developed a sophisticated "state of the arts" open pit operation, now the largest employer in the county. On the border of three counties (Napa, Lake and Yolo) the mine has been subject to hundreds of restrictions due to pollution (especially arsenic) concerns. Reserves of the replacement ores have an estimated "life span" of about a generation.

Another recent source of employment has been

*The Geysers*, the world's largest geothermal operation.

It is located in the *Mayacmas Range* in southwest Lake County and adjacent Sonoma County—both counties have been benefitted financially.

Pacific Gas and Electric has utilized "state of the arts" techniques required by environmental concerns.

A full "build out", utilizing *dry steam*, slowed when petroleum prices dropped in the mid-1980's. P.G. and E. anticipates maximum output by 2000 or so, depending upon demands for electricity.

Lake County houses rising numbers of commuters and other working people.

Increasing commutation is occurring to the northern Bay Area, especially Santa Rosa and Napa. Lower housing cost is an important consideration.

### Little Places

There are no cities in Lake County; most of the small towns are situated along the shores of Clear Lake. And their names sometimes suggest more appeal than these communities possess. While the recreation function is important, save for the summer holiday season, occupance is largely by senior citizens and service personnel. Since mid-century, there has been considerable growth.

Once a sleepy hamlet, the county seat of **Lakeport** (4200) has become a resort center.

**Figure 12-14.** The Geysers, on the border between Lake and Sonoma counties in the Mayacmas Range. This geothermal plant (no.13) began operating in 1980. (Pacific Gas and Electric Company)

Its four small shopping malls haves hurt the downtown area. And imagine a multi-star hotel here! The town retains much charm, with attractive vistas across the lake.

Finally incorporated, **Clearlake** (11,500) has become the largest town. It is suggestive of Atascadero (Ch.7) in the southern Salinas Valley or Paradise (Ch.10) in the Sierran Foothills.

As with the others there are many retirees (and a conspicuous number of mobile home parks), a distended main street and much dispersal. Like Atascadero (but unlike Paradise in the pines) it lies amidst oak woodland.

Clearlake has declined as a resort (some of its waterfront motels are old and shabby) even as it has grown as a residence place. And it will take time to eliminate years "of doing my own thing."

**Middletown** (4000) and **Hidden Valley**, a planned community, both away from the lake, are affected more by mining activities and commuters.

## THE EASTERN HIGHLANDS

The Eastern Highlands, exclusive of southern Lake County (previous section), essentially the confines of Mendocino National Forest, is one of the least-known and infrequently-visited portions of California.

Between Ca. 36 (north) and Ca. 20 (south), a distance of 80 miles, no paved roads yet cross the summits. On the northern edge is the *Yolla Bolly-Middle Eel Wilderness.*

Exclusive of the southern fringe in northern Ventura County, the highest elevations in the California Coast Ranges are here. Loftier summits, such as Black Butte (7488 feet) are apt to be snow-topped in winter.

This realm is covered with pine forests and chaparral. Limited use includes livestock ranching along the canyons, logging and modest water utilization. Hydroelectricity is generated at *Lake Pillsbury* on the western edge. Near the Sacramento Valley three lakes on Stony Creek provide recreational facilities and water for irrigation around Orland.

## THE KLAMATH COUNTRY

This wrinkled land, the Klamath Mountains, occupies the northeastern third of the Northwest and is often ranked with the Sierra Nevada and the southern Cascade as California's stellar highlands.

Not athwart any major travel corridor, it remains somewhat isolated, sparsely peopled and unknown to many Golden Staters.

Contemporary inhabitants of the Klamath Mountains, who may total 30,000, are principally lumber workers, cattle ranchers and service personnel.

They usually reside along stream canyons—elsewhere much of the land is within national forests.

Only three communities exceed a thousand resi-

**Figure 12-15.** The Trinity Alps. These ice-scoured highlands in the Klamath Mountains of Trinity County contain the highest points in the Northwest. (dwl)

**Figure 12-16.** "Downtown" Hoopa. The fragmented community is dispersed over considerable area. (dwl)

dents; most places shown on maps are crossroads hamlets with populations of 100 or fewer. The usual visitors are outdoor people (such as fishers and campers).

The Klamath Country was settled early by Anglo-Americans in quest of gold. Many remained; a considerable number of towns originated nearly a century and a half ago as gold period camps.

Much of the Klamath Country is inaccessible by roads. The three state highways tend to follow canyon alignments.

The typical back road remains unpaved, narrow and winding, perhaps impassible in winter and dusty in summer. Private aircraft and helicopters have made the Country more available to affluent outdoor folk and others; there are a number of small landing fields.

### Hupa, Yurok and Karok

The Northwest has been a choice portion of California for Native Americans but even in the Klamath Country arrival of miners and stockmen early eliminated them from much of the area.

Such ephemeral military posts as Ft. Jones and Ft. Humboldt (Eureka), ostensibly created to "maintain peace", tended to protect the white settlers, not the Indians.

The *Hoopa Valley* reservation, and the *Round Valley* preserve farther south in the northern Coast Ranges, were established soon after the Gold Rush.

Although both areas have been penetrated by Anglos, they remain principal foci of Indian habitation in the Northwest.

Surrounding the confluence of the Trinity and Klamath rivers, the Hoopa reserve occupies 144

square miles. It forms the principal Indian preserve and ranks high in accumulation of Native funds. Approximately 1100 Indians live on the reservation with around 2000 in the locality, mainly Hupa, Yurok, and Karok.*

While some individuals maintain private parcels, over 90 per cent of the reserve is held in common by the tribes.

These Native Americans fish, till small parcels of valley land and work for ranchers or lumber operators in the environs. The Tribal Council has developed a campground for vacationers as well as a small shopping center in **Hoopa**. The tribe has much concern about the high dropout rate of its youth from high school, partly due to economic frustration.

Logging of the rich Hoopa timberlands began in 1947—assumedly cutting has maintained sustained yields. Returns have provided a number of tribal benefits.

### Economic Constraints

Economic pursuits in the Klamath Country are modestly based— they have include mining, forestry, livestock ranching, water development and recreation.

Lumbering became important in the mid-twentieth century. Although many logs are transported elsewhere. Local processing has occurred at Happy Camp, Hayfork, Hoopa Valley and Ft. Jones.

The basic land-use in the Klamath Mountains involves livestock ranching.

The Country is handicapped because of limited terrain suitable for irrigated pastures and haymaking. Thus foci of operations are those relatively-few basins and river valleys with larger amounts of arable land.

Like much of the Northwest the Klamath Country contains surplus water beyond present-day local needs.

In past decades sufficient water elsewhere in the Golden State negated developments here. The initial project to divert water from the Klamath Basin began in 1955 with the *Trinity Project,* an adjunct of the Central Valley Project which provides an additional 1.4 million acre-feet of water for use in the Sacramento Valley, Delta Lands, Bay

---

*Humboldt County ranks third, after Los Angeles and San Diego counties, in total present-day Indian population. Numbers in Los Angeles warrant clarification. Many Indians there, such as Hopi and Navaho, migrated from outside California.

Area and San Joaquin Valley.

The chief unit is *Trinity Dam*, which backs up Clare Engle Lake. Water, from the Trinity River northeast of Weaverville, is tunneled into *Whiskeytown Reservoir* on a tributary of the Sacramento River. A second tunnel conducts water into Keswick Reservoir north of Redding. Besides water for irrigation, the Project provides recreation facilities and has reduced flood threats and also provides power development. But lessening of Trinity River flow has diminished downriver fishing resources in such areas as Hoopa Valley. Presently the Klamath and lower reaches of three tributaries (Scott, Salmon and Trinity) are buffeted against further exploitation by the state's *Wild and Scenic Rivers Act*.

Recreation is an increasingly-important use of the Klamath Country.

Despite eccentric location (relative to metropolitan areas) which discouraged greater use in the past, recreation continues to increase. Many spots in the Klamath appeal to the hiker. In recent years white-water rafting has gained popularity, especially on the Klamath and the Trinity. Perennial streams and alpine lakes allow some of California's best sports fishing.

## California Appalachia

Throughout highland California, *even* in more isolated portions of Southern California, terrain has tended to discourage large clusters of people. There are many areas, *especially* in the Northern Highlands, where humans, from Gold Rush miners to loggers to today's *earth people* and retirees abide. Life

**Figure 12-17.** Rusting dredge on the Scott River. (dwl)

is still a bit rough, living standards lower and amenities fewer than in urban California.

The Klamath Country depicts "California Appalachia" better than most of highlands California.

There no institution of higher learning...even the number of elementary schools is limited. The single telephone in a hamlet may be located in a bar or a general store. Hospitals are few and the number of doctors, nurses and dentists limited. Residents tend to be self-reliant. Those born in this area, especially, are likely to be distrustful of city folk, including recent urban "refugees."

Hunting and fishing, ranching, tending of home garden plots, and woodcutting are typical activities. Employment includes much seasonal and part-time work. During Prohibition days, bootlegging was appropriate (and more recently, raising of marijuana). Poaching a deer or out-of-season fishing to feed one's family, or constructing a non-code residence oneself occur—this is a land of individualism. The prized possession may be be a four-wheel drive pickup truck.

Several portions of the Klamath Country are distinctive because of economic use or physical charm. Such areas include (1) **Scott Valley** (2) **Trinity County** (3) the **Klamath Canyon** and (4) the **Wilderness Areas**.

## Distinctive Areas

**Scott Valley** (circa 2000) provides one of California's more scenic intermontane basins.*

Higher summits of surrounding mountains are snow-capped many months of each year. The Scott River meanders across Scott Valley's flattish surface through lush meadows that support herds of beef cattle.

Contemporary utilization is based upon livestock ranching and recreation. A generation ago land priced doubled as "outsiders" bid for properties. There are adequate summer ranges nearby and haymaking is important in summer on the Valley floor.

Expected inter-community rivalry exists between the two leading hamlets.

The principal town, **Etna** (800) began as a gold camp (Fig.12-17) whereas nearby **Ft. Jones** originated as an Army post on the California-Oregon

---

* Possibly this area is better known in San Diego than it is in the Northwest. A Humboldt State University professor comments, "I'll bet 99 per cent of the people in Humboldt and Del Norte counties have never heard of it." Surely this reflects the provincialism imposed by isolation, even today.

Trail. Both house increasing numbers of retirees and commuters to work in Yreka.

## Trinity County

The County forms the southern nucleus for the Klamath Country.

Yet here terrain is a maze of slopes—flat land is limited. Author James Hilton allegedly visualized Weaverville as his idea of an American "Shangri-La." While the county is traversed by three highways (California routes 3, 36 and 299) much of its confines are accessible only afoot or on animals. Its organization as one of the state's original counties was prompted by early-day gold mining.

Livestock ranching is found in small valleys along the tributaries of the Trinity River southwest of Weaverville. Some hay and a little grain is raised as feed.

Population clusters around two communities.

**Weaverville** (2000) is the county seat, service place and way stop (junction of highways 3 and 299). With older structures (some with outside circular staircases) this picturesque ex-mine camp with its "cowpath" street patterns seems larger than it is.

**Hayfork** (2000) prospers because of its lumber mill (Sierra Pacific).

## The Klamath Canyon

The Klamath Canyon provides the single low-elevation east-to-west crossing of the entire Northwest. But "when Los Angeles *really* discovers the Canyon, there will be no wilderness left in Califor-nia," warns one observer.

While the Klamath is perennial, it is still a winding mountain stream unsuitable for navigation. An early wagon trail between the California-Oregon Trail (now Interstate 5) and Weitchpec, Ca. 96, along the river, was not blacktopped until the 1960's. Lumbering and other activities have prompted improvement of this route but opposition of Indians, among other factors, has discouraged construction northwest from Weitchpec to link with U.S. 101 directly.

As a vacation land (fishing, rafting, camping) the Canyon has become more frequented in the late twentieth century. It probably is the most reliable river in the Golden State for annual runs of salmon and steelhead, as much as 200 miles from its mouth. Lodges, still limited in number, tend to be rustic.

While maps show half a dozen communities, there is only one town of significance.

**Happy Camp** (2500), a onetime mine camp, is the hub of the Canyon. It is buoyed by local services, lumbering *(somewhat* uncertain) and seasonal tourism. Considerable retail trade is conducted in Medford—Oregon license plates are on a suspicious number of locally-owned vehicles. Proximity of national forest land explains the number of dwellings scattered at distance from the fragmented core.

## The Wildernesses

Under the Wilderness Act of 1984 ten wildernesses have been established in and about the Klamath

**Figure 12-18.** Scott Valley (*the one* in Siskiyou County) and the Marble Mountains. Boulder Peak rises to 8137 feet. (dwl)

Mountains.* They contain some of California's most spectacular alpine locales. The Trinity Alps Wilderness includes *Thompson Peak* (8936 feet) as well as the impressively-glaciated expansion of the *Trinity Alps* (Fig. 12-15). *Local relief* sometimes exceeds 6000 feet and the serrated ridges and descending spurs are precipitous. Many little lakes in small ice-sculptured canyons are truly gems. Some of the Golden State's best backpacking and trout fishing is found here.

## A HIDDEN CORNER—WITH PROBLEMS

There is no evidence that the Northwest will ever be highly urbanized. It appears certain to remain peripheral to the main course of California activity and economy. Large portions are in fact fittingly described as "California Appalachia."

Prospects for much of the Northwest are closely allied to the future of its forest industries.

Wood by-products factories are no longer expanding and likelihood of additional pulpwood, paper, plywood and more elaborate industries are problematic. Competition from other producing areas, labor-displacing automation and water conservation needs are important constraints.

The Northwest has vexatious problems for years ahead.

In particular the economy of Del Norte and Humboldt counties, where so many people have depended upon forest industries for a livelihood, will need adjustment. Even the pace of recent timber-cutting cannot continue, for it still exceeds growth rate. The Northwest must rely increasingly upon a harvest of planned regrowth, not upon "mining the forest."

Mining prospects are always speculative—and offer no permanent benefits.

New discoveries affect only local areas, such as the large gold operation southeast of Clear Lake. Geothermal too can be expanded but it is unfit to form a local industrial base.

Further development of water resources is uncertain.

*Trinity Dam* suggests the possibility. Assuredly such development should stimulate recreation and conceivably even attract industry. Indisputable results would include flood control, hydroelectricity and improved roads. Repeated disastrous floods (such as those of 1955 and 1964) emphasize the desirability of flood control facilities in this subregion. The Klamath and several forks of the Eel provide good sites. But lamentably dams must be placed in canyons where much local activity takes place. Currently there is strong opposition to additional dams.

The southern fringes of the Northwest are becoming more closely linked to the Bay Area, with additional commuters, retirees and the possibility of industrial development.

Remaining agriculture here must endure the usual vicissitudes of farming statewide. Accessible orchards and vineyards should attract visitors and new residents, as should more remote locales with guest and hobby ranches. The expanding influx of outsiders, while sometimes taking land from production, will more often serve to perpetuate rural pursuits and landscapes in this realm where "ecotopian" value remains paramount for oldtimers and newcomers alike.

In some areas there is a somewhat uneasy summer season truce between the dominant forest industries and vacationers from outside the subregion. Visitation in some instances can be marred by too many fast-moving trucks, smoking mills, cut-over vistas and closed-entry tree farms, even though such things impart "local color" and help support facilities that tourists may use also. A balance of sorts has been attained between industrial and recreational interests of the Northwest. How effectively that balance is preserved or modified may be the most crucial question currently affecting the entire area.

It seems probable that much of the Northwest will continue to have, at most, only tenuous ties with the "Pacific Connection" that is becoming more meaningful to populous portions of the Golden State.

---

*The largest of these is the *Trinity Alps Wilderness* containing 500,000 acres. Others are Siskiyou and North Fork in the Six Rivers National Forest, Marble Mountains, Red Buttes and Russian Peak in the Klamath Forest, Yolla Bolly, Middle Eel and Snow Mountain in the Mendocino Forest and Mt. Shasta, Castle Crags and Chancelulla in the Shasta-Trinity National Forest.

# PART FOUR

# OVERVIEWS

Geographic study can be either regional, through discussion of multi-faceted areas, or systematic, through individual consideration of such topics as agriculture, climate, or urban. In Parts One through Three priority was given to the regional approach. It is felt that the physical subdivisions of California are so well-known and obvious that they afford familiar mental routes for the reader.

Like the legendary Jack Sprat and his wife, food-wise, the authors (and other geographers) differ in their approach to geography. Steiner and Karinen favor a combination of regional and thematic while Lantis prefers the regional.

In the following Overviews a suggestion of the systematic approach is provided although thematic geography has not been treated fully. Rather, the *choice* of Overview themes is based partly on perceived reader preference and partly on the nature of the subject. Some themes lend themselves to state-wide scope better than others. Admittedly with difficulty instructors who desire the topical approach can deal with subject-matter sections in chapters 2 to 12. For those who prefer the combined regional-systematic approach there are topical summaries at the beginning of each of these chapters.

**Figure A-1.** Late afternoon "break" (for a few seconds) in the frequently-foggy, especially in summer, shore of the Central Coast. (dwl)

Overview A

CLIMATE

# CLIMATE *

California's climatic amenity is its prime physical asset, vastly more precious than all the gold taken from the Sierra Nevada. The incentive for immigration, much of the diverse agricultural output and residential satisfaction have resulted from the sunny subtropical weather for which the Golden State has become an American synonym.

Dank fog and radiant sunshine, cooling sea breezes and lip-parching desert heat, the enervating Santa Anas and chilling north winds, driving rains and long droughts—soon the newcomer finds that there is more than one version of "California climate." Even within the city limits of Los Angeles and San Francisco, one finds departures from the legendary type. Despite its nearly ever-present summer dryness, over two-thirds of the state is sufficiently hot, cold, dry, or wet to suggest climatic traits associated more commonly with the other 49 states. This diversity is advantageous also for its contribution to landscape variety and a broad array of economic activities.

Attention is given first to the principal climatic controls to appreciate California's climatic diversity as well as its relation to worldwide climatic patterns. Next the sundry climates of the Golden State are discussed.

## CONTROLS

California climate is influenced much by its *latitude,* a prime determinant of temperatures, prevailing winds and moisture. Further climatic variation is due to the state's *west coast position* and its *altitudinal variations.* These controls are demonstrated in the following discussion; consideration is given also to storms, ocean temperatures and currents and the trend of mountain barriers.

### 'Twixt 32 and 42 Degrees North

Nearly midway between the equator and the North Pole, the latitudinal spread of California creates conditions that are neither tropical nor polar, but rather subtropical and middle-latitude. Subtropical environments would be even more widespread than they actually are in the Golden State if the elevation of the entire state could be reduced to sea level. Reflecting latitude, temperatures tend to decrease northward from Mexico to Oregon and the growing season becomes shorter (Map A-1) Mountain walls

**Figure A-2.** Clearing newly fallen snow from Ca. 4 west of Mt. Reba in late March after a storm brought an additional four feet overnight. (dwl)

and maritime influences locally modify such progression.

California rests between two major east-west belts of worldwide atmospheric circulation—the middle-latitude storm belt (the "westerlies") and the subtropical high. Precipitation comes largely from middle-latitude storms that originate in the north Pacific Ocean and move eastward across North America. California is to the south of the track followed by most storms; hence precipitation tends to decrease southward within the Golden State. Individual storms may be of a young vigorous nature, in which case heavy rains are likely to occur in the lowlands and wet snow in the highlands, or individual

---

* This section has been reviewed by Richard Haiman, California State University, Chico; John James, University of Nevada, Reno and Robert Richardson, C.S.U., Sacramento.

storms may represent dying stages of old but sizable disturbances, in which case less total precipitation may result, with drier snow falling in the mountains. Meteorologists give particular attention to activity in the upper troposphere, using such terms as troughs and waves and to the path that the *jet stream* follows across the north Pacific Ocean and western North America.

The Golden State is also affected by the *North Pacific* (Hawaiian) *High,* which is centered over the subtropical north Pacific Ocean. Air flowing out of this vast oceanic whirl moves toward California in a southeasterly course. As this air descends from the great high-pressure ridge, it becomes compressed and heated and, hence does not normally yield precipitation. Although the Hawaiian High is thus associated with rainless weather in California, coastal fog and air pollution form frequent companions— both are favored by the inability of cooler, heavier surface air to rise through this lighter, warmer air that is subsiding aloft. In its customary position to the west of California, the Hawaiian High produces light to moderate northwesterly winds which in summer are strongly reinforced by sea breezes. Infrequently when the High shifts, so that its edge is to the north or northeast of California, drying winds from the interior may affect the state. In summer the High, which tends to move northward with the sun, exerts its full strength on California; thus middle-latitude storms move eastward across North America so far north of the state that California is virtually rainless.

Almost all of California tends toward summer dryness, receiving its major precipitation during the winter half year.* Mid-summer precipitation is limited almost wholly to the southeastern deserts, adjacent Sierra Nevada and the Transverse and Peninsular ranges (*especially* the eastern slopes), which are sometimes subjected to unusual invasions of moist air masses from the Gulf of Mexico or even from the tropical eastern Pacific Ocean. Migrant storms in the form of easterly waves or even relict hurricanes (including the Mexican *chubasco)* result in winds and flash floods that bring local destruction. Forest fires, lightning-induced, may occur farther north in the mountains of California.

### The Pacific Connection

Much of the Golden State is insulated from polar continental air masses, so familiar in eastern United States, by prevailing westerly winds off the Pacific Ocean. Interior district temperatures tend to be more extreme than those of coastal sites since land surfaces heat and cool more rapidly than oceans. For any given California elevation and latitude summers are usually warmer and winters colder as one moves eastward. Understandably California's all-time record low and high temperatures have occurred at interior locations (Boca, near Lake Tahoe, and the floor of Death Valley, respectively) where effects of oceanic air penetration are reduced.

The Golden State is noted for its moderate coastal temperatures and for its rapid transition to extreme interior temperatures, exaggerated by the summer coldness of the ocean, which is unusually cool from the shores of Mexico to Oregon. This condition is due to the northwesterly winds (blowing off the Hawaiian High), which move surface water southward (and ultimately away from the coast), with resultant replacement by upwelling of colder water from the ocean depths. Air movement landward across the zone of upwelling is then chilled sufficiently to produce coastal fog or low stratus clouds. Cool sea breezes and stratus cover produce uniquely chilly summers along much of the California strand (Map, A-2).

---

\* This statement is belied in the southeastern deserts, as winter precipitation is slight while rare summer cloudbursts yield sufficient precipitation to show "summer maximum" in long-term summations. For example, July is revealed as Blythe's wettest month!

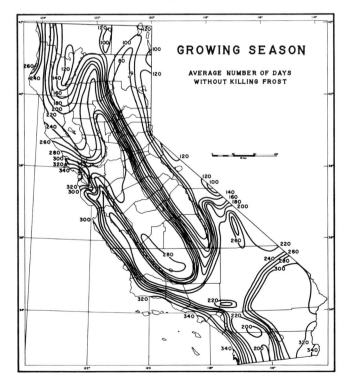

**Map A-1.** Average growing season. A reminder: plants do not keep records. The growth season depends upon the plant.

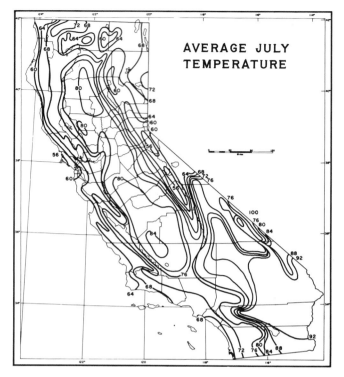

**Map A-2.** The highest temperatures occur in the southeastern deserts and the Central Valley.

### Terrain (Elevation)

Wherever there is sufficient altitude within California effects of latitude are modified markedly. Commonly temperatures decrease with elevation; the more rarified atmosphere of higher altitudes cannot retain upward-rising earth heat as effectively as denser air. Thus the mountains and loftier plateaus of California tend to be colder than adjacent lowlands (Maps A-1, A-2 and A-3). For example, winters along the Del Norte County coast (near the Oregon border) are *warmer* in winter than summits near the Mexican border.

At lower elevations subtropical conditions prevail far into northern California (i.e., the northern end of the Sacramento Valley). In low-lying parts of the state winter mildness is due partly to the fact that invading cold air from the western interior is heated through compression upon descending to lower altitudes. Highlands provide barriers to cold (heavy and "earthbound") air masses. Thus in summer cooler maritime air does not readily rise over coastal hills nor in winter does *polar continental* air from the interior easily cross the Sierra-Cascade and other ranges.

Higher mountains complicate the simple scheme of northward-increasing precipitation in California. Such highlands accelerate the lift of air within cyclonic storms, resulting in heavier *(orographic)* pre-

cipitation. Even near the Mexican border annual amounts approach 40 inches where the Peninsular Ranges have sufficient orographic effect. Precipitation is heavier on windward (Pacific-facing) slopes, where air is rising and oceanic moisture is readily available. Seaward-oriented (windward) slopes, wetter than their interior counterparts (leeward), usually carry a more luxuriant vegetation cover, produce more runoff and afford larger watershed areas (partly as result of more active erosion). As a storm moves inland, its moisture supply is depleted. Air that descends interior-facing mountain slopes becomes warmer and drier to create *rainshadows,* dry belts that extend well to the leeward of the mountains. Thus semiarid or desert climates extend nearly the length of eastern California; even in the southern San Joaquin Valley such conditions prevail (Map, A-5).

### CHANGE AND MODIFICATION

Soils, rocks and fossils (animal and plant) indicate that California, like much of the earth, has known climates in the past differing considerably from those of the present. The Pleistocene epoch, with its alternating advances and retreats of ice, represents the most recent period of significant climatic fluctuation. The *Little Ice Age* of a few hundred years ago evi-

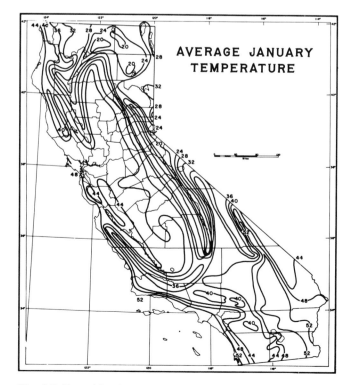

**Map A-3.** The coldest temperatures occur east of the Sierra-Cascade, especially in northeastern California.

dently resulted in the copious spilling of meltwater into the eastern deserts, so that they were more habitable than they are today. Many accept the gradual permanent replacement of forests after fires in parts of California as proof that wetter (or at least cooler) conditions existed at the time of earlier forest growth. Instrumental weather records, maintained for a century, suggest that southern California may be drying very slowly. Cycles of more intense dryness and wetness are revealed but they are too variable to make helpful predictions. Efforts have been made to match precipitation records with the history of flooding, in order to distinguish effects of logging and other practices from "acts of God." Hindered by short-term data, conclusions fail to still the debates between utilitarians and conservationists on this subject.

Climatic modification through air pollution has occurred in the Los Angeles Lowlands and is increasingly apparent in the Central Valley and the San Francisco Bay Area. Remedy lies in pollutant suppression rather than by attempting to alleviate the contributing atmospheric factors of sunshine, stability and stagnation. The growing impact of polluted air upon agriculture, human health and even upon such vegetation as conifer forests in the state lends urgency to the task of finding technical and legal solutions on the surface rather than in an unyielding atmosphere.

Rising urban temperature, humidity (but not rainfall) and fogginess in the irrigated Central and Imperial valleys represent other unintentional climatic modifications. More constructively, citrus growers long ago developed methods of orchard heating that are still employed successfully on frosty nights; such techniques may require further perfection as the citrus producers shift to portions of the state that are climatically more severe. But neither heaters nor other methods have been successful against wintry fogs that sometimes plague Central Valley and coastal travel. Still, experiments in fog dispersal continue, with the realization that dense surficial fogs are sometimes of small duration and volume, unlike the more persistent summer stratus clouds that allow safe ceilings. *Rainmaking,* through addition of chemicals to clouds over some California mountains, has been practiced for decades, although results are subtle at best.

## A DIVERSITY OF CLIMATES

The two principal temperature realms of California, subtropical and middle-latitude* reflect the lati-

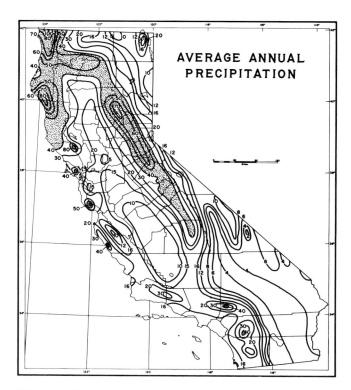

**Map A-4.** The heaviest precipitation falls in the highland areas, especially in the northern Sierra Nevada and in the "far corner" of northwestern California.

tudinal position of the state. Ordinarily, subtropical climates with mild winters prevail between 25 and 40 degrees latitude in both hemispheres; poleward of 40 degrees, middle-latitude climates with colder winters exist.

The latitudinal array is modified by the influence of the adjacent ocean and the patterns of highlands (both trend and altitude). Thus the Sacramento Valley and the North Coast are deemed subbtropical, *even* where they reach poleward of the 40th parallel. However these areas, despite relative mildness, reveal their latitude through angle of the sun's rays and the more extreme seasonal lengths of their daylight period.

The influence of latitude is also modified by the north-south trend of California highlands. While extending appreciably south of 40 degrees, broad

---

* These approach, conceptually, the traditional C and D of Koeppen nomenclature, *modified* to California circumstances. The authors believe that *minimum* temperatures have more relevance to the appearance and habitability of California than do monthly average or maximum temperatures. In Map A-5 and Chart A-1, subtropical climates are indicated for areas where mean minimum temperatures for January are above freezing; where minimum temperature is below 32 degrees, a middle latitude designation is used even though middle-latitude seasonality, in the sense of four well defined "seasons," may be lacking.

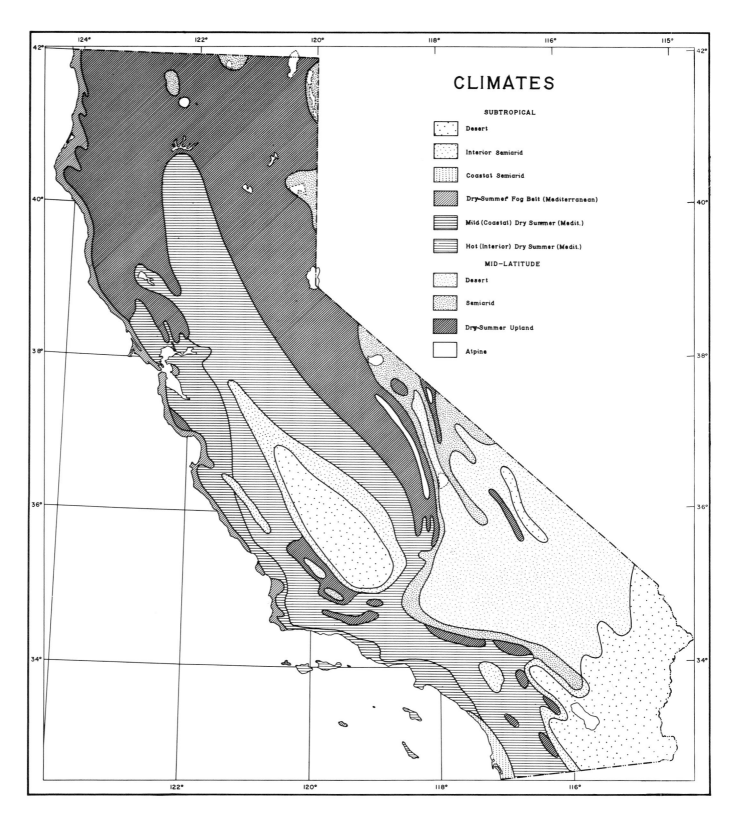

**Map A-5.**

expanses of California mountains have harsher winter conditions than those normally associated with subtropical lands.

A second variable in identifying climatic type is precipitation. All four of the major gradations in moisture— humid, subhumid, semiarid and arid— occur within California. Higher mountains as well as the North Coast generally are relatively humid despite characteristic summer drought; the eastern interior is arid or semiarid; and the northern Central Valley, southern Coast Ranges and southwest fringes of California are essentially subhumid. As actual moisture supply is a function of evaporation as well as precipitation, precise delimitation of moisture categories is difficult. Using a simplified notation portions of California where average annual precipitation is less than 8 inches are designed as *desert,* while areas which receive 8 to 12 inches annually (long-term averages) are deemed *semiarid.*

### Subtropical Realms

California's vaunted reputation as a residence land has been given by this category. It prevails in coastal and near-coastal belts from Mexico to Oregon and inland through portions of the Coast Ranges and the Central Valley—in total about a third of the Golden State. Winters tend to be quite mild and the growing season approaches 12 months annually. Termed "Mediterranean" because of the climatic analogy with portions of the Old World it is found exclusively in California within the United States.* Most of the state's flowers, vegetables and commercial fruits, as well as most of its urban population, are concentrated in these areas. Besides winter mildness, most areas have considerable sunshine interrupted only by cyclonic storms in the lower sun season that bring most of the yearly precipitation. As annual precipitation exceeds 12 inches there is sufficient moisture for forest, woodland, brush or grass and sometimes also for grains and fruit farming without irrigation. Summers are nearly rainless while sunshine and temperatures increase markedly with isolation inland from maritime air of the seashore. Three phases of Mediterranean climate in inland succession are identified accordingly: *Fog Belt, Mild Summer* and *Hot Summer* (Map, A-5 and Chart, A-1).

### Coastal Semiarid

Limited to the San Diego Country, the small zone of *Coastal Semi-Arid Subtropics* indicates the greater dominance of the Hawaiian High than in areas far-

ther north. Many consider it to be one of the nation's choicest residential climates although it is transitional toward the fog desert of Baja California to the south. Morning fog and sea breezes help prevent hot weather. Well-drained slopes are sufficiently fog-free to permit growth of such tropical trees as avocados and lemons. The "frost-free" growing season is essentially year-round with quite-mild winters.

### Interior Semiarid

Between deserts and adjacent more humid areas, the *Interior Semiarid Subtropics* represent transitional zones. They are largely restricted to portions of the San Joaquin Valley surrounding its more arid southwestern segments and to the western periphery of the Colorado Desert. Northeasterly from the San Joaquin desert, semiarid conditions reflect lessening rain-shadow influence as one moves toward the Sierra Nevada with its evident orographic aspects. This climatic subdivision has temperatures and a growing season comparable to the Subtropical Desert.

### Desert **

Basically the subtropical deserts of the world express the effects of the subtropical high-pressure cells (i.e., the North Pacific or Hawaiian High in the instance of California). The Golden State's north-south trending mountain ranges afford an additional control. The Subtropical Desert is restricted to the Colorado Desert, the southeastern Mojave Desert, Death Valley and the southwestern San Joaquin Valley. Irrigation is essential for all crops; natural vegetation is too sparse to afford minimal forage for domesticated animals. The Subtropical Desert, low in elevation, is characterized by intense summer heat and mild winters. The growing season is virtually year-round for hardier crops; in protected sites even more sensitive subtropical crops can be grown in winter.

## MIDDLE-LATITUDE CLIMATES
### Dry-Summer Uplands

The highlands of the Golden State undergo pronounced summer drought; still, these uplands are appreciably wetter in winter and cooler year-round

---

* Koeppen describes this as *Cs.*

** This approximates Koeppen's BWh. As noted previously the authors give primacy to latitude. Hence dry areas (Koeppen's B) are considered dry subtropical or dry middle-latitude.

| Climatic Type | General Characteristics | Representative Stations (with elevation) | July Temp. | Jan. Temp. | Growing Season | Annual Precip. | Annual Snowfall |
|---|---|---|---|---|---|---|---|
| **SUBTROPICAL** | | | | | | | |
| Desert | Summers hot and long, winters mild and brief. Perennial drought and low humidity. Colorado Desert warmer than San Joaquin Valley, with sunnier winters and greater possibility of summer thunderstorms | Brawley (Imperial Cty.), -119 ft. | 93° | 54° | 10.6 mo. | 2 in. | <1 in. |
| | | Maricopa (Kern Cty.), 660 ft. | 86° | 48° | 10.3 mo. | 6 in. | <1 in. |
| Interior Semiarid | Temperatures slightly lower and precipitation a little heavier than adjacent Desert. | Fresno (Fresno Cty.), 331 ft. | 81° | 46° | 10.1 mo. | 9 in. | <1 in. |
| Coastal Semiarid | Mild winters and summers reflect oceanic influences. Higher humidity and much more cloud cover than interior Semiarid. | San Diego (San Diego Cty.), sea level | 72° | 55° | 12.0 mo. | 10 in. | <1 in. |
| Dry-Summer (Mediterranean) Fog Belt | Summer fog and sea breeze. Average July temperature 50° to 64°F. Winters mild for the latitude. Small annual temperature range. Precipitation increases markedly northward. | Del Monte (Monterey Cty.), sea level | 61° | 48° | 9.9 mo. | 15 in. | <1 in. |
| | | Eureka (Humboldt Cty.), sea level | 57° | 47° | 11.1 mo. | 38 in. | <1 in. |
| Mild Dry-Summer (Mediterranean) | Summers warmer and sunnier than Fog Belt but cooler and cloudier than farther inland. Definite maritime influence with some summer fog. Average July temperature 65° to 71°F. | Santa Barbara (S.B. Cty.), sea level | 67° | 53° | 10.0 mo. | 18 in. | <1 in. |
| | | San Jose (Santa Clara Cty.), 95 ft. | 68° | 49° | 10.0 mo. | 13 in. | <1 in. |
| Hot Dry-Summer (Mediterranean) | More continental than other Mediterranean climates. Summers long, hot, and sunny periods. Average July temperatures above 71°F. Winters mild, especially at low elevations with good air drainage. Likelihood of some mid-winter fog (in Central Valley). | Redlands (San Bern. Cty.), 1352 ft. | 77° | 51° | 9.7 mo. | 15 in. | <1 in. |
| | | Colusa (Colusa Cty.), 60 ft. | 78° | 45° | 9.0 mo. | 15 in. | <1 in. |
| **MIDDLE LATITUDE** | | | | | | | |
| Desert | Large annual temperature range. Summers hot but winters longer and more severe than Subtropical Desert. Winter maximum precipitation but occasional summer thunderstorms in Mojave and Basin Range areas. | Trona (San Bern. Cty.), 1700 ft. | 89° | 45° | 8.1 mo. | 4 in. | <1 in. |
| Semiarid | Elevation higher; hence temperatures cooler than adjacent Middle-Latitude Desert. Precipitation heavier, with considerable winter snow common. | Tehachapi (Kern Cty.), 3970 ft. | 76° | 39° | 5.8 mo. | 11 in. | 38 in. |
| | | Doyle (Lassen Cty.), 4280 ft. | 71° | 31° | 3.2 mo. | 10 in. | 24 in. |
| Dry-Summer Upland | Winters longer and more severe than adjacent lowlands, usually with moderate to heavy snowfall. Intensity of winter increases decidedly with elevations and isolation from ocean. Summers generally mild to cool. | Seven Oaks (San Bern. Cty.), 5075 ft. | 63° | 38° | 2.9 mo. | 27 in. | 57 in. |
| | | Placerville (El Dorado Cty.), 1890 ft. | 74° | 40° | 5.9 mo. | 40 in. | 7 in. |
| | | Tahoe (Placer Cty.), 6228 ft. | 61° | 27° | 2.4 mo. | 31 in. | 219 in. |
| | | Weaverville (Trinity Cty.), 2050 ft. | 71° | 37° | 3.9 mo. | 37 in. | 27 in. |
| Alpine | Average July temperature below 50°F., with recurrent mid-summer frost. Precipitation tends to be relatively light; considerable portion in form of snow. | White Mountain (Mono Cty.), 12,470 ft. (short-term record) | 45° | 6° | 0.5 mo. | 13 in. | 131 in. |

**Chart A-1.** Summary of climatic types

than adjacent lowlands. While agriculture may be climatically feasible, the relatively short growing season restricts the variety of crops.

Precipitation is generally adequate to support growth of forest or heavy woodland. The colder northeastern margins receive precipitation in excess of 12 inches; elsewhere the Middle-Latitude Uplands record more than 30 inches, part of which falls as snow. Overall, elevations range from near sea level (in the north) to almost 12000 feet. This climatic type encompasses about a *third* of California! (see Map, A-5). It is the typical climate of the Sierra Nevada, the Southern Cascade Range, Klamath Mountains, northern Coast Ranges and the Modoc Plateau.

A wider range of precipitation and temperatures characterizes this realm which even includes a few lowlands (and highlands in southern California that technically might be classed subtropical. Its small populations and minimal use for agriculture make additional subdivision inappropriate here.

### Semi-Arid

Between the Middle-Latitude Desert and the Transverse Ranges, *and* the Sierra Nevada, this environment provides narrow transition zones with orographic influence which brings slightly higher precipitation than occurs farther east. The type becomes more extensive within the Basin Ranges and is also characteristic of Shasta Valley and the Tule Lake Basin because of rain-shadow location. The more northerly basins have better four-season definition than generally prevails in California yet they too have summer dryness.

### Desert *

North of its Subtropical Desert, eastern California likewise reflects rainshadow position and seasonal dominance of the Hawaiian High. But it is less insulated against outbursts of polar continental air from the northern interior of North America; thus the the virtual year-long growing season of the Colorado desert is much reduced. Moreover, this is *"High Desert"* whose altitudes reach half a mile higher than that of the *"Low Desert"* farther south (and also to the west in the southern San Joaquin Valley). Much of the Mojave Desert as well as the adjoining depressions within the southern Basin Ranges carry Middle-Latitude Desert designation. Altitude may also justify assigning the Cuyama Valley and the Carrizo Plain to this type.

### Alpine **

Generally, above 12,000 feet conditions *suggestive* of polar environments exist in California. The Sierra Nevada contains the largest extent, with lesser areas on Mount Shasta, Lassen Peak, the Warner Range, and the White Mountains. As along Arctic coastlines, temperatures (and also terrain) are too low for agriculture or even for true forest growth. There are diminutive perennial snowfields (especially on north slopes) but the seasonal conditions of continuous light or darkness of polar lands is absent. Stunted vegetation is found in favored locales yet windswept expanses of barren rock are common.

---

\* This *approximates* Koeppen's BWk.
\*\* Koeppen would identify this type as *ET.*

**Figure B-1.** The Mojave Desert, a land of worn mountain blocks, alluvial-filled basins and many playas. (dwl)

Overview B

LANDFORMS*

* This section was reviewed by
Bruce Bechtol, C.S.U., Chico.

# LANDFORMS

The geographic intricacy of the Golden State has evolved upon its diversified topography. Mountains, hills, plains and plateaus —all of the major landform types occur in California. The geologic history of the state has greater complexity than most states—exposed formations range from contemporary (Cenozoic) to ancient (pre-Cambrian). Shoreline and contiguous submarine surfaces add variety. Hence California provides a remarkable natural laboratory for students of geology, geography and other earth sciences.

## LANDFORM DIVISIONS

For purposes of statewide comparison, individual mountains, hills, plains and plateaus are organized into physiographic divisions. The State Division of Mines delineates eleven major units,* listed below (also see Fig. B-1). When California landforms are

related to the remainder of the continent, larger groupings are recognized; thus this list includes the broad North American physiographic provinces of which the California divisions form segments:

### North American Cordillera

**Intermontane Plateau System**
1. Basin Ranges
2. Mojave Desert
3. Colorado Desert
4. Modoc Plateau

**Pacific Mountain System**
5. Cascade Range
6. Sierra Nevada
7. Klamath Mountains
8. Coast Ranges
9. Transverse Ranges
10. Peninsular Ranges
11. Great Valley

*N.E.A. Hinds, *Evolution of the California Landscape,* Bull. 158, Ca. Div. of Mines, 1952. Further reading is listed in the bibliography.

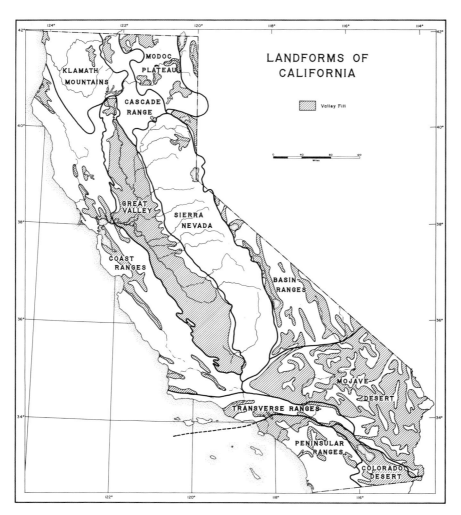

**Map B-1.** The primary landform divisions in California. Most of the lowlands are filled with unconsolidated sediments (commonly alluvium).

The importance and dramatic character of California terrain prompted arrangement of this book primarily in terms of physiography; details of the eleven landform divisions are included in individual chapters. To facilitate comparison, rocks and structures are summarized in map B-1(table) and map B-2.

## GEOMORPHIC PROCESSES

The Golden State reaches along the contact zone between the Pacific Ocean and North American crustal plates—to the pleasure of nature lovers but the misfortune of prospective earthquake victims. Opposing movement of these two subsurface masses along a north-south interface accounts for much of the state's seismic notoriety and diverse ridgetops plus many of California's mineral resources, soils and detailed climatic and hydrologic patterns. Of the various (and complex) plate movements, two chronologic phases are identified here to explain California's broad landform design (further details can be found in the cited geologic literature).

Landform Division Major Lithic Type
General Structure

| Landform Division | Major Lithic Type | General Structure |
|---|---|---|
| Basin Ranges | complex[a] | fault blocks |
| Mojave Desert | complex[a] | fault blocks |
| Colorado Desert[b] | sedimentary | faulted downwarp |
| Modoc Plateau | volcanic | lava flows as fault blocks |
| Cascade Range | volcanic | igneous tableland capped by volcanoes |
| Sierra Nevada | granitic-metamorphic | tilted fault block |
| Klamath Mountains | granitic-metamorphic-sedimentary | folds-faults |
| Coast Ranges | sedimentary | folds-faults |
| Transverse Ranges[c] | sedimentary (western), granitic-metamorphic (eastern) | folds-faults (western) fault blocks (eastern) |
| Peninsular Ranges[d] | sedimentary (western), granitic-metamorphic (eastern) | folds-faults (western) fault blocks (eastern) |
| Great Valley | sedimentary | downwarp |

[a] i.e., sedimentary, volcanic, and granitic-metamorphic rocks occur widely.

[b] Also called "Salton Trough."

[c] Also called "Los Angeles Ranges."

[d] Also called "San Diego Ranges."

**Chart B-1.** Characteristic rocks and structures of the landform divisions.

## First Phase: Subduction, Intrusion, Metamorphosis

Less than 200 million years ago (in Mesozoic time) the eastward-moving *Pacific Plate* was subducting beneath the California segment of North America, producing *geosynclines* (in this case elongated north-south troughs) where the earth's surface sagged into the zones of initial descent. The Great Valley persisted during much of the subduction process—likewise also, to a lesser degree, have the Los Angeles Basin and its adjacent sea floor (Diagram B-1). Eventually topographic lowlands were filled with in-washed sediments and then elevated; their sedimentary rocks today form California's western highland fringes.

Concurrently moving westward, the *North American Plate* has acquired a western fringe that extends roughly from San Diego to Crescent City. The continental crust, east of this boundary, was deformed and elevated as it overrode the descending Pacific Plate. Masses of molten granitic rock (*batholiths*) intruded upward from the deeper disturbed crust to create foundations for California's principal mountain backbone. Lowered considerably through long erosion, this batholithic spine has been uplifted again recently along fault blocks to produce (south to north) most of the present-day Peninsular and Transverse Ranges, as well as the Sierra Nevada and Klamath ranges. Atop the batholiths, or upon their edges, there remain pre-existing sedimentary and other materials, commonly *metamorphosed* (i.e., much altered by heat and/or pressure).

## Second Phase: Rupture, Compression, Eruption, Tension

Subduction yielded, some 30 million years ago, to a reorientation of the Pacific Plate, which assumed a northwestward movement that still continues. * Consequently, western California has been detached from the remainder of North America along the present-day San Andreas fault system, the most critical high-hazard seismic belt in California. The crust of southernmost California is parting from North America proper along this rupture, thus producing the trough that is occupied by the Colorado Desert and by the Gulf of California to the south (Diagram B-2).

---

* Advent, then stoppage of subduction, is believed the result of relocation of North America relative to the E*ast Pacific Rise*, a north-south belt of upmoving oceanic crust, spreading laterally (Diagram B-2). This entire Rise apparently lay to the west of California, causing the segment of the Pacific Plate vicinal to California to subduct eastward. In time, however, westward movement of the North American continent reached a position west of the Rise and thus atop the westward moving portion of the Pacific Plate.

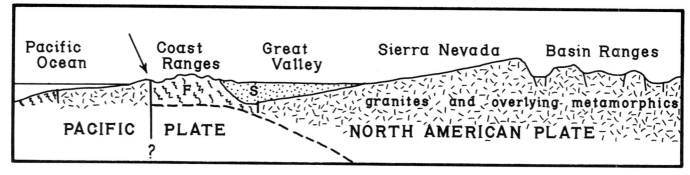

**Diagram B-1.** Cross section along 37th parallel, showing hypothesized crustal structure and major faults. The vertical scale is exaggerated. Meaning of letters: F=Franciscan and overlying rocks; S=Younger sedimentary materials. The vertical arrow points to San Andreas Fault. The dashed line is the former subduction surface of the Pacific Plate. (After Bateman, Yates, et al).

Despite the doomsday predictions of California's impending instant seaward plunge, however, the continental and oceanic plates are converging in the latitude of Los Angeles rather than *separating*, since the Pacific Plate encounters but is unable to displace the North American Plate. Thus resulting crustal compression along an east-west zone is elevating the North American fringe into the narrow but definitive Transverse Ranges, bisected by the San Andreas system with minimal effort. This uplift is aligned with, and assumedly relates to, the *Murray Fracture zone* which extends westward beneath the Pacific (and probably eastward as well beneath the North American continent).

Coastal California, north of the Transverse Ranges, is sliding northwestward relatively freely, with historic evidence of persistent crustal creep amounting annually to one half inch (or more in some locales). Still friction is not absent there either. Instead, the coastal and continental masses have converged sufficiently along the San Andreas system to compress the overlying sedimentary rocks. Resultant folding and faulting of these plastic materials have produced linear northwest-trending ridges to form the Coast Ranges.* The San Andreas system turns westward into the ocean at the latitude of Cape Mendocino. Its northward trend is blocked by the Klamath Mountains, which appears to have moved westward after detaching from this lithic counterpart, the northern Sierra Nevada. As in southern California, this abrupt geologic dislocation coincides with an east-west crustal break of uncertain origin (i.e., the Mendocino fracture zone) which extends far westward upon the sea floor and perhaps into the North American continent as well.

The Cascade Range and the Modoc Plateau of northeastern California differ from most of the Golden State in displaying vast expanses of eruptive rocks which originated as magma beneath the continental plate. Volcanism, apparently in its late stages, must be considered contemporarily active (*perhaps dangerously so!*): Mt. Shasta erupted in the 1700s and Lassen Peak about seventy years ago. The volcanic

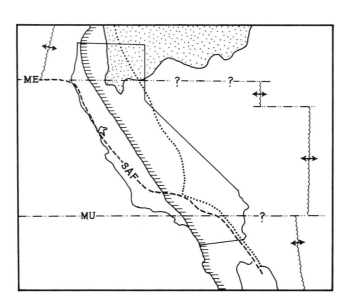

**Diagram B-2.** Contemporary lithic and tectonic setting of the Golden State. Stripes indicate west margin of the continental batholithic belt; stippling indicates the primary eruptive zone; dotted line marks west edge of the tensional fault block region; wavy lines with arrows show hypothesized positions of the East Pacific Rise and its crustal speeding; ME is the Mendocino fracture; MU is the Murray fracture; SAF is the San Andreas Fault (adapted from Hamilton and Myers).

---

* Some segments of southern Coast Ranges contain granitic masses where none would ordinarilly exist, suggesting that northwest conveyance away from a locale in the batholithc belt perhaps near the south end of the Sierra Nevada. Also there are many faults that parallel or branch from the San Andreas with a similar sense of movement. Thus the separation of the Pacific and North American plates along the San Andreas rupture is not clear cut. In fact California's apparent position mostly west of the East Pacific Rise argues for a semi-coordinated westward (or northwestward) movement of both plates— obviously there is much to be learned.

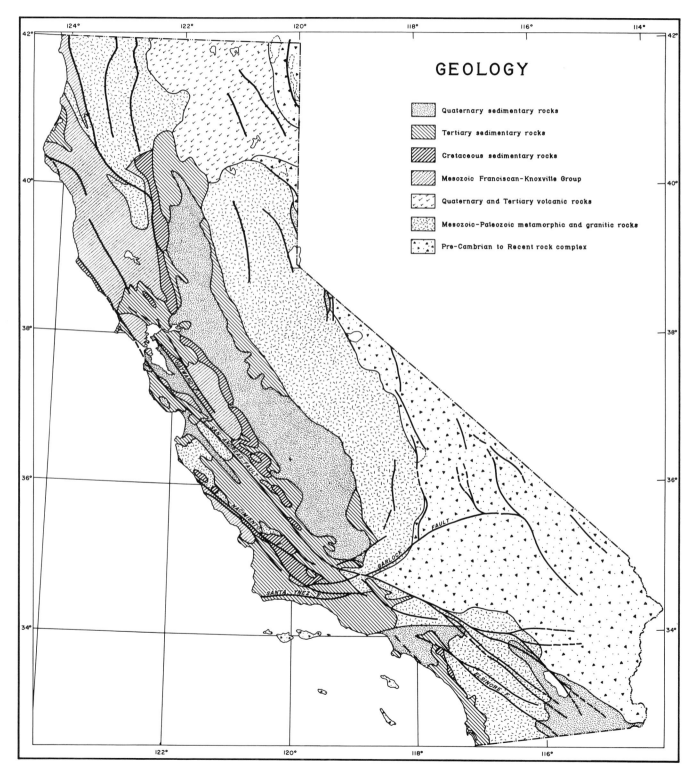

GEOLOGY

Quaternary sedimentary rocks

Tertiary sedimentary rocks

Cretaceous sedimentary rocks

Mesozoic Franciscan-Knoxville Group

Quaternary and Tertiary volcanic rocks

Mesozoic-Paleozoic metamorphic and granitic rocks

Pre-Cambrian to Recent rock complex

**Map B-2.** Major lithic types. Heavy lines locate the principal faults, active and inactive.

materials of this area have overlapped an older terrain, including the northern Sierra Nevada batholith, in possible response to stretching and thinning of the continental crust behind (eastward of) the rapidly west-moving Klamath Mountains.

Numerous fault lines penetrate the lava tablelands of the Modoc Plateau. Hence there are abrupt north-trending scarps along which crustal segments have been elevated, lowered or tilted in response to east-west tension (stretching) of the continental plate.

More spectacular fault blocks occur in the Basin Ranges province. Here, for example, Death Valley has dropped below sea level while nearby mountains have risen two miles above it.

Contemporary faulting in the Mojave Desert diminishes southward while westward it assumes horizontal rather than vertical motion, much like the nearby San Andreas system. Hence Mojave terrain is more subdued while its sedimentary basins are larger than those farther north.

## THE HAZARDS OF EARTHQUAKES

Given the worldwide tendency of the earth's crust to drift horizontally, few places remain continuously free from earthquakes. However seismic disturbances are more profound in areas such as California which lie at the junction of two unequally shifting crustal plates. Within the state locally, historic experience reveals the San Andreas and affiliated fault as a zone of maximum probable earthquake intensity (Map B-3). Additional high-severity areas appear to be the Basin Ranges, the Garlock fault belt and the Santa Barbara Channel. By contrast the lowest probable seismic intensities occur in the eastern Mojave and in a belt through the Klamath Mountains, the northern Sacramento Valley and the northern Sierra Nevada. But the Oroville tremors (1975) reiterated the maxim of an universally-vulnerable state. Quake hazards, in contrast to national or worldwide perspectives, are "high" *everywhere* in California.

**Figure B-2.** Wave action has played an important role in creation of California's much-indented coast. This is a view of the south shore of Anacapa Island (National Park Service).

Coincidence between the state's maximum earthquake risk zones, particularly metropolitan Los Angeles and San Francisco, are of special concern. Worse, weak lithology may reinforce proximity to fault lines in producing damage; California's urban areas tend to be positioned too often upon unconsolidated "valley fill" (Overview D) which affords minimal support, especially when water saturated. Accordingly predictions of devasting (though not apocalyptic) earthquake shocks during the lifetimes of most present Californians and their structures seem plausible. There is no early prospect of prevention although with advancing seismic knowledge earthquake predictions may become usefully specific. The most effective preparations are the most obvious ones (though so far inadequate)—better provision for emergency services and improved structural standards.

A statewide project under the Alquist-Priolo Act to delimit hazardous fault zones is an ongoing phase of earthquake preparation. Hence future California urban developments may avoid the past errors of placing buildings (including schools and hospitals) directly atop active crustal rifts. More accurate delimitation of seismic probablity also would facilitate evaluation of present land usage, leading to crucial

**Figure B-3.** This is the basal tableland of the Cascade Range. Seen here is Deer Creek Canyon northeast of Chico. This is some of the most rugged non-alpine country in California (dwl).

corrections (as siting and design of hospitals) and perhaps to a more effective fiscal insurance system.

## MANY MINERAL COMMODITIES

With its lithic diversity California understandably has been a potential treasure house of economic minerals. Top-score individual items appear on current production lists; prospective and historic tallies are larger. Mineral discovery has been favored by extensive mountain and desert outcrops without soil or vegetative concealment. Extensive public holdings admitting mineral claim entries have also facilitated exploitation. Yet ultimately occurrence and needs must determine the state's mineral exploitation. Thus construction minerals (as aggregates and cement) are usually produced near urban markets; more abundant but distant reserves depend upon future demands. Other plentiful California minerals (as chrome) remain untouched; economics and strategic needs dictate importance.

Only the Modoc Plateau and the Cascade Range, among the state's major physiographic units, are nearly devoid of commercial mineral output. Present-day mining is likewise infrequent in much of the granitic-metamorphic mountain backbone belt where gold deposits once lured thousands. Assorted metallic "vein and replacement" deposits in these areas have been much worked or are too diffused for current economic production. Long noted for cinnabar (mercury), the central and northern Coast Ranges also are a subordinate producing realm. In fact metals account for only three per cent of California's mineral output with recent cutback in tungsten and iron ore (map B-4). The "new" Gold Rush, prompting major ac-

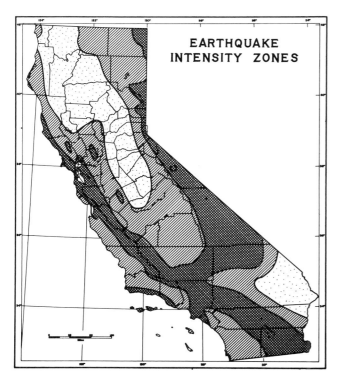

EARTHQUAKE
INTENSITY ZONES

**Map B-3.** Earthquake zones based upon three levels of probable maximum intensity; severity increases with darkness of shading. (based upon preliminary map by California Division of Mines and Geology, 1973).

tivity in the northern Coast Ranges, the Sierra Nevada and the deserts, is still of uncertain consequence.

Fossil fuels (natural gas and petroleum) lead the California mineral group, contributing over 60 per cent of the total value. Fuels are treated separately in Overview G because of their prominence. The aforementioned construction commodities rank next, furnishing 20 per cent of the state's mineral output value.

Among California minerals, the industrial minerals designated as salines (or "evaporites") rank third in value economically. They have accumulated or are derived from brine concentrations that occur in oceanic or former desert lake environments. Most important are the boron minerals, chiefly from the Mojave and Basin Ranges areas. Other salines from the California deserts include bromine, calcium chloride, lithium and potassium salts. Some, along with magnesium, are coastal products, especially from the shores of San Diego, Monterey and San Francisco bays. The salines (especially borates) are important beyond their 10 per cent contribution to the state's total mineral output. California , one of the world's few sources, is an important exporter of these commodities.

California's current mineral output centers locationally on portions of the desert and shoreline, the fossil fuel provinces (increasingly oceanic) and the metropolitan peripheries. Secondary locales include the southern Coast Ranges and the Sierra Nevada-Central Valley borderlands. The former realm yields asbestos and diatomite, consumed in diverse indus-

trial products; the latter area contributes asbestos and refractory clays, as well as construction materials (as clay, sand and gravel and building stone) for the Central Valley and the San Francisco Bay Area.

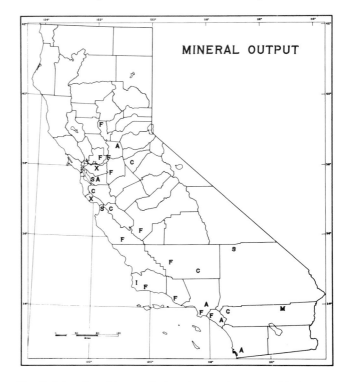

**Map B-4.** Locales with annual mineral output in excess of $10 million (county basis). Commodities identified by letter: A is construction aggregates; C is cement; F is fossil fuels; I is special industrial materials; M, metals; S, salines; X indicates counties where product value is based upon two or more unspecified minerals (based upon California Division of Mines Geology, U.S. Bureau of Mines and author's research).

**Figure C-1.** Ceanothus abloom, Topanga Canyon, Santa Monica Mountains. The several dozen different ceanothi are widespread within chapparal. (dwl)

Overview C

NATURAL
VEGETATION

# NATURAL VEGETATION

Despite its foremost status among the fifty states in agricultural output and population, California is still widely clad, more or less, in natural vegetation. A mere 14 per cent of the Golden State is cultivated or urbanized. California's ranking as a lumber and range cattle producer stems from its biotic resources. Sudden removal of plant cover, as by fire, adversely affects soils, water runoff, wildlife population and scenery. However, purposeful substitution of grassland for dense brush may reduce transpirational water wastage, and careful thinning of woodlands and forests may enhance growth of smaller plants upon which game animals depend. Thus vegetation "management" is a widespread concern and poses important issues, especially in habitats where the vegetation has more than one use.

Marked correlation exists between climatic expression and plant distribution. At opposite extremes in California are the desert shrubs of the arid southeast and the verdant forests of the *humid* northwest (Figure C-1). However more than half of California (its subhumid and semiarid segments) is climatically intermediate and exhibits a considerable mixing of trees, shrubs and grasses. In this *"tension zone"*, ground conditions, fire history and even short-term variations in climate may exert critical influence upon plant life. Seasonal changes are more striking than in bordering deserts or forests and vegetation is more distinctive from that of neighboring states.

The natural vegetation map (map C-1) reflects broadly the climatic modification which results from elevation differences. In eastward sequence across the Sierra Nevada and the Cascade, for example, prairie is replaced by woodland which in turn gives way to forest with increasing altitude. Such *vertical zonation* is common in mountainous habitats; hence many wetter, greener isles are found on the vegeta-

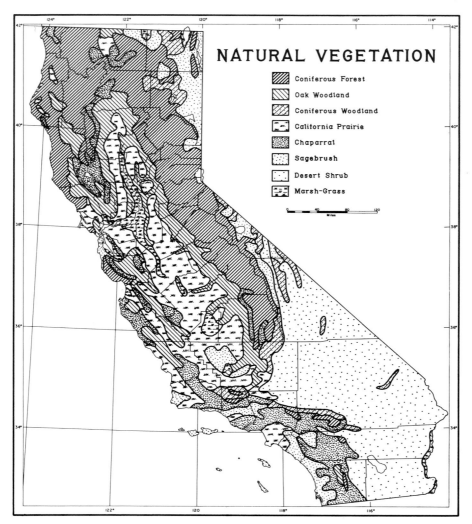

**NATURAL VEGETATION**

- Coniferous Forest
- Oak Woodland
- Coniferous Woodland
- California Prairie
- Chaparral
- Sagebrush
- Desert Shrub
- Marsh-Grass

**Map C-1.** Sixty percent of the different types of plants found within the conterminous 48 states are represented in California.

| Category | Original Coverage | Aspect and Composition | Utilization |
|---|---|---|---|
| coniferous forest | 21% | Needleleaf evergreen trees. Density, growth rate, and understory thickness tend to increase northwestward. One or two species often clearly dominant, especially redwood along North Coast, Douglas fir inland from redwood belt, ponderosa-Jeffrey pines in lower Sierra Nevada and Modoc Plateau, red fir at 8000–9000 feet in Sierra Nevada, and lodgepole-whitebark pines above 9000 feet in Sierra Nevada. Over half the forest area is more mixed, with common associates of ponderosa-Jeffrey pines including Douglas fir, white fir, sugar pine, and incense cedar. | Most species commercially useful. One half of original timber has been cut. Annual loss is about 2.5 times the annual net growth. One-tenth of remaining original timber is within national and state parks. Grazing common except in redwood and Douglas fir belts. Most cutover areas are in brush and woodland or have returned to forest. |
| oak woodland | 11% | Grassland as described for California Prairie, with trees scattered or in groves. Several species of deciduous and evergreen oaks are dominant; subordinate trees are mostly broadleaf deciduous. | Primarily grazing. Heavy forage growth especially in winter and spring. Trees mainly unused. |
| coniferous woodland | 3% | Sagebrush as described below, with pinon pine and/or juniper bushes scattered or in groves. | Primarily grazing. Fair forage growth. Pinon and juniper mainly unused. |
| grassland ("California prairie") | 22% | Treeless grassland, originally dominated by perennial bunchgrasses and other herbaceous plants. Majority of associations now consist of introduced annuals of inferior quality. | More than one-half displaced by farming and urban. Remainder grazing. Heavy forage growth, especially winter and spring. |
| chaparral | 9% | Broadleaf evergreen shrubs, dominated by chamise, scrub oak, manzanita, and ceanothus. Forms impenetrable thickets when well developed. Replaces forest and oak woodland following fire in some localities. | Minimum use other than for watershed covering. |
| sagebrush | 8% | Shrubs and semishrubs dominant but considerable understory of grasses, especially in interior areas. Shorter and less dense than fully developed chaparral. | Primarily grazing. Fair forage in the interior, especially in winter. Poor forage in coastal areas. |
| desert shrub | 25% | Shrubs, usually small and scattered, are dominant, particularly creosote bush, burroweed, and shadscale. Much bare ground despite presence of grasses, cacti, wildflowers, etc. | Largely unused. Relatively small portions displaced by farming and urbanization. |
| marsh grass | <1% | Mostly perennial herbs to 9 feet high. Dominated by bulrushes (including common tule), cattails, spike rushes, sedges. | Largely displaced by farming. Remainder used for grazing and recreation. |
| barren | 1% | | |

**Chart C-1.** California vegetation includes grasslands, woodlands, shrublands, and forests.

The Northeast

    bitterbrush or Antelope brush *(Purshia tridentata)*
    grass, bunch *(Festuca idahoensis)*
    juniper *(J. occidentalis)*
    sagebrush, Great Basin *(Artemisia tridentata)*
    salt brush *(Atriplex spp.)*

Trans-Sierra

    creosote bush *(Larrea divaricata)*
    holly, desert *(Atriplex hymenelytra)*
    juniper *(J. californica)*
    mahogany, mountain *(Cercocarpus spp.)*
    pine, piñon *(P. monophylla)*
    shadscale *(Atriplex confertifolia)*
    pine, bristlecone *(P. aristata)*

Mojave Desert

    burroweed *(Franseria dumosa)*
    cottonwood *(Populus fremontii)*
    ironwood *(Olneya tesota)*
    Joshua tree *(Yucca brevifolia)*
    mesquite *(Prosopis juliflora)*
    palo verde *(Cercidium floridum)*
    pickleweed *(Allenfolfia spp. and Salicornia spp.)*
    Spanish dagger *(Yucca schidigera)*

Colorado Desert

    cholla *(Opuntia spp.)*
    grass, galleta *(Hilaria rigida)*
    ocotillo *(Fouquieria splendens)*
    smoke tree *(Dalea spinosa)*

Southern California

    buckwheat *(Eriogonum spp.)*
    chamise *(Adenostoma fasciculatum)*
    manzanita *(Arctostaphylos spp.)*
    oak, live *(Quercus agrifolia)*
    oak, valley *(Q. lobata)*
    sage, purple *(Salvia leucophylla)*
    sage, white *(Salvia apiana)*
    sagebrush, California *(Artemisia californica)*
    walnut, black *(Juglans californica)*

Great Central Valley

    bulrush *(Carex spp.)*
    grass, needle *(Stipa spp.)*
    oak, California black *(Quercus kelloggii)*
    oak, interior live *(Q. wislizenii)*
    tule *(Scirpus acutus)*

Sierra Nevada

    aspen *(Populus tremuloides)*
    azalea, western *(Rhododendron occidentale)*
    cedar, incense *(Libocedrus decurrens)*
    coffeeberry *(Rhamnus californica)*
    dogwood *(Cornus nuttallii)*
    fir, Douglas *(Pseudotsuga menziesii)*
    fir, red *(Abies magnifica)*
    fir, white *(Abies concolor)*
    gooseberry *(Ribes spp.)*
    hemlock, mountain *(Tsuga mertensiana)*
    maple, bigleaf *(Acer macrophyllum)*
    pine, digger *(Pinus sabiniana)*
    pine, Jeffrey *(P. jeffreyi)*
    pine, lodgepole *(P. murrayana)*
    pine, sugar *(P. lambertiana)*
    pine, western yellow *(P. ponderosa)*
    pine, white-bark *(P. albicaulis)*
    giant sequoia, big tree *(Sequoiadendron giganteum)*

Northwest

    bay *(Umbellularia californica)*
    chamise *(Adenostoma fasciculatum)*
    cedar, Port Oxford *(Chamaecyparis lawsoniana)*
    hemlock *(Tsunga heterophylla)*
    laurel, California *(Umbellularia californica)*
    madrone *(Arbutus menziesii)*
    myrtle, wax *(Myrica californica)*
    oak, tanbark *(Lithocarpus densiflora)*
    redbud, *(Cercis occidentalis)*
    redwood, coast *(Sequoia sempervirens)*
    toyon *(Photinia arbutifolia)*

---

Botanic names were obtained from Munz and Keck, *A California Flora.*

**Chart C-2.** Common and scientific names of plants listed in the book.

tion map in dry realms of the state where mountains are present.

In all landscapes save forests, abnormally dense plant growth occurs where water runoff is locally abundant. Tules and other plants of the marsh-grass group once dominated waterlogged bottomlands such as along the Colorado River and in the Great Central Valley. Where water tables, even though subsurface, are still accessible, *riparian* vegetation, commonly arboreal, is supported. Thus strips of floodplain woodland follow streams which cross the Great Valley. Soil quality is also relevant. Chaparral, particularly, is associated with thinner soils; sagebrush, coniferous woodland and desert shrub are likewise tolerant of inhospitable sites, whereas grass and oak woodland grow more often on deeper, moisture-retentive soils.

Only a limited statewide reduction of area covered by natural vegetation has occurred in recent decades. Tillage long ago occupied prime lowlands, particularly areas of grassland. Farming has since expanded only through intensification rather than through areal growth (except on the West Side and in the South End of the Central Valley). In turn urbanization has replaced more farmland than woodland. Hence the pre-European vegetation distribution remains largely unaltered; still its composition has been modified vastly. Grazing and logging have over-exploited the plant resource, causing deterioration that in places may be irreversible. Wildfire is another immediate influence upon California vegetation; it is questionable, however, whether fire or, for that matter, logging and grazing are as influential today as in earlier decades when they occurred almost unchecked. The sum product of these varied forces has been the substitution of less useful plants for more valuable grass or forest. But it has been demonstrated that, under proper management, all the agents of burning, cutting and grazing can also be controlled to benefit the vegetation cover.

Eight principal categories of native vegetation may be delineated within the state (Chart, C-1). These include two contrasting types of woodland and two sometimes-admired kinds of *brush* (sagebrush and chaparral). The basic vegetation categories may in turn be sudivided into more localized units so as to recognize speciation or difference in usage. Further descriptions of plant cover and its significance are given in chapters two through twelve.

To assist readers who are more technically-oriented, this overview concludes with a listing of many of the plant species noted in the main text, including equivalent common and Latin nomenclature (Chart C-2).

**Figure D-1.** Cultivation of *Vina loam,* a deep (20 feet or more) alluvial soil that developed under the *California Prairie* on the Chico alluvial fan in the central Sacramento Valley. Once used for Chinese (and later Japanese) truck gardens, this particular field, only a few blocks from the University campus, has been subdivided. Because geographers, agronomists, botanists, planners and the general public are aware of the productivity of this soil, much of it may remain in agriculture (currently almond orchards) for many decades. (dwl)

Overview D

SOILS

# SOILS

The by-products of California's oft-stated geologic, climatic and botanic diversity, the soils of the Golden State are exceedingly variable. Nine of the world's ten primary soil orders are represented in the state and more than 500 distinct soil series are recognized. The statewide transition southeastward from humid forest to arid shrub is an important influence; soil alkalinity increases, color lightens and organic matter decreases southeastward in California. Particle size (soil texture), contrari-wise. is often more directly influenced by parent rock than by vegetation or climate. Hence sandy loams commonly occur on granitic surfaces, clay-textured soils are prevalent on the volcanics of the northeast and clay loams are typical on Coast Range sandstone and shale.

Another determinant of soil, through its effects upon erosion and deposition, is slope. Because of California's strongly contrasting terrain, its overall soil qualities are more dependent upon landforms than upon other controls. Hence the primary distinction is between *lowland* (or transported) soils as one category and *upland* (or residual) soils as another. Transported soils normally are favored for cultivation while residual soils are used less intensively, often not at all.

## TRANSPORTED (Lowland) SOILS

Most California soils rated *excellent*, as well as those rated *good* or *fair*, are mostly transported; they are derived from alluvium or other unconsolidated deposits. Situated in the lowest, and hence usually the warmest localities, these soils tend to be deep and even surfaced. Gentle relief alone may impart to them primary consideration where farming involves mechanization and irrigation. More often than not, problems such as drainage, encountered in some transported soils, are outweighed by their aforementioned advantages.

Three groupings of transported soils *(valley, valley basin* and *terrace)* are commonly found in larger California lowlands. Where water levels once stood relatively higher, along coastlines and valley margins, benchlike terraced topography is common (Map, D-1). Terrace soils tend to be older than other lowland

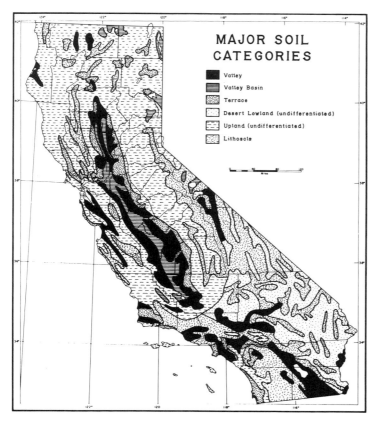

**MAJOR SOIL CATEGORIES**

- ▮ Valley
- ▦ Valley Basin
- ▨ Terrace
- ▢ Desert Lowland (undifferentiated)
- ▢ Upland (undifferentiated)
- ▨ Lithosols

**Map D-1.** There are over 500 different soil types in California. Of the world's ten soil orders, only the *oxisols* of the wet tropics are absent.

| Category | Extent of State | Source and Depth | Site | Quality Rating | Comments |
|---|---|---|---|---|---|
| valley | 11% | Slightly weathered alluvium. Deep. | Elevation intermediate between valley basins and terraces. Surface mostly smooth to gentle sloping. Drainage good. | 89% excellent to good | The state's best all-purpose agricultural soils. Nearly all farmed or urbanized. |
| | | | | 11% good to fair | Undulating and droughty due to sandy, wind-modified nature. Found especially along coast, in desert, and in Merced and Fresno districts, San Joaquin Valley. |
| valley basin | 5% | Mostly slightly weathered, heavy-textured alluvial or lake deposits. Deep | Lowest portions of valleys. Surface nearly flat. Drainage poor. | 50% mostly good | Requires artificial drainage. Peat and muck in Sacramento—San Joaquin Delta rates excellent when drained. |
| | | | | 50% very poor | Excessive salinity or alkalinity common in San Joaquin Valley and Mojave Desert. |
| terrace | 6% | Extensively weathered alluvium; lake, or marine deposit. Deep. | Higher portions of valleys and coastal benchlands. Surface gently sloping to undulating with occasional steep dropoffs. | 59% good to fair 41% fair to poor | Moderately dense subsoils. Permeability limited by extreme claypan or hardpan, especially East Side of Great Central Valley and portaions of deserts. |
| desert lowland (undifferentiated) | 16% | Weathered alluvial and lake deposits. Deep. | Valley, valley basin, and terrace soils for which surveys incomplete. | Excellent to very poor | Uncultivated, commonly because of water deficiency. |
| upland (Undifferentiated) | 41% | Moderately weathered underlying bedrock. Deep to fairly shallow. | Surface rolling, hilly to steep. Usually higher than tthe above-listed soils in a given locality. | 88% fair to poor | Generally too steep for cultivation. Productive for forest or forage. |
| | | | | 12% good to fair | Surface rolling, depth moderate; developed under grasss cover. Mainly Coast Ranges and Sierrra Nevada foothills. |
| lithosol | 21% | Slightly weathered underlying bedrock. Very shallow and stony. | Surface rough; slopes steep. | Nonagricultural | Generally associated with chaparral, desert shrub, or noncommercial forest. |

**Chart D-1.** Summary of major soil categories.

categories, are more subject to erosion and have denser subsoils (Chart, D-1). They occupy benchlike topography were water levels once stood relatively higher.

By contrast, present depositional surfaces tend to be fresher and smoother. In their lowest portions, valley basin soils are often excessively alkaline or acidic, and often are poorly drained. Such soils have frequently been improved remarkably through tillage, drainage and other corrective measures. Valley soils, found on gently sloping alluvial plains, tend to have the fewest handicaps and are superior for agriculture. Yet their fertility has tended to be their undoing, for they have attracted the rise of farm towns where nonfarming activities also gravitate. Unfortunately urbanization has thus focused on some of the Golden State's best farmlands.

## RESIDUAL (Upland) SOILS

Residual soils form directly upon the underlying bedrock. Accordingly many residual soils are shallow and erosion in varying degrees is almost everpresent. Upland location tends to produce colder climate, another handicap. Such soils are more widespread and perhaps more diverse than transported types. But their lack of intensive use makes it inappropriate to consider their many subdivisions here.

The most extreme residual soil is classed as *lithosol* (literally "stony soil"), found on slopes prohibitively steep for tillage and generally shallow. Representative locations include mountain summits and fault scarps. Even for forest or pasture such sites are considered nonproductive. Other upland soils may be more useful but they vary widely in depth, slope and fertility. Only a small portion of such soils is cultivated. The best of them are under restricted cultivation, commonly for tree crops and unirrigated grains.

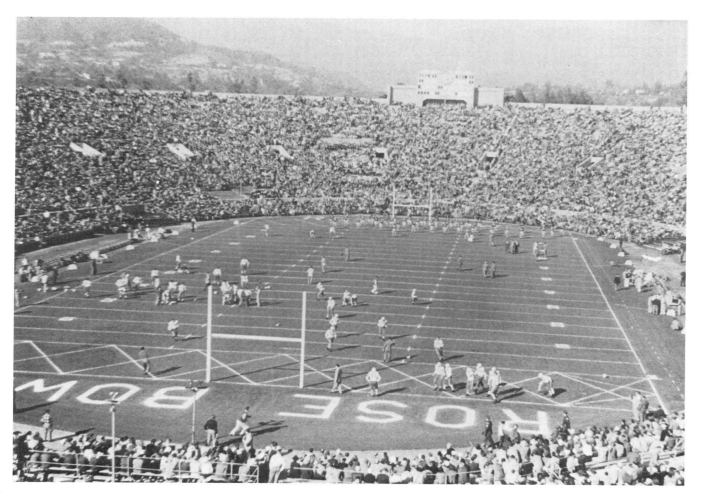

**Figure E-1.** Unless one is at a major sport event or caught in rush hour traffic of a major metropolis, it is usually difficult to appreciate that the population of the Golden State is rising toward 30 million. (dwl)

Overview E

POPULATION

# POPULATION

Now approximating 28 million, total inhabitance determines much of the Golden State's influence. Ongoing population increase and its nature underlie some of California's prestige and contributes both to social strengths and problems. General aspects of population have been noted in Chapter 1. Here discussion concerns the detailed distribution of people and their traits within the Golden State.

## DISTRIBUTION PATTERNS

Within California population arrangement has changed considerably through the years. The most consistent trend, from pre-Spanish times until the present, has been toward coastal locations, as contrasted with dry and mountainous habitats (Map, E-1). California's Indians also favored foothill canyons and other wooded riverine sites where their descendants still reside. The never-numerous colonial Span-

ish and Mexicans remained close to the strand; they created the nuclei for at least a dozen contemporary cities. In the northern interior, gold camps, briefly abustle, experienced lengthy stagnation. Yet they spawned enduring commercial and industrial communities about San Francisco Bay and adjacent waterways. Agricultural settlement of central California lowlands followed, to a lesser extent, the evolution of northern lumber camps. By 1920 the sundry industries and varied attractions of Southern California had created a population balance away from the Bay Area (Map, E-1). This development has moved the geographical population center to the Los Angeles Coastal Plain.

### An Urban Land

Urban population in California has exceeded rural numbers throughout the twentieth century. The state is the nation's most urban—three-fourths of the inhabitants occupy a mere one per cent of the state's expanse. The Los Angeles Lowlands and the San

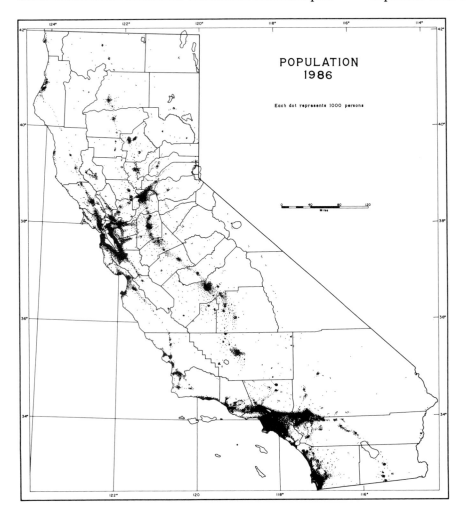

**Map E-1.** The megalopolitan populations of Southern California and the San Francisco Bay Area are conspicuous. Increasingly apparent are the *evolving* metropolitan areas of the Central Valley. In the late twentieth century fewer than half of the U.S. states have a population larger than the Central Valley.

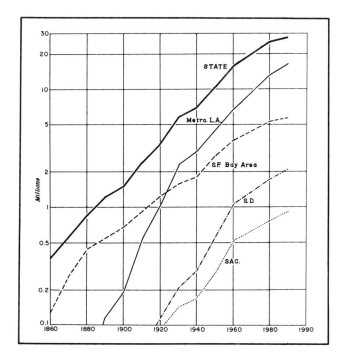

**Chart E-1.** Population of California and its largest urban centers, 1860-1975. Metropolitan Los Angeles consists of Los Angeles and Orange counties while the San Francisco Bay Area includes the nine counties bordering the Bay. Metropolitan San Diego and Sacramento include only their respective counties. Growth, which slowed in the 1960's essentially accelerated after 1980 with Pacific Basin migration from Latin America and eastern Asia.

Francisco Bay Area form the nation's second and fourth ranking conurbations. Each cluster is a giant urban continuum with tangled socioeconomic linkages. Both areas are vigorously expanding into their hinterlands and enmeshing once-rural vicinal countrysides. An enlarging share of the state's people are found in communities peripheral to Los Angeles and the Bay; by contrast most other portions of California, despite population growth, register relative decline (see table following).

Metropolitan dispersal reflects the mobility allowed by automobiles and freeways, tract housing promoted by Federal lending and tax policies, the rise of peripheral employment centers and an exodus from deteriorating neighborhoods. Expanding fringes, as exemplified by Irvine, Riverside and Walnut Creek, tend to be partially suburban and partially independent centers with self-contained employment and services. Central city revitalization, while providing more multi-unit housing, has not offset fringe-area expansion. Inner metropolitan areas, including the cities of Oakland, San Francisco and Los Angeles, have lately gained population through foreign immigration but at rates below the metropolitan fringes.

San Diego and Sacramento, the next largest focii of growth, are nominally independent but each is sufficiently close to one of the two leading conurbations to profit economically—the most-traveled intercity highways in California link San Diego with Los Angeles and Sacramento with the Bay Area.

### Location of California Residents
(by percentage)

|  | 1950 | 1960 | 1970 | 1980 |
|---|---|---|---|---|
| **Los Angeles Area** | | | | |
| Los Angeles County | 39 | 38 | 35 | 32 |
| adjacent counties (4) | 7 | 11 | 13 | 17 |
| **San Francisco Bay Area** | | | | |
| central counties (San Francisco | | | | |
| and Alameda) | 14 | 10 | 9 | 8 |
| adjacent counties (7) | 11 | 13 | 14 | 15 |
| San Diego County | 5 | 7 | 7 | 8 |
| Sacramento Area | 3 | 3 | 3 | 4 |
| Balance of state | 21 | 18 | 17 | 16 |
| Total State | 100 | 100 | 100 | 100 |

Source: Based on U.S. Census Data.

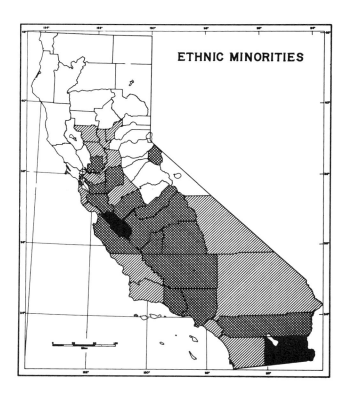

**Map E-2.** Non-Anglo population is increasingly apparent as the day approaches when California will be an Anglo-minority state. Combined ethnic minorities as a percent of total county population has been adapted from U.S. Census data. Darkest counties are already Anglo-minority, the next darkest 25 to 49 percent and the lightest shading 15 to 24 percent.

Most California cities have recently gained population; a number of "mini-metropolises" are arising along the coast and in the Central Valley. While most are not keeping pace numerically with the fringes of the major conurbations, many are beset with social, circulatory, ecologic and other "big city" problems. Many of these cities are in fact being augmented by migrants from the larger urban places—as the major centers expand so do the secondary centers but in less impressive magnitude. Lesser urban centers however do not show population gains as a group, in part because some of them have recently been elevated to metropolitan status in Census nomenclature.

### Mixed Rural Trends

Scattered residences and dispersed farmsteads typify sizable portions of California—in such environments market towns tend to be centrally located within their modest hinterlands. A continuing decline in rural farm population results from agricultural automation and consolidation and a probable increase in penchant for town residence.

Rural hamlets and dispersed non-farm occupance have not diminished as consistently as farm settlement. Some communities gain from farm-to-town movement while others survive (and even prosper) on increased consumption of goods and services per remaining farm unit; still others acquire urban-based retirees, commuters or vacation trade. Smaller places, especially, tend to lose retail business yet retain residential population, often augmented temporarily by natural increase.

Most of California is neither urban nor agricultural—almost uninhabited landscapes are punctuated by strings of small to moderate-sized communities, aligned along the coastal strand or overland transit corridors. Those based upon railroad operations or commodity output have generally not expanded. By contrast, places with other functions (such as highway services, military bases, public institutions and recreation) have often become larger.

The Golden State abounds also in scattered country-acreage landscapes with a blending of diminutive farms and small towns. Inhabitants represent mixtures: part-time or erstwhile city folk and local retirees (or semiretirees). Incomes reflect a breadth of sources—examples include arts and crafts, aircraft piloting, pensions and medical practice. Such environs are commonplace on metropolitan margins and often have an older agricultural veneer, such as the Coast Ranges peripheral to the Bay Area, the San Diego Back Country and the Sierran Foothills.

### Population Trends
#### (millions of people, based on size of place)

|  | 1950 | 1960 | 1970 | 1980 |
|---|---|---|---|---|
| State | 10.6 | 15.7 | 20.0 | 23.7 |
| Urbanized Areas | 7.2 | 11.9 | 16.1 | 19.8 |
| Lesser Urban Centers | .13 | 1.6 | 1.9 | 1.8 |
| Rural |  |  |  |  |
| dispersed | 1.8 | 1.9 | 1.6 | 1.8 |
| towns | 0.5 | 0.5 | 0.4 | 0.5 |

From U.S. Census Data. Urbanized areas contain a nuclear settlement of at least 50,000 population. Lesser urban centers range in population from 2500 to 50,000 and are located apart from urbanized areas. Rural towns are small places with lesser than 2500 inhabitants.

### HITHER, THITHER

A notable magnet for migrants, the Golden State displays internal mobility as well. Californians mirror their fellow Americans tendency to move freely, change jobs frequently, upgrade their domiciles and to deliberately seek preferred habitats. Some residents are inherently transient: seasonal farm work-

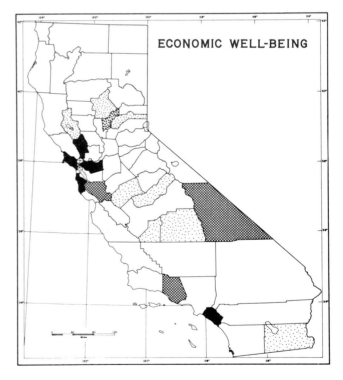

**Map E-3.** Counties are ranked according to three components of economic well-being (percent of labor force employed, median family income, and percent of families above poverty income) according to the U.S. Census data. Darkest counties rank among the 10 wealthiest in all three categories; the cross-striped counties rank among the 10 wealthiest in two of three categories; the large-dotted counties rank among the 10 poorest in all three components and the small dotted counties rank among the poorest in two of three categories.

ers, military personnel and vacation home owners. Impressive numbers of courts, motels, house trailers, barracks (for farm workers or military), desert home-steads and mountain cabins reflect significant sea-sonal fluctuations of population.

Slightly over half of Californians were born out of state, with native scions prevailing in the rural cen-tral and northern sections of the state and being less common in southern urban areas. Recently the number of non-American immigrants has increased dramatically so that California is becoming an Anglo-Hispanic-Asian state. Foreign born inhabitants com-monly reside in the larger cities and in coastal and southern areas, including rural sectors which have much immigrant farm labor.

## STRUCTURE

Human heterogeneity, combined with the state's one-time isolation, has been offered as an explanation for California's legendary penchant for extremes of conservatism and experimentation. The population no longer closely resembles the national aggregate in ethnic balance, age structure and other respects. Still, the population varies considerably around the state and often within small areas. These variations comprise a social geography that has moment for consumer preferences, voting behavior, population forecasts, economic planning and many other inter-ests.

### Getting Older—and Younger

Age distribution and trends in California are similar to those of the nation: the youthful group is declining, the proportion of elderly is rising and the median age is fairly stable. Increased migration of the '80's has slowed the overall aging trend. But in the next decade the "dependency-age ratio" is expected to decline as the number of new adults continues to surpass the group who attain retirement. Movement of the "baby boom" generation into middle age sug-gests the number of new households may decline. But the resultant younger families, expected to be smaller in size than their elders, should continue the popula-tion increase, augmented by immigration.

Population clusters of the elderly occur in portions of the metropolitan districts as well as in rural envi-ronments where retirees accumulate and from which younger persons migrate. By contrast, younger popu-lations are identified with suburbia, some lumber centers of the Northwest, and agriculture in the

southern half of the state. Ethnic minorities of lower income status, both urban and rural, tend to produce a youthful age structure, unlike the general populace.

### Men, Women and Couples

During California's pioneer period males outnum-bered females. Men still predominate in many coun-ties where there is a preeminence of outdoors indus-tries and such activities as military bases. But with metropolitan expansion and expanding tertiary occu-pations the state, like the nation, has a near-balance of males and females; in the large urban centers women constitute the majority.

In rural counties especially, married status is normal, particularly for women. Highest ratios of married men occur in suburban metropolitan areas. Unattached women (working girls, spinsters and widows) are most characteristic of central metropoli-tan areas (such as San Francisco). Single men are most typical where alien farm labor, military person-nel and other special populations prevail, in such diverse areas as Imperial, northern Santa Barbara and Amador counties.

In the "quiet" portions of California where the young depart before marriage, where an established population is aging and retirees resettle, average size of households (reflecting age, marriage and fertility) tends to be small. In central and metropolitan coun-ties, partly for the same reason and partly due to the presence of young working adults, smaller house-holds also tend to occur. Poorer agrarian counties and suburbia tend toward larger family units; the subur-ban areas are sought for child-raising while the agrar-ian populations contain many young adult families with high birth rates.

### Anglos, Hispanics and Asians

California's ethnic groups have long been impor-tant in the cities and farm areas and the "majority" group itself is much-fragmented ethnically. Promi-nent ethnic groups include Mexicans and other His-panics, blacks, east Asians (including Japanese, Chinese, Vietnamese, and Filipino), as well as Indi-ans (both East and American). Less distinct, but locally significant (and large in total numbers) are Jews, Italians, "country Westerners" and many oth-ers.

People of "Spanish/Hispanic origin" constitute the state's largest ethnic group—officially 20 per cent of all Californians. This assemblage includes Cubans, Central Americans and other Latin Americans. Some Spanish-heritage residents are descendants of prestatehood *Californios* or long-time residents—a fact overlooked in the massive Latin immigrations of recent decades.

People from Mexico constituted most of the quarter million illegal California aliens who were detected annually in the 1980's.

Mexican-Americans usually reside in the Los Angeles Basin or the San Francisco Bay Area. They constitute a significant populace in labor-intensive farm districts as far north as Glenn County. They approximate a majority in Imperial and San Benito counties and about a fourth of all San Joaquin Valley residents. The Mexican-American segment is young and more fertile, less affluent and has less formal education than the total populace. Traditionally strong family orientation is lessening, as is that of California generally. Internally-distinctive Mexican-American barrios represent segregated residential communities. Yet in larger cities, appreciable diffusion is evidenced including "suburban"—"colonies" originated with rural employment.

Blacks more on the basis of fertility than recent migration remain a fairly stable eight per cent of the California populace. Residence is predominantly metropolitan, since that is where employment and housing have been available. Family sizes exceed statewide averages, while single-parent households are commonplace. Income levels and education remain well below those of the total populace, although differences are less marked than in some parts of the nation.

Black ghettos persist as the most segregated of California's larger identifiable poor neighborhoods. Often they contain older (and more time-worn) dwellings. Suburbanization of employment, farther from the ghettos, has centered recent fair-employment thrusts. In several California cities and unincorporated areas, blacks form majority populations; in others, growing black communities contribute to (though are not necessarily essential for) election of blacks to public offices.

Other nonwhite peoples, consisting foremost of Filipino, Chinese, Japanese, Native American, Korean, Vietnamese, comprise an additional six per cent of the California populace—a share that has been growing in recent decades. Predominantly urban, these groups differ appreciably from one another in economic well-being, degree of segregation, residence places and other traits. A majority of the Japanese live in the Los Angeles area while the Chinese majority resides in the San Francisco Bay Area. Filipinos and Native Americans are more dispersed; one-fourth

of the latter are rural but nearly half are out-of-state migrants who live in the San Francisco and Los Angeles areas. The Native Americans of Los Angeles probably represent the nation's second largest concentration.

The aforementioned ethnic peoples now constitute over a third of the state's total population—already a majority in some cities and counties. Major metropolitan centers (especially San Francisco) rank high in ethnic concentrations, as do the labor-dependent agricultural sectors of the Central Coast, Central Valley and southern deserts. Ethnic groups are fewer in the northern Sacramento Valley and in the Northern Highlands. In a dozen counties they number less than 10 per cent of the populace. Indians form the chief group in sparsely-populated Alpine and Inyo counties.

### Rich—and Not Rich

A prime criterion in comparing areas for their liveability is affluence, for material well-being tends to favor higher education, mental and physical health, longevity, housing quality and sociopolitical participation. California long has ranked among the wealthier states—fewer Californians are toward the bottom and more are toward the top of the income scale. Median family income for Californians runs 10 per cent above the nation's median; the state ranks among the top 10 highest in average per capita income. "Real" incomes as purchasing power, however, depend upon many circumstances, including place of residence within Calilfornia—San Francisco is costlier and Bakersfield is cheaper in comparison to nationwide urban living costs.

"Economic health" varies sharply among communities and even between proximate neighborhoods. Some fundamental differences around the state are suggested by county patterns of employment and income (Map, E-3). Thus defined, peaks of affluence occur in metropolitan counties serving as peripheral bedrooms and as expanding economic satellites for older core districts. The core areas contain greater extremes of poverty and wealth, but lean toward affluence. San Francisco has the state's highest per capita income while Alameda, Los Angeles, Marin and San Mateo are also among the leaders. Conversely the least affluent counties encompass nonmetropolitan (often rural) settings. Low-ranking counties within or peripheral to the Northern Highlands reflect the frequency of lower income retirees or fluctuating outdoors employment. Numerical poverty indicators, however, may neglect to show otherwise favorable natural and social settings. Agricultural sectors in the Imperial and San Joaquin valleys also suffer seasonal work cutbacks and generally low wages.

### Schooling

The anticipated nationwide correlation between educational attainment and affluence is exhibited by Californians. Both variables are high in the Golden State and causitive connections are often claimed. California's urban dwellers usually have higher levels of schooling. The difference is especially marked between suburbia and some of the southern agricultural lowlands where minority groups prevail. Variations occur in some northern counties where the Anglo-Saxon population is rather well-educated yet incomes (often retirement) are lower. Likewise some central cities, with large ethnic clusters and older residents, lack the educational attainment found in more prosperous rural areas. Educational quality, as opposed to years attained, is another question. Standardized test scores should not give California pride, perhaps in consequence of the state's extremely low rank in per capita outlays for public education.

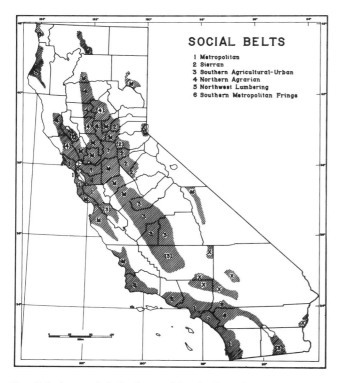

**Map E-4.** Areas of distinctive social traits based on recent county census data. Striped belts have a density of ten or more people per square mile. Numbers in parentheses denote major variations from group traits. The symbol M denotes *mixed traits*, while X indicates that data are unavailable.

### Employment and the Work Force

For decades the ratio of Californians in the work force has remained constant. Trends towards retirement, automation and student status have been offset by an expanding proportion of employed women. Fullest female participation occurs in metropolitan centers (including Sacramento) and in the Trans-Sierra. Smaller proportions of women find work in Northwest lumber towns or the Sierran counties. Apart from military service, youthful males are most completely in the work force where farm populations are least well off and have the least education. More than a fourth of the retirement age group is also employed; participation is highest in Modoc County, the western Sacramento Valley and the Bay Area; percentage is lowest in such retirement areas as Santa Cruz and Lake counties.

The official unemployment rate is probably understated for some "invisible" ethnic peoples, seasonal farm workers, and the state's large numbers of resident aliens plus semi-retirees and the "homeless." For such jobless or unemployed, California's high living costs are a special handicap. Yet part of the unemployment occurs from employee turnover and job mobility; hence it is not necessarily indicative of deprivation. Most persistent unemployment is found in the Central Valley, the Northwest and in some Sierran and other northern counties. In less populous areas work opportunities are drastically impacted by public works construction and operation of public institutions. Cyclic unemployment has resulted from cutbacks of federal aerospace and other defense-related activities, with more dependent areas being more sensitive (thus San Diego more than San Francisco or Los Angeles).

### SOCIAL BELTS

The social belts identified here, based on county census data, delimit areas that are similar relative to the social traits previously discussed (Map, E-4). They provides a comprehensible, albeit generalized, human geography of California. Six belts are described; readers may refine and subdivide them using further information in the main body of this book and in the census itself.

### Metropolitan Belt

The eleven counties where population is more than 80 per cent urban include eight of the nine richest counties. The metropolitan counties also display matching educational attainment. Their ethnic groups are sizable and varied with fewer native-born Californians. Less definitive characteristics include high proportions of working women, high employment rates and large population increases.

Inner metropolitan segments, represented by Alameda, Los Angeles and San Francisco counties, have slower-growing and less-affluent populations with more foreign-born and ethnic residents (minority children constitute a majority of the public school enrollment in San Francisco). Households are smaller and a larger share of both women and men are single. Females outnumber males and a greater proportion of women are employed.

### Sierran Belt

In the central Sierra Nevada four adjacent counties, and one in the northern Sierra, have a California-born majority with limited numbers of ethnic inhabitants. Chiefly rural nonfarm, the residents are older and households are small. The percentage of males is higher, and the ratio of married women higher, than in California overall. Educational levels are fairly high, but modest incomes partly reflect retirement residence. Conservative viewpoints are evident.

In the mid-nineteenth century these areas experienced a dramatic population boom followed by lengthy decline or stagnation. A majority of the present population was attained before World War II. Recent residential influx has brought about social change in a belt between Sacramento and Lake Tahoe. Other counties that share most of the "Sierran" traits just described include Sierra, Mono, and to a lesser extent, Colusa, Lake and Mendocino although they are non-Sierran counties.

### Southern Agricultural-Urban Belt

Centering upon Fresno, five contiguous counties reveal *rural farm, rural nonfarm* and *urban* settlement all to be important; urban classification contains at least 40 per cent of the total population. Numerically, incomes are among California's lowest (and below the national median). Mexicans are numerous as are Anglos who came from the southern Great Plains. Residents tend to be young and families large. Percentage of women in the work force is below the statewide figure. Except for fewer farm residents, Imperial County is similar to the five San Joaquin counties; Kern and San Benito counties also have most of the same characteristics.

### Northern Agrarian Belt

Social resemblance to the Sierran belt is found in several of the northern counties. Historically however there was no mining boom and farming and ranching developed somewhat later. There is definite urbanization (more than a third), an appreciable farm population and rather typical average age and household size. As in the Sierran counties, California-born residents prevail, ethnic groups are limited and there is a pronounced conservatism. There is no marked affluence despite moderate educational attainments. Population growth has been below the statewide average. Besides the four indicative counties shown on the map, several adjacent ones are similar despite important variations. For example both Sonoma and Butte counties are more urban, with older populations (more retirees), equal numbers (or even a predominance) of females, and more active recent growth, thus decreasingly justifying such categorization. More affluent, Colusa is more rural than other counties and has a more prominent ethnic component.

### Northwest Lumber Belt

Effects of the lumber boom of the 1940's and 1950's is revealed in Trinity, Humboldt and Del Norte counties, including the in-migration that accompanied it. Many people came from the Pacific Northwest; native Californians have been outnumbered. Still, rural non-farm settlement is dominant. Ethnic ratios are less than half of statewide percentages. There are many younger households, and they tend to be larger than the California average. A quite-high proportion of both men and women are married and the percentage of employed females is below average. Formal education attains 90 per cent of statewide values. Since the end of the lumber boom in the 1960's population growth has slowed or even reversed and unemployment has become acute. Hostility toward metropolitan areas is strong, particularly in more isolated locales.

### South Metropolitan Periphery Belt

Expansion of population and activities from metropolitan San Diego and Los Angeles is reflected in four rapidly-growing Southern California counties. Previously they were more independent and agriculture-oriented; now they have urban majorities with sizable rural nonfarm (suburban and rurban) occupance. The residents are younger and households larger than statewide averages. Ethnic representation is considerable, especially Hispanics. The native-born segment is about 40 per cent. Education attainment is high while median income generally ranks between that of the state and the nation. Kern and Monterey counties share most of the indicated traits although both are slower-growing; Monterey, with military, penal and farm labor population, has a large unmarried and male element. Kern, with its lower educational status and its greater component of native-born Californians, is transitional to the Southern Agricultural-Urban group.

**Figure F-1.** Almond harvest near Chico, late summer. Mechanized shaker "gently" knocks the tree trunk and a "rain" of nuts descends. (California Almond Growers Exchange)

Overview F

AGRICULTURE

# AGRICULTURE

California remains the nation's agricultural leader even though it is the nation's most urban state in terms of the residence of its people. It is visually apparent that farming and ranching have much consequence, apart from metropolitan areas, desert wastes and steep slopes.

For 80 years after the heyday of gold agriculture remained the predominant factor in the growth of California population. Farming and ranching provided many opportunities for newly-immigrating landowners and laborers as well as disenchanted miners. They also furnished enticing advertisement of the Golden State's charms to prospective tourists, senior citizens and investors. Agriculture has also stimulated other facets of the California economy, such as transportation. Until World War II agricultural processing was the leading industrial type.

Although it is less dominant today than at any time since the Gold Rush, farming still occupies a basic position in the California economy. Agribusiness continues to be a voracious consumer of such items as energy (five per cent of the state's total goes to farming), container wares (from tin plate mills, forests and glass factories), insecticides, fertilizers, machinery and water. Agricultural products far exceed annually the value of all gold recovered since 1849 and surpass the combined annual values obtained from fish, lumber and mines. In most years the Golden State is the nation's agricultural leader—thus it is not surprising that food processing ranks second (after aerospace industries) in value and employment among major industrial types.

In its related aspects agriculture is a common concern too of urban Californians. There is an ongoing debate over such issues as rural and urban legislative representation, agricultural versus urban land zoning, farm size regulation, biotic and soil conservation practices, crop price supports, acreage quotas, use of toxins and establishment of retail food prices—especially for milk.

Repeated struggle with drought marked the first two centuries of California farming; irrigation expansion was perhaps the most far-reaching trend during these decades. It has been the principal instrument in expanded agricultural output—a role perpetuated now by the California Water Project (Overview G). Expanded irrigation in the past led to a growing number of small farms and an accompanying increase in rural population. More recently irrigation has been

| | 1959 | 1964 | 1969 | 1974 |
|---|---|---|---|---|
| Number of Farms (thousands) | 99 | 81 | 78 | 63 |
| Average Farm Size (acres) | 372 | 458 | 459 | 575 |
| Workforce (thousands) | 405 | 291 | 292 | 289 |
| Farmers—Unpaid Family (thousands | 153 | 93 | 82 | 71 |
| Hired Year-Around (thousands) | 120 | 94 | 94 | 98 |
| Hired Temporary (thousands) | 132 | 104 | 116 | 120 |
| Harvested Cropland (millions of acres) | 8.6 | 8.2 | 7.9 | 8.9 |
| Field Crops | 6.7 | 6.2 | 5.9 | 6.5 |
| Fuits and Nuts | 1.2 | 1.3 | 1.3 | 1.5 |
| Vegetables | 0.7 | 0.7 | 0.7 | 0.9 |
| Crop Output (millions of tons) | 31.9 | 38.5 | 38.9 | 45.5 |
| Field Crops | 18.3 | 23.3 | 22.0 | 25.1 |
| Fruits and Nuts | 7.6 | 8.0 | 8.6 | 8.7 |
| Vegetables | 6.0 | 7.2 | 8.3 | 11.7 |
| Cattle and Calves Slaughtered (millions) | 2.7 | 3.3 | 3.2 | 3.1 |
| Milk Produced (millions of pounds) | 8.0 | 8.5 | 8.9 | 10.3 |
| Eggs Produced (billions) | 5.2 | 7.8 | 8.6 | 8.5 |

**Chart F-1.** Agricultural trends, 1959-1974.

unable to offset the trend toward farm consolidation—the number of farms is continuing to decline.

More varied output has been another persistent trend, afforded by irrigation, technological innovations (in transportation, farm mechanization and refrigeration) and affluent consumers. In the early pastoral and dry-farming eras sheep, beef cattle, grains and grapes formed California's principal agrarian products. They were followed, around 1900, by a more diversified output. Since the 1920's, more than half of the state's farms have been irrigated and over a third of the total crop value has been in orchard and vineyard products. The dramatic Central Valley Project and the All-American Canal systems of the 1940's permitted more opportunity for irrigated crops—cotton and vegetables gained prominence. Since 1960, arrival of California Aqueduct water has encouraged additional crops in the once dry-farmed expanses of the San Joaquin Valley.

## LAND AND FARMS

About a third of California is regarded as agricultural land, although scarcely a tenth of the state is actually cropped. Numerous "farms" in the north are partly timbered while some in the south have unused tracts awaiting irrigation. Most of the state's "farmland" is solely pastoral—grazing (including leased public acreage) is the most widespread form of productive land-use in California (Map, F-1) and there are many huge livestock ranches.

In contrast to the total acreage the number of individual properties is diminishing. The trend to fewer farmers involves both giant ranches and "normal" holdings. From an all-time minimum size per unit common around 1930, the "average" California property has become larger. But the present mean value of nearly 600 acres conceals the fact that half the state's farms contain less than 50 acres—many of the small properties are part-time or other less viable operations. The seven per cent of the properties that exceed 1000 acres contain a third of the crop land and account for two thirds of the sales. They contain an especially large portion of California's livestock, feed, cotton and rice producers.

There is considerable variation among commodities in return per acre; the size of holding tends to correlate with the type of product. Thus livestock ranches "average" thousands of acres each whereas cash-grain farms approximate a thousand acres, cotton and vegetable farms average several hundred and vineyard, orchard and poultry farms tend to be much smaller. Water costs and circumstances of settlement are other major determinants of farm size, accounting for the fruit "ranches" and cotton "plantations" that are far larger than the usual feasible minimum.

## OWNERS AND WORKERS

About half of the commercial farms are owner-operated; the remainder are generally supervised by part owners or managers. Reflective of the prevalence of corporate and multiple-farm ownership is the fact that nearly half of the commercial farms are without resident operators.

Although its subtropical climate allows "non-stop" harvest "somewhere", the Golden State still experi-

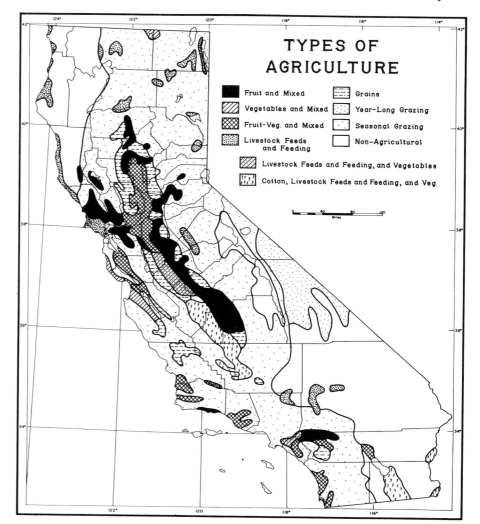

**Map F-1.** Generalized types of agriculture. Fruit has expanded into some vegetable, grain and feeding areas (especially in the San Joaquin Valley) since this map was compiled and some areas shown as agricultureal have been urbanized. (U.S. Dept. of Agriculture and Ca. Agri. Experim. Station data)

ences marked seasonal fluctuations in labor needs. During the peak harvest month (September) the temporary labor force is double that of the slack season (November through April). Automation has increased but labor costs remain the largest single expense for California farmers (although forming only a small share of final retail prices). The seasonal workforce has remained large while the number of farm owners and farm workers has decreased. Growing numbers of year-round workers reflect trends toward corporate organization with its managerial and other skilled and semi-skilled personnel.

The use of foreign labor for the state's harvests has long characterized California farming, fostered by active grower encouragement of immigration from labor-cheap countries (Overview E). Worker camps, barracks and low-rent housing in towns have been a familiar part of rural California.

Despite accelerated mechanization in harvest of such crops as canning tomatoes, nuts and olives, and some shift to commodities demanding less labor, substantial numbers of foreign citizens— especially Mexicans—have continued to work. But efforts of domestic workers to raise their standards, coupled with lessened labor requirements as a consequence of farm automation, and the relative poverty of local rural laborers amid California affluence, have argued for many years against officially imported workers. Tens of thousands of illegal entrants have been employed in California agriculture at the time the federal Immigration Reform Act of 1986 took effect. Regardless of the outcome of that legislation, history suggests that Mexican workers—whatever their immigration status—will continue to provide much agricultural labor.

**THE MARKET PLACE**

Despite rising consumption by Golden State population, California still depends significantly upon the rest of the United States and other nations for disposal of its farm products. An estimated 50 per cent of its agriculture has been thus committed. Approximately two-thirds of its fresh fruit and about 80 per cent of its canned fruits and vegetable have been shipped out of state. Such exports have been based partly on California's status as supplier of near-monopoly commodities like almonds, dates, artichokes, English walnuts, figs, garlic, lemons, olives, and Brussels sprouts. For crops grown more widely in the nation California growers have depended upon

seasonal "gaps" elsewhere. Thus the Golden State has been the chief supplier of the nation's late-spring potatoes while accounting for only a modest share of the total national potato producion annually.

Grower organizations to achieve quality control, operating efficiencies, and promotion of greater consumption has been stimulated by the rigorously commercialized nature of fruit and vegetable marketing. Golden State agriculture has been noted for its use of farmers' cooperative bargaining associations, growers' marketing associations and government marketing orders as well as corporate-like groups and other grower-shipper combinations.

Policies of the federal government have influenced California agriculture both directly and indirectly. Price supports and other direct payments have been applied to production of cotton, barley, flaxseed, hops, rice, sugar beets and dry beans—the list has been variable over time. Other crops, such as alfalfa, voluntarily expand and contract with the directly controlled crops. Federal size-quality standards, tariff policies and subsidy for overseas exports have formed important but fluctuating influences on the composition of California agriculture. Another consideration is the strength of the American dollars against other currencies, which fosters or hinders overseas sales—

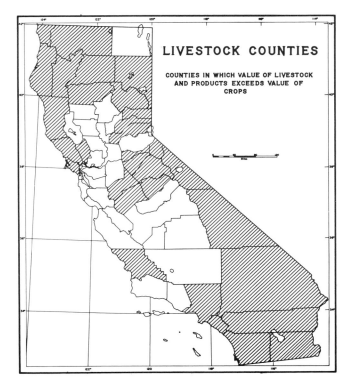

**Map F-2.** Relative livestock-crop values, by county.

a high dollar during parts of the 1980's severely impeded sale of farm exports. Likewise the trade and production policies of other nations have had growing impacts on California agriculture.

## SCORES OF COMMODITIES

The variety of California agricultural products is legendary. While most commodities raised elsewhere in the United States are also grown in California, many of its crops are unique in the nation. Among the nation's important crops, only peanuts, soybeans and tobacco are insignificant here. Half of California's farm income comes from five ranking commodities (cattle, cotton, hay, milk and grapes). No other individual item totals more than five per cent; hence grouping of similar products facilitates an overview of California's farm commodities and land utilization. In order of value, major groups are (1) livestock and livestock products (2) fruits and nuts (3) vegetables and (4) cotton.

## Beef, Milk, and Eggs

Milk, poultry, eggs, and fresh beef are mainly consumed within California. Perishability, coupled with ability to produce feeds locally and California's distance from the Middlewestern farm belt has encouraged in-state production. The number of consumers is rising though dietary trends and consumer resistance have inhibited per capita sales. Much land is devoted to feed production, with more emphasis upon cultivated crops such as barley, sorghum and irrigated hay; the peak carrying capacity for grazing land came many years ago. Byproducts of California's abundant harvests of fruits, sugar beets, rice, cotton and other crops have further encouraged the feeding of livestock concentrates.

Livestock products commonly dominate in climatically handicapped areas and urban fringes (Maps, F-1 and F-2) of California. Income from livestock and products exceeds that from crops in nearly half of the state's counties, many with habitats too cold or too rugged for high-value cropping—in these areas "cul-

**Figure F-2.** This chicken house, one of scores in the San Joaquin Valley and adjacent Sierran Foothills that supplies Foster Farms in Livingston, contains about 20,000 chickens. They will be processed at the age of 52.8 days (San Francisco Chronicle, photo by Jerry Telfer).

tivated land" is devoted solely to production of supplemental feed. Livestock operations that are peripheral to large cities are supported by feeds and replacement livestock from less congested localities, including other states. In areas where high-value export crops take precedence, producers place greater emphasis on beef cattle and sheep feeding, manufactured milk and turkey and broiler-fryer raising than do those farmers in crowded metropolitan fringes where fresh milk and eggs are dominant commodities.

### Grapes, Oranges and Almonds

Orchard and vineyard products have accounted for a steady fifth of California output for several decades. Sometimes individual items in this group are hampered by inflexible yields; overplanting in relation to market has also been characteristic. Lately some acreage has expanded significantly, including that of almonds and grapes; the near-future suggests the specter of oversupply.

Vineyards and orchards once dominated irrigation agriculture in the past. They were located where climate, soils and water supply were superior—especially on gently-sloping alluvial plains of the eastern

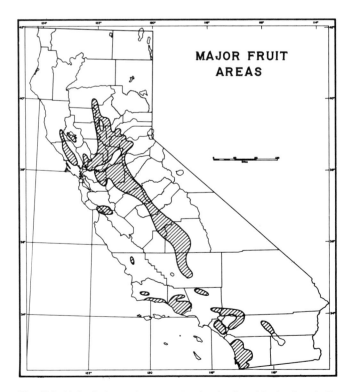

**Map F-3.** Major fruit growing areas tend to be found in the Coachella Valley, Southern California, the San Francisco Bay Area and a few counties to the north and the Central Valley. Deductions should be made for extensive urbanization—orchards expecially have been favored for residential sites.

Central Valley and in many outer lowlands from the Russian River Valley south to San Diego County (map F-3). Anchored by superior incomes and perhaps by inertia, and constituting a way of life, these well-established vineyards and orchards have persisted in their location despite California's shifting agricultural emphasis.

Individual crops tend to be strongly localized within major fruit districts of the state, owing to microenvironments and to economic and social organization of participating farmers. Such areal specializations permit more efficient use of harvesting, processing and shipping facilities, which tend to be expensive and complex for many nuts and fruits. Frost-sensitive avocados, citrus and dates are restricted mostly to the southern half of the state while deciduous fruits prevail farther north. Grapes, California's single most valuable fruit, are grown widely despite concentration in the San Joaquin Valley, where districts tend to specialize in certain favored varieties.

Early establishment of fruit and nut farms as small, owner-operated holdings has produced a legacy of diminutive units with elderly but still active resident proprietors. Larger entrepreneurs (as Tenneco and Gallo) have become more conspicuous.

### Tomatoes, Lettuce and Many More

Vegetables, besides perishability and much reliance on out-of-state consumption, share other traits with nuts and fruits: intensive application of labor, climatic sensitivity, high output per acre and diversity of products. Lettuce and tomatoes are dominant and account for nearly 40 per cent of vegetable value and acreage. Among the vegetables of which California provides more than half the national supply are artichokes, Brussels sprouts, broccoli, celery, garlic and lettuce.

Some vegetable farms in California are small properties on high-value urban fringes, some leased for agriculture while awaiting development. These may be commonly single-family operations such as by Japanese. Even in more rural sectors California truck farming has high tenancy. Nearby 30 per cent of operators rent while another 40 per cent are only part owners. Leasing, quite common among larger operators, reflects "newness" amid the desire of many growers to retain year-to-year flexibility and focus their resources on production and marketing. Production for processing or for fresh export to distant markets originates on larger farms sufficiently removed from metropolitan areas to reduce land costs appreciably.

Vegetables are widely grown in milder winter districts of California (Map, F-4). Fruit and vegetable districts tend to coincide but there is greater emphasis upon vegetables in southern desert and cool-summer coastal valleys. Vegetables, locally, are sometimes relegated to more poorly-drained soils not preempted by the more sensitive (and historically earlier) vineyards or tree crops. Season of harvest is often the crucial location factor. Thus potatoes are raised in such climatically-different areas as Tule Lake and Kern County, broccoli along the Santa Cruz Coast and in Imperial Valley, and tomatoes in the Sacramento Valley and the San Diego Coast—at different seasons. Lettuce is harvested throughout the year somewhere in California.

Since many vegetables are processed locally, major locational considerations include assembly of such materials as water, sugar and containers, availability of labor, disposal of waste and momentum of early start are major locational considerations. Vegetables for processing have tended to be raised near the factories that consume them—historically around the Bay Area and in adjacent sections of the Central Valley. For these crops, notably asparagus and summer tomatoes, successful out-of-state sales has de-

pended more on high yields, overall production efficiency and "brand names" than upon harvest season.

## Cotton

Cotton, like vegetables, did not become a major California product until the 1920's. Thereafter exodus of cotton from southeastern United States had profound impact upon California agribusiness. By the late 1940's cotton had become California's leading crop, a status more recently shared with grapes. This was stimulated by available land, growing industrial consumption, high Golden State yields and freedom from the weevil (until the 1960s).

Upswing in textile-markets during the 1970's resulted in expanded plantings—California became (and remains) the leading cotton-producing state. Despite varied usage, the bulk of cotton output is shipped to eastern United States or Japanese mills after local ginning and compressing. Storability helps minimize isolation from eastern consumers.

Cotton is strongly localized in the southern San Joaquin Valley and the southeastern desert (Map, F-1; elsewhere there is definite climatic limitation. In both growing areas introduction of cotton was favored by abundance of land. Subsequent competition from high-value vegetables has hampered expansion in the Imperial Valley. In the south-central San Joaquin Valley cotton has tended to be "king". Feeds, as alfalfa and barley, and to a lesser extent vegetables, have been commonly associated "cotton belt" filler crops, which help defray investment, improve the soil and provide alternative income in years when cotton quotas are reduced. Cattle feeding, another common enterprise in cotton districts, reflects the presence of abundant feeds. Cotton farms average hundreds of acres but many acreages number in the thousands— the initial cost of deep-well irrigation in the San Joaquin has favored large-scale operations.

## The Other Tenth

Unrelated to the four groups just described are products that furnish a tenth of California's farm income. They include (1) rice, associated with the water-plentiful bottomlands of the Central Valley (2) sugar beets, from the 1920's an expanding crop that is affiliated with expensive refineries in the Santa Maria, Imperial, San Joaquin and Sacramento valleys (3) cut-flower gardening and other nursery products, traditionally confined to coastal valleys, particularly near Los Angeles and San Francisco markets but now more widespread.

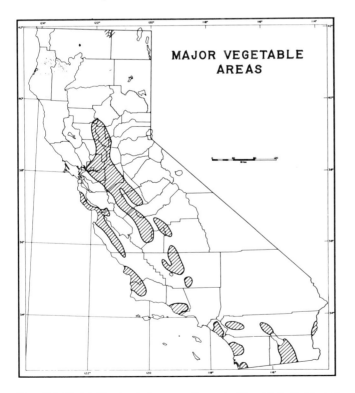

MAJOR VEGETABLE AREAS

**Map F-4.** Vegetable growing areas often coincide with fruit growing areas although they are more extensive in the Central Coast and absent north of the San Francisco Bay Area. Urbanization is deleting some of the indicated districts.

## IS THERE SPACE?

Conspicuous intrusion into farmland by urban and other non-agricultural developments in recent decades has caused fears for agribusiness prosperity and for the loss of scenic open space. The state's Williamson Land Conservation Act (1965), providing lower taxes for participating landholders who agreed to maintain agricultural usage, was hailed in the belief that it would help preserve both agribusiness and rural landscapes by slowing needless urban sprawl. Millions of acres have been set aside under the Act but results have been disappointing. Urban expansion has continued as farmers have elected to take a profit and move elsewhere. Moreover properties far removed from cities have gained financial benefit, including some of the state's largest ranches. No effective legislation to preserve farmland has materialized.

Despite loss of such choice lands as the San Fernando and Santa Clara valleys in recent decades, California farm acreage, rather than diminishing, has been maintained and crop and livestock outputs have increased—farms and people, statewide, continue to coexist. But the lands that have been lost have represented some of the state's choicest farmland, particularly with respect to frost-free crops for which no analogous climates may be substituted.

There is concern too that new water delivery projects may at best only manage to keep pace with groundwater overdraft, salinzation of older farm acreage and further urbanization. While gross farmland thus seems sufficient (and even surplus in times of economic recession) its long-range adequacy and that of its needed water supplies, is more questionable.

**Figure G-1.** The California Aqueduct and pumping station west of Bakersfield. (dwl)

Overview G

WATER*

* This section has been reviewed by Frank Seawall, California State University, Chico.

# WATER

Along with neighboring Southwestern states, California ranks high in per capita water consumption reflecting the presence of reflecting the presence of vast irrigated farmlands. Nearly 70 per cent of the state's water usage is agricultural. There are manyfold examples of waste, urban and rural—eventually excess consumption may prove critical. In the meantime society will continue to seek more water supplies in preference to conserving existing sources. Thus attention is focused first on supply considerations.

Presently consumption equals only three-fourths of California's natural streamflow annually, an absolute water deficit does not yet prevail statewide. Surface flow furnishes only 60 per cent of the usage; the balance is derived from groundwater. While some subsurface reserves are diminishing as extraction exceeds the safe yield, the immense Sacramento Valley aquifers, by contrast, remain lightly tapped. Drainage needs rival supply problems there and in other northern locales.

Seasonal and cyclical fluctuations in stream flow preclude complete use of surface runoff. In smaller basins whose streams enter the ocean directly, peak flows correlate with midwinter rains. In contrast, rivers which receive snowmelt tend to crest later in the season. Accordingly rivers in northwestern California and the northern Sierra Nevada, fed by winter rains augmented by some snowmelt, tend to peak in early spring. Rivers rising in the High Sierra, dependent more on higher elevation snowpack, tend to crest in late spring or early summer. Statewide, river runoff tends to be minimal between August and November. Unfortunately urban consumption and maximum irrigation needs (late summer) seldom coincide with runoff regime. This discordance is lessened somewhat by providing reservoirs and by extraction of ground water—both sources also assist in times of cyclical drought.

Statewide runoff is inbalanced geographically more than seasonally relative to California's needs. Seventy per cent of the stream flow (plus much subsurface runoff) originates in the wettest 20 per cent of California. This area includes the Sierra Nevada plus the northern Coast, Klamath and Cascade ranges. Fortunately the Sacramento River system (with a fourth of the state-wide runoff) flows southward in the direction of greater need. Thus San Francisco Bay receives stream which originates in the in the Warner Mountains near the Oregon border. Lamentably though too much water drains away from population centers eastward into the Great Basin. Moreover, the voluminous rivers of the Northwest (with a third of the state's stream volume) flow northwestward through high-walled canyons, away from easy access. The San Joaquin River network also trends northward, away from the deficit areas.

## THE QUEST FOR WATER

Elaborate means to supply water have been encouraged by California's summer desert climates. Assumedly "irrigation" began with Native American flood farming along the Colorado River. The ditches which supplied Hispanic missions and pueblos followed. In the mid-1800's elaborate canal networks were created to serve gold mining—later some of these were adapted to supply farms and towns. The advent of commercial agriculture and hydraulic technologies promoted farm reclamation works. These included dams, levees, wells and canals from the late 1800's.

On its present-day scale, exploitation of California's water resources has demanded the construction of dams sufficiently large to contain a safe summer-long runoff. The accidental creation of the Salton Sea in 1905 spectacularly demonstrated this need for concomitant dams to provide for irrigation and flood control with stored water used for irrigation before winter rains.

When possible major dams are operated in conjunction with hydroelectric generation for economic gain. Sales of electricity help pay for irrigation and flood control structures. Other reservoirs (such as lakes Huntington and Almanor in the Sierra) exist exclusively for power output. Such "run of the river" structures provide little storage capacity. Moreover, wintry releases tend to be ill-timed for irrigation needs or flood control. Still their stable water levels and scenic locations (upstream, providing cheaper storage and greater hydraulic "head") often have recreation value. Moreover such power dams do not preclude other structures downstream (such as Oroville Dam below Lake Almanor). And of course their electricity can be used for pumping (for drainage or irrigation purposes).

Despite decades of irrigation expansion, the urban share of statewide consumption has increased markedly. Allocations earlier in the century were made according to a doctrine of the "greatest need for the greatest number", thus favoring urban needs. Los

Angeles (in 1907), San Francisco (in 1913) and East Bay cities (in 1925) tapped distant Sierran rivers. The Metropolitan Water District of Southern California (in the early 1930's) went to the Colorado River for water for urban uses.

Lately there has been increasing concern for questions of water esthetics, quality and recreational usage as well as rising energy costs in water conveyance. Established agricultural users must increasingly contend with these concerns as well as the rising water demands of the cities. Urban California likewise must respect all these questions—no untapped water sources remain without challenge; even present supplies are sometimes insecure.

The most impressive (and expensive) aspects of California's quest for water has been its series of integrated systems for storing and moving supplies across vast distances, usually with provision for flood control, hydroelectric output and recreation as well. Lesser augmentations to these extant systems seem

likely. But no wholly new projects of compoarable scale are imminent despite the Golden State's mushrooming population.

In the 1930's "public works" era two major agricultural-water transfer works were initiated in California by the federal government. These were the All-American Canal (Ch. 5) and the Central Valley Project (Ch. 9). Both acquired their prime agricultural impact after World War II and both yield hydroelectric power revenues, further helping to minimize their water prices, already heavily subsidized. These two irrigation systems led to the California application of the "160-acre limit" of traditional federal reclamation law, now abandoned. While effective in the Coachella Valley and in some districts of the Central Valley, federal acreage limits were often honored in the breach. Their chief effect waterwise was to hasten projects by another federal agency, the Army Corps of Engineers, which refrained from practicing acreage restrictions. Thus some San Joaquin

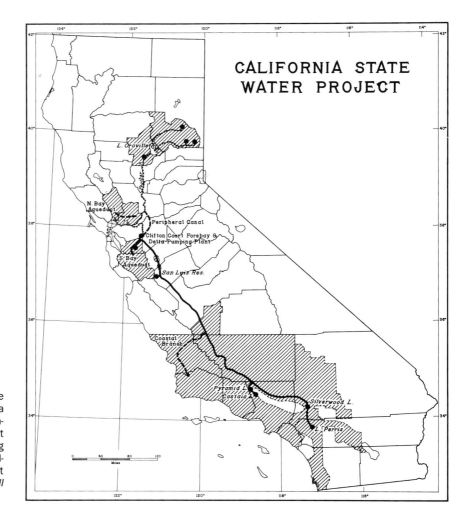

**Map G-1.** Major features of the California State Water Project. Solid lines show the California Aqueduct and adjunct canals *presently* in operation. Dashed lines indicate projected aqueduct extensions. The dotted lines indicate connecting rivers. Large dots indicate major reservoirs. Shading delineates agency areas which hold Project contracts for water *(note that all portions will receive deliveries).*

locales secured water storage (through "flood control" dams built by the Army Corps of Engineers, as Pine Flat and Isabella, without restriction of property size. The subsequent California Water Project (state controlled) likewise has no acreage restrictions.

## THE CALIFORNIA WATER PROJECT

After 1940 expanded agricultural and urban usage prompted additional water needs in southern portions of California. The preferred scheme was to tap additional water from northern rivers,* as the Colorado River and Central Valley projects had done.

Entitled the Feather River Project after its chief water source, the California Water Plan was authorized by the state legislature in 1957 and revenue bonds were approved by the electorate in 1960. The intent is to obtain water within California where available for wherever needed.

Presently Oroville Dam backs up the principal reservoir (Figure 10-35). Water released at Oroville flows in the Feather and thence the Sacramento River as far as the Delta Lands (see Ch.9), where electricity generated at Oroville pumps the water upslope into the California Aqueduct, which flows southward along the western border of the San Joaquin Valley.

The full Aqueduct delivery capacity (about four million acre-feet annually) has contractually already been fully allocated but is far from physical achievement. In addition to small supplies for headwaters areas, some 30 per cent of Aqueduct flow is eventually destined for San Joaquin Valley farms. In the Delta another eight per cent is diverted westward to serve portions of the San Francisco Bay Area. Nearly 60 per cent of Project water is ultimately committed to southern California. Most of this water will go to metropolitan areas between Ventura and San Diego** (and inland as far as San Bernardino and Riverside. The remainder goes to the western Mojave Desert (Antelope Valley and the Mojave River Valley). A projected South Coast branch to serve San Luis Obispo and Santa Barbara counties remained conjectural in the late 1980's.

Small-scale deliveries by the C.W.P began (in Alameda and Plumas counties) in 1962. A decade later (1973) the first water was delivered to Lake Perris, the southern terminus of the Project. From Lake Perris water is delivered by the previously-developed Metropolitan Water District to final destination. Full capacity operation, initially planned for the 1990's, may be delayed. Environmental concerns

(principally relating to the Delta Lands and San Francisco Bay) exist in the northern half of California. While a Peripheral Canal project designed to transfer larger is apparently "dead", state legislators from southern California continue to try to find a way to sending more water south.

Conceived in an era of prosperity and rapidly-increasing water demands, the Project was possibly underpriced. Critics claimed that it was premature and possibly too large. If user revenues fail to meet construction repayment costs the California taxpayers will be burdened.

The Project's built-in energy deficit remains problematic. Under ultimate operation it will reach seven billion kilowatt-hours annually. Power generation at Oroville and elsewhere will not provide electrical self-sufficiency south of San Luis Reservoir (Figure 9-5) yet the highest water "lifts" are in southern Kern County (Figure G-2) and thence across the Transverse Ranges. Sources for eventual energy consumption remain undeveloped. While water consumption at less-than-planned amounts will defer energy gy shortages but will peril Project financing.

Allied with the Project is the San Luis Unit (Figure 9-5), a joint state-federal development in the Coast Range west of Los Banos. Federal (Central Valley Project) water is brought south via the Delta-Mendota Canal during periods of "spare" capacity (i.e., winter) and stored in San Luis Reservoir. Thence it is deliveredthrough a 100-mile segment of the California Aqueduct to federally-watered lands of the Westlands Water District in western Fresno County. Another combined federal-state operation is water import into Napa Valley via the C.W.P.'s North Bay Aqueduct which leads from Putah South Canal (an unit of the Central Valley Project).

## ADDITIONAL PLANS

Other water projects have been under consideration. Some would involve state and federal coordination (deliberate or implied) where supplies and/or destinations are intermixed—this is most probable in the Central Valley. Some future projects would affect or contribute to full utilization of the California Aqueduct capacity.

---

* In the instance of the Colorado River the "northern" sources are the snowfields of the Rocky Mountains.
** In the minds of many residents of central and northern California, there is the mistaken idea that the sole purpose of the Project is to provide water for Los Angeles.

## Northwest Diversions

The Northwest (Ch.12) is California's "last big waterhole." Plans to integrate Eel River water into the California Water Project met much opposition and were thwarted by passage (in 1972) of California's Wild and Scenic Rivers Act which forbids further damming of the Klamath, Trinity, Smith and American North Fork rivers. At the time a 12-year moratorium was imposed on diversion from the Eel, deemed the best source for southward water shipment. Subsequent legislation gives further protection to the Eel, at least temporarily.

## Trans-Delta Shipment

Full utilization of the California Aqueduct will necessitate a means of conveying Sacramento basin water across the Delta Lands. Plans for a Peripheral Canal, a joint federal-state undertaking which would deliver water into the California Aqueduct and the Delta-Mendota Canal intakes failed to allay concerns about potential salinity in Delta farmland and sufficient fresh water flow into San Francisco Bay to "flush out" excessive pollutants. The proposal was rejected by statewide referundum. Currently alternative methods for trans-Delta shipment are being explored.

## The San Joaquin Drain

Another controversial matter is disposal of mineral-laden waste waters from expanded irrigation in the desert of the western and southern San Joaquin Valley. While excess application of water to the farmlands is essential to prevent excessive salt build-up in the soil, there is much concern about the possible impact of saline waste waters into the Delta and San Francisco Bay.

## East Side Canal

Expansion of the Central Valley Project has been envisaged for many years. Assumedly this would allow more irrigation for the eastern San Joaquin Valley. Although preliminary work was done for Auburn Dam on the American River, no federal allocation for construction has been made. But a long-sought aqueduct to bring American River flows owned by East Bay Municipal Water District into the Bay Area appears closer to realization.

## The San Felipe Plan

A projected extension of the Central Valley Project, still unfunded, would convey water westward across the Coast Ranges from San Luis Reservoir to supply portions of Santa Cruz, Santa Clara, Monterey and San Benito counties. Effects on the delicate Central Valley water balance are unclear.

## LOOKING AHEAD

Further water developments in California are highly conjectural. A cutback in federal funds during the 1980's has made additions to the Central Valley Project uncertain. There is strong opposition to constructing additional dams in the Northwest. The Central Arizona Project, which became operational in 1986, means Southern California will "lose" 500,000-acre feet of Colorado River water annually. Some feel that the high cost of water, despite frequently large subsidies may "drive" many out of farming, making water available for urban use.

Innovative movements toward cooperative developments, though halting, present offer alternatives to "water wars" in the Golden State. The Metropolitan Water District has sought arrangements with desert irrigators to obtain seasonal surplus and conserved supplies—water presently wasted would be purchased for urban use while lowering irrigation costs. A Coordinated Operation Agreement is being initiated between the Central Valley and California Water projects to govern their mutual activities in the Delta and the San Joaquin Valley. Ways to store surface deliveries underground, during wet winters, in Kern County and elsewhere are being explored. These and other new schemes may constitute the largest and most effective water developments in the near future.

**Figure H-1.** Harbor Freeway, downtown Los Angeles, 4:30 p.m. "Early" in the rush hour the traffic was moving smoothly. (dwl)

Overview H

ENERGY*

* This section has been reviewed by Frank Seawall, California State University, Chico.

# ENERGY

California's era of infinite energy was terminated abruptly with the nation's energy "crisis" of 1973-74. That event led to to the first comprehensive appraisal of the Golden State's electricity and fuel status. But the decline in price of petroleum in the 1980's lessened concerns while curbing the state's own important petroleum industry and reducing its tax revenues. Little preparation for recurrent energy shortfalls was undertaken. Yet barring major technologic breakthroughs (seemingly always "around the corner"), a cheap supply of energy appears to be historic. Certainly California sources have been found problemical and subject to emergency nationwide reallocation.

The Golden State has a lower-than-normal per capita consumption (10 per cent of the nation's population but only 7 to 8 per cent of the national energy

| Markets | Per Cent of Usage | |
|---|---|---|
| | CA. | USA |
| Industrial | 26% | 29% |
| Electric Utilities | 24 | 26 |
| Transportation | 34 | 25 |
| Residential-Commercial | 18 | 19 |

Data are for the early 1970's, from Federal REserve Bank of San Francisco and Californiá Division of Oil and Gas.

**Chart H-1.** Comparative energy uses, California and the nation.

consumption). California differs appreciably from other states in its specific supply and use patterns. More of California's consumption is needed for transportation, reflecting a large state and extreme reliance on automotive travel. Conversely, California devotes lesser energy to manufacturing or electricity output.

The state and nation employ comparable proportions of their energy for "household and commercial"

| Sources | Per Cent of Supply | |
|---|---|---|
| | CA. | USA |
| Oil | 49% | 44% |
| Coal | 2 | 18 |
| Natural Gas | 40 | 33 |
| Hydroelectricity | 9 | 4 |
| Nuclear & Geothermal | <1 | <1 |

Data are for 1971, from U.S. Department of Commerce and California Division of Oil & Gas. California data include imports from other states, including energy used to generate electricity.

**Chart H-2.** Comparative energy costs, California and the nation.

purposes; California's per-person heating costs are lower but other demands cancel out this advantage. Supply-wise, too, California departs from the national picture in employing hydroelectricity, oil, and natural gas in place of coal. Nuclear energy is a lesser source in both areas. The Golden State does have unique geothermal power output and a brace of new aeolian generators and functional solar electric facilities but all these cater only modestly to statewide demands.

## CONSUMPTION AND CONSERVATION

Energy more than water is a commodity with demand elasticity. Thus one public response to energy deficits has been introduction of conservation measures—as yet small in proportion to ultimate potentials.

There is frustration with technological inertia. Only half of our "energy" output does useful work; the rest is wasted, largely as heat loss—and much waste appears irreducable, as in electric generation from fossil fuel (oil, gas, coal), which is only about one-third "efficient." Moreover, added energy is required for such environmental improvements as reduced auto exhaut emissions and purification of waste waters. Energy materials themselves are consumed also in the form of vital products such as nitrogen fertilizer from natural gas. California's petrochemical industry incorporates five per cent of the state's annual energy output into its material products.

The Golden State is bedeviled particularly by its energy-consumptive enterprises normally regarded as luxuries, such as recreational travel and the resort industry, upon which thousands of jobs depend—California sales of luxury cars, motor boats and private aircraft scarcely reflected the previous oil crisis. Challenging also is the wide diffusion of energy consumers; although other "villains" are frequent, automobiles are the prime consumers. For their entire electrical needs factories utilize a mere three per cent of California's energy output. Aircraft take five per cent of the energy, home applicances only three and commercial lighting about four. Conservation thus requires many approaches which resist simple prioritization.

Four particular user-groups are recognized to identify further the consumption of energy in the Golden State: transportation, industry, electric utilities, residential and commercial structures.

### Trucks and Automobiles

California has an abnormally high energy consumption in the transportation category. Automobiles alone absorb more than 20 per cent of the state's annual energy output. Trucks consume only half the automotive quantities and aircraft only about one-fourth as much. Trains and buses are minor energy users in the Golden State.

### Fabrication

Heat processes fueled with oil and natural gas constitute the principal energy utilization by California manufacturers. By comparison electricity usage in factories though significant in quantity, is modest. Five industrial types—steel, aluminum, petroleum refining, paper and petrochemicals—collectively account for 40 per cent of industrial energy usage in California.

### Light Bulbs and Air Conditioners

Generated in-state and imported as well, electricity is shared about equally by residences, commerce and industry. The commercial proportion exceeds the national ratio while industrial usage is lower—this reflects employment differences. National and state residences have comparable electric consumption. Over half of California's electric supply is generated from natural gas and other fossil fuels and another third from waterpower. These shares include consideration of the state's sizable imports of electricity from elsewhere in the West.

**Figure H-2.** Nuclear power plant, Diablo Canyon. This controversial plant became operative in 1986. It can supply the electrical needs of nearly two million people. The domed structure houses the "nuclear" area. (Pacific Gas and Electric Co.)

### Family Rooms and Offices

Air temperature control and illumination form the prime energy commitments in both commercial and residential categories—up to three-fourths of total usage. Partly owing to domestic water heating and food preparation and storage, residential energy consumption exceeds that of commerce. Commercial markets and dwellings combined consume two-thirds of California electrical output and more than a third of the natural gas. During the recent energy crisis prompt and substantial savings were achieved by merchants, institutions and householders. Future *insulated* construction may lessen per capita energy use. Yet many new California residences include central air conditioning as do totally-enclosed shopping malls—even in milder sectors of the state.

## ENERGY SOURCES

California has been endowed naturally with four relatively-abundant energy sources: steep-flowing rivers, oil, gas and geothermal steam as well as ocean water for electric generation cooling needs. Coal and uranium, though present, are insignificant and must be imported, as increasingly, are most other energy resources. Next, the various energy sources are outlined relative to their current and prospective availability.

### Petroleum

About half of the Golden State's entire energy supply comes from oil. It is almost the sole transportation fuel, the second-ranking source of energy for industry, commerce and homes. California, despite its status as the nation's third-ranking producer, lost its petroleum self-sufficiency after the mid-1960's. Production generally declined subsequently and has increasingly been outpaced by consumption increments—now there is a heavy import demand.

California's off-shore fields apparently offer the final major untapped petroleum source. Although they already produce a fourth of the state's oil, they have posed a public quandry since the Santa Barbara oil spill of 1969. The subsequent moratorium on new drilling was soon challenged by supply shortages. Federal authorities in particular moved to expand sea-floor exploration in the 1980's. The widely debated activation of the Elk Hills Naval Petroleum Reserve (Ch. 9) for civilian usage has added to the state's oil output. Secondary recovery systems, injecting steam or water into oil-bearing strata to boost yields, now widely applied, are already computed in estimates of remaining reserves. California's capacious shoreside refineries are natural destinations for Alaska Arctic Slope crude oil. Expansion of deep-water unloading facilities has been sought, with attendant safety concerns. Thus, California's thirst for oil appears to satiable, but only by means of further offshore recovery, more tanker shipments and larger refineries. These are ecologically risky but perhaps an inevitable stopgap awaiting better energy sources.

### Natural Gas

Natural gas supplies 40 per cent of the total energy intake of the Golden State. Normally it is extracted from oil fields in southern parts of the state, where part is used in oil production , and also separately from "dry gas" fields (chiefly in the Central Valley between Madera (south) and Corning.

Beginning in 1948 and now coming from Southwestern states and Canada, gas imports satisfy three-fourths of the state's consumption. Electric utilities and industries, having "interruptable" contracts, were the first to shift to other fuels in event of international shortages. But ultimate adequacy even for conventional residential and commercial supplies seemed doubtful. One alternative would be gas manufactured from such fuels as coal, then piped to California from southern or western states. Efforts were initiated, then suspended, in the 1970's to import gas in low-temperature, pressurized liquid form by tanker ship. Costs would be several times the present market price, with shipping hazards yet to be defined.

### Hydropower

Hydroelectricity, as an energy source, has justifiably received such compliments as "quiet", "clean", "good rural tax revenues" and "recreationally useful." Unfortunately the better in-state sites are now almost preempted. In fact much hydroelectricity comes from the Colorado and Columbia rivers. These sources are expected to diminish.

Additional capacity in-state will be seemingly at the deterioration of wild rivers, which have many defenders. Water transfers around the state (Overview G), although yielding considerable hydropower, also are major electric consumers where pumping is needed. Of especial concern is the California Water Project, whose designed at-capacity operation will require much additional electricity. Multiferous small-scale hydro units, while ecologically preferable to major installations and staunchly advocated by some groups, remain of dubious feasibility where

water run-off is highly seasonal.

### Nuclear Power

Harnessed to generate electricity from steam turbines driven by the heat of nuclear fusion, uranium became the internationally-acclaimed glamour fuel of the 1960's. Output in California began with a pilot plant at Humboldt Bay, now dismantled, in 1963, followed by San Onofre (north of San Diego) in 1968 and Rancho Seco (near Sacramento) in 1974. Massive nuclear reactors at Diablo Canyon (southwest of San Luis Obispo) were put into operation in the mid-1980's after much delay along with large capacity increments at San Onofre. California utilities will gain a further nuclear supply from Arizona's emergent plant.

Disadvantages of nuclear power have multiplied. They have included prolonged construction times, mechanical breakdowns (*especially* at Rancho Seco), vulnerability to malfeasance, risks of accidental emissions (seemingly higher in quake-prone California), unproven methods of long-run waste disposal, and of much concern, escalating costs relative to other energy sources. The search for additional generating sites has included consideration of Point Arena and Bodega Bay on the north coast, Wasco in the San Joaquin Valley and Vidal Junction in the Mojave Desert. While such sites would be isolated from sizable populations, compared to existing plants, strong antinuclear public sentiment makes new plants doubtful.

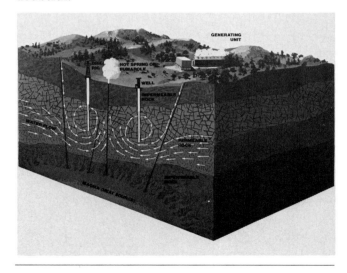

**Diagram H-1.** California, destitute of coal and with declining petroleum reserves, is fortunate to have a sizable geothermal potential. This is a schematic of The Geysers, the world's ranking geothermal producer. Generating capacity should be reached early in the twenty-first century (Pacific Gas and Electric Co.)

**Figure H-3.** An alternate source of energy: solar energy "farm" near Daggett in the Mojave Desert. (Southern California Edison Co.)

## Geothermal Power

Since 1960 underground natural steam in Lake County has been harnessed for electricity. This is the nation's first operation of its kind, now larger than facilities in other countries. Initial capacity has been expanded markedly and additional output is planned. So far less than one per cent of California's total energy comes from this source. Existing pollution is minor, leading to hopes of replication elsewhere. Facilities in Imperial County were underway in the 1980's. Other potential locales are found in the Northeast (Modoc Plateau), Southern Cascade and Trans-Sierra subregions. The currently-utilized "dry steam" type seems best but is also the least widespread. Exploitation of Imperial Valley steam has been hindered by its brininess.

## Coal

Coal, never significant as a California energy source, was reevaluated after the oil shortfalls in the 1970's. It has been imported for steel-making and indirectly in the form of electricity generated in Arizona and Nevada. Because of its air-polluting tendencies and hauling expense it has previously been disregarded. But expanding energy demands and opposition to new coal-burning plants in western interior states have prompted reconsideration. Tentative plans for an coal-burning electric generation on the north edge of the Delta Lands in 1975 were shelved, in part because of much public opposition.

**Figure H-4.** *Another* alternate source of energy, from the winds. In addition to this locale (San Gorgonio Pass), there are wind machines near Tehachapi Pass, Altamont Pass (east of Livermore) and Carquines Strait. (Southern California Edison Co.)

## THE FUTURE FOR ENERGY

It is probable that significant technologic changes will occur in energy production. Public policies and subsidies to promote such changes and to reach critical-scale output from known but marginal technologies have been slow to emerge in view of vested interests and traditional attidues.

Solar distillation has been used to purify seawater along the coast and small solar heating units are seen on a growing number of buildings. Eventually, the fabled sunshine of the Golden State may become a significant energy source—southeastern portions of California rank high nationally in solar energy potential. The state's first commercial solar electric plant, now operating at Daggett, has inspired plans for several others.

Aeolian power, at present technologically marginal, is viewed as an eventual source along California's north coast where maximum winter wind velocities counter-balance the seasonally lower sun of the southern deserts. In the 1980's there are four operational farms at Carquinez Strait, Altamont Pass Tehachapi Pass and San Gorgonio Pass. These were hastily installed in response to short-lived federal tax provisions—their long-run efficiency is un-certain.

Other possibilities include harnessing of the tides along the often-straight California coast. The tidal range is low and the prospects do not seem too promising. Various esoteric energy-yielding substances, including methanol, hydrogen and urban waste, are additional possibilities.

One enduring benefit of the oil crisis of the 1970's was its effect upon popular and official energy attitudes. Californians were given to see for the first time the extent of their dependence on other places and upon energy itself as a valuable commodity. Impelled by rising costs the public economized with more fuel-efficient automobiles, appliances and new buildings. New thrusts for public mass transportation systems arose and new residential preferences with journeys-to-work emerged. Heretofore unapppreciated potentials for energy conservation and production were recognized and given preliminary implementation. Many of these were put "on hold" with the reappearance of the oil "glut" in the 1980's, as Californians returned to "business at usual." But beginnings had been made—the state's energy pictures for producers and consumers would never be the same.

# BIBLIOGRAPHY

In deference to the "knowledge explosion" and usage experience, many works predating 1970 are not included or have been deleted. Effort has been made to cite useful bibliographic aids. See the predecessorial work, *California, Land of Contrast* (published in 1963, 1970, 1977 and 1981) for additional listings, especially older materials.

## BIBLIOGRAPHY, STATEWIDE

The Readers Guide to Periodicals helps in finding Californiana in popular magazines such as *California, Sunset, Travel* and the *National Geographic.* For setting-oriented works of fiction, see D. Diehl, "Best Books," *California,* 11 (1986), 44-48.

For many scholarly journals the *Social Sciences Index* performs a like service. The series of *Snipe's Guide* index article in leading geography journals. Recent government documents are found in the *Catalog of Federal Government Publications* and in the *Annual Listing of California State Publications.* Comprehensive in nature are "California" entries in *Books in Print* and the *National Union Catalog* of the Library of Congress. For unpublished studies the handiest reference is S. Lamprecht, California: A Bibliography of Theses and Dissertations in Geography *(Council of Planning Librarians, Exchange Bibliog.* no. 753, 1975). Among leading statewide bibliographies are T.C. Trzyna and W. Shank, *The California Handbook* (Center for Ca. Public Affairs, 3rd ed., 1975) and R.W. Durrenberger, *Elements of California Geography* (National Press Books,

1968). For appreciation of Ca. history and literature in terms of landscape see D. Wallace and M. Baer, *The Wilder Shore* (Sierra Club, 1984).

## SOURCE BOOKS

The *California Almanac,* published under various titles from 1947 to 1987, has been the most comprehensive factual reference. Good statistical sources include the *California Statistical Abstract* and the *California County Fact Book.* E.G. Gudde, *California Place Names* (U. Ca. Press, 3rd edit., 1969) is a standard work. See also M.B. Hoover and others, *Historic Spots in California* (Stanford U. Press, 3rd edit., 1966) and Ca. Dept. Parks, *State Historical Landmarks* (1979). J.D. Hart, *A Companion to California,* is a worthy history-oriented encyclopedia. See also *Encyclopedia of California* (Somerset, 1985). Current tourist guidebooks do not equal the stature of the Federal Writers' Project, *California, A Guide to the Golden State* (Hastings House, rev. 1967), despite the latter's obsolescence.

## GENERAL GEOGRAPHIES AND RELATED STATEWIDE LITERATURE

The "classic" is C. Zierer, ed., *California and the Southwest,* (Wiley, 1956). Sufficiently current is the reader edited by R.W. Durrenberger, *California: Its People, Its Problems, Its Prospects* (National Press Books, 1971). A popular introductory textbook is C. Miller and R. Hyslop, *California, The Geography of*

*Diversity* (Mayfield, 1983). The provocative C. McWilliams, *California: The Great Exception* (1944 et seq.) has been updated by M. Davie, *California, the Vanishing Dream* (Dodd, Mead, 1972). J.J. Parsons, "The Uniqueness of California," *Am.Qtr.* 7 (1955) remains a succinct overview. Widely-read L.C. Powell has sampled from 31 authors among California's literary "great," for *California Classics* (Ward Ritchie Press, 1971). More recent is J. Eisen and D. Fine, *Unknown California. Classic and Contemporary Writing on California Culture, Society, History, and Politics* (Collier, 1985). See also C. McWilliams (ed.), *The California Revolution* (Grossman, 1968). While they concern broader areas, J. Garreau, *The Nine Nations of North America* (Avon, 1981); R.D. Gastile, *Cultural Regions of the United States* (U.Wa.Press, 1975); and R. Boywer & D. Savageau, *Places Rated Almanac* (Rand McNally, 1985) have much pertinence to California. Of interest also is D. Wyatt, *The Fall into Eden: Landscape and Imagination in California,* Cambridge, 1986 and The nitty-gritty realm of Golden State politics, regional and state-wide, is presented in N.R. Pierce, *The Megastates of America* (Norton, 1972) while the state's persistent north-south dichotomy is examined by R.E. Wolfinger and F.I. Goldstein, "Comparing Political Regions: The Case of California," *Am.Pol.Sci.Rev.* 63 (1969), 74-85. See also R.M. Pierce and S.D. Brunn, "The Classification and Regionalization of California Politics," *Ca. Geog.* 15 (1975), 16-24. Administrative demarcations are described in the following: S.Scott et al, *Local Governmental Boundaries and Areas* (U.Ca. Bur. Publ. Adm.,1961), O.C. Coy, *California County Boundaries* (Valley Publ., 1973), F.D. Uzes, "California's Riparian Boundary Problems," *Surveying and Mapping* 29 (1969), 41-48 and the classic by B.E. Thomas, "The California-Nevada Boundary," *Ann. Assn. Am. Geog..* 42 (1952), 51-68.

## MAPS AND ATLASES

Every Californian should know the outstanding *Atlas of California* by M.W. Donley and others (Pacific Book Center, 1979), which presents a gazetteer, an almanac of statistics and a reference to sources of information. A smaller atlas is David Hornbeck, *California Patterns: A Geographical and Historical Atlas* (Mayfield, 1983). More specific are W.A. Beck and Y.D. Haase,*Historical Atlas of California* (U.Ok. Press, 1974). Recent sectional atlases are *Southern California Atlas and Gazetteer* and *Northern California Atlas and Gazetteer* (De Lorme, 1987).

For socioeconomic coverage of metropolitan areas consult R.Abler,ed,,*A Comparative Atlas of America's Great Cities* (U.Mn. Press, 1976) and the series by U.S. Bur. of Census titled *Urban Atlas, Tract Data* (GPO, c.1974). Topographic map sheets published by the U.S. Geol. Survey are sold at Survey offices and local map dealers and are available for reference use in larger libraries. They include the 1:125,000-scale series of 31 sheets covering the entire state and the newer 1:100,000-scale metric series. While commercial road maps are growing scarcer (and not necessarily better), state and local maps issued through the *Am. Auto Assn.*, the *Auto. Club of So.Ca.* and the *Ca. State Auto. Assn.* remain among the best of their type.

## PHYSICAL ENVIRONMENT

The series of *Natural History Guides* published by U.Ca. Press cover sundry aspects. For the viewpoint of conservationists see such sundry sources as the *Sierra Club Bulletin*, *Landscape* and pertinent issues of *Cry California* (no longer published). Despite its biases, R.F. Dasmann, *The Destruction of California* (Macmillan, 1965) has been much praised. Also see H. Aschmann, "People, Recreation, Wild Land and Wilderness," *Yrkb. Assn. Pac. Coast Geog.* 28 (1966), 5-15. For broad managerial concerns see *Public Lands in California* (Ca. State Land Comm.,1973) and E.A. Williams, *Open Space: The Choices Before California* (Diablo Press, 1969). Also see A.S. Leopold, *Wild California* (U. Ca. Press, 1985).

### Climate

G.R. Stewart, *Storm* (Modern Library, 1947) gives a "good" feel for winter weather. *Climate and Man* (Yrbk. of Agri., USDA, 1941) gives statistical data as does *Climates of the States* (Water Information Center, 1974). Three differing ways of describing California climatically are: J.W. James, "A Modified Koppen Classification of California's Climates," *Ca. Geog.,* 7 (1966), 1-12; M.H. Kimball and F.A. Brooks, "Plantclimates of California," *Ca. Agri.* (May 1959), 7-12; and W. Terjung, "Physiological Climates of California," *Yrbk. Assn. Pac. Coast Geog.* 28 (1966), 55-73. See C.R.Elford, "Climatography of California," in *Climatography of the United States*, No. 60-4 (GPO, 1970), 46-55 and O. Granger, "Increasing Variability in California Precipitation, " *Ann. AAG*, 69 (1979), 533-543. Air quality is summarized by P.A. Leighton in "Geographical Aspects of Air Pollution," *Geog. Rev.* 56 (1966), 151-174 and by Peter Mason, "The Distribution of Air Pollution in California," *Jr. Geog.* 73 (1974), 32-37. See also P.J. Taylor, "A Pedagogic Application of Regression Analysis: Precipitation in California," *Geography,* 65 (1980), 203-212. See also Ca. Energy Comm., *Wind Atlas,* Sacramento, April 1985.

### The Land and Shoreline

Ca. Div. of Mines and Geology, which issues the monthly journal *California Geology,* the *Geologic Map of California* (in 27 sheets at scale 1:250,000), *Evolution of the California Landscape* (Bull. 158, 1952, and numerous other items, is the principal source. On hazards see the agency's *Urban Geology Master Plan for California* (Bull. 198,1973); R. Iacopi, *Earthquake Country* (Lane, 1971) and N. Meyer, "There Are 15,000 Earthquakes in This State Every Year,' *Ca.* 10 (1985), 80-86. On this topic also see B.A. Belt and G.B. Oakeshott, "The Danger from Earthquakes in California," *Pac.Discovery* 36 (1983), 25-31 and D.C. Engebretson, *Relative Motions between Oceanic and Continental Plates in the Pacific Basin* (Geol. Soc. Am., 1985). See also J.J. Parsons, "California as a Hazardous Environment". G. Oakeshott, *California's Changing Landscapes*(McGraw-Hill, l978) and R.M. Norris and R.W. Webb, *Geology of California* (Wiley, 1976) are basic geology texts. The standard reference on soils is *Generalized Soil Map of California* (U.Ca. Agri. Exp. Sta. Manual 6, 1953).soil. A basic source is *California Soils* (Ca. Dept. of Conservation, 1979). Productive soil "capability" is mapped in L.R. Wohletz and E.F. Dolder, *Know California's Land*(Ca. Dept. Nat. Rescs. and U.S. Soil Conserv. Svc., 1952). Many references are found in *California Forest Soils* (U.Ca. Div. of Agri. Sc., Priced Publ.4094). A series of Soil Surveys for many of California's counties, with other environmental qualities, has been published by the U.S. Soil Conserv. Svc. Status of the shoreline is presented in G. Griggs and L. Savoy, *Living with the California Coast* (Duke U. Press, 1985), G.E. Bailey and P.S. Thayer, *California's Disappearing Coast* (U.Ca. Inst. Gov. Studies, 1971). The *California Coastal Plan* (Ca. Coastal Zone Conserv. Cmsn., 1975) describes policies and resources. See also J.E. Petrillo and O. Gresnell, eds., *The Urban Edge: Where the City Meets the Sea* (Ca. Coastal Conser), William Kaufmann, 1985), M. Heiman, *Coastal Recreation in California: Policy, Management, Access* (U.Ca. Instit. Gov. Stud., 1987); and for individual areas, the *Coastal Wetland Series* (Ca. Dept. of Fish and Game, 1970+).

### Vegetation

The standard all-around reference is M.G. Barbour and J. Major, *Terrestrial Vegetation of California* (Wiley, 1977). E.S. Bakker, *An Island Called California* (U.Ca. Press, 1971) deals with the major ecological communities. The standard statewide taxonomy, with an overview as well, is P. Munz and D.D. Keck, *A California Flora* (U.Ca. Press, 1973). Large-scale vegetation maps (the newer ones showing soils as well) are issued by the U.S. Forest Svc., San Francisco. Vegetation management is covered in the following: L.T. Burcham, *California Range Lands* (Ca. Div. Forestry, 1957); M. Rosenthal, *Symposium on Living with the Chaparral* (Sierra Club, 1974); and *California's Forest Industry* (U.S. Forest Svc. Gen. Tech. Report PSW-23, 1977). See also N.W. Thrower and D.E. Bradbury (eds.): *Chile-California Mediterranean Scrub Atlas* (Acad. Press, 1977) and T.R. Plumb, *Oak Management in California*(U.S. Forest Service, PSW-54, 1981).

## WATER RESOURCES

The currently-indispensable reference is W.L.Kahrl, *California Water Atlas* (Wiley, 1979). *Bulletins of the Ca. Dept. of Water Resources* are a principal source of recent information; for titles to 1974 see Bulls. 170-69 and 170-74. Comprehensive books include J.S. Bain et al, *California's Water Empire* (Johns Hopkins Press,1966); E. Cooper, *Aqueduct Empire* (Arthur Clark, 1968) and D. Seckler (ed.), *California Water: A Study in Resource Management* (U. Ca. Press, 1971). See also H.F. Gregor, "Water and the California Paradox," in C. McWilliams (ed.), *The California Revolution* (Grossman), 1968). See also E.A. Engelbert (ed.), *Competition for California Water* (U.Ca. Press, 1983). Recent sources dealing with broader areas include M.P. Reisner, *Cadillac Desert. The American West and Its Disappearing Water* (Viking, 1986); D. Worster, *Rivers of Empire: Water, Aridity and Growth of the American West* (Pantheon, 1985), with its commendable bibliography. Another good source is D.J. Pisani, *From Family Farm to Agribusiness: The Irrigation Crusade in California and the West* (U.Ca. Press, 1984). More specific is T.L.McKnight, "Center Pivot Irrigation in California," *Geog. Rev.*73 (1983), 1-14.

## ENERGY

Considerable data are presented in *Meeting California's Energy Requirements, 1975-2000* (Stanford Resch. Instit., 1972) and *Energy in California* (Ca. State Rescs. Agency, 1973). See also *California Energy, the Economic Factors*(Federal Reserve Bank of San Francisco,1976), publications of the Ca. Energy Comsn., including *Energy Choices for California* (1979), and P.A. Morrison, *The Energy Sitatuion and the World of Californians* (Rand Corp.,1981). The Ca. Dept. of Water Rescs.(see preceding section) has issued studies on development of geothermal, hydroelectric, nuclear, solar and wind energy. See also R. Banham, "The Most Beautiful Power Plant in the World," *California*, 10, 1985)) 98-103) about the Solar One plant at Daggett. For petroleum prospects see W. Rintoul, *Drilling Ahead: Tapping California's Richest Oil Fields* (Valley Publ., 1981). For minerals generally, see H.E. Pemberton, *Minerals of California* (Van Nostrand Reinhold, 1983).

## AGRICULTURE

The five-year federal census of agriculture provides overall data. Monthly reports are presented by the Ca. *Crop and Livestock Reporting Scv.* and in annual reports of the county agricultural commissioners. For recent trends see *Projections of California Crop and Livestock Production to 1985* (U.Ca. Agri. Exp. Sta.Info. Ser. 77-3, l977). A good agricultural history is presented in C.B. Hutchison, *California Agriculture* (U.Ca. Press, 1946). Many concerns are considered in *Agricultural Policy Challenges for California in the 1980s* (U.Ca. Div. of Agri. Scis., Sp. Pub. 3250, l978). A recent overview is presented in A.F. Scheuring, *A Guide-book to California Agriculture* (U.Ca. Press, 1983). See too H.F. Gregor, *An Agricultural Typology of California* (Aka. Kiado, Hungary, 1974). A topic of potential concern is discussed in N. Gary et al, "The Africanized Honey Bee: Ahead of Schedule," *Ca. Agri.* 39 (1985), 4-7. For bibliography, see R.J Orsi, *A List of References for the History of Agriculture in California* (U.Ca. Davis, 1974). Economic research apppears in a lengthy monograph series issued by the *U.Ca.Giannini Foundation,* including *Technological Change, Farm Mechanization and Agricultural Employment*(Found. Pub. 4085, 1978). A number of publications deal with workers and working conditions. For example, see four articles by P. Martin et al, "A Profile of California Farm Workers," *Ca. Agri.* 39 (1985), 16-18, "Immigration Reform and California Agriculture," *Ca. Agri.*, 37 (1983), 14-15, "Farm Labor Contractors," *Ca. Agri.* 40 (1986), 12-15, and "The Fragmented California Farm Labor Market," *Ca.*

*Agri.* 39 (1984), 14-16 and "Changing Patterns in California's Harvest Labor Force," *Ca. Agri.* 38 (1984), 6-8, V. Fuller and B. Mason, "Farm Labor," *Am.Acad. Pol. and Soc. Sci.* 419 (1977), A. Schmitz and D. Seckler, "Mechanized Agriculture and Social Welfare... " *Am.J. Agri. Econ.* 52 (1970), 569-577; J. Hightower, *Hard Tomatoes, Hard Times* (Schenkman, 1973); S. Kushner, *Long Road to Delano*(International, 1975); and J. London & H. Anderson, *So Shall Ye Reap* (Crowell, 1970). A reissue of classic, still provocative studies of the 1940's is W. Goldschmidt, *As You Sow: Three Studies in the Social Consequences of Agribusiness* (Osmun Allenheld). R.C. Fellmeth, *Politics of Land* (Grossman, 1973) is a critique by the Ralph Nader group of agribusiness and of rural real estate practices. For pleasure see G.T. McClelland and J.T. Last, *California Orange Box Labels* (Hillcrest, 1985). The literature on the Golden State's most-renowned beverage is voluminous. See California is *Wine Country* (Ca. Wine Institutes, 1986), D. Holtgrieve, *The California Wine Atlas* (Eucumene Assoc., 1978), B. Thompson, ed., *California Wine Country* (Lane, 1972) and M.F.K. Fisher, *The Story of Wine in California* (U.Ca. Press, 1962). A good overview is given in G.L. Peters, "Trends in California Viticulture," *Geog. Rev.* 74 (1984), 455-467.

## POPULATION

The decennial federal censuses and annual estimates and projections issued by the Ca. Dept. of Finance are essential. *County and City Data Book*(U.S. Bur. of the Census, about every five years) is a treasure trove. Still worthwhile is H. Gregor, "Spatial Disharmonies in California Population Growth," *Geog. Rev.* 53(1963), 100-122. Also see *California Population Issues* (Sierra Club, 1977) and K. Drager, "Should California Act to Restrict Population Growth," *Ca. J.* (Dec. 1980), 472-474. A thoughtful study is L.J. Kimbell and D. Shulman, *Growth in California: Prospects and Consequences* (U.Ca. Insti. of Govt. Studies, 1981). The literature on ethnic California is much expanded. General in nature are R. Olmstead and C. Wollenberg,eds., *Neither Separate nor Equal, Racism in California* (Ca. Hist.Soc.,1971), G.E. Frakes and C.B. Solberg, *Minorities in California History* (Random House, 1971), and K.F. McCarthy, *Immigration and California: Issues for the 1980s* (Rand Corp., 1983). Individual ethnic groups are covered in a series of volumes by *Ca. Dept. of Industrial Relations,* 1963-1966. Literature about the Hispanics includes J. Vigil, *From Indians to*

Chicanos. *The Dynamics of Mexican American Culture* (Waveland, 1985), R.G. del Castillo, *La Familia: Chicano Families in the Urban Southwest* (Notre Dame U. Press, 1986), E. Galarza, *Farm Workers and Agribusiness in California*(Notre Dame U. Press, 1978); A.Camarillo, *Chicanos in a Changing World: From Mexican Pueblos to American Barrios in Santa Barbara and Southern California, 1848-1930* (Harvard U. Press, 1979); R.L. Nostrand, "'Mexican American' and 'Chicano': Emerging Terms for a People Coming of Age," *Pac.Hist. Rev.*42 (1973), 389-406; and K.F. McCarthy & R.B. Valdez, *Current and Future Effects of Mexican Immigration in California* (Rand Corp., 1985). Information on Asians is also expanding; see T.Muller, *The Fourth Wave; California's Newest Immigrants: A Summary* (The Urban Institute, 1984); L.J. Crouchett, *Filipinos in California from Days of the Galleons to the Present* (Downey Place, 1983). For the Japanese, see *Japanese Americans, Tradition and Change in Three Generations* (Nelson Hall, 1977). For the Chinese see Anon., *Cathay in Eldorado: The Chinese in California* (Book Club of California, 1972). For the Indochinese, see P.J. Strand & W. Jones, Jr., *Indochinese Refugees in America* (Duke U. Press, 1985). On the First Americans the classic work is A.L. Kroeber, *Handbook of the Indians of California* (reprinted, Ca. Book Company, 1953). Much newer are works by R.F. Heizer, including *Handbook of North American Indians: California* (Smithsonian, vol. 8, 1978); R.F. Heizer & S.B. Elsassir, *The Natural World of the California Indians* (U.Ca. Press, 1980); W.H. Garner, *The Broken Ring: The Destruction of the California Indians* (Westernlore, 1982); and J.J. Rawls, *The Indians of California. The Changing Image* (U. Ok.Press, 1984). D.W. Johnson et al,*Churches and Church Membership in the United States* (Glenmary, 1974) provides statewide and county data by denomination. For early peoples, see M.J. Moratto et al, *California Archeology* (Academic Press, 1984) and J.L. and K.K.Chartkoff, *The Archeology of California* (Stanford Univ. Press, 1984). For conditions before 1769 see D. Hornbeck, "The California Indian before European Contact," *Jr. Cult. Geog.* 2 (1982), 23-39.

## HISTORY

With California's rich heritage, the literature is understandably voluminous. The classic is H.H. Bancroft, *History of California* (San Francisco, 7 vol., 1884-1890). Bibliography is provided in R.E. Cowan, *Bibliography of the History of California* (Reynolds,

1964) and Ca. Libr. Assn., *California Local History; a Centennial Bibliography* (Stanford U. Press, 1950). Most geographic of the one-volume summaries is highly-readable W.H. Hutchinson, *California, The Golden Shore by the Sundown Sea* (Star, 1988). A must is K. Starr, *Inventing the Dream: California Through the Progressive Era* (Oxford, 1985). Others include H.W. DeWitt, *California Civilization* (Kendall/Hunt, 1979); A.F. Rolle, *California, A History* (Crowell, 3d, 1978); W. Bean, *California, an Interpretive History* (McGraw-Hill, 4th, 1982); J.W. Caughey, *California: A Remarkable State's Life History* (Prentice-Hall, 4th, l982), is a long-time favorite. Additions to the literature can be found in *Pacific Historical Review, Ca. History* and *Historical Society of Southern California's Publications and Quarterly*. A number of county historical societies also issue publications. For the viewpoint of a geographer, see J.E. Vance, Jr., "California and the Search for the Ideal," *Ann.AAG* 6 (1972), 185-210.

## THE NORTHEAST (Chapter 2)

The literature on this area is limited. The outstanding work is the comprehensive monograph by R.W. Pease, Modoc County. A Geographic Time Continuum on the California Volcanic Tableland, (U.Ca. Pubs. in Geog., 17, 1965). See also Northeastern Counties Ground Water Investigation (Ca. Dept. of Water Rescs., Bull.98, l963). Also refer to the publications of the Modoc and Lassen county historical societies, especially R. Middleton's study, "The Honey Lake Basin, Ecumine of Northeastern California", Lassen County Historical Society, no. 15, July 1963, entire issue.

## THE DESERTS (Chapters 3,4,5)

E.L. Edwards, *The Enduring Desert; A Descriptive Bibliography* (Ward Ritchie, 1969), suggests the scope of the literature. For "feel" read E. Corle, *Desert Country* (Duell, Sloan & Pearce, 1941). Broad physical aspects are given in E.C. Jaeger, *The California Deserts* (Stanford U. Press, 1965) while R.P. Sharp, *Southern California Field Guide* (Kendall/Hunt, 1978) deals with the geology. Despite title, G.P. and S.M. Hannes, "A Cluster Analysis of Southern California Desert Climate Data," *Ca. Geog.* 24 (1984), 39-46 is quite readable. For mining see W.H. Kerns, "The Mineral Industry of California," *Minerals Yearbook,* 1976, *Vol.II, Area Reports: Domestic* (GPO), 113-142;

*Mineral Resources of California* (Ca. Div. Mines and Geol., Bull.191, 1967); U.S.Bur. Mines, *Mining and Mineral Operations in the Pacific States: A Visitor Guide* (GPO, 1976) and R. Nadeau, *Ghost Towns and Mining Camps of California* (Ward Ritchie, 1965). Studies by Ca. Dept. of Water Rescs. on general physical environment and land use include *Mojave River Ground Water Basin Investigation* (Bull. 84, 1967), *Desert Areas of Southern California Land and Water Use Survey* (Bull.101, 1963); *Coachella Valley Investigation* (Bull. 108, 1964); *Ground Water Occurrence and Quality: Lahontan Region* (Bull.101-1, l964) and *Long Range Potential of Antelope Valley-Mojave River Basin* (Bull.78, App. A, 1959). Recreation and preservation concerns are presented by the U.S. Bur.Land Mgm. in relation to its current desert conservation area. See that agency's *The California Desert* (1970), *High Desert Recreation Resources Guide* (1976) and *Final Environmental Impact Statement and Proposed Plan* (1980).

### The Trans-Sierra (Ch.3)

Vivid description is given in M. Austin's classic, *The Land of Little Rain* (Doubleday, 1962). W.A. Chalfant presented the case for Owens Valley in *The Story of Inyo* (Chalfant, 1933). Different views are presented in R. Nadeau, *The Water Seekers* (Peregrine Smith, 1974). More recent are W.L. Kahrl, *Water and Power: The Conflict over Los Angeles's Water Supply in Owens Valley* (U.Ca. Press, 1982); G. Smith(ed.), *Owens Valley Groundwater Conflict* (Wm. Kaufmann, 1978) and D.J. Chasan, "Mono Lake vs. Los Angeles," *Smithsonian,* 11 (1981), 42-51. See also G.S. Smith, *Deepest Valley* (Genny Smith Books, rev, 1986). C.B. Hunt, *Death Valley. Geology, Ecology, Archeology* (U.C. Press,1975) covers the national monument.

### The Mojave Desert (Ch.4)

R. Mitchell, *Exploring Joshua Tree* (La Siesta, 1964). Also, R. Cowles and E. Bakker, *Desert Journal. Reflections of a Naturalist* (U.Ca. Press, 1983). A specific problem is described in R.A. Luckenbach, "What the ORV's are Doing to the Desert," *Fremontia* 2 (1975), 3-11.

### The Colorado Desert (Ch. 5)

A.J. Lang, "William P. Blake's Desert of the Colorado River," *Ca. Geog.*, 21 (1981), 81-94. C.H. Steere, *Imperial and Coachella Valleys* (Stanford U. Press, l953) is a bit old. More recent is L. and D. Lindsay, *The Anza-Borrego Desert Region* (Wilderness Press, 1978). S.W. Edmunds & A.Z. Rose (eds), *Geothermal Energy and Regional Development: The Case of Imperial Valley* (Praeger, 1979). See also Ca. Dept. of Water Res., So. Dist., *...Use of Water by Imperial Irrigation District, 1981* and *Coachella and Imperial Valley Agricultural Land Use Study,* 1980.

### SOUTHERN CALIFORNIA (Ch. 6)

For regional literature an older source is F.D. Walker, *A Literary History of Southern California* (U.Ca. Press, 1950). The *Geology of Southern California* (Ca.Div.Mines & Geol., Bull. 170) is broad areally and topically. See also R.P. Sharp, *Coastal Southern California* (Kendall/Hunt, 1978) and H.P. Bailey, *The Climate of Southern California* (U. Ca. Press, 1966). Some of it is dated but C. McWilliams, *Southern California Country* (Duell, Sloan & Pearce, 1946) gives a "feel." The same is true of R. Lillard's witty *Eden in Jeopardy* (Knopf, 1966). Urban evolution is seen too in G.S. Dumke, *The Boom of the Eighties in Southern California* (Huntington Libr., 1944), W.W. Robinson, *Ranchos Become Cities* (San Pascual Press, 1939) and D. Hornbeck, "The Patenting of California's Private Land Claims, 1851-1885," *Geog. Rev.* 69 (1979), 434-448. D.Gebhard and R. Winter, *A Guide to Architecture in Los Angeles and Southern California* (Peregrine Smith, 1977), encompassing townscapes and history, ranges into central California. J.McKinney, *Day Hiker's Guide to Southern California* (Olympus, 1987) is recommended for the stroller. Also see D. Gagnon, *Hike Los Angeles* (Western Tanager, 2 vol., 1984). See also W.H. Miller, "Where is Southern California," *Ca. Geog.* 22 (1982), 67-95.

Although old, L.C. Powell, *Land of Fiction; 32 Novels and Stories About Southern California* (Dawson, 1952) identifies much cultural heritage. An anthology, with many journal articles, is D. Fine (ed), *Los Angeles in Fiction* (U.N.Mex. Press, l984). A recent view of the entire area is given in *Southern California: A Region in Transition* (So. Ca. Assn. of Govt.), 3 vol., (1984). The same agency has prepared *A Status Report on the Southern California Economy: Profile of an Economic Transition* (1985). Much more specific, on a topic of concern, is *The Problems and Needs for Management of Hazardous Waste in Southern California* (So. Ca. Assn. Govt., 1985). Also specific is P.R. Pryde, "On Farmland Protection in Southern California," *Prof. Geog.* 38 (1986), 365-367.

## San Diego Country

P.R. Pryde, *San Diego: An Introduction to the Region*(Kendall /Hunt, 2nd, 1983) is the standard reference with extensive bibliography. N. Morgan and T. Blair, *Yesterday's San Diego* (E.A. Seemann, Hist. Cities Series #21, 1976) examines evolution. Physical aspects are considered by G.G. Kuhn & F.P. Shephard, *Sea Cliffs, Beaches and Coastal Valleys of San Diego County* (U.Ca. Press, 1984). An outdoor guide is J. Schad, *Afoot and Afield in San Diego County* (Wilderness, 1986). Ethnic aspects are discussed by L. Ford and E. Griffin, "The Ghettoization of Paradise," *Geog.Rev.*60 (Apr.1970, 140-158). J.Van der Veer, *My Valley in the Sky* (Messner, 1959) describes yesteryear's Back Country. See also R. Leadabrand, *A Guidebook to the Sunset Ranges* (Ward Ritchie, 1965).

## The Los Angeles Basin (Lowlands)

There is a lengthy, ever-expanding literature on metropolitan Los Angeles. "Coffee table" photographic impressions are provided by A. Seidenbaum and J. Malmin, *Los Angeles 200* (Abrams, 1980) and R. Cameron, *Above Los Angeles* (Cameron, 1976). The past is discussed well in J. and L.Caughey, *Los Angeles: Biography of a City* (U.Ca. Press, 1977) and A. Rolle, *Los Angeles* (Boyd and Frazer,1981). See also B. Henstell, *Sunshine and Wealth, Los Angeles in the Twenties and Thirties* (Chronicle Books, l984) and B. Marchand, *The Emergence of Los Angeles* (Pion, 1986). Comprehensive current geographies of Los Angeles have been prepared by R. Steiner, *Los Angeles, the Centrifugal City* (Kendall/Hunt,1981) and H.Nelson, *The Los Angeles Metropolis* (Kendall/Hunt, 1983). More restrictive in scope are R. Cooke, *Geomorphic Hazards in Los Angeles* (Allen Unwin, 1984) and D.Brodsly, *L.A. Freeway* (U.Ca.Press, 1981. For contrast, see A. Hylen, *Los Angeles Before the Freeways* (Dawson's, 1982). More comprehensive is *Regional Transportation Plan*, 4 vol.(So. Ca. Assn. Govt., 1985). See also C.F. Queenan, *Long Beach and Los Angeles. A Tale of Two Ports* (Windsor, 1986). Another recent work is W.H. Miller, "The Port of Los Angeles-Long Beach in 1929 and 1979," *So. Ca. Qtr.* 65 (1983), 341-378. Relative to motion pictures, see J.P. Beaton, "Why the Movies Chose Hollywood," *Jr. of Cult. Geog.*, 4 (1983), 99-109. D.B. Nunis,*Los Angeles and its Environs in the Twentieth Century* (Ward Ritchie, 1975) approximates a comprehensive bibliography. The standard geographical guide is J.E. Spencer (ed.),

*Day Tours In and Around Los Angeles* (Pacific Books, 1979); it includes adjacent mountain and desert areas. D.W. Lantis, "Bicentennial Los Angeles: Comments on the Metropolis and the Pertinent Literature," *Ca. Geog. 21* (1981), 67-80 lists 29 items. Besides those already noted, of particular merit are J. Halpern, *Los Angeles: Improbable City* (Dutton, 1979), Jack Smith, *Jack Smith's L.A.* (McGraw-Hill, 1980), and L.L. Meyer et al, "Los Angeles, 1781-1981," (entire spring 1981 issue of *Ca. Hist., 60*). More recent is E. Soja et al, "Urban Restructuring in Los Angeles," *Econ.Geog.* 59 (1983) 195-230. Much literature deals with the ethnic complexity. Examples include R. Romo, *East Los Angeles; History of a Barrio* (U.Tx. Press, 1983), J. Desbarets, "Thai Migration to Los Angeles," *Geog. Rev.*, 69 (1979), 302-318; S.J. Fiske and J.C. Weibel, "Navajo Social Interactions in An Urban Environment," *Bull.So.Ca. Acad. Sci.*, 79 (1980), 19-37; and R. Wilson and B. Hosokawa, *East to America* (Morrow, 1980).

Pertinent literature on Orange County tends to be limited. See B.A. Weightman, "Arcadia in Suburbia: Orange County, Ca.," *Jr.of Cult. Geog.* 2 (1981), 55-69. For the San Fernando Valley a recent study is L.C. Jorgensen (ed), *The San Fernando Valley: Past and Present* (Pacific Rim Research, 1982).

## Transverse Ranges

Old but worthwhile is W.W. Robinson, *The Forest and the People* (Ward Ritchie, 1946). A classic study is R.G. Cleland, *A Place Called Sespe* (Huntington Libr., 1957). Still valid is R. Steiner, "Reserved Lands and the Supply of Space for the Southern California Metropolis," *Geog. Rev.*,56 (1966), 344-362. Forest preservation and multiple-use are the concerns of R.F. Lockmann, *Guarding the Forests of Southern California* (A.H. Clark, 1981).

## Channel Islands

K.O. Emery, *The Sea Off Southern California* (Wiley, 1960) and C. Hillinger, *The Channel Islands* (Academy, 1958) still have merit. See also S. Medders, "California's Channel Islands," *National Parks and Conservation,*49 (1975), 11-15 and B. Hansen, "Santa Cruz: An Island Reborn," *Nature Conservancy Notes* (June & July, 1987), 9-13; and J. James, "Channel Islands Climate: Addenda to a Modified Koppen Classification of California's Climate," *Ca. Geog.* 22 (1982), 33-49.

## THE CENTRAL COAST (Ch.7)

Long-recognized studies of coastal climate include C.P. Patton, "Climatology of Summer Fogs in the San Francisco Bay Area," *U.C.Publ. in Geog.*, 10 (1956), 113-200 and H.R. Byers, "Summer Sea Fogs of the Central California Coast," *U.C. Publ. in Geog.*, 3 (1930), 291-338. A feel for rural landscapes is presented in R. Peattie (ed.), *The Pacific Coast Ranges* (Vanguard, 1946). For the Western Lowlands see V.F. Carlson, *This Is Our Valley,* (Westernlore, 1959); C. Wilvert, "San Luis Obispo County: Heart of the San-San Gap," *Ca. Geog.*, 19 (1979), 69-85 and "San Diego/San Francisco=Sansan," *Geog. Mag.* 53 (1981), 268-272. G. Lee et al, *An Uncommon Guide to San Luis Obispo County* (Padre, 1977); S.T. Buczacki, "The Land that is the North American Salad Bowl," *Geog. Mag.*,53 (Feb. 1981), 297-299. Relative to The Coast see D.D. Cook, "The Fight to Conserve California's Coast," *Geog. Mag.*,54 (Nov. 1982), 623-629, on a topic of ongoing importance. O. Lewis, *Fabulous San Simeon* (Ca.Hist.Soc., 1958) provides a good feel for a fabled spot. B.L. Gordon, *Monterey Bay Area: Natural History and Cultural Imprints* (Boxwood, 1975) considers an area of much significance. More specific is J.R. Curtis, "The Boutiquing of Cannery Row," *Landscape* 25 (1981) 44-48. See also S. Lydon, *Chinese Gold: the Chinese in the Monterey Bay Region* (Capitola Book Co., 1985) Geographer/planner D. Vokac finds most of his *The Great Towns of California* (West, 1986) in the Central Coast, the northern periphery of the Bay Area and the Sierran Foothills. The novel by J. Steinbeck, *East of Eden* (Viking, 1952) gives good background for the Salinas Valley. More recent is S.T. Buczacki, "The land that is the North American salad bowl," *Geog.* 53 (1981), 297-299. For The Ranges an old source by J.W. Coulter, "Land Utilization in the Santa Lucia Region," *Geog. Rev.* 20 (July 1930, 469-479) provides background.

## THE SAN FRANCISCO BAY AREA (Ch. 8)

D. Herron, The *Literary World of San Francisco and its Environs* (City Lights, 1984) updates F.D. Walker, *San Francisco's Literary Frontier* (Knopf, 1939). A good geographical summation is made by J. Vance, *The Cities of the San Francisco Bay* (Ballinger, 1976). See also J.E. Vance, Jr., *Geography and Urban Evolution in the San Francisco Bay Area* (U.Ca. Instit. of Urban Stud., 1964). More recent are C. Wollenberg, *Golden Gate Metropolis: Perspectives on Bay Area History* (U. Ca. Press, 1985) and P.

Wayburn, *Adventuring in the San Francisco Bay Area* (Sierra Club, 1987). For aerial impressions see R. Cameron, *Above San Francisco* (Cameron, 1969). Physical aspects are presented in *Geologic Guidebook of the San Francisco Bay Counties* (Ca. Div. Mines & Geol., Bull. 154, 1951); A.C. Smith, *Introduction to the Natural History of the San Francisco Bay Region* (U.Ca. Press, 1960) and H. Gilliam, *Weather of the San Francisco Bay Region* (U.Ca. Press, 1962). For planning aspects, a good historical summary is M. Scott, *The San Francisco Bay Area* (U.Ca. Press, 1985, 2nd); N.A.,*Future Development of the San Francisco Bay Area* (U.S. Ofc. of Area Develop., 2 vol., 1959); I.M. Heyman, "Symposium: The San Francisco Bay Area—Regional Problems and Solution," *Ca. Law Libr. Rev.* 55 (1976), 695-855. A lengthy history is provided by L. Kinnaird, *History of the Greater San Francisco Bay Region* (Lewis, 3 vol., 1966). D.E. Dowall, *The Suburban Squeeze: Land Conversion and Regulation in the San Francisco Bay Area* (U.Ca. Press, 1984) deals with a major current problem. D. Gebhard et al, *A Guide to Architecture in San Francisco and Northern California* (Peregrine Smith, 1976) covers many aspects and has an extensive bibliography.

### San Francisco Bay

There is considerable literature. See H. Gilliam, *Between the Devil and the Deep Blue Bay* (Chronicle Books, 1969); *San Francisco Bay Plan* (San Francisco Bay Conserv. and Develop. Cmsm., 1969); R. Odell, *The Saving of San Francisco Bay* (Conservation Foundation, 1972); T.J. Conomos et al, *San Francisco Bay: The Urbanizing Estuary* (Ca. Acad. of Sci., 1979); R. Pestrong, "San Francisco Bay Tidelands," *Ca. Geol.* 25 (1972), 17-40. Also see W.J. Kockelman et al (eds.), *San Francisco Bay: Use and Protection* (Am. Assn. for Adv. of Sci., 1982).

### The East Bay

*A Community Guide to the Greater East Bay* (Security Pacific Bank, 1979); *Berkeley, the First Seventy Five Years* (American Guide Series, Hasting, 1940) still has merit, as do M.S. Hellman, "Port Costa, California Wheat Center," *Ca. Geog.* 4, 1963, and *Diablo's Guide to the East Bay* (Diablo Press, 1962). Useful is S. Fisher and A. Rubin, *Environmentalist's Guide to the East Bay* (Bay Press, 1973). See also A. Bradsford, *Oakland's Not for Burning* (McKay, 1968) and B. Bagwell, *Oakland, Story of a City* (Presidio Press, 1982). M. Baldassare et al, ". . The Impact of the

Bay Area Rapid Transit System on Residential Mobility," *Environ. & Behav.*,II (1979), 435-450.

## South Bay

P.F.Griffin and R.L. Chatham, "Urban Impact on Agriculture in the Santa Clara Valley," *Ann. Assn. Am.Geog.*, 48 (Sept. 1958), 195-208 tells of the urban transition. *Focus on Santa Clara County* (Bank of America, 1969). Dirk Hanson, *The New Alchemists: Silicon Valley and the Micro-Electronics Revoultion* (Little, Brown, 1982) and R.A. Walker and M.J. Williams, "Water from Power: Water Supply and Regional Growth in the Santa Clara Valley,"*Econ. Geog.* 58 (Apr. 1982), 95-120. Other sources include A.L. Saxenian, "The Urban Contradictions of Silicon Valley," *Intern. Jr. of Urban and Reg. Research*, 7 (1983), 237-262 and J.R. Wolch and S.A. Gabriel, "Develpment and Decline of Service-Dependent Population Ghettos," *Urban Geog.* 5 (1984), 111-129.

## The Peninsula

W. Chapin et al, *The Suburbs of San Francisco* (Chronicle Books, 1969) considers other parts of the Bay Area as well. E.K. Burns, "Subdivision Activity on the San Francisco Peninsula, 1860-1970," *Yrb. Assn. Pac. Coast Geog.* 39 (1977), 17-32 summarizes urban evolution. For one city, see J.A. Blum, "South San Francisco: The Making of an Industrial City,"*Ca. Hist.* 63 (1984), 114-134.

## San Francisco

A number of works provide background. For example, see E. Rostlund, "Geographic Setting of San Francisco,"*Jr. Geog.* 54 (1955), 441-448; G. Atherton, *My San Francisco* (Bobbs-Merrill, 1946); J.C. Altrocchi, *The Spectacular San Franciscans* (Dutton, 1949); H. Caen, *Baghdad by the Bay* (Doubleday, 1949); W. Bronson, *The Earth Shook, the Sky Burned* (Doubleday, 1959). More recent is C. Hartman, *The Transformation of San Francisco* (Rowman & Allanheld, 1984). See also L.K. Loewenstein, *The Streets of San Francisco: the Origin of Street and Place Names* (Lexikos, 1984). On ethnic aspects see C. Salter, *San Francisco's Chinatown* (R. & E., 1978); V.G. Nee and B.DeBary, *Longtime Californ'; A Documentary Study of an American Chinatown* (Pantheon, 1972). R. Dillon, *The Italian Heart of San Francisco* (Presidio, 1985); D. Cinel, *From Italy to San Francisco: the Immigrant Experience* (Stanford U. Press, 1982). Specialized items include R. Clary, *The Making of Golden Gate Park: The Early Years, 1865-1906* (Ca. Living Books, 1980).

## Marin County

The literature is limited, despite J. Futcher, *Marin— The Place, the People: Profile of a California County* (Harcourt, Brace, Jo., 1985).

## North Bay

There is a considerable literature dealing with viticulture and related tourism. See W.K Crowley, "...Vineyard and Winery Expansion in Sonoma County," *Ca. Geog.*,17 (1977), 11-14. See also J. Hoch & N. Tryphonopoulos, *A Study of the Economy of Napa County,* (U.Ca. Giannini Found. Res. Report 303, 1969). Also see C.H. Exline, ". . .The Conversion of Agricultural Land to Suburban Uses in Sonoma County, 1950-1970," *Ca. Geog.* 23 (1983), 14-35 and D. Edwards, *Making the Most of Sonoma: A California Guide* (Presidio, 1982).

## The Borderlands

See H. Gilliam & P. Hyde, *Island in Time: The Point Reyes Peninsula* (Scribner, 1974).

## THE GREAT CENTRAL VALLEY (Ch. 9)

The rich literary heritage is reviewed in G. Mastlam and J.D. Houston, *California Heartland: Writing from the Great Central Valley,* (Capra, 1978). For statistics there is the *Monthly Summary of Business Conditions, Central Valley Counties* (Security Paccific Bank. For environmental aspects, see *Central Valley Basin* (U.S. Dept. Interior, 1949); K. Thompson, "Riparian Forests of the Sacramento Valley," *Ann. Assn. Am. Geog.*, 51 (1961), 294-315; H.J. Wood, "The Agricultural Value of California Soils," *Geog. Rev.*, 29 (1939), 310-313; and C.F. Cole, "The Salt and Sodium Affected Soils of the Eastern San Joaquin Valley," *Yrbk.Assn. Pac. Coast Geog.*, (1958), 27-34. Much has been written about water. An example is D.F. Anthrop, "The Peripheral Canal and the Future for Water in California," *Yrbk. APCG* 44 (1983). 109-128. See also section on Water.

Background includes D.C. Cutter, *The Diary of Ensign Gabriel Moraga's Expedition of Discovery in the Sacramento Valley, 1808* (Dawson, Los Angeles, 1957), J.P. Zollinger, *Sutter, the Man and his Empire* (Oxford, 1939), J.A. McGowan, *History of the Sacramento Valley* (Lewis, 3 vol., 1961) and W. Smith, *Garden of the Sun*, (M.Hardison, 3d ed., 1956).

There is a voluminous literature concerning agribusiness; see preceding references under "Agriculture." For general background see E. A. Yeary, *So*

..*You Want a California Farm* (U.Ca. Agri. Exp. Sta. Circ. 556, 1971). Publications of the U.Ca. Giannini Foundation include *Mixed-Feed Manufacturing in the Central Valley* (1960) and *Leasing on California Rice Farms*(1971). Also worthwhile are M.E. Baker, "Challenge of the '80's for California agribusiness," *Ca. Jr.*, 423-424 and A. Jackson et al, *Cry California*, 14 (1980), no. l, entire issue. A "classic" is C.C. Colby, "The California Raisin Industry," *Ann. Assn. Am. Geog.* 14 (1924), 49-108. Studies of other enterprises include K.Thompson, "Location and Relocation of...English Walnuts,"*Econ. Geog.* 37(1961), 122-149, P.F. Griffin, "The California Olive Industry," *Jr. Geog.* 54 (1955), 429-440; and D.C. Large, "Cotton in the San Joaquin Valley," *Geog. Rev.* 47 (1957), 365-380. There is considerable literature on floods. See R. Kelley, "Taming the Sacramento: Hamiltonianism in Action," *Pac. Hist. Rev.*,34 (1965), 21-49; *The Big Flood, California 1955* (Ca. Disaster Office, Sacramento, 1956); and K. Thompson, "Historic Flooding in the Sacramento Valley," *Pac. Hist. Rev.* (1960), 349-360. For effect of mining methods, see R.L. Kelley, *Gold vs. Grain, the Hydraulick Mining Controversy in California* (Arthur C. Clark, 1959).

### The Sacramento Valley

Yesteryear's life along California's largest river is described in J. MacMullen, *Paddle-Wheel Days of California* (Stanford U. Press, 1944) and J. Dana, *The Sacramento*(Rinehard, 1939). One of the now-stagnant river towns is described by C.H. Hisken, *Tehama, Little City of Big Trees* (Exposition, 1948). For the Redding District see E.G. Zelinsky and N.L. Olmsted, "Upriver Boats: When Red Bluff was the Head of Navigation," *Ca. Hist.*, 24 (1985), 86-117. For the West Side, see W. Duffy, *The Sutter Basin and Its People* (Galbreath, 1972). Concerning the Flood Basins, there is considerable older material. For a more recent item, see J.N. Rutger and D.M. Brandon, "California Rice Culture," *Scientific American* 244 (1981), 42-51. Literature dealing with the East Side tends to be limited. R. Lowry, *Who's Running This Town*(Harper and Row, 1965), a dated sociological study of Chico, could refer to other Central Valley cities. A historically-important ethnic group is discussed in S. Hardwick, *The Chinese in Butte County, California: 1860-1920* (R.& E. Res., 1976). For an economic activity of much importance in urbanized areas in the Central Valley, see G.J. Smith, "Medical Centers Compete for Markets," *No. Ca. Bus. Rev.*, 12, #4 (1987) 4-5. W. Anderson, *The Sutter Buttes: a naturalist's view* (Natural Selection, 1983) tells of an area seen by many but known to few. There is understandably more literature on metropolitan Sacramento. See J.A. McGowan and T. Willis, *Sacramento, Heart of the Golden State* (Windsor, 1983); S. Hardwick, "A Geographical Interpretation of Ethnic Settlement in an Urban Landscape: Russians in Sacramento," *Ca.Geog.* 19(1979), 87-104; A considerable portion of E. Galarza, *Barrio Boy* (U. of Notre Dame Press, 1971 deals with Sacramento. R. Dillon, *Fool's Gold* (Coward-McCann, 1967); K. Thompson, "Prospects for the Port of Sacramento," *S.W. Soc.Sci. Qtr.*, 39 (1958), 133-144. Awareness of the rising metropolitan status is presented by S. Magagnini, "Is Sacramento Ready for the Big Time? Yup," *Ca.* (July 1987), 54-56 ff. See also E. Heaser and L. Kong, *The Sacramento Region...a Bibliographic Guide* (Vance Bibliog.'s, 1981)

### The Delta Lands

Much has been written on this area. R. Dillon, *Delta Country* (Presidio, 1982) provides a good summary, attractively illustrated. See also C.A. Bohakel, *The Historic Delta Country. A Guidebook to State Highway 160, the Bayou of the West* (priv. publ.,1979), R. and P. Miller, *Delta Country* (La Siesta,1971) and D.D. Arreola, "The Chinese Role in the ...Sacramento-San Joaquin Delta," *Ca. Geog.* 15 (1975), 1-15 and D.J. Blackburn, "Switch on the Delta," *Ca. Jr.* XII (1981), 88-92. J. Thompson, in addition to his excellent dissertation, has written extensively. Examples include "Reclamation Sequence in the Sacramento-San Joaquin Delta,*Ca. Geog.*, 6 (1965), 29-35, *The Tule Breakers,* written with E.A. Dutra (U. of the Pac.,1983) and "From waterways to roadways in the Sacramento Delta," *Ca. Hist.* 59 (1980), 144-169. Also see *Laypersons' Guide to the Delta* (Western Water Educ. Found., 1985) and G. Newmarch, "Subsidence of Organic Soils," *Ca. Geol.* 34 (1981), with worthwhile data, island by island. Fragile levees have been studied by Ca. Dept. Water Rescs. in Bulls. 167 (1967) and 192 (1975). J.M. MacDiarmid, "The State Water Plan and Salinity Control in the Sacramento-San Joaquin Delta," *Yrbk, Assn. Pac. Coast Geog.* 37 (1975),39-54 is a good source on water. Also see D.F. Anthrop, "The Peripheral Canal and the Future for Water in California," *Yrbk. APCG*, 44 (1983), 109-128.

### The San Joaquin Valley

J.J. Parsons provides an outstanding summary in "A Geographer Looks at the San Joaquin Valley," *Geog. Rev.* 76 (1986), 371-389.

For the East Side see N.P. Hardeman, *Harbor of the Heartlands: A History of the Inland Seaport of Stockton* (U. of Pac. Press, 1986) and J. Roberts, "The Future of Manufacturing in Stockton," *Ca. Geog.* 6 (1965), 49-57 for Stockton; for the Fresno District, O.E. Granger, "Climatic Variations in the California Raisin Industry," Geog. Rev. 70 (1980), 300-313 and S. Ungar, "Fresno, Number 277," Atlantic Monthly 256 (1984), 18-26 on metropolitan evaluation.

Considerable literature concerns the Trough, West Side and South End. For example, see B. Wallach, "The West Side Oil Fields of California," *Geog. Rev.* 70 (1980), 50-59, U.Ca. Giannini Found. Res. Repts. on agricultural potentials of the West Side, No. 312 (1970) and 316 (1971). M. Mitchell considers an area and topic of much recent controversey in "Westlands Water District...Problems with the National Reclamation Act,"*Yrbk.APCG* 46 (1984), 117-128. Much information can be gained from W. Preston, *Vanishing Landscapes: Land and Life in the Tulare Lake Basin* (U.Ca. Press, 1981), with good maps and bibliography. For large-scale farming, especially here, see J..J. Parsons, "Corporate Farming in California," *Geog. Rev.* 67 (1977), 354-357; R. Steiner, "Large Private Landholdings in California," *Geog.Rev.*, 72 (1982), 315-326; and E. Liebman, *California Farmland: A History of Large Agricultural Holdings* (Rowan & Allanheld, 1983). There is considerable literature on drainage problems. See *Status of San Joaquin Valley Drainage Problems* (Ca. Dept. of Water Rescs., Bull. 127-74, l974); G. Wiggett and J. Alfords, "Selenium," *Ca. Geol.* 39 (1986), 99-107; M. Bowker, "Putting a Lid on Kesterson," *Sierra* 71 (1986) 33-37; R. Burau, "Evironmental Chemistry of Selenium," *Ca. Agri.* 39 (1985), 16-18; and K. Tanji, "Selenium in the San Joaquin Valley,"*Environment* 6 (1986), 6-11 ff.. W.J. Stein, *California and the Dust Bowl Experience* (Greenwood, 1983) tells of an difficult period in the Valley.

## THE SIERRA NEVADA (Ch. 10)

R.Peattie (ed), *The Sierra Nevada: The Range of Light* (Vanguard, 1947) whets one's enthusiasm as does R. Kauffman, *Gentle Wilderness* (Sierra Club, 1967). J. Muir, *My First Summer in the Sierra* (Houghton Mifflin, 1979) and C. King, *Mountaineering in the Sierra Nevada* (U. Neb. Press, 1970) are reprinted classics. Two additional classics by F.P. Farquhar are *Yosemite, the Big Trees and the High Sierra* (U.Ca. Press, 1948), with a selective bibliography and *History of the Sierra Nevada* (U.Ca. Press,

1966), which reveals how much additional research is needed. An "update" is provided by P. Browning, *Place Names of the Sierra Nevada* (Wilderness, 1986). Environmental works include T.I. Storer and R.L. Usinger, *Sierra Nevada Natural History* (U.Ca. Press, 1963); M. Hill, *Geology of the Sierra Nevada* (U.Ca. Press, 1975); O.P Jenkins, *The Great Watershed of California* (Angel Press, 1978; J.E. Kesseli, "Studies in the Pleistocene Glaciation of the Sierra Nevada," *U.Ca. Pubs. in Geog.* 6-8 (1941); D.H. Miller, "Snow Cover and Climate in the Sierra Nevada,"*U.Ca. Publ. in Geog.* 11 (1955); H.W. Anderson, Managing California's Snow Zone Lands for Water(*U.S. Pac. S.W. For. & Range Exp. Sta.*, 1963); and N.A., *Timber Marketing and Ownership in the Central Sierra Nevada Region* (U.Ca. Agri. Exp. Sta. Bull. 774, 1960) and *The Lumber Industry in the Central Sierra Nevada Region* (Bull.811, 1965). For a thorough review of the vegetation see V. Johnston, *Sierra Nevada* (Houghton Mifflin, 1970). Material on the High Sierra includes H. Roth, *Pathway in the Sky* (Howell-North, 1965) and such guides as J.P.Shaffer et al, *The Pacific Crest Trail*, Vol.1: California (Wilderness Press,1977); L. and G.Clark, *John Muir Trail Country* (Western Trails Pubs., 1978); and T. Winnett, *Guide to the John Muir Trail* (Wilderness Press, 1978). For the Eastern Slope see D. Goldman, "Landscape, Water and Outdoor Recreation in the Eastern Sierra," *Ca.Geog.* 3 (1962), 41- 46; G.S. Smith (ed.),*Mammoth Lakes Sierra* (Wm. Kaufmann, 1976) and L. Simon, "Proposed Hydroelectric Power Plant Locations: Inyo and Mono Counties," *Ca. Geog.* 23 (1983), 51-64. Material on the Southern Prongs is limited. See A. Woodward, *The Story of El Tejon* (Los Angeles, 1942. Also see J.C. Jenkins, *Self-Propelled in the Southern Sierra* (Wilderness Press, 1978). Considerable material has been published on the Park Belt. See J. Harper, *Mineral King: Public Concern with Government Policy* (Eureka Printing, 1982); L.M. Dilsaver, "Land-Use Conflict in the Kings River Canyons," *Ca. Geog.* 26 (1986), 59-80; D.G. Yeager, *California National Parks* (Lane, 1969); F.E. Matthes, *Sequoia National Park, A Geological Album* (U.Ca. Press, 1950); and J.R. Whited and J.L. Vankat, "Fire and Man in Sequoia National Park," *Ann. Assn. Am. Geog.*, 67 (1977),17-27; *Sequoia and Kings Canyon National Parks* (Stanford U. Press, 1949). The extensive literature on Yosemite includes F.E.Matthes, *The Incomparable Valley, A Geologic Interpretation of the Yosemite* (U.Ca. Press, 1950); N.A., *The Influence of Modern Man on the Vegetation of Yosemite Valley* (U.Ca. Agri. Exp.Sta., 1967); P.

Schaffer, *Yosemite National Park—A Natural History Guide. . .* (Wilderness Press, 1978); *Natural Resources Management Plan and Environmental Assessment. Yosemite National Park* (U.S. Nat. Park Svc., 1977). Much has been written on The Foothills. Old but good introductions include R. Dillon, *Exploring the Mother Lode Country* (Ward Ritchie, 1974), R. Baugh, "Mother Lode, 1949," *Yrbk. Pac. Coast Geog.* 11 (1949), 3-18; *Geologic Guidebook along Highway 49*(Ca. Div. Mines & Geol., Bull.141, 1948); and B. Brasch, *Gold Rush Country*, (Lane Book, 1972). For earlier literature, see C.I. Wheat, *Books of the California Gold Rush* (Colt Press, 1949) and *The Maps of the California Gold Region* (Grabhorn Press, 1942). Also see E.K. Gudde et al, *California Gold Camps* (U.Ca. Press, 1975); L.M. Dilsaver, "After the Gold Rush," *Geog. Rev.* 75 (1985), 1-18 and F. Scott, "California Gold Mining Landscapes," *Ca. Geog.* 1971), 38-44. Additional literature includes W.T. Jackson & S.D. Mikesell, *The Stanislaus River Drainage Basin and the New Melones Dam*, (U.Ca. Davis, 1979); P.B. Smith, "Highway Planning in California's Mother Lode," *Ca. Hist.*, 59 (1980), 204-221; P. Guiness, "The Changing Location of Power Plants in California," *Geography* 65 (1980), 217-220; and F. Egan, "Suburbanizing the Sierra," *Cry Ca.*, 13 (1978), 7-12. For the Northern Sierra there is more literature about the Donner-Tahoe area than elsewhere. A classic about Lake Tahoe is G.W. James, *The Lake in the Sky* (C.T. Powner, 1956), with additional background in E.B. Scott, *The Saga of Lake Tahoe* (Sierra-Tahoe Publ. Co.,1957). A trail guide, J.P. Schaffer, *The Tahoe Sierra*(Wilderness, 1975) has a physical summary. On environmental questions see C.R. Pagter and C.W. Wolfe, Jr., "Lake Tahoe: The Future of a National Asset," *Ca. Law Rev.* 52 (1964) 563-622; *Tahoe Basin Studies Report* (Ca. State Water Rescs. Bd., 1974) and Research Reports on management by U.Ca.,Davis, Insti. for Govt. Studies. For areas nearby see E. Huggins and J. Olmstead, *Adventures On and Off Interstate 80* (Tioga, 1985). J. Morley, *Gold Cities* (Howell-North, 1965) tells of Grass Valley and Nevada City.

## THE SOUTHERN CASCADE (Ch. 11)

The literature is somewhat limited. For this and adjacent subregions see *Geology of Northern California* (Ca. Div. Mines & Geol., Bull.190, 1966); D.D. Alt & D.W. Hyndman, *Roadside Geology of Northern California* (Mountain Press, 1975). For the famed volcanic park, see P.S. Kane, *Through Volcan's*

*Eye* (Loomis Museum Assn., 1980). The area is touched upon in R. Peattie (ed), *The Cascade*(Vanguard 1949) and A. Powers, *Redwood Country* (Duell, Sloan & Pierce, 1949). See also R.O. and V. Case, *Lost Mountains* (Doubleday Doran, 1945). On the First Americans, see T.Kroeber, *Ishi in Two Worlds* (U.Ca. Press, 1961). On the lumbering and allied activities there are R.H. May, *A Century of Lumber Production in California and Nevada* (U.S. Ca. For. and Range Exp. Sta. Forest Surv. Release 20, 1953), J.A. Zivnuska et al, *The Commercial Forest Resources and Forest Products Industries of California*(U. Ca. Agri. Exp. Sta., 1965), and C.L Bolsinger, *Timber Resources of Northern Interior California* (U.S. For. Svc. Res. Bull. PNW—65, 1976). W.H. Hutchinson, *California Heritage, A History of Northern California Lumbering* (Diamond Gardner, 1957). R.M.Hanft, *Red River* (Ca. State Univ., Chico, 1980) provides long-needed information on the logging empire of Thomas Walker in Mn. and Ca.. His *Pine Across the Mountains* (Golden West Books, 1970) tells of the McCloud Lumber Company and its railroad while K. Stephens, *Matches, Flumes and Rails* (Trans-Anglo Books, 1977) gives historic background into logging in the Sierra-Cascade border country.

## THE NORTHWEST (Ch. 12)

For general impression, R. Peattie (ed.), *The Pacific Coast Ranges* (Vanguard, 1946) is of some help. An old regional novel is Peter B. Kyne, *The Valley of the Giants*(Doubleday, 1919). For environment, see references listed for Ch. 11 and also A.D. Sokolow, "California's New Migration to the Towns of the 'Cow Counties,'" *Ca. Jr.* 8 (1977), 348-350; J.J. Parsons, "Slicing up the Open Space: Subdivisions without Homes in Northern California," *Erdkunde* 26 (1977), 1-8; D.E. Hansen et al, *California Remote Subdivisions* (U.Wisc.Press, 1976); and F. Coleberd, *Hidden Country Villages of California* (Chronicle Books, 1977). Relative to the concept of a separate state, see P.Berg(ed.) *Reinhabiting a Separate Country: A Bioregional Anthology of Northern California* (Planet Drum Found., 1978) and M. Dileo & E. Smith, *Two Californias: The Truth about the Split-State Movement* (Island Press, 1983).

Sundry sources include *Northern Coastal California. Economic Trends in the Seventies.* (Security Pacific Bank, 1977); *North Coastal Area Investigation* (Ca. Dept. Water Rescs. Bull. 136, 1964-65), and *Water, Land and Related Resources, North Coastal Area of California* (U.S.Dept. Agri. & Ca. Dept. of

Water Rescs., 1970). Timber resources have been inventoried by U.S. For. Service for Humboldt County (Resource Bull. PNW-26, 1968) and for Mendocino and Sonoma counties (Resource Bull. PNW-40, 1972. A more recent appraisal is B.T. Cullen, "Changes in the Size and Location of Northwestern California's Wood Products Industry," *Ca. Geog.*, 25 (1985), 45-64. For the Redwood area see E. Fritz, *California Coast Redwood—An Annotated Bibliography* (Recorder-Sunset Press, 1957); F.I. Jewett, "The Impact of a National Park upon a County's Economy," *Ann. Reg. Sci.* 2 (1968), 247-287; L.C. Merriam, "The Redwood Park Proposal," *Jr. of For.* 65 (1967), 306-321; A. Powers, *Redwood Country* (Duell, Sloan, & Pearce, 1949). S. Nixon, *Redwood Empire* (Dutton, 1966); *Humboldt Harbor and Bay* (U.S.Corps Engin., 1968); T.R. Vale, "Conservation Strategies in the Redwoods," *Yrbk. Pac. Coast Geog.* 36 (1974), 102-112; and G.W. Dean et al, Structure and *Projections of the Humboldt County Economy: Economic Growth Versus Environmental Quality* (U.Ca. Giannini Found., Res. Rept. 318, 1973). Also see W. Boly, "Travels in Humboldt," Ca. 7 (1982), 64-72; and R. Sullivan, "Growing Pains. A Report from . . . Humboldt (1975-1985)," Ca. 11(1986), 136-140 ff.

For information on other parts of the Northwest, see D. Wallace, *Klamath Knot* (Sierra Club, 1983); H.K. Maudlin, *Your Lakes, Valleys and Mountains, History of Lake County* (East Wind Printers, 1960); F.T. McBeth, *Lower Klamath Country* (U.Ca. Press, 1950); R.Raphael, *Cash Crop. An American Dream* (Ridge Times Press, 1985) gives insight into California's Appalachia and marijuana growing; On the same topic see E.E. Parsons, *Humboldt Homegrown. The Golden Age* (Egret,1985); *Engineering Geology of the Geysers Geothermal Resource Area* (Ca.Div.Mines & Geol., Sp.Rept. 122, 1976); *Ten Counties Investigation* (Ca.Div. Water Rescs. Bull. 184, 1971); D. Green, *Marble Mountain Wilderness* (Wilderness Press, 1980); D.R. Wallace, *The Dark Range* (Sierra Club, 1978); and J. and C. Robertson, "The Town of Last Resort: Mendocino, Ca." *Small Town 9* (1978), 4-11.

# LIST OF
# PHOTOGRAPHS

# LIST OF MAPS

# LIST OF CHARTS AND GRAPHS

# INDEX

vertical zonation, 417-419
Victorville, 59
Vietnamese, 158, 373
View Park, 152
Vina District, 354
vineyards. *See* grapes and wine
Visalia, 387
Vista, 117
Vizcaino, 218
Volcanic Tableland (Modoc Plateau), 23
Volcanic Tableland (Mono County), 37
volcanoes and volcanic Areas, 41, 460-462, 479

**W**

Walker, T.B., 469
Walker Pass, 421
Walnut (city), 175
Walnut Creek, 274
walnuts, 372
Warm Springs Valley, 27
Warner Range, 23, 26-27
Warner Springs, 120
Wasco, 405
Washoe Indians, 419
water, 100-101, 201, 417, 445. *See* also specific rivers, lakes, dams, reservoirs, irrigation districts, canals, aqueducts, and projects
waterfowl, 351
Watsonville, 234
Watts, 151
weather. *See* climate
Weaverville, 500
Weed, 467
Weedpatch, 406
West Adams District, 134
West Covina, 175
West Hills College, 395
West Hollywood, 136
West Los Angeles, 138
West Mesa, 70, 86

West Oakland, 265
West Pittsburg, 272
West Valley College, 283
West Walker Valley, 41
Westbay, 254
Westchester, 148
Western Addition, 304,
Western Pacific Railroad. *See* Union Pacific
Western Terraces (Santa Barbara County), 196
Westlake, 206
Westlands Irrigation District, 395-396
Westminster, 158-159
Westwood, 467, 472
Westwood Village, 137
wetbacks. *See* immigration and agricultural labor
Whaleback, 460
wheat, 6, 28, 237, 337-338
Whiskeytown Reservoir, 499
White Mountain Peak, 37
Whitewater River, 35
Whitney Pass, 421, 425
Whitney, Mount, 414
Whittier, 153
wild rice, 350
Wilderness Act of 1964, 501
Wildernesses, 423-424. *See* also specific wilderness
wildfire, 102, 138, 174, 201, 311, 526
wildlife refuges, 29. *See* also specific refuges
William Land Park, 361
Williams, 347
Williamson Act, 552
Willits, 494
Willows, 347
Wilmington, 143
Wilshire Corridor, 136
wine, 177, 230, 230-231, 273, 282, 319, 320-321, 325, 354, 372, 377, 382, 496. *See* also Grapes
Winnemuca-To-The-Sea Highway, 27

Winship, Jonathon, 482
winter sports. *See* Snow and specific ski centers
Winterhaven, 79
Wintun Indians, 337
Wintun Lodge, 471
women, 539
wood processing. *See* forests and forest industries
Woodland, 348
Woodland Hills, 168
Woodside, 323
Wright Act, 338, 375
Wrigley family, 209

**Y**

Yang-Na, 121
Yerba Buena, 294
Yokut Indians, 337
Yolla Bolly-Middle Eel Wilderness, 497
Yolo By-Pass, 350
Yountville, 321
Yolo County, 347-349
Yreka, 471-472
Yuba City, 357
Yuba River Country, 454
Yosemite National Park, 431-432
Yountville, 321
Yucaipa Valley, 181
yucca, 52
Yucca Valley, 59
Yugoslavs, 386
Yuki Indians, 480
Yuma, 71, 79
Yuma Crossing, 78
Yuman Indians, 95
Yurok Indians, 463, 498

**Z**

zeolite, 36

# THE AUTHORS

Each of the three authors has been active in California geography for more than a third of a century. All three have served as presidents of the California Geographical Society.

David W. Lantis, born on the Bluegrass fringe of Cincinnati, first visited California over 60 years ago. A permanent resident of California since 1949, he received his Ph.D. from The Ohio State University. Before joining the faculty at California State University, Chico, he had taught at various institutions in Southern California (University of Southern California, Los Angeles City College, Los Angeles Valley College, Compton College, and California State University, Long Beach). He has authored sundry shorter works on California topics.

Rodney Steiner is a native of Los Angeles. He prepared a master's thesis on the San Gabriel Mountains at U.C.L.A. then was awarded the Ph.D. at the University of Washington. He has taught at California State University, Long Beach since 1953. He is the author of Los Angeles, The Centrifugal City (Kendall/Hunt, 1981) as well as shorter works.

Arthur E. Karinen is a native of Mendocino County and grew up in Fort Bragg. His M.A. thesis at U.C., Berkeley dealt with the historical geography of the Mendocino Coast. He was awarded the Ph.D. at the University of Maryland, where he taught for over a decade before joining the faculty at C.S.U., Chico. Besides his interest in California, he is a leading American authority on Finland.